W9-AXF-297

THE PRINCIPAL DISEASES
OF LOWER VERTEBRATES

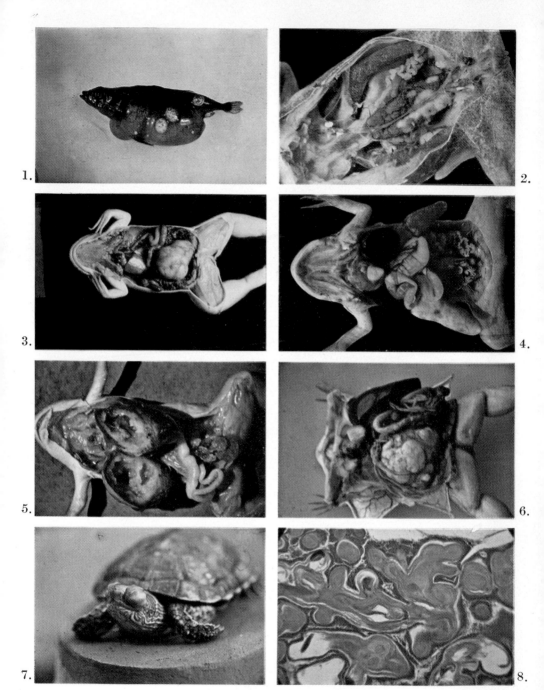

FRONTISPIECE

1. *Gasterosteus aculeatus* infected with *Glugea anomala* and *Schistocephalus solidus*. 2. *Xenopus laevis*. Tuberculosis of kidneys. 3. *Xenopus laevis*. Tuberculosis of rectum. 4. *Xenopus laevis*. Lobar tuberculous pneumonia. 5. *Xenopus laevis*. Biliary adenoma with extensive central necrosis. 6. *Xenopus laevis*. Nephroblastoma. 7. *Clemmys leprosa*. Hyperplasia of Harderian gland. 8. *Chinemys reevesii*. Hyperplasia of Harderian gland. Microscopic section.

THE PRINCIPAL DISEASES
OF LOWER VERTEBRATES

H. Reichenbach-Klinke

*Technische Hochschule and Bayerische Biologische Versuchsanstalt
Munich, Germany*

and

E. Elkan

*Group IX Laboratories, Shrodells Hospital, Watford
Hertfordshire, England*

ACADEMIC PRESS

London and New York

1965

ACADEMIC PRESS INC. (LONDON) LTD
Berkeley Square House
Berkeley Square
London, W.1.

636.089
R 27p

U.S. Edition published by
ACADEMIC PRESS INC.
111 Fifth Avenue
New York, New York 10003

54063
Aug. '66

Copyright © 1965 By ACADEMIC PRESS INC. (LONDON) LTD

LIBRARY OF CONGRESS CATALOG CARD NUMBER: 64–16699

PRINTED IN GREAT BRITAIN BY
THE UNIVERSITY PRESS
ABERDEEN

Preface

The "Principal Diseases of Lower Vertebrates" presents the material published by Heinz H. Reichenbach-Klinke between 1957 and 1962 in three separate volumes as "Krankheiten der Aquarienfische" (Alfred Kernen, Stuttgart), "Krankheiten der Amphibien" and "Krankheiten der Reptilien" (Gustav Fischer, Stuttgart). The scope of the work has been enlarged with material contributed by E. Elkan who has also done the translation. We have tried to extend the pathology of fish beyond that of the species kept in aquaria. The scope of fish pathology is, however, widening so rapidly at the present time that no textbook can ever hope to be completely up-to-date even for a short period. Representatives of the main groups of parasites affecting fish have been presented as far as possible.

Experience has shown that those who keep, or are interested in, one kind of lower vertebrate will sooner or later also take an interest in one of the other groups. It was therefore thought expedient to include what is at present known of lower vertebrate pathology in one volume, even at the risk of some repetition where fishes, amphibians and reptiles suffer from similar diseases or are the victims of identical parasites.

Since with the exception, perhaps, of the fishes, the lower vertebrates are of little economic importance, little attention had been paid to their diseases until the day when their usefulness in the laboratory was recognized. Since then, a host of highly technical papers on the pathology and the parasitology of lower vertebrates has appeared in journals inaccessible to the general public. Even so, the textbooks on pathology, bacteriology, zoology and parasitology devote at best only very little space to the diseases of animals not classified as "domestic" or "agricultural".

In trying to fill this gap we have been aware of the fact that we are dealing with an almost unexplored area of science, and that our knowledge in this field is expanding rapidly. Even so it is hoped that the book may be of use to those interested in any specific problem and may help them to locate the original papers dealing with that particular item.

No attempt has been made to make this book in the widest sense of the word "popular". The disciplines of anatomy, physiology, pathology and zoology are too complicated in their demands of some basic knowledge of the relevant terminology to make that possible. Yet it is hoped that the book—and particularly the illustrations—may be of use to those who keep lower vertebrates for scientific and non-scientific purposes.

If, in many of its parts, this book reads like a pure textbook of parasitology, this is simply due to the fact that, as we descend the evolutionary ladder, more and more diseases are due to parasites and the primary and secondary damage they cause. A basic knowledge of parasitology is therefore indispensable for anyone wanting to keep fish, amphibians or reptiles in good condition.

The production of this book would have been impossible without the kind permission of editors of various scientific journals to reproduce material and illustrations first published in their pages. This refers particularly to the Zoological Society of London, The British Herpetological Society, *Nature*, the *Journal of Protozoology, Cancer Research, Copeia* and others. To all of them and the many individual authors who gave us permission to use some of their material, we are sincerely grateful.

Acknowledgements are equally due to the German publishers Alfred Kernen Verlag, Stuttgart, and Gustav Fischer Verlag, Stuttgart, who generously allowed us to reproduce material published by them under the titles quoted above and who were kind enough to agree to our plans for this English edition in one volume. Finally we wish to thank Academic Press, London, for their helpful collaboration in the production of this book.

Particular thanks are due to a number of authors who allowed us to use or to photograph some of their material; in particular Dr. E. Amlacher, Berlin, Mr. C. Arme, Leeds, Dr. W. Foersch, Munich, Dr. P. Ghittino, Turin, Dr. W. Meyburg, Bremen, Dr. T. Roskam, Ijmuiden, and also the Bavarian Institute for Experimental Biology, Munich, as well as to two technical assistants in the Department of Chemistry of the same Institute, Miss H. Amtmann and Mr. W. Schlagbauer, who assisted in the execution of some of the drawings.

Since both authors hope to continue working in the field of lower vertebrate pathology they will be grateful to receive relevant material dead or alive. A great deal of collaboration between zoologists, parasitologists and pathologists will be needed before a complete text of lower vertebrate disease can be written.

H. REICHENBACH-KLINKE

January 1965   E. ELKAN

Contents

PART II. AMPHIBIA

PART III. REPTILIA

Part I

Fishes

CHAPTER 1

Method of Investigation

A. SYMPTOMS OF DISEASE—LIFE SPAN OF FISHES

No diagnosis of the disease that has befallen an animal can be made without proper investigation and, if possible, extended observation of the "patient". Just as our knowledge of the number of possible diseases of animals increases year by year so must our methods of investigation multiply and become more and more complicated. Equally, it must be remembered that many symptoms may not be typical of one disease only but may be present in many quite unrelated conditions.

The fish, an actively motile aquatic creature, necessarily shows its own characteristic range of symptoms. One of the first symptoms to be observed is usually a change in the normal mode of swimming. Locomotion, obviously out of control, becomes aimless: the fish swims jerkily and in small circles, is unable to keep on an even keel, or to raise itself when it sinks to the bottom. In extreme cases the loss of equilibrium can go so far as to make the fish swim upside-down, the abdomen turned towards the surface. If symptoms like these appear among fish under observation one specimen should be sacrificed for investigation. Less serious, perhaps, are attempts on the part of the fish to scrape along stones or to butt against the wall of the container in an attempt to rid itself from irritating parasites attached to its skin.

The recognition of feeding anomalies is extremely difficult. Complete refusal to feed is not necessarily a sign of illness. Many fish fast while their ovaries mature simply because, besides the enormously swollen ovaries, there is no space left for the other intestines. Also, like many other animals, a fish may take only one special kind of food and starve to death if this is not available.

Loss of colour and general pallor is a typical and alarming sign usually caused by metabolic or circulatory disturbances. Bacteria and microsporidia, affecting the skin or the muscles, may cause the same symptoms. On the other hand a fish may lose colour for lack either of light or of oxygen, if not of both, without being organically diseased. If the discoloration is confined to circumscribed areas of the skin, parasites should be suspected.

The appearance of an abnormally dark discoloration may equally be a sign of disease, particularly if the patches are black or brown. They may often be caused by the presence of subcutaneous parasites. Dark spots accompanied by local swelling may be due to tumours.

General degeneration of the skin occurs in the course of metabolic disturbances. It usually starts at the fins, which look torn and shredded, and continues with patchy losses of epidermis, haemorrhage and the development of ulceration. To this group belongs a kind of inflammation of the skin characterized by rough scales. In severe cases the scales may stand out at right angles.

Even a slight dullness of colours that should be brilliant may be of importance, particularly if the cornea of the eye is involved. It need hardly be mentioned that any swelling or protrusion of an eye must be regarded as a grave symptom.

Parallel with diseases of the skin, skeletal degenerations develop, affecting the jaws, the gill covers, and finally the spine and the tail, which may become shortened and distorted.

Apart from the localized symptoms the general behaviour of the fish should be watched, particularly if an otherwise active specimen hides in dark corners and seems unable to move its fins normally.

A seriously diseased fish, when caught in the net, fails to make the typical jerky movements in an attempt to escape. The absence of this escape reflex must be regarded as a grave symptom, particularly if it is accompanied by an absence of eye movement. The normal fish moves its eyes in relation to the source of light striking the tank. Absence of these eye and escape reflexes deserve particular attention where other symptoms of disease may be lacking.

The observer who knows his fish and their normal behaviour well will easily notice one of the many symptoms mentioned and this will allow him to isolate the affected individual before the disease has spread to others.

Symptoms due to disease should be distinguished from signs of old age. To assess these we should have some information on the expectation of life in the fishes. This varies from about 3 years for small species to about a hundred in large ones. Some of the observations available are set out on p. 5.

B. Killing and Detailed Examination of Specimens

Laboratories equipped to carry out such examinations prefer to obtain their material fresh and as soon after death as possible. The ideal method would therefore be to chill the dead fish and send it to

Species	Average expectation of life (years)
Nannostomus aripirangensis Meinken	3
Amia calva L.	7
Pristella riddlei Meek	8
Danio malabaricus Jerdon	9·5
Lepidosiren paradoxus Fitz	10
Anguilla anguilla L.	10–11*
Pterophyllum scalare C. & V.	11
Hemichromis bimaculatus Gill	14
Corydoras paleatus Jenyns	16
Melanotaenia nigrans Rich.	17
Puntius lateristriga C. & V.	18
Clupea harengus L.	18
Puntius semifasciolatus Gthr.	19
Puntius binotatus C. & V.	20
Eleotris marmorata Blkr.	20
Gadus callarias L.	25
Carassius carassius auratus Bloch	30
"Flatfish"	60–70
Acipenser ruthenus L.	72
Huso huso L.	up to 75
Silurus glanis L.	up to 100
Cyprinus carpio L.	up to 100

* If migration and ovulation is suppressed   55   and more

the laboratory in a Thermos flask. It should be remembered that haematological, bacteriological and virological examinations cannot be carried out on fixed material. The dissection of many of the intestines, too, is much more difficult in material that has been passed through formaldehyde or alcohol. On the other hand it must be considered that post-mortem fish material deteriorates within 1–2 h, particularly in the hot season. If, therefore, conditions should be particularly favourable, diseased fish should be sent in alive, in large cans holding water with oxygen sufficient for the journey and water-weeds to counteract excessive shaking. It is now possible to send small live fish with about a litre of water in a well closed polythene bag suitably packed in a cardboard box by rail. If available, some oxygen can be blown into the bag before closing it. Water plants will not produce oxygen in the dark but they will protect the fish from trauma.

In the case of external parasites answers may be expected soon. Any microscopical investigation, particularly those involving bacterial culturing or cutting of sections, may take one to several weeks. If more than one diseased specimen is available, the laboratory will be glad to have several, which will allow the use of a variety of methods to find the cause of the disease.

Fish can be killed by the time-honoured method of a blow on the head or by decapitation. Chemical methods, however, which do not damage any part of the fish's body, are much to be preferred. Ether and chloroform are miscible with water in sufficient quantity to effect anaesthesia or death. Urethane (2–5%) can be used for the same purpose. Among the latest arrivals MS 222 Sandoz (Basle) has become popular. Kodak recommend Quinaldine in low concentration.

The following parts deserve our particular attention: skin, including eyes; nasal aperture and lateral line system; gills and oral cavity; blood and intestinal contents; brain and spinal cord; muscles; peritoneal cavity and the remaining intestines and reproductive organs.

The skin is first inspected with a hand lens which will reveal any of the larger ectoparasites. Smears are made next and examined under the microscope. Later the fish may be scaled and skinned so that the skin can be examined for dermal or subcutaneous cysts. Among the ectoparasites we may expect to find bacteria, flagellates, ciliates, sporozoa, gyrodactylids, metacercariae, parasitic copepods and fungi.

The gills are dissected out after removal of the gill cover. They may be the seat of bacteria, flagellates, ciliates, sporozoa, trematodes and fungi.

As in many human diseases the blood picture often gives a hint of the nature of the disease, but the usefulness of blood counts and of the determination of the relation of white to red corpuscles is limited if we are in ignorance of the normal figures for the species. These figures change in the presence of parasites and in more than one species an unparasitized specimen would be difficult to find. Nor can we be sure that laboratory-bred animals will give figures comparable with those normal to the species in its natural environment. Gross leucocytosis, in particular eosinophilia, is however significant. The white blood corpuscles found in fish are lymphocytes, monocytes, neutrophile granulocytes and eosinophile granulocytes. Fish have no bone marrow and the leucocytes develop in lymphoid tissue in the kidney where it lies dispersed between the uriniferous tubules. In selachians (cartilaginous fish) such tissue is also found between the mucosa and the muscular coat of the oesophagus. The acidophile granules in the leucocytes of rays are much larger than those of higher vertebrates and in the electric rays (*Torpedo*) they are "bacilliform", i.e. they occur in the shape of small rodlets. Schäperclaus determined for the healthy carp a relation of red to white corpuscles of 332 : 1. The erythrocytes of fish are on the whole smaller than those of amphibians and reptiles but larger than those of mammals. They are oval and nucleated. Those of the cyclostomes, no longer grouped with the fish, are round. Fig. 1 shows a few examples of fish erythrocytes and that of man; Fig. 2 shows fish leucocytes.

The eyes should be carefully removed from their orbits with a small sharp scalpel and the contents investigated for bacteria, sporozoa,

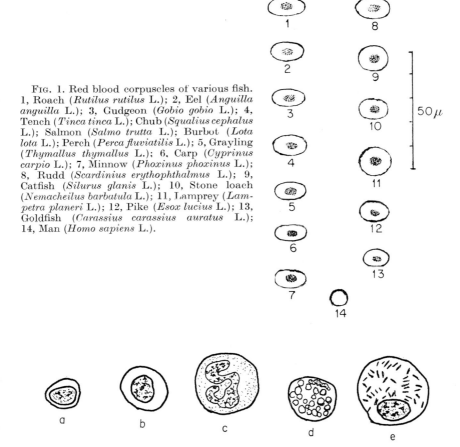

FIG. 1. Red blood corpuscles of various fish. 1, Roach (*Rutilus rutilus* L.); 2, Eel (*Anguilla anguilla* L.); 3, Gudgeon (*Gobio gobio* L.); 4, Tench (*Tinca tinca* L.); Chub (*Squalius cephalus* L.); Salmon (*Salmo trutta* L.); Burbot (*Lota lota* L.); Perch (*Perca fluviatilis* L.); 5, Grayling (*Thymallus thymallus* L.); 6, Carp (*Cyprinus carpio* L.); 7, Minnow (*Phoxinus phoxinus* L.); 8, Rudd (*Scardinius erythophthalmus* L.); 9, Catfish (*Silurus glanis* L.); 10, Stone loach (*Nemacheilus barbatula* L.); 11, Lamprey (*Lampetra planeri* L.); 12, Pike (*Esox lucius* L.); 13, Goldfish (*Carassius carassius auratus* L.); 14, Man (*Homo sapiens* L.).

FIG. 2. White blood corpuscles of fish. (After Bohn.) (a) Lymphocyte; (b) monocyte; (c) neutrophil of trout; (d) leucocyte with large granulation from ray; (e) leucocyte with fusiform granula from *Torpedo*.

trematodes, fungi, rarely ciliates. If fungi are found the adjacent parts of the brain should be carefully scrutinized. The brain may be examined fresh or in sections. Here too we may find bacteria, ciliates, sporozoa or fungi.

A similar array of parasites—bacteria, microsporidia, myxosporidia, haplosporidia, metacercaria and fungi—may be expected to occur in the muscle. Areas which look pale, swollen or hardened should be teased apart under the dissecting lens so that isolated muscle fibres can be examined.

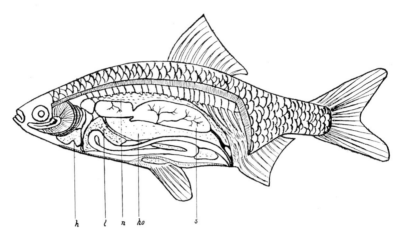

Fig. 3. Dissection of a roach (*Leuciscus rutilus* L.). *h*, heart; *ho*, testis; *l*, liver; *n*, kidney; *s*, swim-bladder. (After Schnakenbeck.)

The intestinal canal, being the obvious port of entry for many kinds of infestation, should always be scrutinized for the presence of parasites and signs of disease. From mouth to anus we may find flagellates, ciliates and fungi; in the gut, bacteria, sporozoa, trematodes, cestodes, acanthocephala, nematodes, and fungi. Examination of the intestinal wall in sections is of great importance because it is here that we may find the early stages in the reproductive cycle of sporozoans which penetrate the intestinal epithelium after hatching from spores swallowed by the host. Fungi like *Ichthyosporidium hoferi* may be found in the same area. It is practical to cut through the oesophagus immediately behind the oral cavity and to pull out and straighten the gut, gradually detaching it with scissors from the mediastinum along its whole length down to the anus, where it is again cut through. It is impossible to open the whole length of the gut without having straightened it out first and the scissors used should have at least one blunt tip.

The peritoneal cavity is opened by a curved cut beginning at the anus and following its upper border to the dorsal edge of the operculum returning to the anus along the mid-ventral line (Fig. 3). Fluid or any foreign bodies found should be examined.

Next to the gut it is the liver which is most frequently the seat of disease. The organ may be examined in squashes or in sections. Bacterial cysts, sporozoa, fungal cysts and encapsuled larvae of various worms may be encountered.

Kidney, spleen and heart are frequently the seat of parasites; the swim-bladder may be infected by sporozoans. Testes and ovaries may be destroyed by the presence of nematodes or fungi.

For details of the techniques required in the investigation of so many different diseases and parasites special textbooks on animal histology must be consulted. This applies particularly to the many selective staining methods available and to the culture media used in the separation and recognition of bacterial strains. For the diagnosis of solid tumours microtome sections are indispensable. In rare cases of skeletal anomalies radiography may also be useful.

C. Rules to be Followed on Sending in Fish for Investigation

The more closely these rules are followed the easier will be the task of the investigator.

1. Avoid delay. Send live specimen. If this is impossible despatch immediately after death.
2. Send dead animals frozen and, only if this is impracticable, in preserving fluids.
3. Never send any material without a detailed history of the case.

The following details may be kept in mind. It is of the utmost importance to the investigating laboratory to receive either live or very fresh material since new strains of bacteria or fungi may grow during decomposition, obscuring the original infection and leading the investigator to faulty conclusions. In some cases, where it is necessary to determine the species of a fungus or a bacterium from cultures, preserved material can obviously not be used at all. In others, certain fine structures typical of the offending organism may be lost through preservation as well as through decomposition. From all that has been said it will be clear how superior live material is to anything else that may be sent to the laboratory.

The use of Thermos flasks for the sending of small pieces of chilled material has already been mentioned. Very careful packing of these fragile containers is highly recommended since it is not very convenient

1*

to fish out a morsel of dead fish from among a heap of broken glass. Cans made for the transport of fish usually have a wide bottom and a conical roof to make the surface of the water, where oxygen may be absorbed, as large as possible. On long journeys arrangements will have to be made for the water to be renewed. Water-weeds may absorb a certain amount of the oxygen but leafed branches may be introduced to protect the fish from excessive shaking in transit. In the summer, ice should be added at regular intervals; in the winter, warm water— particularly when tropical fish are sent. If a packing crate is used, ice may be conveniently included, packed in plastic bags.

Post-mortem material, whether whole small fish or parts of larger ones, should be sent wrapped in cotton wool soaked in 5% formaldehyde. Packing in plastic bags or plastic containers saves much postage and avoids breakage in transit. Alternatively alcohol (50–70%) may be used. S.V.I. (Spiritus Vini Industrialis), stocked by all chemists, has a concentration of about 96% and is suitable as a fixative in adequate dilution. The intestines of large specimens decompose even if the whole fish is immersed in fixing fluid, and this danger is the greater the higher the air temperature of the day. Such specimens must be thoroughly injected before despatch. In medium-sized fish it is sufficient to inject 5% formaldehyde into the body cavity.

The case history is of great importance to the investigator. It should indicate all abnormalities recorded in the diseased fish, deviation from normal behaviour as well as changes in appearance noticed while the fish was still alive. Symptoms like the following will easily bring themselves to the notice of the observer: pallor or abnormal darkening of parts or of the whole body; jerky scraping along stones; loss of equilibrium; persistent swimming at the surface with gasping for oxygen and refusal to feed. The case history should also mention on what type of food the fish has been fed and whether, for any reason or other, a change in diet has been attempted. Finally, it may be of interest to have a view of the kind of cage or tank that was used, whether or not it was overgrown with algae, whether artificial or daylight was used for illumination, how much lime the water contained and what the pH figures were. Every detail may be of interest in the investigation of a particular case.

REFERENCES

Andrew, W. (1959). "Textbook of Comparative Histology." Oxford University Press, New York.

Bohn, G. (1934). " Leçons de Zoologie et Biologie générale." Hermann, Paris.

Brown, M. E. (1957). " The Physiology of Fishes." Academic Press, New York.

Cunningham, J. T. (1912). Chapter on Fishes. *In* "Reptiles, Amphibia, Fishes and Lower Chordates" (Lydekkar *et al.*, eds.). Methuen, London.

Duijn, C. v. (1956). "Diseases of Fishes", publ. *Water Life*, London.

Goodrich, E. S. (1930). "Studies on the Structure and Development of Vertebrates." Macmillan, London.

Gresham, G. A. and Jennings, A. R. (1962). "An Introduction to Comparative Pathology." Academic Press, New York.

Guyer, M. F. (1933). "Animal Micrology", 5th edn., University of Chicago Press.

Hirschmann, H. and Partsch, K. (1954). Zur Methodik der Fischuntersuchung (mit besondereer Berücksichtigung der Fischkrankheiten). *Mikrokosmos* **42**, 160–165.

Humason, G. L. (1961). "Animal Tissue Techniques." W. H. Freeman and Co., San Francisco.

Jung, T. (1958). Zur Kenntnis der Ernährungsbiologie der in dem Raum zwischen Harz und Heide vorkommenden Hirudineen. *Zool. Jahrb. Phys.* **66**, 79–128.

Plehn, M. (1924). "Praktikum der Fischkrankheiten." Stuttgart.

Romeis, B. (1948). "Mikroskopische Technik", 15th edn., Munich.

Roth, W. (1922). "Die Krankheiten der Aquarienfische und ihre Bekämpfung", 2nd edn., Stuttgart.

Saunders, J. T. and Manton, S. M. (1931). "A Manual of Practical Vertebrate Morphology." Oxford University Press.

Schäperclaus, W. (1954). "Fischkrankheiten", 3rd edn., Akademie Verlag, Berlin.

Schulz, F. N. and Krüger, F. v. (1925). Das Blut der Wirbeltiere. *In* "Handbuch der vergleichenden Physiologie" (H. Winterstein, ed.). Vol. I, 1. Jena.

Young, J. Z. (1950). "The Life of Vertebrates." Clarendon Press, Oxford.

Chapter 2

Infectious Diseases

A. Diseases due to Bacterial Infection

Arranging the bacterial infections common in fish according to "Bergey's Manual" (1957) the preponderance of the Pseudomonadaceae is very striking. The following types may be encountered:

Pseudomonadales
  Pseudomonadaceae
    Pseudomonas fluorescens Migula
    Pseudomonas ichthyodermis Zobell and Upham
    Aeromonas punctata Snieszko
    Aeromonas salmonicida Griffin
    Aeromonas hydrophila Stanier
    Photobacterium phosphoreum Ford
  Spirillaceae
    Vibrio anguillarum Bergmann
    Vibrio piscium David
Eubacteriales
  Corynebacteriaceae
    Erysipelothrix insidiosa Langford and Hensen
    Corynebacterium spp.
  Enterobacteriaceae
    Escherichia coli Castellani and Chalmers
    Paracolobactrum aerogenoides Borman, Stuart and Wheeler
    Haemophilus piscium Snieszko, Griffin and Friddle
Actinomycetales
    Mycobacterium fortuitum Cruz
    Mycobacterium piscium Bergey *et al.*
    Mycobacterium marinum Aronson
    Mycobacterium platypoecilus Baker and Hagan
    Mycobacterium salmoniphilum Ross
    Streptomyces salmonicida Rucker
Myxobacteriales
    Cytophaga columnaris Davis-Garnjobst

Chondrococcus columnaris Fish and Rucker
Spirochaetales
    Spirochaeta spp.
    Treponema spp.
Rickettsiales
    Neorickettsia helminthoeca Phillips *et al.*

Diseases caused by pseudomonad Bacteria

The infective ascites of cyprinids is usually due to an infection with *Aeromonas punctata* Sn., a very variable aquatic bacterium which occurs in harmless and pathogenic strains. Schäperclaus described the latter as *"forma ascitae"*. But it must be remembered that the pathogenic strains are well able to live elsewhere than in the body of fish. The varying lesions caused by this bacillus have been studied by Schäperclaus (1952–53), Dombrowski (1953) and Liebmann (1954). The leading symptoms are always ascites with green discoloration and degeneration of the liver, enlargement of the spleen and anaemia. Ulcers may develop and, if the fish survives the ascites, deformities of the skeleton of the head, the spine or the fins may remain. The inhabitants of ponds frequently show nothing but the ulcerative form of the disease (Figs. 4 and 5).

Fig. 4. Carp suffering from ulcerative ascites. (Photo.: *Bayr. biol. exp. Inst.*)

The responsible bacterium is a short, Gram-negative rod with one flagellum, length $0.9–1.5\,\mu$, width $0.4–0.5\,\mu$. The length of the flagellum is about three times that of the body (Fig. 6).

Schäperclaus recommends immediate isolation of specimen, disinfection and, if possible, the introduction of bacteriophages suitable to attack the bacillus. The same author (1955a) reports good results with antibiotics like streptomycin or chloromycetin. They be may administered:

(a) In the form of injections. A fish of 10 g receives 0·1 mg of chloromycetin dissolved in 0·1 ml of water.

(b) Mixed into the food. A fish of 10 g receives 1 mg of chloromycetin mixed with 1 g of rye meal daily.

(c) As a bath. 80 mg of chloromycetin to be dissolved in 1 litre of water. The fish to remain in the bath for 8 h. The drug should not be added to the water in an aquarium.

Duijn (1951) recommends sodium chloride baths at daily-rising con-

FIG. 5. Siamese fighting fish (*Betta splendens* Regan) ♂ suffering from ascites. (Orig.)

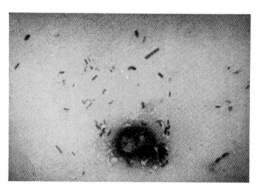

FIG. 6. *Pseudomonas punctata* Zimmermann. Smear from a swordtail (*Xiphophorus helleri* Heckel) suffering from ascites. × 400. (After v. Duijn.)

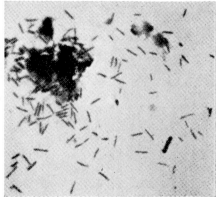

FIG. 7. *Pseudomonas fluorescens* Flügge. Smear from a Gurami. × 1320. (After v. Duijn.)

centrations, or baths in solutions of ammonia of 1 : 2 000 for 5–15 min. Liebmann puts more emphasis on keeping the fish under natural conditions with sufficient administration of the vitamins A and D and the trace elements of copper, cobalt and magnesium. His results refer in particular to the keeping of carp.

Aeromonas punctata Snieszko has been blamed for the freshwater ascites of eels and the patchy discoloration of bream, pike, whiting and perch.

Symptoms of the freshwater disease of the eel are a patchy or general reddening of the skin, particularly on the ventral side near the anus and on the fins. The diseased fish may be listless with white or ulcerated patches or localized swellings. Blindness, enteritis and internal haemorrhages may supervene.

Similarly the disease common among whiting is characterized by patches of reddened skin developing into ulcers, loss of parts of fins and internal haemorrhages. The offending bacteria cannot always be found. Pike seem to suffer from an analogous disease which, however, is said to be caused by a virus (see p. 149).

Aeromonas salmonicida G., another pseudomonad bacterium, is to blame for the boils of salmon (Snieszko and Bullock, 1957). Boils appear first along the dorsal fin and gradually spread all over the body. Haemorrhagic ulcers teem with bacteria. Once they gain entrance into the general circulation the fish dies from septicaemia. In some cases the fish even die before external symptoms have been noticed. *Haemophilus piscium* S., G. and F. causes a very similar disease among trout in North America, where the complaint is well known and feared as the "Ulcer Disease of Trout".

Yolk hydrops of embryonic fish has been ascribed to *Aeromonas liquefaciens* van Betegh. These cases may, however, rather be due to developmental disturbances than bacterial infection (Fig. 148).

Pseudomonas fluorescens Flügge is a Gram-negative rod of $1\cdot6-3\,\mu$ length and a width of about $0\cdot5\,\mu$. The presence of 2–6 flagella distinguish it from *A. punctata*, but both forms occur in harmless and pathogenic strains. These bacteria have so far only been isolated from the skin of diseased fish, not from internal organs. They were found on *Trichogaster trichopterus* Pallas, *Macropodus opercularis* L., *Colisa lalia* H-B., the barbel, some characids and some cichlids (Duijn, 1938) (Fig. 7). The bacterial invasions seem to occur mainly in specimens debilitated through other, metabolic disturbances, but they are in most cases lethal.

Vibrio, which produces similar symptoms, commonly attacks marine fishes. The saltwater eel disease, for instance, is caused by *Vibrio anguillarum* Bergmann, a curved Gram-negative bacterium without spore formation or capsule. Its length is $1\cdot5\,\mu$, its width $0\cdot5\,\mu$. This disease, too, begins with the appearance of red skin patches which develop into boils and ulcerations. The muscles, particularly those in the cardiac region, become affected and the eel dies exhibiting spastic movements. *Vibrio anguillarum* was found by Schäperclaus to occur among pike in the Baltic. In these and in other Baltic species the bacillus produced erythema and petechiae.

Freshwater or saltwater fish, kept for long periods in an aquarium, are prone to develop bacterial fin rot, particularly of the tail. The disease is caused by a Gram-negative non-sporulating pleomorph bacillus. Affected fish usually die on the third day after the disease has been noticed. Damage to the skin, which may have been caused by careless use of the net, involving loss of scales, may help the bacillus to gain entrance. The symptoms are similar to those of the epizootic of whitings: inflammation of scale pockets; loss of scales; ulceration; eventually septicaemia and death. Bacterial fin rot is common both among fish taken from their natural habitat and among those born in captivity. Schäperclaus described (1950) a case of this kind in a black Molly. The rod-shaped bacteria had a tendency to form chains. The disease is without doubt infectious.

Fig. 8. *Colisa lalia* H.-B. with severe fin rot of skin and eyes. × 2. (Orig.)

An explosive spread of a disease of this kind was observed among a batch of *Colisa lalia* H.-B. freshly imported from S.E. Asia. The fish survived the transport to Europe but fell ill on arrival and died without exception within a day or two. The skin became grey, matt and patchy, the cornea, sometimes the whole eye, degenerated (Fig. 8) and every smear showed the presence of masses of rod-shaped bacteria.

The addition of various disinfectants to the water has been recommended. Albucid (1 g in 10 l of water) or Trypaflavin (1 g in 100 l) may be tried. Antibiotics will probably mostly come too late. In any case the addition of common salt (0·4–0·6%) to the water may be equally effective, at least in the treatment of freshwater fish. Whatever the treatment, even if it proves successful, it should be continued for some time after all signs of disease have disappeared.

Chlamydobacteriales

These thread-forming bacteria which Duijn found on the skin of Siamese fighting fish (*Betta splendens* Regan) seem to be comparatively harmless. The threads formed by the bacteria give the skin a velvety aspect and the condition may easily be confounded with a fungal infection. The bacterial threads, however, are much thinner than those produced by fungi. Duijn states that water containing an excess of iron favours the growth of these bacteria.

Eubacteriales

Dermatitis in fish, recognized by roughening of the scales due to oedema, may also be caused by "*Bacterium*" *lepidorthosae* Duijn 1951, a small, very motile Gram-negative flagellated rod allied to the *coli* group. The bacteria were found in the skin as well as in internal organs. After the initial dermatitis the tail becomes paralysed; the fish linger for a while at the surface but die within a few days. *Betta* and *Macropodus* seem to be particularly affected.

Paracolobactrum aerogenoides Borman, Stuart and Wheeler is allied to the paracolon group. It has recently been found in the body cavity of several freshwater fish (Griffin and Snieszko, 1961) and experimentally the infection could be transferred to young trout.

Haemophilus piscium causes the condition commonly referred to as "ulcer disease" (Snieszko *et al.*, 1950). White papillary spots quickly develop into round ulcers accompanied by inflammation of the jaws and the palate. The tissues may be ulcerated down to the bone and the infection may equally destroy the fins. In some cases the condition resembles furunculosis.

A small Gram-positive diplobacillus (?*Moraxella*) was suspected by Snieszko and Griffin to cause the kidney disease of N. American salmonids. The kidneys appear oedematous and show grey-white necrotic areas. The gut is filled with yellow fluid; a similar, transparent, often slightly pink fluid fills the peritoneal cavity. Petechiae may be seen in the skin and the peritoneum, necrotic areas in the gills, the liver and other organs. The disease seems similar to the virus causing septicaemia of trout (see p. 149). The authors suggest that the bacillus responsible may also cause the "Salmon poisoning" of dogs which

Cordy and Gorham ascribed to a Rickettsia *Neorickettsia helmin-thoeca.*

Reference to the erysipelas of fish is made on p. 190.

Actinomycetales. Tuberculosis of Fish

The term of "fish tuberculosis" was suggested by Bertarelli and Bocchia (1910) and Betegh (1910) who found numerous cases of fish affected by foci containing the typical acid-fast cold-water tubercle bacilli. Later investigations showed that here too we are dealing with a whole group of bacteria all of which produce similar morbid conditions in fish. The symptoms heralding an infection of this kind are again refusal to feed; loss of weight; pallor and milky turbidity of the skin; defects of the integument, with haemorrhages and ulcers which may develop into deep craters, exophthalmos, open wounds and fin de-generation of any degree up to complete loss of the distal parts. The progress of the disease is a slow one and at the start the animals appear to be perfectly well. Gradually they lose weight, their move-ments become jerky and the fish retire to dark and inaccessible corners

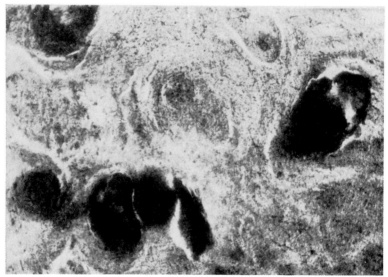

FIG. 9. Heart of *Trichogaster leeri* Blkr. with tubercular foci. × 110. (Photo.: Reichen-bach-Klinke.)

of the aquarium. Internal organs show at this stage the appearance of small gray necrotic foci, sometimes with a dark centre (Fig. 9). In the course of time these grow and coalesce, gradually displacing and des-troying the healthy tissue. Eventually the specimen dies when some of the larger tumours completely block the circulation of the diseased organs. These symptoms are unfortunately not so specific that a certain diagnosis can be made *in vivo*. Only the presence of acid-fast bacilli in smears or sections proves the specific origin of the disease. Since, however, we are here dealing not with one but with a group of very similar bacteria, the symptoms they produce may not be exactly alike in every case and every kind of fish. An exact diagnosis can only be made by a laboratory equipped to use intricate culture methods to distinguish one of these closely allied species of bacteria from another. The common ground among all types of *Mycobacterium* remains that they produce exactly the same symptoms when transferred to other fish, that they are acid-fast, and that they are not pathogenic for warm-blooded animals. All these bacteria, however, belong to the order Actinomycetales genus *Mycobacterium* Lehmann and Neumann. They are Gram-positive and, when stained with fuchsin, are not decolorized by weak acids. Those which infect warm-blooded animals grow best at 37°C; those which infect fish at 25–30°C. Cultures of the latter type die off when grown at the higher range of 37°C. The two types cannot be distinguished morphologically. Branched types may occasionally be seen. The bacteria are aerobic and do not liquify gelatine. Grown on broth they form thin fragile surface skins, some cultures producing an odour typical of tuberculin. Positive tuberculin reactions have not been elicited in the cold-water types. Their growth is enhanced by the addition of glycerine and glucose to the medium.

A few further details about bacteria belonging to this group may be of interest.

The most commonly distributed type seems to be *Mycobacterium piscium* Bergey *et al.* (*Bacillus tuberculosis piscium* Dubard) which attacks all kinds of freshwater fish in cold and tropical climates. The bacillus is an acid-fast rod, Gram-negative, non-motile, of a length varying from 0.3–0.5 $\mu \times 3$–12 μ. Star-shaped colonies are typical (Reichenbach-Klinke, 1954). The actual size of the bacteria seems to vary according to the host in which they grow (Table 1).

Bacteria found in one and the same fish are of equal length. In cultures their length may be uniform but as soon as they are again transferred to fish their length begins to vary. For details see Jahnel (1940) and Reichenbach-Klinke (1954).

Transferred to glycerine–agar these bacteria produce round, button-like colonies; on more solid media they may have a violet tinge. Both glucose and lactose are accepted, galactose is rejected.

Mycobacterium piscium may be identical with the "Aquarium organism" mentioned by Baker and Hagan (1942) which was highly pathogenic for the goldfish but did not affect *Platypoecilus maculatus* Gthr. and was of variable length. Equally the rodlets described by Shin Maie (1922) in goldfish may have been of the same kind.

TABLE 1

Bacteria Observed in Cases of "Fish Tuberculosis" (Reichenbach-Klinke, 1954)

Host	Length of bacteria (μ)	Author
Xiphophorus helleri Heckel	below 3–5	J. Jahnel
Gymnocorymbus ternetzi Boul.	3–3·5	J. Jahnel
Danio malabaricus Jerdon	3–7	J. Jahnel
Haplochromis multicolor Hilg.	4–9	J. Jahnel
Aphyocharax rubropinnis Papph.	4–10	J. Jahnel
Cichlasoma meeki Brind	3–5	R.–K.
Hyphessobrycon innesi Myers	5–7	R.–K.
Trichogaster leeri Blkr.	3–5	R.–K.
Pterophyllum scalare C. and V.	6–10	R.–K.
Lebistes reticulatus Peters	6–10	R.–K.
Tanichthys albonubes L.	5–7	R.–K.
Symphysodon discus Heckel	6–8	R.–K.
Apistogramma ramirezi M. and H.	5–7	R.–K.
Barbus conchonius Ham.–Buch.	10–12	R.–K.

Any tissue may fall a victim to the invasion by these bacteria. Discoloration and milky turbidity of the skin may be the first signs, ulcers of varying depth supervene as muscular and even bony parts are destroyed. Eventually even the liver, the intestine, the kidney, the spleen and the heart may be affected (Fig. 10). Bony tuberculosis

FIG. 10. Spontaneous tubercular infection of *Danio malabaricus* Jerdon. Tubercles on skin and internal organs. (After Jahnel.)

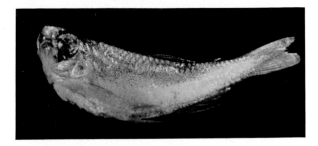

FIG. 11. Spinal deformity caused by tuberculosis in *Hyphessobrycon innesi* Myers. (After Reichenbach-Klinke.)

FIG. 12. Spinal deformity caused by tuberculosis in *Rasbora heteromorpha* Duncker. (After Reichenbach-Klinke.)

FIG. 13. Destruction of skull through tuberculosis in *Cichlasoma meeki* Brind. (After Reichenbach-Klinke.)

may manifest itself in deformation of the jaws and spinal curvatures (Figs. 11, 12 and 13.) The disease is common among fish and may cause great losses when it assumes the extent of an epizootic. Jahnel took tuberculosis to be the commonest cause of death in fish. This may be correct for some localities but is hardly true generally.

A bacterium, apparently belonging to this group and discovered by Baker and Hagan (1942) has already been mentioned. Growth started at 25°C, was optimal at 30°C and ceased at 37°C. There was no change in length as observed in *M. piscium*. Suitable media were glycerol–egg, glycerol–phosphate–agar and Söhngen's mixture. The lesions equal those seen in *M. piscium* infections.

Nigrelli (1943), listing deaths which occurred in the New York Aquarium, mentions only three cases (2·5% of the total death-rate) attributable to these bacteria. The figure seems astonishingly low, for he had already mentioned an epizootic of "tuberculosis" among these fish for 1942 which had killed numerous specimens of *Hyphessobrycon innesi* Myers, *Tanichthys albonubes* L. and species of *Brachydanio*. All these deaths were presumably due to *Mycobacterium piscium*.

Mycobacterium marinum, described by Aronson in 1936, is non-motile, acid-fast and shows the variability in length typical of the genus. It was found in the liver, the spleen, the gills, the kidney, the ovary, the pericardium and the eye of tropical coral fish like *Abudefduf mauritii* Bloch, *Micropogon undulatus* L. and *Centropristes striatus* L., which were at the time kept at the Philadelphia aquarium. Colonies grown on agar were first lemon-coloured but darkened to orange later on. Grown on glycerol–agar they were greyish-white at first, some changing towards orange later on. Gelatine was not liquefied. Galactose was rejected while fructose was metabolized. The optimal growth temperature was 18–20°C. Growth stopped completely at 47°C.

Another acid-fast rodlet, described as the "Halibut Strain", was seen by Griffith (1930) and Sutherland (1922) in *Hippoglossus vulgaris* Fleming. It produced the typical picture of dermal tuberculosis with granulomatous degeneration but without the presence of giant cells. The acid-fast bacilli ceased to grow at 37°C and were not pathogenic for frogs and goldfish. Agglutination and absorption tests allowed a strict differentiation of this strain from *Mycobacterium marinum*. Thin, grey-white, later white, pearl-like colonies grew on egg, while growth on broth produced a grey surface film with white patches.

Only four strains of cold-water *Mycobacterium* can at present be said to have been well established as valid. They are *Mycobacterium piscium* Bergey *et al.*, *M. platypoecilus* Baker and Hagan, *M. marinum* Aronson and the "Halibut Strain" of Griffith and Sutherland. Taking into account strains isolated from amphibians and reptiles and typing them according to agglutination and absorption, Griffith (1930) established four serological types. Type I: *Mycobacterium marinum* and crocodile strain (Cayman strain); Type II: frog strain; Type III: carp strain (probably = *M. piscium*), snake strain and turtle strain; Type IV: halibut strain.

Important observations, showing that the infection of salmon is not always due to natural causes, have been made by Ross *et al.* (1957, 1960) working at the U.S.A. Western Fish Disease Laboratory, Seattle, Washington, who summed up their conclusions as follows: "The inclusion of viscera and carcases of tuberculous adult salmon in the diet of juvenile salmonids is considered to be the major source of mycobacterial infections in hatchery-reared fish." Compared with this source of infection all other possible modes were found to be of very minor importance and a substantial reduction of the tubercular infection among salmon could be achieved if feeding methods at the hatcheries were adjusted so as to exclude salmon carcases altogether. Ross described the causative organism as *Mycobacterium salmoniphilum* (1960).

Recent observations have shown the adaptability of acid-fast bacteria to be much greater than formerly supposed. Ross and Brancato, working on *Mycobacterium fortuitum*, recently found the thermal adaptability of this strain to be even greater than previously determined. Their strain, derived from *Hyphessobrycon innesi* but also known from guinea-pigs, rabbits and mice, continued to grow even at 37°C (see also Gordon and Smith, 1955).

Observations of this nature would also make us pay particular attention to the temperature. It has been suggested that higher temperatures, even if tolerated by the fish, favour bacterial infection while varying or lower temperature ranges seem to have a protective effect. Obviously the adaptability of the fish has to be considered, but attempts at protecting them by varying their temperature seem to be well worth while. This, of course, can only be a first approach to the problem. The full fight against these bacteria can only be conducted with the aid of drugs, particularly sulphonamides (Elster and Mann, 1949). It is still doubtful at present to what degree they may be supported by antibiotics. Wherever possible the selection of resistant races of fish and the strict imitation of their natural habitat presents the best guarantee of success.

It cannot be denied, however, that all these investigations represent only a beginning in the investigation of cold-water tuberculosis. Further investigations are very likely to lead to the discovery of other well-definable strains. Our present knowledge of the host specificity and the specific requirements of the various strains is very incomplete, but since infections of this nature occur commonly both in natural habitats and in collections, it is likely that further investigators will take up the quest for the nature of these important bacteria.

Considering the limits of our present knowledge, the fight to ward off infections of this kind still presents a difficult problem. Where fish are kept more or less crowded it cannot surprise that the disease usually assumes the nature of an epizootic. Free-living fish seem to be much better able to ward off infections of this nature because only the healthiest individuals survive anyway. Any fish weakened by deficient feeding or uncongenial surroundings is in much greater danger of falling a victim to bacterial infection, and it is not at all surprising that aquarium life, often accompanied by deficient light (particularly in the blue part of the spectrum), deficient food and accumulation of metabolic end-products, should predispose to a general weakening of the natural defences of the fish.

Streptomyces

Infection of fish with members of the genus *Streptomyces* is fortunately uncommon. Rucker (1949) found an infection of this kind in the liver

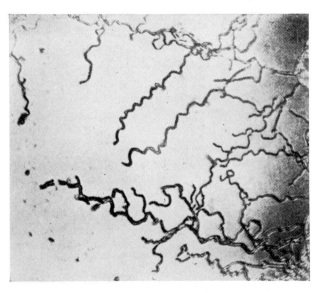

FIG. 14. Aerial hyphae of *Streptomyces salmonicida* Rucker from the liver of *Oncorhynchus nerka* Walbaum. × 1 000. (After Rucker.)

and the kidney of young American Salmonids (*Oncorhynchus nerka* Walb.). The parasite produced forked threads of 0·5–1 µ width and chains of oval spores (Fig. 14).

Myobacteriales and Spirochaetales

Members of these genera are held responsible for a bacterial oedema of the gills in young trout. The disease is highly infectious and causes great losses among the stock (Klingler, 1958; Machado-Cruz, 1962). Externally the disease can be recognized by the inability of the fish to close the operculum. Breed *et al.* (1950) mention the occurrence of the genera *Spirochaeta* and *Treponema* in the gut of marine fishes like gadids and blenniids.

Bacterial Diseases of Uncertain Origin

Davis (1922) described a condition under the name of "Peduncle Disease" caused apparently by a rod-shaped bacterium of 3 5 µ length. The disease affected particularly the fry of rainbow trout. It began with a greyish discoloration of the fin edges and gradually destroyed skin and muscles. The exact nature of the offending organism has not been determined.

Rickettsiales

A Rickettsia, *Neorickettsia helminthoeca* Phillips *et al.*, was described from salmon by Cordy and Gorham in 1950. Attention was drawn to the salmon after the occurrence of cases of "Salmon poisoning" in people who had eaten uncooked salmon. It was suggested that the disease is transmitted by metacercariae.

REFERENCES

Aronson, J. D. (1926). Spontaneous tuberculosis in salt water fish. *J. infect. Dis.* **39**, 315–330.

Baker, J. A. and Hagan, W. A. (1942). Tuberculosis of the Mexican platyfish (*Platypoecilus maculatus*). *J. infect. Dis.* **70**, 248–252.

Bataillon, Dubard and Terre (1897). Un nouveau type de tuberculose. *C.R. Soc. Biol., Paris* **49**, 446–449.

Bertarelli, E. and Bocchia, J. (1910). Neue Untersuchungen über die Tuberkulose der Kaltblüter. *Zbl. Bakt.* I, **54**, 385–389.

Betegh, L. v. (1910). Weitere Beiträge zur experimentellen Tuberkulose der Meeresfische nebst Studien über die Transmutationsfrage der Warmblütertuberkelbazillen. *Zbl. Bakt.* I, **53**, 374–377; **54**, 211–216.

Breed, R. S., Murray, E. G. D. and Hitchens, A. P. (1950). *In* "Bergey's Manual of Determinative Bacteriology", 7th edn., Ballière, Tindal and Cox, London.

Bullock, G. L. (1961). A schematic outline for the presumptive identification of bacterial diseases of fish. *Progr. Fish Cult.* 1961, 147–151.

Cordy, D. R. and Gorham, J. R. (1950). The pathology and etiology of salmon disease in the dog and fox. *Amer. J. Path.* **26**, 617, 637.

Davis, H. S. (1922). A new bacterial disease of freshwater fishes. *Bull. Bur. Fish.* **38**, 261–280.

Davis, H. S. (1956). "Culture and Diseases of Game Fishes." Berkeley and Los Angeles.

Dombrowski, H. (1953). Vergleichende morphologische und physiologische Untersuchungen zwischen *Pseudomonas punctata* (Zimmermann) und *Pseudomonas fluorescens* (Flügge) sowie deren Vorkommen in der Natur. *Biol. Zbl.* **72**, 449–464.

Duijn, C. van (1951). "Diseases of Fishes." Chap. 13, Tuberculosis disease, pp. 69–70. Publ. *Water Life*, London.

Elster, H. G. and Mann, H. (1949). Bekämpfung der Verpilzung von Fischeiern mit Sulfonamiden. *Allg. Fischereiztg.* **74**, 24.

Gordon, R. E. and Smith, M. M. (1955). Rapid growing of acid-fast bacteria. II. Species description of *Mycobacterium fortuitum* Cruz. *J. Bact.* **69**, 502–507.

Griffin, P. J. and Friddle, S. B. (1953). A more comprehensive description of *Bacterium salmonicida*. *Trans. Amer. Fish. Soc.* **82**, 129.

Griffin, P. J. and Snieszko, S. F. (1961). A unique bacterium pathogenic for warm-blooded and cold-blooded animals. *Fish. Bull. U.S. Dept. Int.* **52**, No. 68, 185–190.

Griffith, A. S. (1930). Tuberculosis in cold-blooded animals. *In* "A System of Bacteriology in Relation to Medicine", Vol. 5, pp. 326–332.

Jahnel, J. (1940). Spontaninfektionen mit säurefesten Stäbchen bei Fischen. Neue Beobachtungen bei Fischtuberkulose. *Wien. tierärztl. Mschr.* **27**, 289–302.

Jahnel, J. (1940). Die Fischtuberkulose. *Wschr. Aqu. Terrk.* **37**, 317–321.

Klingler, K. (1958). Entzündliche Kiemenschwellung bei Regenbogenforellen. *Schweiz. Fischereiztg.* **66**, 98–99.

Ledoux-Lebard (1900). Le bacille pisciaire et la tuberculose de la grenouille due à ce bacille. *Ann. Inst. Pasteur* **14**, 535–554.

Liebmann, H. (1956). Ernährungsstörung und Degeneration als primäre Ursache der Bauchwassersucht bei Fischen. *Berlin. Münchn. tierärztl. Wschr.* 1956, 21–34.

Machado-Cruz, J. A. (1962). Sur l'apparition récente de "Bacterial gill disease" en Europe et sa caractérisation histopathologique. *Publ. Inst. Zool. Porto*, No. 82.

McCraw, B. M. (1952). Furunculosis of fish. *U.S. Dept. Int. Rep. Fish.* **84**.

Maie, S. (1922). Experimentelle Versuche bei Goldfischen (*Carassius auratus*.) mit säurefesten Bazillen. *Zbl. Bakt.* I, **88**, 28–38.

Nigrelli, R. F. (1943). Causes of diseases and death of fishes in captivity. *Zoologica*, **28**, 203–216.

Offhaus, K., Brunner, G. and Riedmüller, S. (1955). Gedanken über die Entstehung der Bauchwassersucht des Karpfens auf Grund bakteriologischer Ergebnisse und elektrophoretischer Untersuchungen. *Arch. Fischereiwiss.* **31**, 316–327.

Parisot, T. J. and Decker, A. H. (1960). A comparative study of the causative agent of a mycobacterial disease of salmonid fishes. *Amer. Rev. resp. Dis.* **81**, No. 1, 60–67; **82**, No. 2, 212–222.

Peruansky, A. (1912). Über die Bakterienflora des Fischdarms und ihre Beziehungen zu den Fischvergiftungen und Fäulnisvorgängen. *Diss. Heidelberg* 1912.

Reichenbach-Klinke, H. H. (1953). Schädelzerstörung bei Aquarienfischen als Folge einer Mangelerkrankung. *Nachr. Naturwiss. Mus. Aschaffenburg* **40**, 49–56.

Reichenbach-Klinke, H. H. (1954). Untersuchungen über die bei Fischen durch Parasiten hervorgerufenen Zysten und deren Wirkung auf den Wirtskörper. I, Teil. *Z. Fischerei* N.F. **31**, 564–636.

Reichenbach-Klinke, H. H. (1955). Beobachtungen über Meeresfisch-Tuberkulose. *Pubbl. Staz. Zool. Napoli* **26**, 55–62.

Ross, A. J. (1959). *Mycobacterium salmoniphilum* sp. nov. from salmonid fishes. *Amer. Rev. resp. Dis.* **79**, 241–250.

Ross, A. J. and Brancato, F. P. (1959). *Mycobacterium fortuitum* Cruz from the tropical fish *Hyphessobrycon innesi*. *J. Bact.* **78**, No. 3, 392–395.

Ross, A. J., Earp, B. J. and Wood, J. W. (1959). Mycobacterial infections in adult salmon and steelhead trout returned to the Columbia river basin and other areas in 1957. Special Scientific Report-Fisheries No. 332, U.S.A. Dept. of the Interior. Fish & Wildlife Service.

Ross, A. J. and Johnson H. E. (1962). Studies of mycobacterial infections in Chinook salmon. *Progr. Fish Cult.* 1962, 147–149.

Rucker, R. R. (1949). A streptomycete pathogenic to fish. *J. Bact.* **58**, 659–664.

Schäperclaus, W. (1950). Über einen Fall von Flossenfäule beim schwarzen Molly. *Wschr. Aqu. Terrk.* **44**, 167–170.

Schäperclaus, W. (1952–53). Infektionsablauf und natürliche Infektionsabwehr bei der ansteckenden Bauchwassersucht des Karpfens. *Z. Fischerei*, N.F. **1**, 273–249.

Schäperclaus, W. (1954). "Fischkrankheiten", 3rd edn., Akademie Verlag, Berlin.

Schäperclaus, W. (1955a). Aufsehenerregende Heilungs- und Bekämpfungserfolge bei der infektiösen Bauchwassersucht der Karpfen durch antibiotische Mittel. *Dtsch. Fischereiztg.* **2**, 330–334.

Schäperclaus, W. (1955b). Die Rolle der Bakteriophagen im Stoffhaushalt der Gewässer und bei der Entstehung von Fischkrankheiten. *Arch. Hydrobiol. Suppl.* **22**, 488–493.

Schäperclaus, W. (1956). Neue Möglichkeiten zur Bekämpfung von Infektionskrankheiten bei Aquarienfischen. *Aqu. Terr. Z.* **9**, 213–215.

Snieszko, S. F. and Bullock, G. L. (1957). Determination of the susceptibility of *Aeromonas salmonicida* to sulphonamides and antibiotics, with a summary report on the treatment and prevention of furunculosis. *Progr. Fish Cult.* 1957, 99–107.

Snieszko, S. F. and Griffin, P. J. (1955). Kidney disease in brook trout and its treatment. *Progr. Fish Cult.* 1955, 3–13.

Snieszko, S. F., Griffin, P. J. and Friddle, S. B. (1950). A new bacterium (*Hemophilus piscium* n. sp.) from Ulcer disease of trout. *J. Bact.* **59**, 699–710.

Sutherland, P. L. (1922). A tuberculosis-like disease in a salt-water fish (halibut) associated with the presence of an acid-fast tubercle-like bacillus. *J. Path. Bact.* **25**, 31–35.

Weber, A. and Taute (1904). Zur Frage der Umwandlung der Tuberkelbazillen im Kaltblüterorganismus. *Dtsch. med. Wschr.* **30**, 1019–1020.

B. Diseases Caused by Flagellates

Costia necatrix **Leclerq**

The unicellular flagellate *Costia necatrix* Leclerq is a common parasite of the aquarium and causes a skin condition in fish sometimes referred to as "infectious turbidity of skin and gills". The small parasite is kidney-shaped when seen sideways; fusiform in dorso-ventral view. It has two flagella (Fig. 15) and is 10–20 μ long and 6–10 μ wide. The

Fig. 15. *Costia necatrix* Leclerq. (Orig.)

shorter flagellum measures about 9 μ; the longer one about 18 μ. Where four flagella are seen the individual is probably engaged in division. The parasite adheres to the skin of the host not with the flagella but with the opposite part of the cell. Its mode of feeding is as yet undetermined. Division progresses rapidly and if the parasite population becomes excessive the skin reacts by inflammation and loss of surface epithelium. This in turn opens the way for secondary invaders like *Saprolegnia* or *Gyrodactylus* and may eventually cause the loss of the fish.

Separated from the host, *Costia* dies within an hour. No viable resting stages have so far been observed.

The following means of defence against this parasite have been recommended:

1. A 20 min bath in 1% NaCl (1 g in 100 cm³ of water) repeated four to five times within intervals of 2–3 days. Larger fish tolerate a slightly higher concentration;
2. A 15 min bath in formaldehyde 1 : 2 000–1 : 5 000 repeated as above;
3. A 2 day bath in one of the quinine salts (1 g in 50 l of water);
4. A 2 day bath in trypaflavin (1 g in 100 l of water).

A second *Costia* species, *C. pyriformis* Davis, distinguished by its smaller size (9–14 ×5–8 μ) occurs on N. American trout. It has, so far, not been seen on this side of the Atlantic.

Hexamita

This parasite, recognizable by its numerous flagella, is mostly found in body cavities. *H. truttae* Duj. for instance is a pathogenic inhabitant of the fish gut and may also be found in the gall bladder. It has eight flagella which measure $7 \cdot 4$–$12 \cdot 3 \times 3$–6μ. Schäperclaus (1951) described these parasites from *Pterophyllum scalare* C. and V. and from *Cichlasoma severum* Heckel where they occurred in the gut. *Hexamita* only becomes dangerous if a heavy growth occurs in small fish but we cannot be certain whether in every case *Hexamita* is the primary parasite and not a follower in the wake of some other invader. Optimal food should usually suffice to protect the fish. Some means of drug treatment have been suggested as follows: admixture of $0 \cdot 2\%$ of calomel to the food for 2 days; or admixture of $0 \cdot 2\%$ of Carbasome to the food for 4 days.

Trypanoplasma (= Cryptobia)

Trypanoplasma is a blood parasite particularly known from free-living freshwater fish. The flagellates are slender and fusiform and move with the aid of two long flagella (Fig. 16). Numerous species

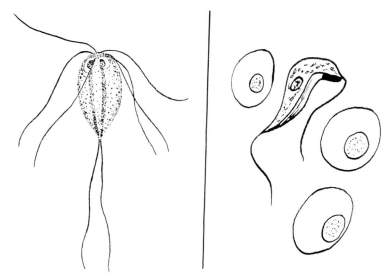

FIG. 16. Left: *Hexamita truttae* Duj. Right: *Trypanoplasma* (= *Cryptobia*) *cyprini* Plehn.

are known. *T. cyprini* Plehn occurs in the goldfish. The flagella of this species measure 15μ, the body 10–30×3–4μ. They are probably harmless when they occur in small numbers. Heavy infestation produces loss of weight and listlessness ("sleeping sickness of goldfish").

Trypanosoma

Trypanosoma, another blood parasite, is distinguished from the 2-flagellate *Trypanoplasma* by the presence of only one flagellum. Numerous species of both genera may be found in fish (Fig. 17). The intermediate hosts are probably leeches.

Flagellates of the Gut

Other parasitic flagellates allied to *Trypanoplasma* may be found in the gastro-intestinal canal of fish. The genera *Bodomonas* and *Cryptobia* (Fig. 17), for instance, occur in the stomach and in the gut of marine

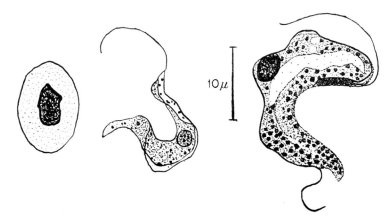

FIG. 17. Left: Erythrocyte of *Caulopsetta scapta* Forster. Middle: *Trypanosoma caulopsettae* Laird. Right: *Cryptobia gurneyorum* L. (After Laird.)

species. Equally *Trichomonadina*, more commonly seen in vertebrates, may invade fish in the form of *Monocercomonas* and *Tritrichomonas*, both of which have been seen in marine fish. Occasionally *Chilomastix* species have been reported from the same source (Reichenow, 1953).

Parasitic Dinoflagellates. *Oodinium*

The dinoflagellates may be distinguished by the presence of a single, posterior-trailing flagellum. The genus includes a number of parasitic forms which were formerly thought to occur in marine fish only. In 1934 epizootics of *Oodinium ocellatum* Brown were reported among coral fish kept in sea-water aquaria.

Recently, however, the genus has been noticed to parasitize freshwater fish as well. Weiser (1949) pictured a protozoon of this group from *Salmo trutta* L. in Bohemia and this was probably allied to the "Colisa Parasite" mentioned by Schäperclaus from *Colisa lalia* and

Carassius carassius L. in 1951. In 1946 Jacobs described a further species of this genus, *Oodinium limneticum*, from freshwater fish in N. American aquaria and further details came from the pens of Hirschman and Partsch (1953) and Schäperclaus (1954) on the European species *Oodinium pillularis* Schäperclaus.

This is an egg- or pear-shaped protozoon of slightly varying shape. Its length varies between 15 and 150 μ, the width between 15 and 70 μ. The cytoplasm is described as foamy, with numerous small granula suspended in it. The nucleus may be spherical or egg-shaped. The cell membrane contains chitin and has, at one pole, a funnel-shaped aperture. This "cytostome" allows the parasite to attach itself to the host and to penetrate the epithelium with plasmatic pseudopodia (Fig. 18).

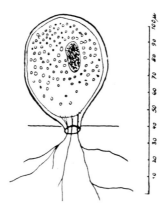

FIG. 18. *Oodinium pillularis* Schäperclaus. Parasitic stage, anchored to the fish skin. Specimen with long rhizoids.

During division the parasite becomes spherical, falls off, and sinks to the ground. During the resting period it divides into 32 or 64 daughter cells which swarm as soon as they have acquired their flagella. These "dinospores" are recognized by the presence of an annular furrow and a red eye spot. They perish unless they succeed in attaching themselves to a fish within 12–24 h. Once they are fixed the flagella disappear and the parasite quickly assumes the adult form.

Oodinium limneticum does not show the eye spot in the swarming stage; the number of flagellate swarmers produced in division is 256.

A fish attacked by this parasite loses its glossy skin and seems covered with a yellow to brown varnish. Hence the popular names of Rust-, Gold Dust-, or Velvet Disease. Microscopic examination reveals the pear-shaped protozoa particularly on the fins (Figs. 19 and 20). In heavy infections the parasites completely cover the skin and even

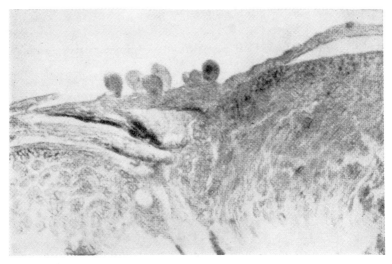

FIG. 19. *Oodinium pillularis* Sch. Several specimens attached to the skin of *Ctenops vittatus* Cuv. Azan stain. × 100.

FIG. 20. *Oodinium pillularis* Sch. on *Aphysosemion calliurus*. (Photo.: Matthes.)

penetrate to the gill chamber and the oral cavity, where they may interfere with the fish's ability to breathe. We have recently seen that these parasites are even capable of burrowing deeply into the epidermis, which then closes over them, changing them from ecto- to endo-parasites (Reichenbach-Klinke, 1956). They are, in such cases, usually found in the subcutaneous connective tissue. In tropical fish *Oodinium* has been seen to produce considerable oedema of the gill cover.

The parasite feeds by absorbing cytoplasmic liquid from the host by way of the pseudopodia, which issue from the cytostome. The pseudopodia penetrate into the epidermal cells and seem to have histolytic power enabling them to liquefy and absorb the host's protoplasm.

Both *Oodinium* species mentioned attack freshwater fish in moderate and tropical climates. They are not host-specific and we know of no species of fish immune to this parasite. Epizootics have been seen in aquaria and among free-living fish. The infection usually has an explosive character, killing the fish within a few days. Fish have also been found carrying a mild infection without, apparently, any danger to their general health.

The following measures for the eradication of the infection have been recommended:

A permanent bath of 2–3 days duration in a solution of quinine dihydrochloride (1·5 g : 100 l of water); or a careful application of salt baths (NaCl 3–5% for 1–3 min); or a bath in a solution of trypaflavin (1 g : 100 l of water) for 2–12 h.

If our assumption that these parasites are unable to produce resting stages or spores is correct, planted aquaria may become free from infection if left without fish for 8–10 days. All we know at present is that such resting stages have as yet not been observed.

Dempster (1956) eradicated *Oodinium limneticum* with copper sulphate. Making a stock solution of 1 g : 1 litre of water he used 2 cm^3 of this in 1 litre of water in the aquarium.

Opalina

These large ciliate protozoa are much less frequently found in fish than in amphibians and reptiles. They occur, after Sanden (1949), regularly in the fishes of the upper White Nile. Our knowledge of their further distribution among freshwater fish is as yet incomplete but they are not known to cause any alarming epizootics. The commonest species, *Opalina ranarum* Ehrenberg, can be found in the large intestine of any frog. It is flat, oval, a little more pointed at one pole than at the other, 200–350 μ long, multinucleate and diagonally striped (Fig. 21). They are continually on the move, rotating slowly around their longitudinal axis while swimming in the intestinal juice of their hosts. They feed on

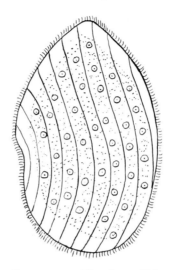

Fig. 21. *Opalina ranarum* Ehrenberg. (After Doflein.)

small particles which are engulfed by the cytostome. When fully grown their large size makes them visible to the naked eye.

REFERENCES

Brown, E. M. (1931). Note on a new species of Dinoflagellata from the gills and epidermis of marine fishes. *Proc. zool. Soc. Lond.* 1931, 1, 345–346.

Davis, H. S. (1953). "Culture and Diseases of Game Fishes."

Dempster, R. P. (1955). The use of copper sulphate as a cure for fish diseases caused by parasitic dinoflagellates of the genus *Oodinium*. *Zoologica* **21**, 133–137.

Dempster, R. P. (1956). Copper sulphate as a cure for oodinium disease. *Aqu. J.* **27**, 193–199.

Henry, H. (1913). A summary of the blood parasites of British sea fish. *J.Path. Bact.* **18**, 218.

Hirschmann, H. and Partsch, K. (1953). Der "Colisaparasit" ein Dinoflagellat aus der *Oodinium* Gruppe. *Aqu. Terr. Z.* **6**, 229–234.

Jacobs, D. L. (1946). A new parasitic dinoflagellate from fresh-water fish. *Trans. Amer. micr. Soc.* **65**, 1–17.

Laird, M. (1951). Studies on the trypanosomes of New Zealand fish. *Proc. zool. Soc. Lond.* **121**, 285–309.

Reichenbach-Klinke H. (1954). Untersuchungen über die bei Fischen durch Parasiten hervorgerufenen Zysten und deren Wirkung auf den Wirtskörper. *Z. Fischerei* N.F. **31**, 565–636.

Reichenbach-Klinke, H. (1956). Die Artzugehörigkeit der in Mitteleuropa vorkommenden *Oodinium* Art und Beobachtungen über ihr parasitäres Stadium. *G. Microbiol.* **1**, 106–111.

Reichenbach-Klinke, H. (1956). Die Dinoflagellatenart *Oodinium pillularis* Schäperclaus als Bindegewebsparasit von Süsswasserfischen. *G. Microbiol.* **1**, 263–265.

Reichenow, E. (1953). "Lehrbuch der Protozoenkunde", 6th edn., G. Fischer, Jena.

Sanden, H. (1949). Opalinids from Nile Fish. *Nature, Lond.* **164**, 410.

Schäperclaus, W. (1951). Der Colisaparasit—ein neuer Krankheitserreger bei Aquarienfischen. *Aqu. Terr. Z.* **41**, 169–171.

Schäperclaus, W. (1954). "Fischkrankheiten", 3rd edn., Akademie Verlag, Berlin.

Weiser, S. (1949). Parasites of freshwater fish. II. *Vestnik csl. zool. spolecn.* **13**, 364–371.

C. DISEASES CAUSED BY RHIZOPODA

Rhizopoda do not play an important part in fish pathology. Reichenow (1951–53) lists only *Entamoeba salpae* Alexeieff as occurring in the intestinal tract of various species of *Box*.

D. DISEASES CAUSED BY SPOROZOA

Coccidia

Cases of coccidiosis occur not infrequently both in marine and freshwater fish. *Eimeria subepithelialis* Moroff and Fiebiger, for instance, parasitizes the gut of cyprinids. In young carp it causes enteritis and where it penetrates deeply into the mucosa polyps and cysts may develop. The parasite is most easily recognized in the macrogamete stage which contains the developing oocyst, an oval structure 18–21 μ long (Fig. 22). After fertilization by motile microgametes the oocyst,

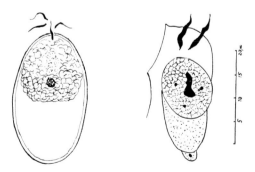

FIG. 22. Developmental stages of *Eimeria*. Left: Fertilization of the macrogamete of *Eimeria propria* Schn. Right: Fertilization of the macrogamete of *Eimeria subepithelialis* M. and F. (After Schäperclaus.)

now surrounded by a capsule, divides into four fusiform sporoblasts, each of which in turn produces four sickle-shaped spores. Pustular coccidiosis may not remain confined to the gut but can lead to severe general deterioration of the fish with great loss of weight and destruction of the fins.

A common parasite of carps is *Eimeria cyprini* Plehn (? = *E. carpelli* Léger and Stankovitch) which causes enteritis with intense inflammation. *Eimeria* may also be found in the testis of the sardine, the liver of herrings and the swim-bladder of gadid fish.

Parasites attacking the red blood corpuscles may also be found in fish. Laird (1952, 1958) described such forms from several marine fish, one of the commonest being *Haemogregarina bigemina* Laveran and Mesnil and *Haemogregarina mugili* Carini (Fig. 23).

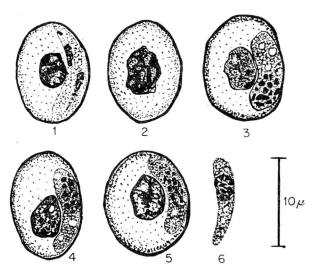

FIG. 23. Coccidial blood parasites. 1, 2, *Haemogregarina bigemina* Lav. and Mesn. from *Clinus perspicillatus* Val. 3–6, *Hamogregarina mugili* Carini from *Awaous ocellaris* Broussonet. (After Laird.)

Myxosporidia

It is a remarkable fact that the Myxosporidia which cause some of the most deadly and infectious epizootics among free-living fish, like the furunculosis of barbs and the staggers of trout, are rarely found to cause any damage to aquarium fish. In their natural habitat myxosporidiosis is one of the most dreaded infections of fish, yet it is difficult to recognize such an outbreak because the Myxosporidia attack mainly internal organs. Even there an exact diagnosis of the species responsible is only possible if spores can be demonstrated which show the characters distinguishing the invader from other similar species. The plasmodia emerging from the spores—here called trophozoites—are shapeless amoebulae lacking all distinguishing diagnostic features.

The oval spore of a myxosporidium is covered by a bivalve chitinous membrane (Kudo, 1921). In the genus *Myxobolus* one pole of the spore capsule is occupied by two or four polar capsules, the rest of the available space by the sporoplasm, which may still show the separate nuclei of the gametes and a vacuole which may be stained with iodide (Fig. 24). The shell of the genus *Henneguya* Thélohan is drawn out into two long appendices while in *Ceratomyxa* similar processes protrude laterally (Fig. 25).

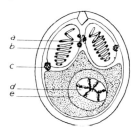

FIG. 24. *Myxobolus pfeifferi* Thel. spore. × 2 500. *a*, Granule of polar capsule; *b*, polar capsules with threads; *c*, shell forming nucleus; *d*, nucleus of amoebula; *e*, iodophira vacuole. (After Keysselitz from Reichenow.)

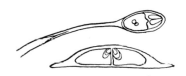

FIG. 25. Spores of a *Henneguya* sp. and a *Ceratomyxa* sp.

The spores of the family Chloromyxidae (*Sphaeromyxa, Zschokkella*) are fusiform, those of the Myxosomatidae (*Lentospora*) lens-shaped, those of *Hoferellus* blunt pyramidal. Their sizes vary between 5–10 μ the longest reaching up to 40 μ in length.

The myxosporidian spore, once it is introduced into the intestinal tract of the host, throws out threads from the polar capsules. It is as yet doubtful whether this is done in response to mechanical or to chemical stimulation. It is equally in doubt whether the amoebula emerges through or along the polar thread. It certainly enters the intestinal epithelium and from there finds its way, carried either by the lymph- or the blood stream, to those organs in which the further development can proceed. Here the parasite multiplies by plasmotomy, a process which quickly leads to the development of very large numbers of parasites by asexual reproduction. Eventually spores with the characters described are formed. Details of the life cycle vary from species to species.

Myxosporidia may be encountered in hollow organs like the gall-bladder, uriniferous renal tubules, and lymphatic spaces—but also in the muscle, the connective tissue, in nerves, even in the bone. Apart from some exceptional cases the seat of myxosporidians is extracellular or intercellular, not within the cells of the host.

Dunkerly (1920) investigating the Myxosporidia occurring in fish caught off Plymouth listed the following species:

Host	Parasite
Blennius ocellaris	*Myxidium incurvatum* Thél.
	Ceratomyxa arcuata Thél.
Blennius pholis	*Myxidium incurvatum* Thél.
Bothus maximus	*Myxidium incurvatum* Thél.
Callyonimus lyra	*Myxidium incurvatum* Thél.
	Ceratomyxa arcuata Thél.
Capros sanglier	*Ceratomyxa lata* sp.n.
Clupea pilchardus	*Ceratomyxa truncata* Thél.
	Coccomyxa morovi Léger Hesse
Cottus bubalis	*Ceratomyxa dubia* sp.n.
	Plistophora typicalis Gurley
	Chloromyxum quadratum Thél.
Gadus merlangus	*Myxidium sphaericum* Thél.
	Ceratomyxa arcuata Thél.
Gadus minutus	*Sphaeromyxa longa* sp.n.
	Myxidium sphaericum Thél.
Lophius piscatorius	*Ceratomyxa appendiculata* Thél.
	Glugea lophii
Mustelus vulgaris	*Chloromyxum leydigi* Ming
Onos mustela	*Sphaeromyxa balbiani* Thél.
	Sphaeromyxa ovata sp.n.
Onos tricirratus	*Sphaeromyxa cirrata* sp.n.
Platophrys laterna	*Myxidium incurvatum* Thél.
	Ceratomyxa arcuata Thél.
Pleuronectes flesus	*Myxidium intermedium* sp.n.
Pleuronectes limanda	*Ceratomyxa lata* sp.n.
Labrax labrax	*Ceratomyxa arcuata* Thél.
Scylliorhinus stellaris	*Chloromyxum leydigi* Ming
Squalus acanthias	*Chloromyxum leydigi* Ming

One of the best known and much feared myxosporidian infections of fish occurs in young salmonids where *Myxosoma cerebralis* Plehn invades the cranial cartilage causing first a loss of co-ordination (staggers) and later, bony deformities like pugheadedness and spinal deformities. The posterior part of the fish may become black. The disease has spread all over Europe and in 1960 has also been seen in N. America. The offending organism is a lens-shaped myxosporidium with two long polar threads (Fig. 26).

Examples of the genera *Myxobolus, Sphaerospora, Lentospora, Hoferellus, Thelohanellus, Henneguya* and *Kudoa* may be found in various marine and freshwater fish. They all parasitize muscle tissue, the body cavity or internal organs (Figs. 26, 27). *Myxobolus pfeifferi* Thélohan

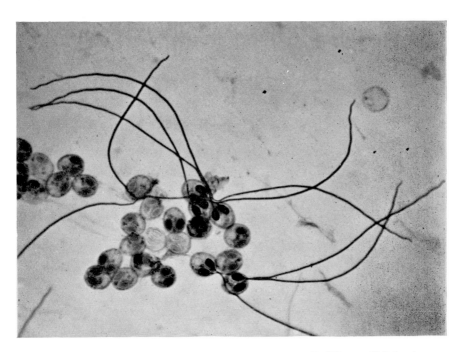

FIG. 26. *Lentospora* sp. from *Rutilus rutilus* L. × 740. (Photo.: Ghittino.)

produces furunculosis in barbels, *Myxobolus luciopercae* Schäferna and Jirovec produces cysts in the gill chamber of the giant pike-perch (*Lucioperca lucioperca* L.), *Thelohanellus pyriformis* Thél. is found in large muscular cysts (Fig. 28) and *Myxobolus neurobius* Schuberg and Schröder parasitizes the spinal cord of Salmonids. *Hoferellus cyprini* Plehn causes obstruction of renal tubules in carp, several species of *Henneguya* produce tumours in the gills of pike, *Henneguya zschokkei* Gurley (Fig. 29) causes boils in salmonids (*Coregonus* spp.) and *Sphaerospora tincae* Plehn is responsible for a serious epizootic among tench fry. The genus *Kudoa* occurs mainly among marine fish where, for instance, *Kudoa histolytica* Pérard affects the mackerel (*Scomber scombrus* L.). Sindermann (1957) reported on myxosporodiosis among herring of the Western Atlantic. The parasite responsible, *Kudoa clupeidae* Linton, produces translucent intramuscular cysts which hamper the motility

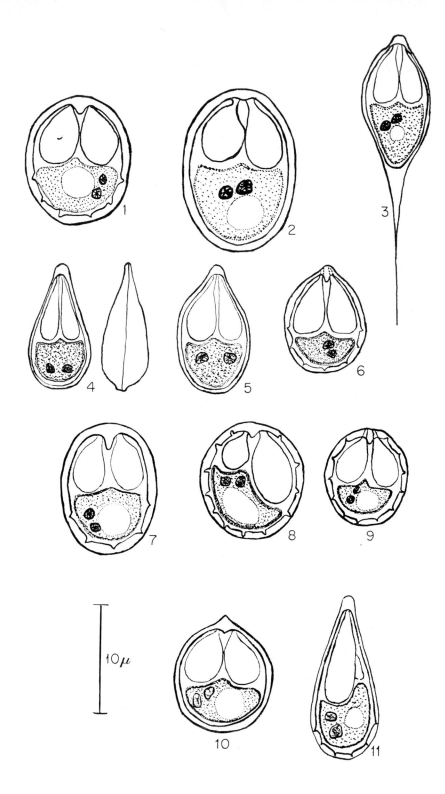

10μ

of the fish. An extensive review of myxosporidiosis occurring among Indian fish was published by Tripathi in 1953.

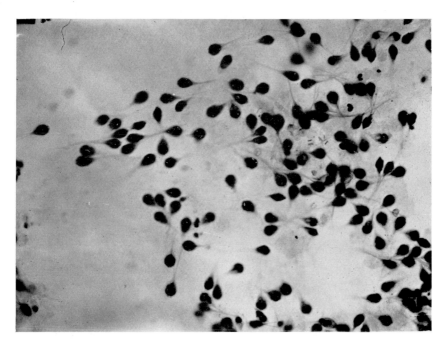

FIG. 28. *Henneguya zschokkei* Gurley from *Coregonus acronius* Rapp. × 500. (Orig.)

Microsporidia

While Myxosporidia are rarely seen in aquaria it is not uncommon to encounter Microsporidia among captive fish. They are again mainly recognized by details in the structure of their spores which, since they

←——

FIG. 27. Myxosporidia pathogenic to fish.
1, *Myxobolus mülleri* Bütschli. (*Cyprinus carpio*, skin).
2, *Myxobolus ellipsoides* Thél. (*Tinca tinca*, kidney).
3, *Henneguya psorospermica* Thél. (*Esox lucius*, gills).
4, *Myxosoma dujardini* Thél. (*Leuciscus leuciscus*, gills).
5, *Myxosoma dujardini* Thél. (*Squalius cephalus*, gills).
6, *Myxosoma branchialis* Markew (*Barbus meridionalis* Risso, gills).
7, *Myxobolus cycloides* Thél. (*Blicca björkna*, gills).
8, *Myxobolus dispar* Thél. (*R. rutilus*, gills).
9, *Myxobolus exiguus* Thél. (*Chondrostoma nasus*, gills).
10, *Myxobolus obesus* Gurley (*Alburnus alburnus*, gills).
11, *Thelohanellus fuhrmanni* Auerbach (*Noemacheilus barbatulus*, gills). (After Lom, 1960.)

2*

measure only 4–8 μ in length, are not always easy to establish. The
Microsporidia have only one polar capsule and one polar filament
which nearly fills the spore and may be up to 0·5 mm long (Fig. 29).
The shape of the spore is oval. Development is similar to the mode
mentioned for Myxosporidia. The spore releases the polar thread
(thought to be an organ of fixation) and the amoebula in the intestine
of the host. The amoebula enters an epithelial cell and is eventually

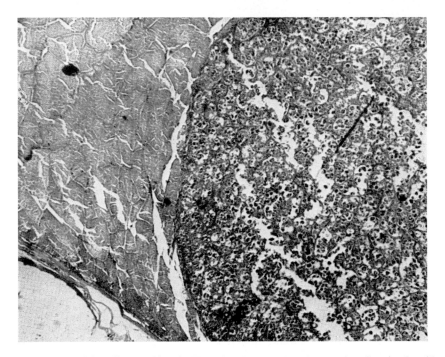

Fig. 29. *Thelohanellus pyriformis* Thél. in the muscle of a marine Cyprinodontid.
×75. (After Schlumberger.)

carried to the particular organ where it completes its reproductive
cycle, having enormously multiplied its numbers in the process. The
sporoblast, a stage in this cycle, produces varying numbers of spores.
These numbers are typical of the particular microsporidium and are
used to determine the species. They may vary from 1 to 100.

Contrary to the Myxosporidia, which are found between cells, the
Microsporidia develop intracellularly in the cytoplasm or, in some
cases, even within the nucleus of the host cell. Their presence must
therefore be taken as a very serious attack on the host whose reaction
to the infection is however an unexpected one. Instead of showing

signs of degeneration the affected cells and their nuclei grow out of all proportion and develop into giant cells, eventually forming veritable tumours which, as happens in *Gasterosteus*, can deform the fish completely (Fig. 33) or, as happens in *Lophius piscatorius* L., can severely damage the nervous system. In the former species it is *Glugea anomala* Moniez, in the latter *Nosema lophii* Doflein which are responsible. Apart from the skin and the nervous system the muscle, the intestine and the gonads may be affected by microsporidians.

As in the Myxosporidia the species are determined by the number of spores produced by the spherical sporoblast. In *Nosema*, well known from its devastating effect on silkworms, the figure is one, in *Glugea* (called after the Belgian zoologist, Gluge) two, in *Thelohania* (after the French microbiologist, Thélohan) eight and in *Plistophora* (from the Greek *pleistos* = many) 16–100 spores per sporoblast. Of these genera, some of which are very common in insects and crustaceans, *Glugea* and *Plistophora* cause the greatest damage in fish.

Nosema

Small tumours due to this parasite have been seen in the subcutis and the ovary of the stickleback (*Gasterosteus aculeatus* L.) and in the

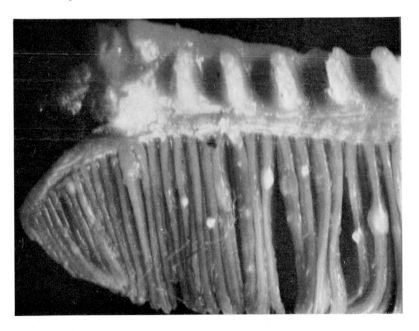

Fig. 30. Gill arch of a haddock (*Gadus aeglefinus*), caught off S. Iceland, infected with *Nosema branchiale* Nemeczek. × 2. (Photo.: Elkan.)

minnow (*Phoxinus phoxinus* L.), but these findings were rare and did not amount to epizootics. *Nosema girardini* Lutz and Splendore parasitizes the gut of the poeciliid *Phalloceros caudomaculatus* Hensel. *Nosema branchialis* Nemeczek is commonly found on the gills of the haddock (*Gadus aeglefinus* L.) where it produces small white tumours without, apparently, interfering much with the life of the fish (Fig. 30).

Glugea

We do not know as yet why some animals are so much more infested by parasites than others. Like the common toad among the Amphibia, the stickleback among fish also attracts a remarkable number of parasites of all kinds. One of the commonest of these is *Glugea anomala* Moniez which produces cysts in the subcutis of the fish which may grow to the size of a pea, completely distorting and disfiguring the fish. The spores which measure $3 \times 4 \mu$ develop in the cortical part of the cyst. The latter represents only one—enormously enlarged—cell of the host (Figs. 31–34).

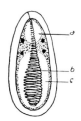

FIG. 31. *Glugea anomala* Moniez spore. × 5 000. *a*, Anterior vacuole; *b*, polar thread; *c*, posterior vacuole. (After Stempell.)

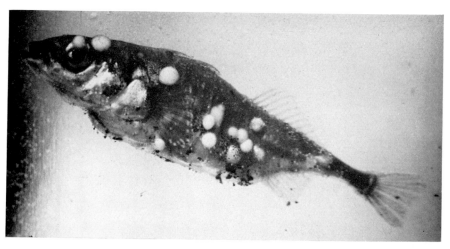

FIG. 32. *Gasterosteus aculeatus* L. infected with *Glugea anomala* M. Note cyst covering part of cornea. × 2. (Photo.: Elkan.)

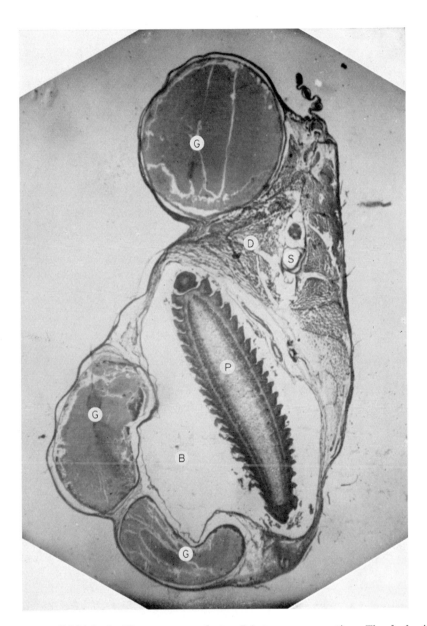

FIG. 33. Stickleback (*Gasterosteus aculeatus* L.) transverse section. The body is completely deformed by cysts of *Glugea anomala* M. The parasite in the body cavity is *Schistocephalus solidus*. *B*, Body cavity; *D*, dorsal muscles; *G*, *Glugea* cysts; *P*, plerocercoid larva of *Schistocephalus solidus*; *S*, spine. (Photo.: Elkan.)

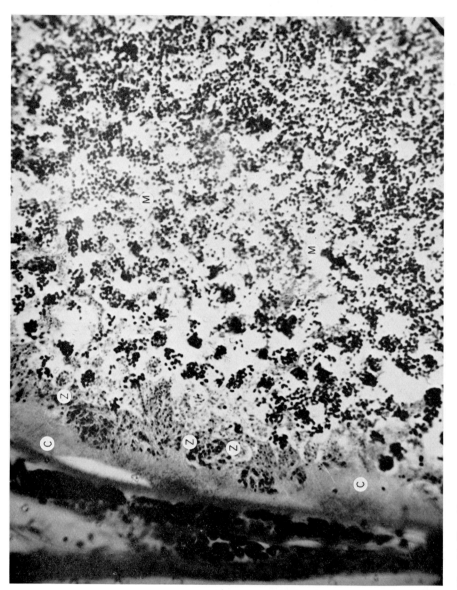

Fig. 34. Magnified section through front of a cyst of *Glugea anomala* M. from a stickleback. *M*, Mature spores; *Z*, zone of developing spores; *C*, cyst wall. × 100. (Photo.: Elkan.)

Glugea pseudotumefaciens Pflugfelder (1952) was described as responsible for the so-called "rest-body" of *Cyprinodontidae* and *Cyprinidae*. The spores are ovoid, have a long polar filament and lie in pairs within the sporoblast. Ovary, liver, kidney, spleen, eyes and central nervous system are affected. The infection develops in the shape of small tumours with concentric layers which show the developmental stages of the parasite. The round or oval amoebulae appear intracellularly in the ovary and divide into small rods looking almost like bacteria. These divide transversely and form chains. The host cell may die, leaving masses of detritus behind. If the host cell survives, the parasite changes into spores, each sporoblast producing two. The spores have one polar capsule. Pflugfelder (1952) could transfer the infection to *Poeciliidae*, *Cyprinidae* and *Colisa lalia* H.-B., whereas *Hyphessobrycon innesi* M., *H. flammeus* M., *H. gracilis* R. and D. and *Macropodus opercularis* L. were found to be immune. (Fig. 35.)

Undetermined types of *Glugea*

W. H. Cotton (quoted by Duijn, 1956) found undetermined types of *Glugea* in *Hyphessobrycon gracilis* and *H. innesi*, barbels, *Danio* species and fighting fish. (*Betta* spp.) He blamed the parasites for a type of muscular degeneration similar to that caused by *Plistophora hyphessobryconis* and thought he was dealing either with *Glugea anomala* M. or *Glugea hertwigi* Weissenberg, both of which, however, produce spherical cysts and not a general muscular disease. No such cysts were seen in Cotton's fish.

Another, equally undetermined type of *Glugea* was seen by Johnstone (quoted by Herald and Rakowicz, 1951) in a sea horse (*Hippocampus hudsonius*) also producing muscular degeneration. On the skin white patches appear gradually, spreading from the tail and destroying the glossy surface of the fish. Attempts at treatment with various baths were unsuccessful (Fig. 36).

Plistophora hyphessobryconis Schäperclaus

This infection, which has become popularly known as the "Neon fish disease" often occurs among tropical species kept in the aquarium. Thirty-two spores lie in the spherical sporoblast measuring 4–6 ×2–2·5 μ. The diameter of the sporoblast is 50–60 μ. Twelve to thirty of these may be found united within a cyst wall (Fig. 37). The parasite mainly occupies those parts of the muscular system which lie next to the skin. It may destroy large parts of the muscle and produce local swelling, but no cell hypertrophy as seen in other *Glugea* species. Occasionally the parasite penetrates the connective tissue. It appears that this microsporidium exercises a chemical histolytic action on the muscle fibres which are widely destroyed, leaving a granular debris behind. The swelling of the diseased parts is due to the presence of great numbers of parasite-filled cysts. The whole muscle becomes pale and transparent, thereby causing the patchy appearance of the surface of the fish.

FIG. 35. *Glugea pseudotumefaciens* Pflugfelder. Spores in a host cell. (After Pflugfelder).

FIG. 36. Sea horse (*Hippocampus* sp.) with Microsporidiosis (grey patches). (Orig.)

If one fish among the stock kept in a tank falls a victim to this disease the whole population will quickly suffer the same fate. The progressive disease causes congestion and muscular paralysis, secondarily loss of balance and fin degeneration. Infection of other fish is due to water pollution by parasite-loaded excreta. Within the fish the infection spreads by the continuing multiplication of the invading organism.

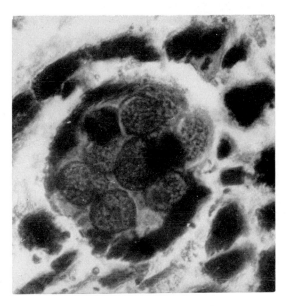

FIG. 37. *Plistophora hyphessobryconis* Sch. Cyst filled with sporoblasts in the muscle fibre of a Neon fish. Azan stain. × 450.

This infection has so far only been seen in characids of the genera *Hyphessobrycon* and *Hemigrammus* as well as in cyprinids like *Brachydanio rerio* H.-B. Experimental attempts at infecting tench (*Tinca tinca.* L.), *Cichlasoma severum* H. and *Barbus semifasciolatus* Gthr. were unsuccessful (Schäperclaus, 1941). Richert (1956) points out that the disease affects *Carassius carassius* L. and is by no means host specific.

Plistophora typicalis Gurley

This microsporidium parasitizes several marine fish and the stickleback *Gasterosteus pungitius* L. The spores measure $3 \times 5 \mu$, the sporoblasts $25–35 \mu$. Other *Plistophora* species have been described from marine fish but have, so far, not invaded aquaria.

The only possible way of fighting an infection of this kind, which starts inside the fish and not on the surface, lies in early removal of any suspect-looking specimen and thorough disinfection of the tank in which the stock was kept.

Haplosporidia

This group, whose spores have a lid instead of a pole capsule, were first seen to occur in some localities in N. Germany (Reichenbach-Klinke, 1950). The species observed was *Dermocystidium percae* which produces oval cysts in the subcutis of the perch (*Perca fluviatilis* L.). Cysts are found particularly in the fins, the head, and between the pectoral fins. They are 1–2 mm long and 0·24–0·18 mm wide. The spores are spherical and are recognized by an inclusion body occupying nine-tenths of the cell content. The diameter of the spores is between 6 and 7·75 μ, the lid being clearly visible (Figs. 41, 42).

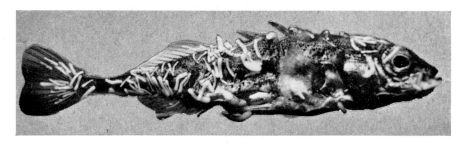

Fig. 38. *Gasterosteus aculeatus* L. with cysts of *Dermocystidium gasterostei* Elkan. (From Elkan, 1963.)

Attempts to transfer the infection to roach (*Rutilus rutilus* L.) did not succeed. The parasite seems to be host specific. The infection was first noticed among perch and has only been seen in freshwater fish. Heavily affected specimens suffered from anoxaemia and loss of substance, but true epizootics have not been observed. A few other members of the genus *Dermocystidium* Pérez are known, all from freshwater fish: *Dermocystidium branchialis* Léger produces spherical cysts in the gills of the brook trout (*Salmo trutta fario* L.); *Dermocystidium vejdovskyi* Jirovec is found in similar cysts in the pike (*Esox lucius* L.). Another member of this group was recently seen in two species of stickleback (*G. aculeatus* and *G. pungitius*) (Elkan, 1962). The cylindrical cysts covered the whole body of the fish, including the cornea of the eye, and some penetrated deeply between the bones of the skull. The spores showed the typical large inclusion body but no lid (Figs. 38–41). The species, described as *Dermocystidium gasterostei* Elkan, may be identical with *D. cuticulare* found by Scheer (1956) on *Pungitius pungitius* L. It did not affect perch or other fish living in the same

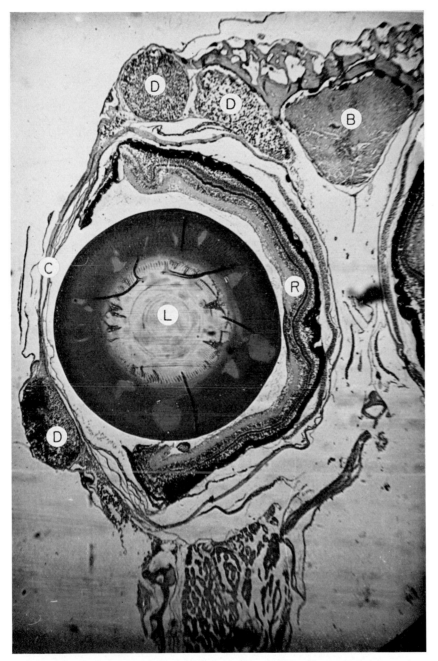

FIG. 39. *Dermocystidium gasterostei* Elkan. Transverse section through the head of *Gasterosteus aculeatus* showing three cysts, one of which is in the cornea. × 40. *B*, Brain; *C*, cornea; *D*, cysts filled with spores of *Dermocystidium*; *L*, lens; *R*, retina. (Photo.: Elkan. Courtesy *Nature, Lond.*)

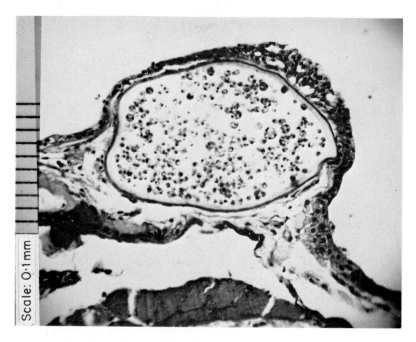

Fig. 40. *Dermocystidium gasterostei* Elkan. Cyst in skin of stickleback with maturing spores. (Photo.: Elkan. Courtesy *Nature, Lond.*)

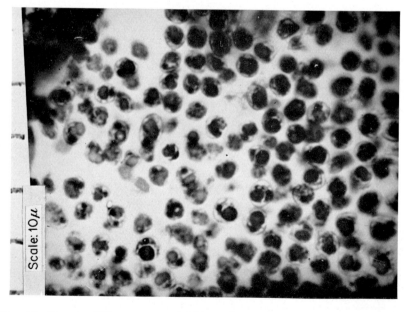

Fig. 41. *Dermocystidium gasterostei* Elkan. Spores with large inclusion bodies. Giemsa. (Photo.: Elkan. Courtesy *Nature, Lond.*)

waters and did not seem to inconvenience the affected sticklebacks overmuch, even when they were covered with cysts.

Sporozoon tincae Wolf and Dvorak, another *Haplosporidium*, has been found to produce a lethal skin disease in tench. Tumours arise in the skin and break through to the surface causing severe ulceration. Masses of the organism show up as white depots in internal organs (Jirovec *et al.*, 1947).

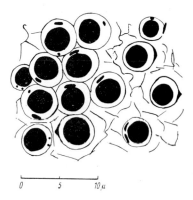

0   5   10 μ

FIG. 42. *Dermocystidium percae* Reichenbach-Klinke. Spores.

The allied genus *Dermosporidium carini* is only known from salmonids and from frogs. The spores have no lid and the inclusion body is missing. *D. truttae* Weiser forms small tumours in the gills of the trout (*Salmo trutta fario* L.). The systematic position of many members of the genus *Haplosporidium* is as yet uncertain. Small outbreaks occur in unrelated places and die down again without causing much damage. The difficulty experienced in the experimental transfer and in observation under controlled conditions has so far limited our knowledge of this order.

REFERENCES

Duijn, C. v. (1956). "Diseases of Fishes", publ. *Water Life*, London.
Dunkerly, J. S. (1920). Myxosporidia from Plymouth. *Parasitology* 12, 328–333.
Elkan, E. (1962). *Dermocystidium gasterostei* n. sp. a parasite of *Gasterosteus aculeatus* L. and *Gasterosteus pungitius* L. *Nature, Lond.* 196, 958–960.
Gurley, R. (1894). The myxosporidia or psorosperms of the fishes and the epidemics produced by them. *Rep. U.S. Comm. Fish* 18, 65–304.
Herald, E. S. and Rakowicz, M. (1951). Stable requirements for raising sea horses. *Aqu. J.* 22, 234–242.
Hoffman, H. L., Dunbar, C. E. and Bradford, A. (1962). Whirling disease of trouts caused by *Myxosoma cerebralis* in the United States. *U.S. Dept. Int. Rep. Fish*, 427.

Jirovec, O. (1939). *Dermocystidium vejdovskyi* n. sp. ein neuer Parasit des Hechtes, nebst einer Bemerkung über *Dermocystidium daphniae* (Rühberg). *Arch. Protistk.* **92**, 137–146.

Jirovec, O., Schäferna, K. and Skorpil, F. (1947). *Sporozoon tincae,* a pathogenic parasite of the tench. *Parasitology* **38**, 145–149.

Laird, M. (1952). New Haemogragarines from New Zealand marine fishes. *Trans. roy. Soc. N.Z.* **79**, 589–600.

Laird, M. (1953). The protozoa of New Zealand intertidal zone fishes. *Trans. roy. Soc. N.Z.* **81**, 79–143.

Laird, M. (1958). Parasites of South Pacific fishes. *Canad. J. Zool.* **36**, 153–165.

Léger, L. (1914). Sur un nouveau protiste du genre *Dermocystidium,* parasite de la truite. *C.R. Acad. Sci., Paris* **158**, 807–809.

Lom, J. (1961). Protozoan parasites found in Czechoslovakian fishes. I. Myxosporidia, Suctoria. *Zool. Listy* **10**, 45–58.

Opitz, H. (1942). Mikrosporidienkrankheit *Plistophora* auch bei *Hemigrammus ocellifer* und *Brachydanio rerio. Wschr. Aqu. Terr. Z.* **39**, 83–85.

Pflugfelder, O. (1952). Die sogenannten Restkörper der *Cyprinodontidae* and *Cyprinidae* als Abwehrreaktionen gegen Mikrosporidienbefall. *Z. Parasitenk.* **15**, 321–334.

Reichenbach-Klinke, H. (1949) Microsporidien als Fischparasiten. *Wschr. Aqu. Terrk.* **43**, 158–160.

Reichenbach-Klinke, H. (1950). Der Entwicklungskreis der Dermocystidien sowie Beschreibung einer neuen Haplosporidienart *Dermocystidium percae* n. sp. *Verh. dtsch. Zool. Mainz.* 1949, 126–132.

Reichenbach-Klinke, H. (1952). Neue Beobachtungen über den Erreger der Neonfischkrankheit *Plistophora hyphessobryconis* Schäperclaus (Sporozoa, Microsporidia). *Aqu. Terr. Z.* **5**, 320–322.

Reichenow, E. (1951–53). "Lehrbuch der Protozoenkunde", 6th edn., Jena.

Richert, F. (1958). Über das Auftreten des Erregers der Neon-Fisch Krankheit (*Plistophora hyphessobryconis*) bei Süsswasserfischen der gemässigten Zone. *Mikrokosmos* **47**, 327–330.

Schäperclaus, W. (1941). Eine neue Mikrosporidienkrankheit beim Neon-Fisch und seinen Verwandten. *Wschr. Aqu. Terrk.* **38**, 381–384.

Scheer, D. (1956). Die Fischparasiten der Haplosporidiengattung *Dermocystidium. In* " Probleme der Parasitologie." Vorträge der II. Parasitol. Arbeitstagung. Berlin. 268–276. Also *Z. Fischerei* **6**, N.F. 1957, 127–134.

Sindermann, C. J. (1957). Diseases of fishes of the North Atlantic. VI. Geographic discontinuity of Myxosporodiosis in immature herring from the Gulf of Maine. *Res. Bull. Dept. Sea and Shore Fish,* No. 29.

Steffens, W. (1956). Weitere Beiträge zur Kenntnis der *Plistophora*-Krankheit. *Aqu. Terr. Z.* **9**, 153–155.

Tripathi, Y. R. (1953). Studies on parasites of Indian fishes. I. Protozoa: *Myxosporidia,* together with a check list of parasitic protozoa described from Indian fishes. *Rep. Indian Mus.* **50**, 63–88.

Weiser, J. (1949). Parasites of freshwater fish. II. *Vestn. Csl. Zool. Spol.* **13**, 364–371.

E. DISEASES CAUSED BY CILIATES AND SUCTORIA

Among the ciliated protozoa we find a fair number of fish parasites which may give rise to widespread epizootics. The greatest losses are caused by the well known *Ichthyophthirius multifiliis* Fouquet, and by various species of the genus *Trichodina*.

Ciliates mainly parasitize the skin and the gills; few of them penetrate into the subcutis but in a few rare cases they have been found in the small intestine and even in the brain.

The parasitic as well as the free-living members of this class are easily recognized by the cilia which cover either a part or the whole body. This, and the fact that most of them are in continuous rotating motion, distinguishes them from other parasites. *Ichthyophthirius*, for instance, can be seen to move even inside the cutaneous cysts. These ciliates always have more than one nucleus, a large macronucleus (horseshoe-shaped in *Ichthyophthirius*) and several smaller intensely staining micronuclei. The presence of these characters induced Grell (1956) to classify the opalinids within the flagellates because their nuclei are all of the same size so that neither macro- nor micronuclei exist. The reproduction of ciliates takes place either by simple division or after conjugation, which involves exchange of nuclear substance. In parasitic forms conjugation is very rarely seen but it is known to occur in *Trichodina*. Spontaneous division of the cell and production of numbers of small swarmers usually occurs outside the host during a free-living stage. Some ciliates may produce encapsuled resting stages.

The emerging swarmers are extremely dependent on finding a host. If they fail in this quest they perish after 24–48 h. The interposition of free-living stages in the life cycle of these ciliates indicates that they are transitional forms still alternating between the free-living and the parasitic mode of life. Infusoria, finding themselves in putrefying water, may enter fish eggs and thereby become facultative parasites. Those swarmers, on the other hand, which depend on finding a suitable host within 1–2 days, are obviously highly specialized and host-dependent. Treatment with chemical substances is far more effective when directed against these swarmers than if applied to the fish, and it should be repeated until it can safely be assumed that the last of the ciliates has entered the reproductive phase and has been killed while free swimming outside the host.

Ichthyophthirius multifiliis Fouquet

This ciliate, one of the commonest invaders of fish, has been very thoroughly studied. It does not seem to cause severe epizootics in open

waters but frequently does so in breeding ponds and aquaria. In
breeding ponds this parasite may kill thousands of fish; equally all
the fish kept in an aquarium may be killed within a few days or weeks.

Ichthyophthirius multifiliis (Fig. 43) belongs to the order Holotricha

FIG. 43. Young Rainbow Trout with *Ichthyophthirius* infection. (Orig.)

where the entire body surface is covered with cilia. The shape is
spherical or pear-shaped, the diameter varies between 50 μ and 1 mm.
The cytostome, a tubular opening which serves as a mouth, is not
always easily visible. The cytoplasm contains numerous vacuoles, a
macronucleus visible *in vivo* and recognized by its horseshoe shape, as
well as a smaller micronucleus. Larger individuals may also show
dark pigment granules and other cytoplasmic inclusions.

Ichthyophthirius is a typical skin parasite and it is recognized under
the microscope by the uniform distribution of the cilia, its shape and
its permanent rotating motion which continues even if the parasites
lie encysted on the gills. All parts of the skin and the gills may be
affected, but the parasite is rarely seen in the mouth.

The parasitic stage starts when one of the swarmers lands on the
skin of a fish. Its rotating motion allows it to penetrate between the
epidermal cells, but it always remains near the surface and never
reaches the subcutis. The epidermis, irritated by the invader, reacts
by the production of local granulations which gradually overgrow and
enclose the parasite.

Macroscopically this produces the picture popularly known as "White
Spot Disease" and the small white spots may lie so close together that
no normal skin can be seen between them. The ciliate burrows along
below the surface and may, in its progress, be joined by others so that
several parasites may be found lying closely together. They feed on
epithelial debris; possibly also on the products of local cytolysis.
Varying according to external conditions the parasite grows to its full
size in 1–3 weeks. When mature it leaves the fish, surrounds itself with
a transparent membrane, and sinks to the bottom. Very soon, possibly

within the hour, there ensues a rapid sequence of cell divisions leading to the production of from 250–1 000 swarmers. These may leave the cyst at the earliest after 7 h. If they do not find a suitable host within 48 h after hatching they perish.

We know as yet nothing about possible sexual reproduction in this species, nor does it seem to produce resting forms of any kind. Deviations from the described cycle may occur due to a change of water, lack of oxygen or lack of suitable hosts. In such circumstances young parasites may divide while on the fish, or mature forms, swimming free in the water, may produce swarmers without having been encysted.

In the skin the invader may be surrounded by a capsule produced by the host. The gills, however, which are a common seat of the parasite, rarely react by cyst formation. They do, instead, produce a kind of granulation tissue embedding the ciliate. This often leads to adhesions between adjoining gill filaments. The granulation tissue seems to starve the parasite, which eventually may die from inanition.

Only rarely has the parasite been found to invade the oral cavity or the anterior gut.

The number of Ichthyophthirii a fish can tolerate at any time depends on its size, species and defensive power. It is not surprising that small fish, where the relation of surface to mass is unfavourable, succumb easier than larger species. Characids, for instance, are more easily damaged by *Ichthyophthirius* than cyprinids or cichlids, but no species of fish has so far proved to be entirely immune to it. Some fish seem to tolerate an almost complete invasion of their skin by the parasite; exact figures about their power of resistance are, however, not available. The general impression seems to be that small-scaled fish are less resistant to the infection than large scaled species, also that free swimming fish are more exposed than bottom feeders.

The great part this parasite plays in fish pathology is explained by its universal distribution. It has been found in every continent; epizootics have even been observed in marine aquaria (Buschkiel, 1932). Particularly devastating epizootics occur among newly imported stock and these are caused by parasites extremely resistant to treatment. These differences in resistance have been thought to be due to the presence of several sub-species of *Ichthyophthirius*, but it is more likely to assume that the differences lie in the power of resistance of the fish, some of which may be endowed with chemical or physical means barring the adherence or entry of the swarmers. Deterioration in the environmental conditions under which the fish have to live frequently cause explosive outbreaks of *Ichthyophthirius* epizootics. The cause may lie in the temporary failing of the host's resistance. Such epizootics have been observed when fish were transferred from one tank to another. Such a procedure may at the same time weaken the fish and give the invader a particular chance (Figs. 43–47). Mishaps of this type were observed on several occasions when stock of the golden variety of cyprinoid *Idus idus* L. was transferred from one tank to another. The transferred fish were infected, those that were left behind remained healthy.

FIG. 44. Goldfish (*Carassius c. auratus* L.) with *Ichthyophthirius* infection. (Orig.)

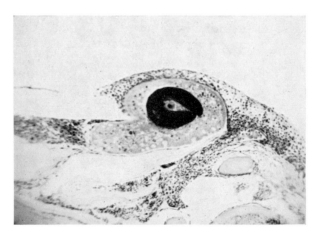

FIG. 45. *Ichthyophthirius multifiliis* Fouquet in the skin of *Scardinius erythrophthalmus* (Rudd). H. and E. (Photo.: Elkan.)

Under favourable circumstances an equilibrium may establish itself between a less aggressive population of invaders and a fish able to keep it in check, a state described as a "latent infection". In such cases only a few parasites may be found on the fish and no reproduction of the ciliate takes place. The slightest change may, however, temporarily weaken the fish, upset the equilibrium and cause an immediate epizootic.

Fish which have survived a number of *Ichthyophthirius* attacks seem to acquire a temporary immunity, but this is speedily lost if no attacks take place for some time.

Fig. 46. Young rudd (*Scardinius erythrophthalmus*) infected with *Ichthyophthirius multifiliis*. Note destruction of caudal fin. × 2. (Photo.: Elkan.)

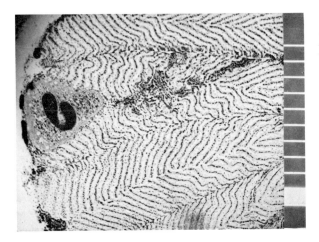

Fig. 47. *Scardinius erythrophthalmus*. Pseudobranch with *Ichthyophthirius multifiliis* Fouquet. Scale: 0·1 mm. (Photo.: Elkan.)

Stable and healthy environmental conditions are therefore the first line of defence against *Ichthyophthirius*. New imports should never be mixed with old stock, since the presence of a few parasites is most difficult to ascertain. A quarantine of 6–8 weeks is recommended, but if parasites have succeeded in establishing themselves prolonged defence is required. Stolk (1956) recommends raising the water temperature for 6 h to 33°C and then cooling to 21°C. Good results are obtained if this procedure is repeated 3–5 times. Only if this method is either inapplicable or if it has proved unsuccessful should disinfecting baths be employed. The following may be tried: a permanent quinine bath (1 g : 51 l of water); a permanent bath in trypaflavine (1 g : 100 l of water). The fish should only be removed from the bath when no further parasites can be recovered. The time this takes may vary between 3–20 days.

The drug Chloramine has lately become popular in the fight against *Ichthyophthirius*. After Schäperclaus (1954) baths should contain 1 g : 15 l of water and should be applied for 2–4 h. A bath containing 1 g in 100 l of water may be applied for several days. The effectiveness of Chloramine seems to stem from the production of nascent oxygen which kills the swarmers.

Other chemical substances like atebrin and "Aquarol", a mixture of salts, have been used successfully. Kristensen (1950) used penicillin (200 000 units : 500 l of water) and Schäperclaus (1956) suggests that other antibiotics might be tried with advantage.

There remains the suggestion to transfer the fish every 12 h to a new tank which is certainly free of parasites. The used tanks rid themselves of the infection if they remain empty of fish for at least 3 days. To apply this method seven tanks are needed, a circumstance which detracts from its practicability.

Where new aquaria are being installed it must be borne in mind that swarmers might be introduced with the aquatic plants. Suspicious material should be kept in a quarantine tank for at least 3 days.

Tubifex, a common fish food, has often been thought to carry *Ichthyophthirius*, but the accusation has never been proved.

The species *Ichthyophthirius cryptostomus* Zacharias is now considered to be a variation of *I. multifiliis* and is no longer considered a valid species (Kahl, 1935).

Chilodonella cyprini Moroff

This comparatively large heart-shaped ciliate is a pure ectoparasite and does not, like *Ichthyophthirius*, burrow in the skin. The appearance of the infected fish is similar to that caused by a *Costia* infection but the patches of dead and infected skin are thicker and whole pieces of skin may be lost.

The cilia of *C. cyprini* cover only the dorsal side; part of the ventral side is non-ciliated. Eight to fifteen rows enclose the ventral side marginally, and some longer cilia lie in front of the cytostome. The species is therefore classed with the Hypotricha. They are recognized by the presence of an oral basket reinforced by 14–26 rods (Fig. 48).

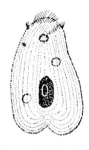
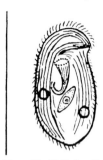

FIG. 48. *Chilodonella cyprini* Moroff.   FIG. 49. *Chilodonella hexasticha* Kiernik.

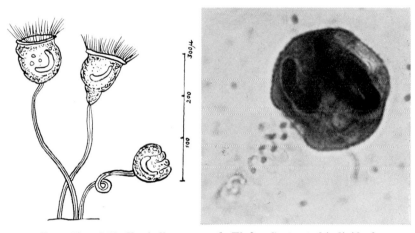

FIGS. 50 and 51. *Vorticella campanula* Ehrbg. Contracted individual.

The oval macronucleus measures one-third of the length of the body. The situation of the micronucleus varies. Two vacuoles are usually present in the cytoplasm. The total measurements of the parasite are 41–63 $\mu \times$ 30–6 μ. It is assumed that it feeds on debris derived from epithelial cells. Reproduction takes place by simple division and spreading by invasion of other hosts. This means that one fish may infect others direct without intervention of swarmers. Detached from its host the parasite perishes within a few hours.

Chilodonella cyprini has been found on a variety of freshwater fish, even on tadpoles. Although it may attach itself to any fish it seems to prefer debilitated specimens. If the infection is heavy the fish dies.

The most suitable treatment consists again in either a bath of 10 min duration in 1% salt (NaCl) or in suitable baths of quinine or trypa-flavine (see pp. 60, 203) for 24 h.

Further Species of *Chilodonella*

Apart from *C. cyprini*, the commonest species, another type, *Chilodonella hexasticha* Kiernik may be encountered. It may reach $42 \times 54 \mu$ in size, is pronouncedly pear shaped and the oral basket presents the aspect of a bent horn (Fig. 49). Schäperclaus (1954) discovered a third species, as yet unnamed, on *Rasbora heteromorpha* Duncker, equal in size to *C. hexasticha* but not heart-shaped and with a straight oral basket.

Infections with *Glaucoma*

Glaucoma, another holotrich ciliate, is the parasite occasionally encountered in the brain of fishes. Epstein (1926) reported on such an infection in *Abramis brama* L.; Shumway (1940) found them in the brain of the axolotl. This ciliate is oval, the whole surface is covered with cilia, the size $20–25 \times 35–60 \mu$. It prefers slightly putrescent water.

Vorticella

Slightly stale water also sometimes favours the development of large "lawns" of Vorticellidae, sessile peritrich ciliates which may cover the whole surface of plants and occasionally of debilitated fish. They are easily recognized by the large annular rows of cilia around the cyto-stome, their bell-shaped appearance and the fact that they are normally attached to a base by a long retractile stalk. Free-swimming forms without stalk may also occur. They feed on matter suspended in the water and their parasitic role is a minor one (Figs. 50 and 51). Duijn reports the appearance of *Vorticella* on fighting fish (*Betta splendens* R.) which had been captive for some time but were not damaged by this infection.

Scyphidiidae

Another family of sessile ciliates, closely related to those already described. Tripathi (1954) described members of the family from Indian cyprinids; Laird (1959) saw them on marine fish. On adult fish these infusoria live as symbionts on the skin of fish but they can cause great damage among fish fry if the infestation becomes too heavy. Several species of *Scyphidia* have been reported from freshwater fish in N. America (Davis, 1956). The cylindrical ciliates adhere by suction to the skin of the fish. For their removal the author recommends baths in formaldehyde (1 : 4 000) or PMA (pyridilmercuroacetate 1 : 500 000).

Glossatella

Glossatella, another peritrich ciliate, is closely allied to *Vorticella*. It rarely appears upon fishes. The contractile stalk is shorter and the cilia surrounding the cytostome are larger than those in the former species. They somewhat resemble pears standing on their stalks (Fig. 52). Like *Vorticella* they feed on suspended matter and have no

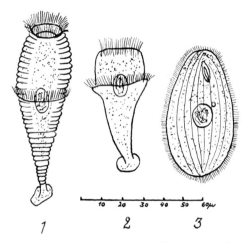

FIG. 52. 1, *Glossatella piscicola* Blanchard; 2, *Glossatella glabra* Roth; 3, *Glaucoma pyriformis* Ehrbg. (This is no fish parasite. Shown as example for *Glaucoma*.)

damaging effect on fish. Among others the following species have been observed:

Glossatella piscicola Blanchard. Body cross-striated, length 62–86 μ, width 23–27 μ. Blanchard (1885) found this species on barbels in the Le Havre aquarium. Roth (1908) saw it on goldfish suffering from *Gyrodactylus*; Schäperclaus (1954) on sticklebacks.

Glossatella glabra Roth. No cross striation as in *G. piscicola*. Length about 70 μ, with 30–40 μ. Generally club-shaped. Found by Roth (1908) on Veiltails.

Glossatella amoeba (Grenfell). A small variable species, rarely seen on fish.

Sessile ciliates may be removed with the help of salt (NaCl) baths of 1·5–2% or, if stronger measures are needed, with a bath of 0·5% of ammonia.

Trichodina and Related Forms

Members of the genus *Trichodina* Ehrenberg (Family Urceolariidae Stein) are very commonly seen on all kinds of aquatic animals. In fish they may settle on the skin in such numbers as to obscure the normal structure and they are easily recognized by their similarity to a suction disk. Genus and classification have been reviewed by Tripathi (1948).

The typical features of the genus are exhibited by *Trichodina domerguei*, a flat, disk-like organism provided with several rows of cilia at the circular periphery (Fig. 53), and a circle of more centrally

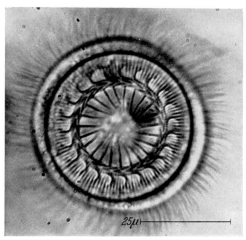

Fig. 53. *Trichodina domerguei* Wallengren. (After Hirschmann and Partsch.)

lying hooklets. The external adhesive ring allows the ciliate to attach itself firmly to the skin of a fish or other aquatic animal. The laterally situated cytostome is surrounded by a special ring of cilia. Next to the sausage-shaped macronucleus a smaller micronucleus can be seen. The diameter of the ciliate is 40–56 μ, the number of the toothed hooklets 21–29. It seems that the parasite is in permanent rotation while attached to a host and that this has an irritating effect on the epithelial cells. *Trichodina* is capable of destroying all layers of the skin down to the subcutis. This happens particularly in fish already enfeebled from other causes. Such specimens soon succumb from the combined attack.

It is difficult to be certain about the mode of feeding in these ciliates. *Trichodina domerguei* appears to live on debris from the vulnerable skin of the fish, from bacteria and other micro-organisms. The fact that they are fairly omnivorous allows these protozoans to live swimming about for some time, not attached to a host. They may therefore be caught together with live fish food.

Methods to remove them are similar to those already mentioned for other ectoparasites. Baths with quinine hydrochloride (1 g : 50 l of water) or trypaflavine (1 g : 100 l of water) for 1–2 days have been found useful. Salt (NaCl) baths (2·5% for 3–10 min) are more harmless but may have to be repeated several times before being successful.

Trichodina domerguei may be found on a variety of freshwater fish. Apart from the skin and the fins its seat of predilection seem to be the gills. Tripathi (1948) described altogether seventeen ectoparasitic species of *Trichodina*, eight of them marine and six which live in the gut and the urinary bladder (*T. urinaria* Dogel parasite of perches). Lom (1963) has revised the whole family. The most common species beside *Trichodina* spp. are *Trichodinella* (macronucleus describes a turn of 180°) *epizootica* (Raabe), *Tripartiella* (macronucleus describes a turn of 180–270°) *incissa* (Lom) and *copiosa* (Lom).

Suctoria

In a second class of the Ciliophora, the Suctoria, we find another fish parasite. Davis (1956) describes two species of *Trichophrya* which attack the gills of N. American freshwater fish. These protozoans are equipped with sucking tentacles allowing them to feed directly on cytoplasm by penetrating the cell wall of the host. They have mainly been found on Centrarchidae (sunfish), where they caused great losses among the fry. According to Lom (1961), *Trichophrya* has also been found on European fish. We ourselves have found it on the gills of coregonids.

REFERENCES

Buschkiel, A. L. (1936). Neue Beiträge zur Kenntnis des *Ichthyophthirius multi-filiis* Fouquet. *Arch. Néerl. Zool.* II. 178–224.
Bychowsky, B. E. (1962). Opredelitel parasitow pressnowodnych ryb. SSSR, Moscow.
Davis, H. S. (1956). "Culture and Diseases of Fishes." Berkeley and Los Angeles.
Duijn, C. v. (1956). "Diseases of Fishes", publ. *Water Life*, London.
Epstein, H. (1926). Infektion des Nervensystems von Fischen durch Infusorien. *Arch. Russ. Prot.* **51**, 169.
Grell, K. G. (1956). "Protozoologie." Berlin, Göttingen, Heidelberg.
Hirschmann, H. and Partsch, K. (1955). *Trichodina domerguei* Wallengren, ein selten schöner Parasit an Fischen. *Mikrokosmos*, **42**, 73–77.
Hyman, L. H. (1940). "The Invertebrates", Vol. I. McGraw-Hill, New York.
Kahl, A. (1935). Wimpertiere oder Ciliata (Infusoria). *In* "Die Tierwelt Deutsch lands und der angrenzenden Meeresteile" (F. Dahl, ed.). Jena.
Kudo, R. R. (1960). "Protozoology", 4th edn., Thomas, Springfield, Ill.

3

Kristensen, J. (1950). Witte stip kinine en drakenwinzalm. *Het Aquarium* **20**, 268–269.

Laird, M. (1959). *Caliperia brevipes* n. sp. (Ciliata: *Peritricha*) epizoic on *Raia erinacea* Mitchell at St. Andrews, New Brunswick. *Canad. J. Zool.* **37**, 283–288.

Lederer, G. (1940). Ichthyophthiriasis und ihre Bekämpfung im Aquarium. *Zool. Garten* N.F. **12**, 111–122.

Lom, J. (1960). *Trichodina reticulata* Hirschmann and Partsch, 1955, from Crucian Carp, and *T. domerguei f. latispina* Dogiel 1940, from *Diaptomus. Vestn. esk. Zool. Spol.* **24**, 246–257.

Lom, J. (1960). On two endozoic Trichodinids, *Trichodina urinaria* Dogiel 1940 and *Trichodina polycirra* n. sp. *Acta parasit. pol.* **8**, 169–180.

Lom, J. (1961). Protozoan parasites found in Czechoslovakian fishes. I. Myxosporidia, Suctoria. *Zool. Listy Fol. Zool.* **10** (24), 45–58.

Lom, J. (1963). The Ciliates of the Family *Urceolariidae. Vestn. Czesk. spol. Zool.* **27**, 7–19.

Pratt, H. S. (1951). "A Manual of the Common Invertebrate Animals." Blakiston, Philadelphia.

Reichenbach-Klinke, H. (1950). H. Ein bemerkenswerten Fall von *Ichthyophthirius. Wschr. Aqu. Terrk.* **44**, 305–307.

Reichenow, E. (1953). " Lehrbuch der Protozoenkunde", 6th edn.

Roth, W. (1908). Beiträge zur Kenntnis des *Ichthyophthirius multifilis* Fouquet. *Bl. Aqu. Terrk.* **19**.

Roth, W. (1922). "Die Krankheiten der Aquarienfische und ihre Bekämpfung", 2nd edn. Stuttgart.

Schäperclaus, W. (1954). "Fischkrankheiten", 3rd edn., Akademie Verlag, Berlin.

Shumway, W. (1940). A ciliate protozoan parasitic in the central nervous system of larval *Ambystoma. Biol. Bull.* **78**, 283–288.

Stolk (1956). Cited by Duijn (1956).

Tripathi, Y. R. (1948). A new species of ciliate, *Trichodina branchicola*, from some fishes at Plymouth. *J. Mar. biol. Ass. U.K.* **27**, 440–450.

Tripathi, Y. R. (1954). Studies on parasites of Indian fishes. III. Protozoa. 2. Mastigophora and Ciliophora. *Rep. Indian Mus.* **52**, 221–230.

Zacharias, O. (1892). Über eine Ichthyophthiriusart aus den Aquarien der biologischen Station in Plön. *Festschr.* 70. Geburtstg R. Leuckart, 289–292.

F. PARASITIC COELENTERATES

There exists in Russia a type of polyp, *Polypodium hydriforme* Ussow, which parasitizes the eggs of the sturgeon. It has only been found in the females of *Acipenser ruthenus* L., *A. stellatus* Pall. and *A. sturio* L. In the parasitic stage the polyp may produce a stolon (a kind of shoot from which the new individual may grow by budding). The parasite lies between the egg membrane and the yolk and hibernates in the egg. Shortly before oviposition takes place the stolons are everted. Raikova (1959) found free-living polyps in the lower Dnieper and in the Volga, parasitic polyps in the lower Danube, the Don, in the Kuban region, the northern Dvina, the Volga and in other tributaries of the Caspian sea and the Aral sea. (Fig. 56.)

REFERENCE

Raikova, E. V. (1959). O Sarashennocti volshskogo Ocetra. *Polypodium hydriforme* Ussow (Coelenterata) *Isw. Inst. ORRC.* **49**, 207–212. (Über den Befall des Wolgastörs mit *Polypodium hydriforme* Ussow.)

G. TREMATODES PARASITIZING FISH

Fish play an important part as hosts of helminths.

Yamaguti (1961) lists for fish 54 Families of digenetic trematodes; 37 Families of cestodes; and 21 Families of nematodes. The nematodes embraced 89 genera with 602 species.

The worms, whose economic importance, consequent on their damaging effect on many fishes, has been recognized for many years, have been extensively studied and described. Our knowledge of the systematics and the biology of this class is therefore more complete than that of most other parasites. So far as the fishes are concerned trematodes may live on their skin and their gills as ecto- or, in their muscles and almost any internal organ, as endoparasites. The majority of trematode species inhabit the sea but there are some equally noxious species in our lakes and rivers.

The Trematoda are classified according to the anatomy of their sucking disks and by their life cycles, which may involve the invasion of one or of several hosts.

The Monogenea or Heterocotylea have sucking disks with chitinous reinforcements. They pass their life cycle on one host. They live as ectoparasites on the skin or the gills of fish where they either produce fully developed offspring or eggs which give rise to the next generation. *Gyrodactylus*, a common gill parasite, belongs to this order.

The Aspidobothria or Aspidogastrea (Faust and Tang) are a trematode group whose place among the Monogenea or the Digenea is still disputed. They parasitize the gut and the bile duct of marine and of some freshwater fish and have large, often subdivided sucking disks devoid of hooks. There is no alternation of hosts and no metamorphosis, the larva developing straight into the adult. According to Hyman (1951) fish acquire these parasites by eating infected clams and snails. The best known genus is *Aspidogaster*.

The Digenea (Malacocotylea) are trematodes with simple sucking disks. They require a change of one or several hosts to complete their life cycle. Most Digenea parasitize vertebrate animals. The number of species is great and many of them are found in marine and freshwater fish. The life cycle of many of these worms is complicated and new knowledge is continually being added to what we know of this large and important Order of parasites.

The first intermediate host entered by the first-stage larva (miracidium) is nearly always a water snail. Further development varies from species to species. Favourite second or third intermediate hosts for the later larval stage (redia, cercaria) are insects, fish or amphibians. If an aquarium or fish tank is scrupulously cleaned of all snails, a repetition of an infection with digenetic trematodes cannot occur. A fish functioning as second intermediate host, may be heavily infested by cercariae but unless the fish is in turn eaten by a bird or a mammal the life cycle of the worm cannot be completed. Only in the final stage does the worm come to sexual maturity. Apart from aquatic birds and mammals, predaceous fish or reptiles may, in some cases, act as final hosts. Some of the more important trematodes will be described.

Order Monogenea

Family Gyrodactylidae

These worms have a double-pointed anterior end and no eye spots. The embryos develop one inside the other. All the species are viviparous (Fig. 53). The species most frequently seen in the aquarium is *Gyrodactylus elegans* v. Nordmann, a worm of 0·5–0·8 mm length. The large adhesive disk at the posterior end is fitted with the two main hooks, each about 60 μ long. The hooks lie approximately parallel and are connected by two broad ridges (Fig. 54).

Gyrodactylus elegans occurs in marine and in freshwater fish, particularly in flatfish, bottom-living fish, sticklebacks, carp and others. The worms are just visible to the naked eye. One end is attached to the fish, while the other floats with the water current. Should the fish die the worms desert it at once (Schäperclaus, 1954). Mann (1951) reported on losses among fish in Hamburg caused by *G. elegans*, and favoured, apparently, by a deterioration in the quality of the water.

Gyrodactylus medius Kath. measures only 0·25–0·5 mm. The principal hooks are 35–45 μ long and are arranged in the shape of a narrow angle. The edge of the hooks is slightly serrated.

Sproston and Malmberg (1956) discuss the differentiation between the various species of *Gyrodactylus*, which is by no means easy. Numbers of specimens have to be studied and minute details measured before a determination of the species responsible for an epizootic can be made with certainty. Because of its small size the worm can easily be transferred from one habitat to another. N. American guppies (*Lebistes reticulatus* Peters) are parasitized by *Gyrodactylus bullatarudis* Turnbull (Fig. 55, 1, 2) and Malmberg (1956) saw a related species on the actinopterygian African fish *Polypterus senegalus* Cuvier which, because of its size, he named *Macrogyrodactylus polypteri*. The genus is distinguished by the presence of sixteen particularly long processes of the adhesive disk (Fig. 55, 3).

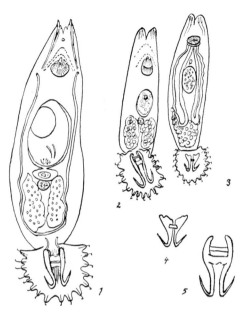

Fig. 54. Freshwater Gyrodactylids. 1, *Gyrodactylus elegans* v. Nordmann; 2, *Gyrodactylus medius* Kathariner; 3, *Gyrodactylus gracilis* Kathariner; 4, Hooks of *G. gracilis*; 5, Hooks of *G. medius*.

Methods of fighting a gyrodactylid infection follow those used against other ectoparasites. Baths in salt (NaCl 2·5% for 10–15 min); trypaflavine (1 g in 100 l of water) as a permanent bath; equally quinine (1 g of quinine sulphate or quinine hydrochloride in 50 l of water) or Rivanol (an acridine derivative) (1 g in 400 l of water). Schäperclaus recommends as particularly useful short baths in a solution of hydrogen peroxide (17 cm³ of a 3% commercial solution in 1 litre of water), the bath not to exceed 5 min. He also recommends formaldehyde (100 cm³ in 100 l of water) for 15 min or Zephirol (alkyl-dimethyl-benzyl-ammonium chloride) (1 : 2–4 000) for 30 min.

Dactylogyridae

The Dactylogyridae, a similar order of the monogenetic trematodes, definitely prefer the gills as a seat of attachment. They may be recognized by the presence of four black eye spots at the anterior end. All species lay eggs which produce ciliated larvae. A few of these worms do no harm to the fish. A heavy infestation produces adhesions between the gill villi and distortion of the whole organ. The main genera are *Dactylogyrus, Neodactylogyrus, Monocoelium* and *Ancyrocephalus*. They may be distinguished as follows:

Dactylogyrus: There is a connecting rod between the two main hooklets of the adhesive disk (Fig. 58).

Neodactylogyrus: There are two connecting rods between the two main hooklets of the adhesive disk.

Monocoelium: Two pairs of hooklets with one connecting rod between the four hooks.

Ancyrocephalus: Anterior end round, four main hooklets on the adhesive disk, two connecting rods between the hooklets.

Of the twenty-six species of *Dactylogyrus* mentioned by Dawes (1946) only a few are found causing greater damage in ponds. Dawes (1946) lists a further twenty-nine species for *Neodactylogyrus* which parasitize the gills of various marine and freshwater fish. They rarely exceed a length of 1 mm.

Ancyrocephalus is a mainly marine species. *A. paradoxus* Creplin, for instance, has been found on the pike-perch (*Lucioperca lucioperca* L.).

The closely allied type *Monocoelium monenteron* Wagner is a common parasite of the gills of the pike (*Esox lucius* L.) (Fig. 57).

The N. American dactylogyrids are of particular interest in so far as, with their hosts (various species of perch), they have been distributed to many countries, among others to Europe. This applies particularly to the genus *Urocleidus* (Mizelle, 1938; Mizelle and Arcadi, 1945).

Diplectanum, another dactylogyrid genus, is well known from the Mediterranean (Fig. 59). It has also been found on S. American freshwater fish. The favourite seat of all these forms are the gills.

The great variety of dactylogyrids was recently described by Bychowsky (1962).

Discocotylidae

The discocotylids are represented among the fish parasites by one of the most curious creatures in the whole animal kingdom, the twin-worm *Diplozoon*. In the adult stage these worms whose length rarely

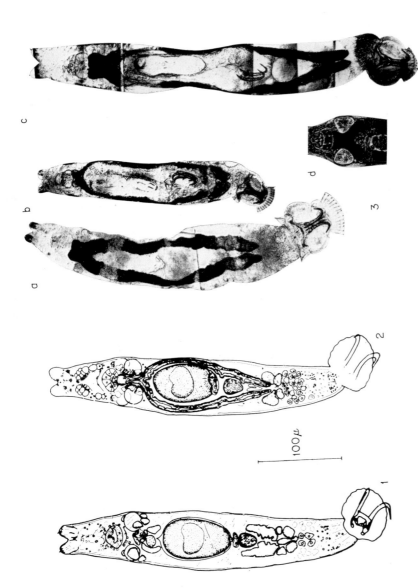

FIG. 55. 1 and 2, *Gyrodactylus bullataredis* Turnbull; 3 (a-d), *Macrogyrodactylus polypteri* Malmberg. (After Malmberg.)

FIG. 56. *Polypodium hydriforme*
Ussow from the egg of a sturgeon.
(After Raikova.)

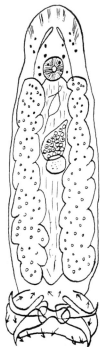

FIG. 57. *Monocoelium monenteron* Wag.
(After Alarotu.)

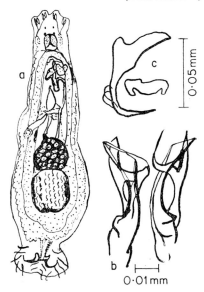

FIG. 58. (a, b) *Dactylogyrus vastator* Nybelin. (After Bychowsky.) (c) *D. auriculatus*
Diesing. (After Nybelin.)

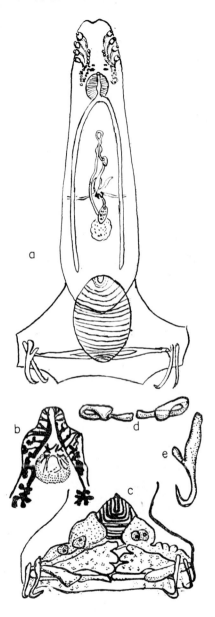

FIG. 59. (a) *Diplectanum aculeatus* Parona and Perugia. ×120. (b–e) *Diplectanum aequans* Diesing. (After Sproston.)

exceeds 1·5 mm, are only seen in permanently united pairs. The adhesive disk has eight hooks. There are no eye spots. The anterior part

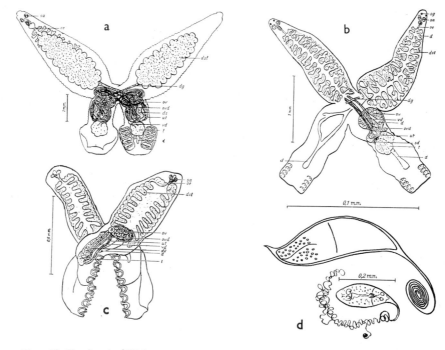

Fig. 60. Freshwater Diplozoa.
(a) *Diplozoon paradoxum* N. Natural size 4–11 mm.
(b) *Diplozoon nipponicum* G. Natural size 1–1 mm.
(c) *Diplozoon barbi* Reichenbach-Klinke. Natural size 1–1 mm.
(d) Above: egg of *D. barbi* with filament. (After Reichenbach-Klinke.)
    Below: egg of *D. paradoxum* with filament. (After Nordmann.)
    d, gut; *dst*, yolk sac; *dg*, yolk duct; *oe*, oesophagus; *ov*, ovary; *ovd*, oviduct; *sg*, cement gland; *t*, testis; *ut*, uterus; *vd*, vas deferens.

is foliate (Fig. 60). The worms are sufficiently transparent to allow recognition of the dark yolk granules filling the yolk sac, the anterior two suction disks, the pharynx and the lateral caeca of the gut. Fig. 60 shows the complicated arrangement of the reproductive organs. One egg only is produced at a time. It is provided with a long filament and adheres to the gills of the host (Fig. 60d). A pair of larvae, once they have reached adequate maturity, attach themselves to each other by way of adhesive disks and fuse so completely that henceforth they cannot be separated and their reproductive organs remain in a state of constant copulation. Larvae which fail to pair up in this way perish.

Twin-worms are pure gill parasites and when too numerous they interfere heavily with the breathing of the affected fish. *Diplozoon barbi* produces adhesions and oedema of the gills (Fig. 61). Excessive infestation may even kill the fish.

Each of the few species of *Diplozoon* described seems to limit itself strictly to one host genus. The largest form known, *D. paradoxum* v. Nordmann, is found on cyprinids in Europe and Asia, while *D. nipponicum*, also found on cyprinids, is confined to E. Asia.

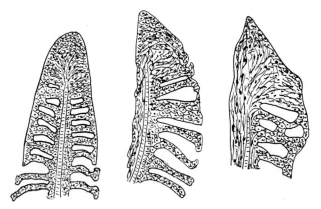

FIG. 61. Gill adhesions in a perch with *Diplozoon barbi* infection.

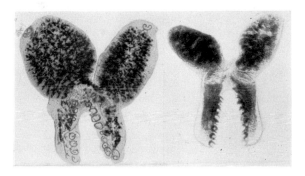

FIG. 62. *Diplozoon barbi* R–K. Two mature specimens.

Diplozoon barbi Reichenbach-Klinke (1954) seems to have been imported from S.E. Asia. So far it has, in Europe, only been found on barbels of the genera *Barbus* and *Puntius* (Figs. 62 and 63). In German aquaria it has been encountered since 1949; it has, however not caused any widespread epizootics. *D. barbi* measures 1–1·3 μ in length, 0·2–0·6 mm in width; the suction disks have a diameter of 0·05–0·06 mm. There are 6–8 pairs of intestinal diverticula. The eggs are about 0·2 mm long and 0·08 mm wide exclusive of the long suspensory filament. For further details of the anatomy see Fig. 60.

Diplozoon tetragonopterini. The species was established by Sterba (1956), from the gills of S. American salmonids. Experimentally it

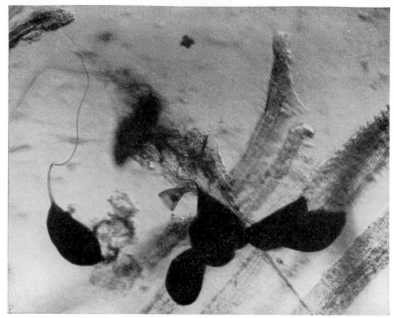

FIG. 63. Eggs of *Diplozoon barbi* anchored by their long filaments in the gills of a perch. × 200.

could only be transferred within the same genus and morphologically it closely resembles *D. barbi* (Fig. 64).

The eradication of *Diplozoon* should follow the methods advised for *Gyrodactylus* (p. 69).

Tripathi (1957) raises the Diplozoidae to the status of a Family.

FIG. 64. *Diplozoon tetragonopterini*. Two joined young stages slightly compressed. Natural length about 1 mm. (After Sterba.)

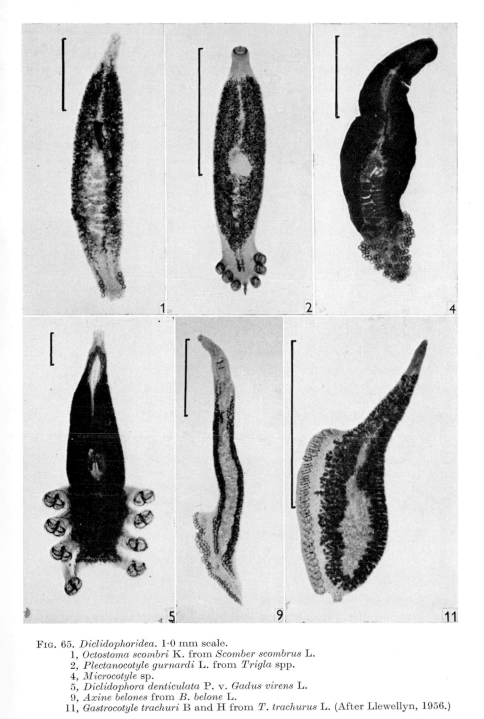

FIG. 65. *Diclidophoridea.* 1·0 mm scale.
    1, *Octostoma scombri* K. from *Scomber scombrus* L.
    2, *Plectanocotyle gurnardi* L. from *Trigla* spp.
    4, *Microcotyle* sp.
    5, *Diclidophora denticulata* P. v. *Gadus virens* L.
    9, *Axine belones* from *B. belone* L.
    11, *Gastrocotyle trachuri* B and H from *T. trachurus* L. (After Llewellyn, 1956.)

Similar forms classed among the Discocotylidae (for instance, *Disco-cotyle sagittata* Diesing from trout) are widely distributed in fresh and marine waters.

Microcotylidae

Together with several other similar families like the Hexastomatidae, the Calceostomatidae, the Udonellidae, the Monocotylidae and the Capsalidae, the Microcotylidae should be mentioned as a particularly widespread family. Of the genus *Microcotyle* alone we know about 100 species although numerous synonyma are possible (Tripathi, 1954).

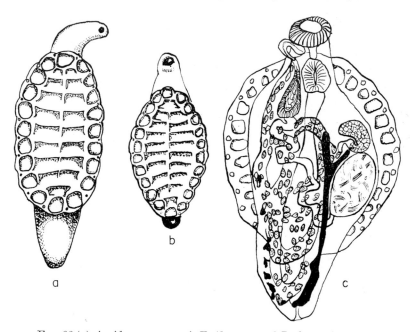

Fig. 66.(a) *Aspidogaster enneatis* E. (from gut of *Barbus* sp.).
(b) *A. decatis* E. (from gut of *Cyprinus carpio*).
(c) *A. limacoides* D. (in gut of cyprinids and gobiids).

Most of these forms are again gill parasites of marine fish. They have been found on bream, perch, labrids and chaetodontids. *Microcotyle* is recognized by the number (30–80) of suctorial disks (Fig. 65). Other genera occurring in marine fish are *Axine* and *Gastrocotyle*.

Mazocraeidae

A representative of this family is the genus *Octostoma* (= *Kuhnia*). *O. scombri* Kuhn is a common gill parasite of the mackerel (*Scomber scombrus* L.).

Diclidophoridae

Another Family of widespread monogenetic trematodes, parasitic on the gills of marine fish, particularly on gadids. The suctorial disk is split into eight separate processes each of which ends with its own small adhesive valve (Fig. 65).

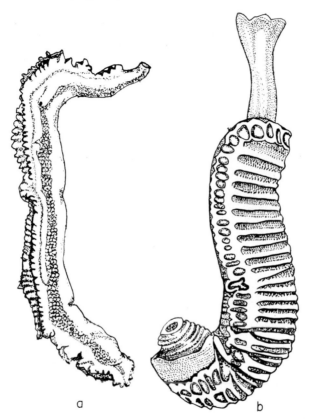

a   b

FIG. 67. (a) *Macraspis elegans* O. (from gall bladder of *Chimaera monstrosa* L.).
(b) *Cotylogaster occidentalis* N. (from *Aplodinotus grunniens* Raf. (After Dollfus.)

Order Aspidobothria (Aspidogastrea Faust and Tang, 1936)

The Class is less notable for its commercial importance, which is not great, than for its fantastic shape. Aspidobothria are occasionally found in marine fish and have been extensively studied by Dollfus (1958). These worms are usually found in internal organs like the gut, the oesophagus, the gall bladder or the bile ducts. Fig. 66 shows *Aspidogaster decatis* Ekman from the gut of a carp. An allied form, *A. enneatis*, is known from various species of *Barbus*. *Aspidogaster limacoides* Diesing lives in the gut of freshwater fish in S. Europe from Austria to the Caspian Sea in cyprinid and silurid fish. *Cotylogaster occidentalis* Nickerson is known from the gut of *Aplodinotus grunniens* Raf., *Macraspis elegans* Olsson from the gall bladder of *Chimaera monstrosa* L. and from *Callorhynchus milli* St. Vincent (Fig. 67).

The marine types have been recorded from rays, sharks, and bream where they may parasitize the gut or the gall bladder.

Class Digenea

Digenetic trematodes may use fish either as intermediate hosts in one of their larval stages or as mature worms where the fish is the final host. In the larval form they may be found in the form of metacercaria free or encysted in almost any organ. Sexually mature digenetic worms may inhabit the intestinal tract, the gills or the circulatory system and may, from there, invade any other part of the fish. Molluscs (snails or clams) are always the first intermediate hosts. Where the fish acts as penultimate host the final host may be another, carnivorous fish, a bird or a carnivorous mammal.

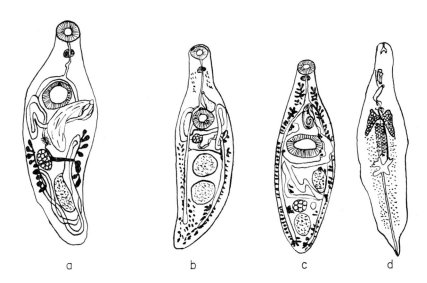

a   b   c   d

Fig. 68. Trematodes parasitic in fish.
(a) *Asymphylodora tincae* Modeer.
(b) *Allocreadium isosporum* Looss.
(c) *Sphaerostoma bramae* Müller.
(d) *Sanguinicola inermis* Plehn.

A complete list of all the digenetic trematodes which may be found in fish would fill a book in itself. A few of the more important species are pictured in Fig. 68. Cercariae damaging the skin and worms circulating in the blood stream should be particularly mentioned because of their damaging effect on the hosts.

In the gut of the tench (*Tinca tinca* L.) we find *Asymphylodora tincae* Modeer and in that of cyprinids *Sphaerostoma bramae* Müller and *Allocreadium isosporum* Looss. They all rely on molluscs as intermediate hosts. Some of the marine trematodes are extremely common. The angler fish, for instance (*Lophius piscatorius* L.), is a frequent host of *Bucephalopsis gracilescens* Rud. In this case the development starts in mussels (*Cardium edule* L. or *Mytilus edulis* L.). There follows a second intermediate host, usually a gadid, where the larva encysts in the brain, more rarely in the skin, the eyes, or the mouth.

Trematodes of the genus *Sanguinicola*, in particular *S. inermis* Plehn, inhabit in the final form blood vessels of fish. The worms, and particularly the profusely produced eggs, may cause complete occlusion of the blood vessels and death of the fish. The snails serving as intermediate hosts are species of the genera *Lymnaea*, *Valvata* and *Buliminus* (Fig. 68).

Fish Losses through Trematode Larvae

Occasionally the infestation of the subcutis of fish by trematode larvae may become extremely heavy, endangering the life of the host. The worm-blindness seen in so many fish in the Bodensee may serve as an example.

Hoffman (1960), reviewing the trematodes parasitizing fish, gave an account of an extraordinarily large number of different species

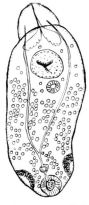

Fig. 69. *Diplostomulum truttae* Lal. (After Hoffman.)

involved. Their morphological differences are often small and quite unrecognizable for anybody but an expert (Fig. 69). The main Families concerned are the Strigeidae, the Diplostomatidae, the Clinostomatidae, the Gorgoderidae and the Cyathocotylidae. We shall give a few examples of each.

Family Strigeidae (= Holostomidae)

The perhaps commonest metacercarial infestation of fish is caused by *Posthodiplostomum cuticula* v. Nordmann (= *Neascus cuticola* v. Nordmann and Hughes). The metacercariae of this species are found in melanin-pigmented cysts in the skin, the fins and the cornea of numerous fish. The final hosts are herons. Many other species parasitize the skin of fishes.

"Worm-blindness" is another condition caused by strigeid trematodes, particularly by *Diplostomum spathaceum* Rud. (= *D. volvens* v. Nordm. = *Diplostomulum spathaceum* Rud.). The larvae may be found in the lens of the eye or in the vitreous body. The intermediate hosts are lymnaeid snails. Final maturity is reached in auks (Alcidae), gulls or pelicans.

Another strigeid metacercaria which may invade the vitreous body is *Tylodelphis clavata* v. Nordm. (= *Diplostomulum clavatus* Diesing).

Family Gorgoderidae

From this Family we may quote the genus *Phyllodistomum* which has the distinction of requiring a fish as second and as final host. Metacercaria are found in dermal pustules of minnows (*Phoxinus phoxinus* L.). The mature worm lives in the gut of trout. Other gorgoderids, some of which occur also in Europe, have as their first intermediate host bivalves (*Sphaeriidae*); as second host some amphibium, a snail or a tadpole; as final host a frog.

Family Clinostomatidae

An infection with these worms may be encountered in aquarium fish imported from tropical countries. Pustules of 2–2·5 mm diameter appear in the skin. They may be grey-white or have a yellow tinge. The preferred site is at the base of the fins, on the ventral area, on the head in the neighbourhood of the eyes, but pustules may arise anywhere else (Figs. 70 and 71). Opened with a fine scalpel the cysts are seen to contain a metacercaria (Fig. 72) which, having left its first intermediate host, a snail, has penetrated into the skin of the fish. The condition is popularly known as "Yellow Grub" disease. The worm only reaches full maturity if the fish is eaten by a bird. The trematode species concerned are mostly *Clinostomum complanatum* Rud. and *Clinostomum marginatum* Rud.

Both species have a wide distribution in southern Asia. Baer (1933) has lately found another eleven, which occur in European, African and Asian fish and mature in various species of heron, more rarely in cormorants or reptiles, where they may encyst in the pharynx or the oesophagus.

FIG. 70. *Colisa lalia* H.–B. Cercarial infection, particularly of the head.

FIG. 71. *Colisa lalia* H.–B. Cercarial infection of head region.

Clinostomum complanatum Rud. occurs along the lower Danube, in S. Asia and in N. America, particularly on sun-fish (*Centrarchidae*), the dwarf cat-fish (*Ameiurus nebulosus* Les.), *Crenicichla saxatilis* L. and *Salvelinus fontinalis* Mitch. The mature worms of some clinostomatid cercariae are as yet unknown. Information is wanting of species occurring in Angola, the Congo and in Ceylon. From the latter country a species named as *Clinostomum piscium* Southwell and Prashad has been described from the fishes *Colisa fasciata* Bl. and Schn. and *Nandus nandus* Cuv. and Val. The larva had a length of 2·8–5 mm.

Transverse sections through an affected fish show the parasite occupying a cyst in the subcutaneous tissue. If the larva is large in relation to the size of the host the cysts may burrow into and displace

Fig. 72. Isolated cercaria in pigmented capsule. From *Colisa lalia* H.–B. (Photo.: Reichenbach-Klinke.)

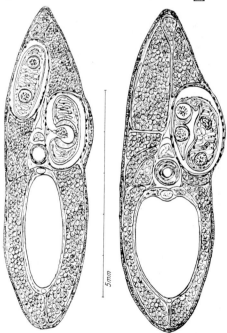

Fig. 73. Transverse sections through two specimens of *Colisa lalia* with cercarial cysts in the muscle. (After Reichenbach-Klinke.)

the muscle and abut on the spinal column. Where the infection is a heavy one the transverse section through the affected fish may seem to show nothing but parasitic tissue, most of the host tissue having been displaced. It is no surprise to learn that small fish suffer considerably from such an infection both in their metabolism and in their motility.

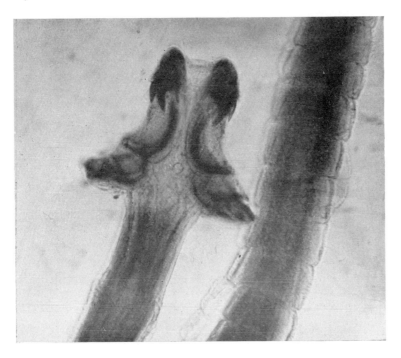

Fig. 74. Scolex of *Acanthobothrium coronatum* Rud. × 60. (Photo.: Reichenbach-Klinke.)

Clinostomatid metacercariae found by Reichenbach-Klinke in dermal cysts of *Colisa lalia* H.-B., a tropical fish, frequently seen in the aquarium, may serve as an example. The larvae, when freed from the cysts, have an extended oval shape and a short, well-defined caudal part (Fig. 72). They are 2–4 mm, rarely up to 6·5 mm long and 1–2 mm broad. In the cysts they are seen partly rolled up and fixed by the ventral sucker. No movement of the larvae has been observed during this resting period but the larvae seem to grow slightly during their term of encystment.

The *Colisa* metacercariae allowed a detailed study of anatomical detail from fixed and stained preparations. The cyst wall is 0·05–0·1 mm thick and is made up from a peripheral connective-tissue layer, derived from the host and an inner membrane provided by the parasite. Star-shaped black pigmented cells (melanophores) can be seen in both layers. The larvae usually show a smooth surface; ridges or irregularities may occasionally occur in the anterior part of the larva. In the epidermis we see numerous mucus-producing cells and similar cells lie elsewhere in the deeper parts of the tissue. Under the epidermis we find first transverse, then longitudinal muscle. The anterior sucker is round and its position is terminal. The ventral sucker, which is a little wider than long, lies close to the anterior one, approximately at the end of the first third of the body. The gut is bifurcate with small dilatations but no diverticula. It reaches as far as the last segment of the worm.

In this case the infected fish is the second intermediate host. The final or main host, mostly a water bird like the heron, catches the fish near the shore in shallow water. The gastric juice of the bird digests the fish and the cercarial cyst, but is unable to attack the cercaria itself. The larvae are thus liberated and start their migration towards the oral cavity of the bird where they attach themselves and mature into fully grown worms within 4 days.

Fertilized eggs pass into the water with the bird's faeces. The miracidium emerges and, within a few hours, penetrates into a snail, the first intermediate host. In S. America this is often the posthorn snail *Helisoma* (*Taphius*) *nigricans* Spix (= *H. lugubris* Spix), a snail frequently kept in aquaria for ornamental purposes. In North and Central America the related species *Helisoma* (*Pierosoma*) *trivolvis* Say and *H.*(*P.*) *tumidum* Pfr. are responsible. In Asia we lack as yet definite information but it seems likely that the native *Planorbidae* function as intermediate hosts there as well as elsewhere.

Once inside a snail the ciliated miracidium grows into a resting stage, the sporocyst. This in turn produces parthogenetically a new generation of trematode larvae, the rediae. The development takes about 3 weeks. The rediae again multiply parthogenetically and produce daughter rediae and the latter eventually change into the sexually immature cercariae.

Family Opisthorchidae

The well known feline liver fluke *Opisthorchis felineus* Rivolta may, during its larval stage, infect edible fish and thereby become of medical importance. The mature worm lives in the bile ducts and the pancreas of cats, dogs and man. The larva infects several freshwater fish of the genera *Idus* and *Leuciscus*. Infections have been reported among the inhabitants of the eastern part of the Baltic coast. The parasite also seems to be common in the region of the river Ob in Western Siberia.

Clonorchis sinensis Cobbold, the closely allied Chinese liver fluke, has a wide E. Asian distribution from Japan to Indo-china, where it occurs in cats, dogs and man. Here again the infection is acquired by the ingestion of raw or lightly smoked fish, mostly cyprinids which act as intermediate hosts for the metacercariae. These may be recognized by the fact that they have small eye spots.

Veterinarians are much concerned with the metacercaria of *Nano-physetus salmincola* Chapin which transmits to canids (their final host) a body resembling rickettsia which goes under the name of *Neo-rickettsia helminthoeca* Phil. *et al.* The Rickettsia produces the clinical picture of the "Salmon Poisoning" of dogs which has been reported as to 90% fatal in the affected canids (Cordy and Gorham, 1950).

REFERENCES

Alarotu, H. (1944). Untersuchungen über die an Fischen in Finnland lebenden monogenetischen Trematoden. *Acta zool. fenn.* **43**, 1–52.

Baer, J. G. (1933). Note sur un nouveau trématode, *Clinostomum apophallum* sp. nov. avec quelques considérations generales sur la famille des *Clinostomidae*. *Rev. suisse Zool.* **40**, 317–342.

Baer, J. G. (1946). "Le Parasitisme." Masson, Paris.

Bychowsky, B. E. (1962). Opredelitel parasitow pressnowodnych ryb. SSSR, Moskow.

Cordy, D. R. and Gorham, J. R. (1950). The pathology and etiology of salmon disease in the dog and fox. *Amer. J. Path.* **26**, 617–637.

Dawes, B. (1946). "The Trematoda. With special reference to British and other European forms." Cambridge University Press.

Dollfus, R. P. (1946). "Parasites (animaux et végétaux) des Helminthes", p. 482. Lechevalier, Paris.

Dollfus, R. P. (1958). Cours d'Helminthologie. I. Trematodes. Sous-classe *Aspidogastrea. Ann. Parasit. hum. comp.* **33**, 305–395.

Hoffman, G. L. (1956). The life cycle of *Crassiphiala bulboglossa* (*Trematoda: Strigeida*). Development of the metacercaria and cyst, and effect on the fish hosts. *J. Parasit.* **42**, 435–444.

Hoffman, G. L. (1960). Synopsis of *Strigeoidea* (*Trematoda*) of fishes and their life cycle. *Fish. Bull.* **60**, 437–469.

Hunter, G. W. and Dalton, H. C. (1939). Studies on the *Clinostomum*. V. The cyst of the yellow grub of fish (*Clinostomum marginatum*). *Proc. hel. Soc., Wash.* **61**, 73–76.

Hunter, G. W. and Hunter, W. S. (1940). Studies on the development of the metacercaria and the nature of the cyst of *Posthodiplostomum minimum* Mac-Callum, 1921 (*Trematoda*, Strigata). *Trans. Amer. micr. Soc.* **59**, 52–63.

Hyman, L. (1951). "The Invertebrates", Vol. II. McGraw-Hill, New York.

Kathariner, L. (1895). Die Gattung *Gydrodactylus* v. Nordm. *Arch. Zool. Inst. Würzburg* **10**, 125–164.

Llewellyn, J. (1956). The host-specifity micro-ecology, adhesive attitudes and comparative morphology of some trematode gill parasites. *J. mar. Biol.* **35**, 113–127.

Malmberg, G. (1956a). Om Förekomsten av *Gyrodactylus* pa Svenska fiskar. *Skrifter Sver. Fiskeriför.* 1956, 19–76.

Malmberg, G. (1956b). On a new genus of viviparous monogenetic Trematodes. *Ark. Zoologi* **2**, **10**, 317–330.

Mann, H. (1951). *Gyrodactylus* als Ursache von Fischsterben bei Aquarienfischen. *Aqu. Terr. Z.* **4**, 261–262.

Mizelle, J. D. (1938). Comparative studies on Trematodes (*Gyrodactyloidea*) from the gills of N. American freshwater fishes. *J. Biol. Monogr.* **17**, 1–81.

Mizelle, J. D. and Arcadi, J. A. (1945). *Urocleidus seculus. Trans. Amer. micr. Soc.* **64**, 293–296.

Palombi, A. (1949). I. Trematodi d'Italia. I. Trematodi monogenetici. *Arch. zool. Ital.* **34**, 203–408.

Reichenbach-Klinke, H. (1952). Eine neue Art der digenen Trematodengattung *Brachyphallus* Odhner (*Hemiuridae*). *Z. Parasitk.* **15**, 335–338.

Reichenbach-Klinke, H. (1954). Weitere Mitteilung über den Kiemenparasiten *Diplozoon barbi* Reichenbach-Klinke (*Trematoda Monogenea*). *Z. Parasitk.* **16**, 373–378.

Reichenbach-Klinke, H. (1956). Muskelcercarien aus einem Zwergfadenfish (*Colisa lalia*). *Mikrokosmos* 45 Jahrg. 81–84.

Schäperclaus, W. (1954). "Fischkrankheiten", 3rd edn., Akademie Verlag, Berlin.

Southwell, T. and Prashad, Bp. (1918). Notes from the Bengal Fisheries Laboratory. III. Some fish trematodes. *Rep. Indian Mus.* **15**, 348–350.

Sproston, N. G. (1946). A synopsis of the monogenetic trematodes. *Trans. Zool. Soc. Lond.* **25**, 185–600.

Sterba, G. (1956). *Diplozoon.* Zur Morphologie und Biologie der Geltung. *Verh. dtsch. zool. Ges., Hamburg,* 1957, *Zool. Anz.* **158**, 181–196.

Tripathi, Y. R. (1954). Studies on the parasites of Indian fishes. IV. Trematoda monogenea. *Microcotylidae. Rec. Ind. Mus.* **52**, 231–248.

Tripathi, Y. R. (1957). Monogenetic trematodes from fishes of India. *Ind. J. Helm.* **9**, 1–149.

Turnbull, E. R. (1956). *Gyrodactylus bullatarudis* n.sp. from *Lebistes reticulatus* Peters, with a study of its life cycle. *Canad. J. Zool.* **34**, 583–594.

Wunder, W. (1925). Untersuchungen über Pigmentierung und Encystierung von Cercarien *Z. Morph. Ökol.* **25**, 336–352.

Yamaguti, S. (1961–63). "Systema Helminthum." Vols. III, and IV. Interscience, London, New York.

H. TAPEWORMS (CESTODES) PARASITIZING FISH

Analogous to the trematodes, cestodes may use fish as intermediate or as final hosts in some period or other of their life cycles. Larvae may be found free or encysted either in the body cavity or within the liver, the muscles or, more rarely, in the gut. Mature tapeworms of fish are only found in the intestinal canal. The early developmental stages of cestodes parasitizing fish are not passed in snails but in small crustaceans (Copepodes) or in worms of the *Tubifex* type, both of which represent the staple food of fish. Those cestodes which pass their early stages in fish reach maturity, either in other, predaceous fish, in birds, mammals or even in man.

As an example we may mention *Caryophyllaeus laticeps* Pallas, recognizable by its flattened, leaf-like anterior end (scolex). The larvae

FIG. 75. Larva from a *Trypanorhynchus* sp. From the marine *Beryx decadactylus* C. and V. cm scale.

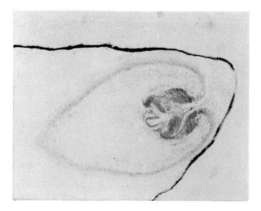

FIG. 76. *Scolex pleuronectis* Müller. Tapeworm larva from intestinal caecum of *Engraulis encrasicholus* Rond. × 62. (Photo.: Reichenbach-Klinke.)

live in tubificid worms. Fish fry may be heavily infected by *Caryophyllaeus*.

Equally, marine fish, particularly sharks and rays, harbour a great variety of cestode worms (Fig. 74) some of which, the Tetraphyllidea, anchor themselves with large hooks which may be part of the scolex or distributed over the surface of a tubular proboscis.

Larvae are frequently found in bony fish (Teleosts) which are plankton feeders. Examples of the few cestode species which inhabit the gut of freshwater fishes are *Cyathocephalus*, *Eubothrium*, *Proteocephalus* and *Triaenophorus*.

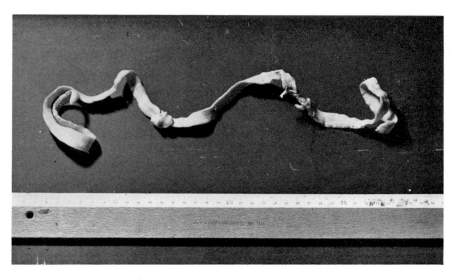

Fig. 77. *Ligula intestinalis* from the body cavity of *Abramis brama* L.

The mature form of *Amphilina foliacea* Rud., also a freshwater parasite, does not live in the gut but in the peritoneal cavity of sturgeons (Fig. 78). The larvae are transmitted by small crustaceans (*Gammaridae*) which share the fresh waters with the fish.

Ligula intestinalis L. may grow to a length of 60 cm in the body cavity of carp or, more rarely, perch. The bulk of the parasite may compress the other organs of the fish to such an extent that they can no longer function (Fig. 77). Such a fish may become sterile. The final hosts in this case are fish-catching birds.

The larval form of another tapeworm, *Schistocephalus solidus* Müller, produces an analogous picture in the stickleback. Seventy-two such larvae were found in one fish (C. Arme, personal communication). No wonder that these fish, which, at the same time, may suffer from a

Fig. 78. *Amphilina foliacea* R. from the body cavity of *Acipenser ruthenus* L. cm scale. (Photo.: *Bayr. exp. biol. Inst.*)

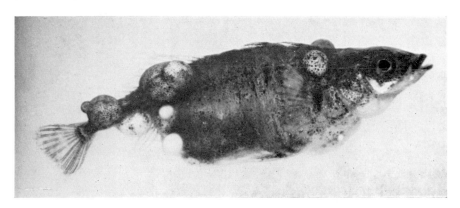

Fig. 79. Stickleback. Double infestation with *Schistocephalus solidus* in the body cavity and *Glugea anomala* in the skin. × 2. (Photo.: Elkan.) Cf. Frontispiece, Fig. 1.

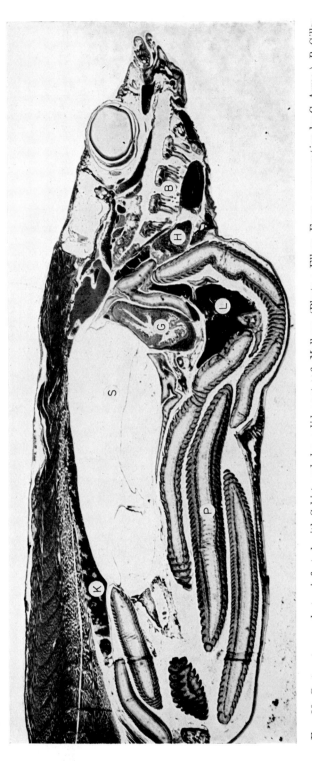

FIG. 80. *Gasterosteus aculeatus* infected with *Schistocephalus solidus* sgt. ×6. Mallory. (Photo.: Elkan. From a preparation by C. Arme.) *B*, Gills; *G*, stomach; *H*, heart; *K*, kidney; *L*, liver; *P*, plerocercoid larvae of *Schistocephalus solidus*; *S*, swim-bladder.

heavy infection by *Glugea anomala* M., have ended their lives with completely distorted bodies (Figs. 79–82, and Frontispiece).

Another cestode, more important perhaps because it may be transferred to humans, is *Diphyllobothrium latum* L. As in the two previously mentioned species the larva, known as a plerocercoid, lives in the body cavity and sometimes in the reproductive organs of the burbot (*Lota lota* L.), the ruffe (*Acerina cernua* L.) and the pike (*Esox lucius* L.). Primary hosts are small crustaceans like *Cyclops* or *Diaptomus*, the final host may be man, the pig and the dog. Cats, according to Kuhlow (1953), are not affected. The parasite is particularly known from the shores of the Baltic Sea and from some Swiss lakes. Lately it has also appeared along the lower Elbe (Kuhlow, 1953). Patients infect themselves by eating unboiled intestines of infected fish, but plerocercoids seen in such fish need not in every case be those of *D. latum* but may be those of other *Diphyllobothrium* species harmless to man. Such larvae mature in various birds or small mammals. The

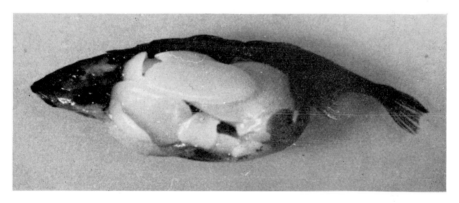

Fig. 81. As Fig. 79. Body cavity opened to show the densely packed plerocercoids of *Schistocephalus solidus*. (Photo.: Elkan.)

finding of *Diphyllobothrium* larvae in edible fish need therefore not always coincide with an outbreak of the infestation in the population. Kuhlow lists:

D. dendriticum Nitsch: Mature in gulls; plerocercoid in sticklebacks;

D. vogeli Kuhlow:? Mature in gulls; plerocercoid in sticklebacks or smelts;

D. osmeri v. Linstow: Plerocercoids in smelts.

D. ditremum Creplin: Mature in gulls and cormorants; plerocercoids in Irish trout.

Fraser (1960) reports finding the plerocercoid of *Diphyllobothrium medium* Fahmy in trout. The final host in this case is the otter (*Lutra*

lutra L.). The only species, besides *D. latum* which affects humans, is
D. cordatum Leuckart, which is confined to Iceland and Greenland.

Some cestode species spend their larval as well as their adult life in
fish. A type much feared by the fishing industry is *Triaenophorus lucii*
Müller (= *T. nodulosus* Pallas). The primary host is again a planktonic
crustacean; the secondary hosts are whiting and trout; the final hosts
other predatory fish like pike, perch, trout or salmon. It is not the

Fig. 82. As Fig. 79. Pleroceroids removed from body cavity. Note the compressed
viscera of the fish. (Photo.: Elkan.)

mature worm, however, which causes the greatest damage, but the
larvae, large numbers of which may entirely destroy the liver of the
intermediate hosts, causing great losses among the fish population.
The mature worm is fitted with strong hooks at the anterior end.
A close relation is *Triaenophorus crassus* Forel, whose larvae live in
the gut of salmonids (*Coregonus* spp.) while the mature worm is found
in the pike.

References

Borradaile, L. A. *et al.* (1959). "The Invertebrata." Cambridge University Press.
Fraser, P. G. (1960). The occurrence of Diphyllobothrium in trout, with special
reference to the outbreak in the West of England. *J. Helminth.* **34**, 59–72.

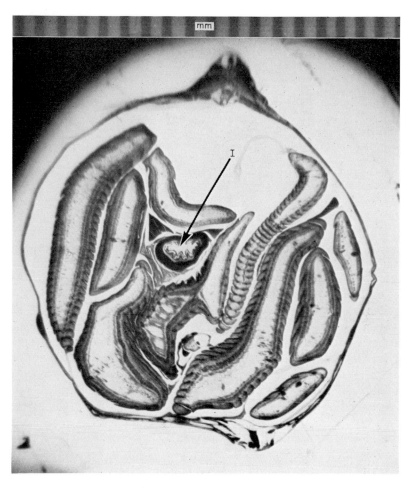

FIG. 83. As Fig. 79. Transverse section. *I*, Intestine. (Photo.: Elkan.)

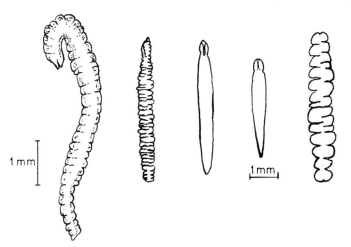

FIG. 84. Plerocercoid larvae of diphyllobothriid worms. Left to right: *D. latum, D. dendriticum, D. osmeri, D. vogeli, D. latum.* (After Kuhlow.)

Hyman, L. (1951). "The Invertebrates", Vol. II. McGraw-Hill, New York.

Kuhlow, F. (1953). Bau und Differentialdiagnose heimischer Diphyllobothrium Plerocercoide. Z. Tropenmed. Parasit. **4**, 186–202.

Kuhlow, F. (1955). Untersuchungen über die Entwicklung des breiten Bandwurms (Diphyllobothrium latum). Z. Tropenmed. Parasit. **6**, 213–225.

Reichenbach-Klinke, H. (1956). Die Larvenentwicklung bei der Bandwurmordnung Tetraphyllidea Braun 1900. Abh. Braunschw. wiss. Ges. **8**, 61–73.

Reichenbach-Klinke, H. (1957). Entwicklung und Artzugehörigkeit der als "Scolex pleuronectis Müller" bekannten Cestodenlarve (Cestoidea: Tetraphyllidea). Verh. dtsch. zool. Ges., Hamburg, 1956, Zool. Anz. Suppl., Vol. 20, pp. 317–324.

Sprehn, C. (1960). Trematoda und Cestoidea. In P. Brohmer et al., "Die Tierwelt Mitterleuropas", I. Quelle and Meyer, Leipzig.

Wardle, R. A. and McLeod, J. A. (1952). "The Zoology of Tapeworms." University of Minnesota Press, Minneapolis.

I. ACANTHOCEPHALA PARASITIZING FISH

Acanthocephala, worms with a tube-like proboscis which is covered with barbed hooks, may produce alarming losses among fish. The parasites anchor themselves securely in the epithelium lining the gut and may even perforate it (Figs. 85–87). Over a hundred or more worms have been counted in barbel (*Barbus barbus* L.) and chub (*Squalius cephalus* L.) sometimes completely obstructing the pyloric outlet of the stomach. The fish look as if they had been severely starved, which is not surprising since they are probably unable to digest any food and may even suffer from severe bacterial infection set up by the intestinal lesions.

One of the commonest acanthocephalan species, both in fresh and marine waters, is *Pomphorhynchus laevis* Müller, recognized by the bulbous neck (Figs. 85 and 87). In salmonid fish we find the genus *Echinorhynchus* (Fig. 86) and the species *Neoechinorhynchus rutili* Müller in many other fish of fresh or brackish waters (Fig. 88).

The Acanthocephala too require intermediate hosts: first intermediate hosts are again small gammarid crustaceans (*Pomphorhynchus*), insect larvae (*Neoechinorhynchus*) or marine crustaceous *Amphipoda* (*Echinorhynchus*). *Pomphorhynchus* requires a second intermediate host (small whitings) while most other species require only a single one.

Acanthocephalus lucii Lühe and *A. anguillae* Lühe, two species with a narrow proboscis which parasitize freshwater fish, develop their larvae in isopod *Asellida*. Of the numerous exotic species we may mention *Pallisentis basiri* Farooqi (Fig. 89). Further details of this large and important phylum may be found in the regional investigations of authors like Bullock (1962) and Haderlie (1953).

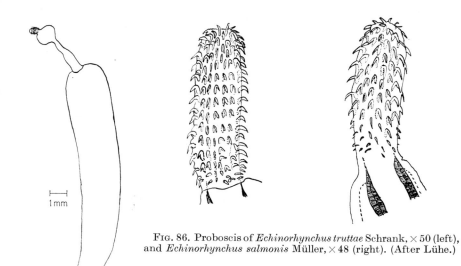

FIG. 86. Proboscis of *Echinorhynchus truttae* Schrank, × 50 (left), and *Echinorhynchus salmonis* Müller, × 48 (right). (After Lühe.)

FIG. 85. *Pomphorhynchus laevis* M. (After Sprehn.)

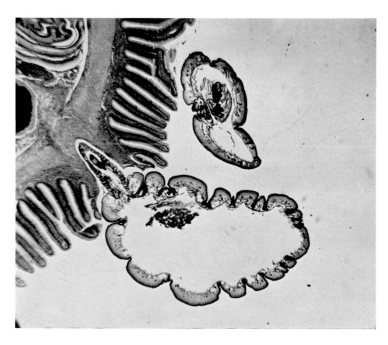

FIG. 87. *Pomphorhynchus laevis* M. attached to the mucous membrane of the gut of *Squalius cephalus.* × 20. (Photo.: Ghittino.)

4

FIG. 88. Proboscis of *Neoechinorhynchus rutili* M. (left) and *Triaenophorus crassus* Forel (right). (After Forel.)

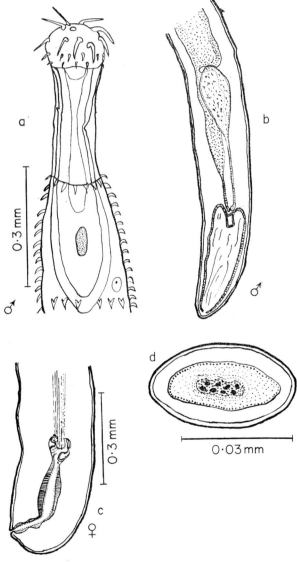

FIG. 89. *Pallisentis basiri* Farooqi. (a) Proboscis; (b) tail of ♂, (c) tail of ♀; (d) egg. (After Farooqi.)

REFERENCES

Borradaile, L. A. *et al.* (1959). "The Invertebrata." Cambridge University Press.
Bullock, W. L. (1962). Acanthocephalan parasites of freshwater fishes of New Hampshire. *J. Parasit.* **48**, 2, 44.
Farooqi, H. U. (1958). A new species of the genus *Pallisentis* from freshwater eel. *Z. Parasitk.* **18**, 457–464.
Haderlie, E. C. (1953). Parasites of the fresh-water fishes of Northern California. *Univ. Calif. Publ. Zool.* **57**, 303–440.
Hyman, L. H. (1951). "The Invertebrates", Vol. III. McGraw-Hill, New York.
Meyer, A. (1930). Acanthocephala. *In* P. Brohmer *et al.* "Die Tierwelt Mitteleuropas", I. Quelle and Meyer, Leipzig.
Petrotschenko, V. J. (1956–58). "Acantocefaly domashnich i dikich shiwotnich." Moscow.
Pratt, H. S. (1951). "A Manual of the Common Invertebrate Animals." Blakiston, Toronto.
Sprehn, C. (1959). Acanthocephala. Supplement. *In* P. Brohmer *et al.* "Die Tierwelt Mitteleuropas," I. Quelle and Meyer, Leipzig.

J. NEMATODA AND NEMATOMORPHA PARASITIZING FISH

Well over a hundred different species of nematode worms play a part in the helminthology of fish, either as larvae or in the shape of mature worms invading internal organic systems. As usual the seat of predilection is the gut; then follow the muscles, the reproductive system and the circulatory organs. Larvae may be found in the skin, the muscles, the gut, the liver and in the body cavity. Heavy infestation may cause great losses among the fish particularly if the branchial blood vessels are affected.

Following the reviews of Schuurmans-Stekhoven jr. (1935) and Skrjabin (1960) we shall give some details of the main Orders.

Order Ascaroidea

Both marine and freshwater fish are parasitized by ascarid worms. *Contracaecum spiculigerum* Rud. and *C. aduncum* Rud. are particularly widely distributed. Larvae may be found in the peritoneal cavity and in the mesentery of many marine fish; the mature worms are found in predaceous fish like gadids and salmonids which, in some regions, may be infested by 50%. This is equally true for the genera *Raphidascaris, Porrocaecum* (larval host, *Sebastes* spp.; final host, seals), *Dujardinia, Paranisakis* and *Goezia. Eustoma rotundata* Rud. may require several intermediate hosts (*Gadidae*); the final hosts are sharks. These are also frequently parasitized by another nematode *Acanthocheilus bicuspis* Wedl. Tinned cod liver has been found infected with larval stages of *Anisakis*; even mature worms have occasionally been found (Amlacher, 1961). According to Bishop and Margolis (1955) 80–100% of the herrings caught along the coast of British Columbia are infected by *Anisakis*, a nematode which also parasitizes dolphins, albatross, delphinid whales and seals.

Baylis (1921) described the following Ascarids from fish:

Clupea harengus	*Contracaecum aduncum* (Rud.)
Gadus morrhua	*Contracaecum clavatum* (Rud.)
Esox lucius	*Raphidascaris acus* (Bloch)
Blennius viviparus	*Contracaecum auctum* (Rud.)
Rhombus punctatus	*Contracaecum auctum* (Rud.)
Silurus glanis	*Goezia ascaroides* (Goeze)

Dutch authors (Thiel *et al.*, 1960) have reported human infections by larvae of *Eustoma rotundata* Rud. The infection arises from the ingestion of raw, only mildly salted herrings, and larvae were found at the centre of a phlegmonous enteritis characterized by large accumulations of eosinophile granulocytes. The focal enteritis is confined to parts of the epithelial mucosa which has already previously been sensitized by nematode larvae. Thirty relevant cases, all ascribed to the effect of nematode larvae, were reported within 7 years.

Order Trichuroidea (Trichinelloidea, Trichocephaloidea)

The various names applied to these worms all pay tribute to the fact that they are almost as slender as hairs. They are perfectly cylindrical, with a pointed anterior and a rounded posterior end. One of the commonest genera of the Order is *Capillaria* (Fig. 90). Those parasitizing fish rarely exceed 20 mm in the female and 10 mm in the male sex. The eggs are easily recognized by the presence of opercular plugs at either pole (Fig. 91). These allow for differentiation between closely allied species. Most of them are intestinal parasites. A few of the rarer types are only known from their eggs.

The smaller the fish are the more they suffer from a *Capillaria* infection. Young infected salmonids look starved and seem to be reluctant to feed.

Many *Capillaria* species have been introduced into Europe from S. America. One of the more common types is *Capillaria pterophylli* Heinze (Fig. 90) the female of which may grow to 19 mm, the male to 8·3 mm. They are never thicker than 0·07 mm and 0·05 mm respectively. Heinze, who first described the worm in 1933, noted fine transverse ridges on the skin, also some light-reflecting dots. The copulatory spicule at the posterior end of the male is blunt at the apex, the surface sculptured (Fig. 90b). The body is slightly broadened on both sides at the posterior extremity. The eggs have smooth shells and are oval, with a shallow constricting groove in the middle which is not always easy to see (Fig. 91). They have a large opercular plug at both poles. Their size is 0·05–0·06 × 0·02 mm.

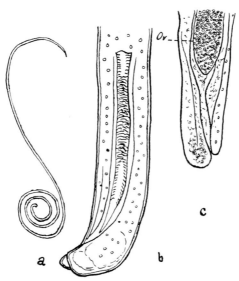

Fig. 90. *Capillaria pterophylli* Heinze. (a) Female, 10 : 1. (b) Tail of male with spiculum. × 330. (c) Anus and part of ovary (*ov*) of female. × 330. (After Heinze.)

The electric catfish (*Malapterurus electricus* Lac.) harbours a similar species, *Capillaria fritschi* Travassos. The female may grow to a length of 15 mm.

All other species of *Capillaria* are much smaller. The female of *C. piscicola* Trav., Art. and Per., for example, reaches only a length of 6 mm and a width of 0·056 mm, the male is 4·2 mm long and maximal 0·044 mm wide. *Capillaria piscicola* lives in the gut of Brazilian characids and has reached us presumably with imported ornamental fish. The eggs may be distinguished from those of *C. pterophylli* by the absence of the equatorial groove and the more lengthy oval shape. Their measurements are 0·043 × 0·018 mm (Fig. 91).

A minute type, *Capillaria minima* Tr. Art. and Per., also lives in Brazilian salmonids. Mature females measure 1·9 mm in length, males 1 mm. The eggs have a slightly thicker membrane than those mentioned before and their opercular plugs are smaller. They measure 0·05 × 0·025 mm (Fig. 91).

Capillaria sentinosa Travassos has conspicuously sculptured eggs (Fig. 91c) which measure 0·04–0·05 mm × 0·02–0·023 mm. Only the male of this worm has so far been found.

Ghittino (1961) described *Capillaria eupomotis* from sun-fish, trout and small Italian cyprinids.

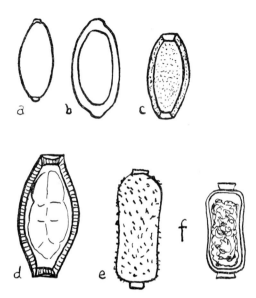

FIG. 91. Eggs of various species of *Capillaria*. (a) *Capillaria piscicola* 450 : 1; (b) *C. minima*; (c) *C. sentinosa*; (d) *C. leucisci*; (e) *C. tomentosa*; (f) *C. pterophylli*. (After Heinze.)

Hepaticola, mostly listed as a separate genus (Hyman, 1951) is, in fish, represented by *H. petruschewskii* Schulman, known from the gut of sun-fish, pike-perch and other freshwater fish, whose livers may be severely affected by the parasite. We may further mention the genus *Skrjabinocapillaria* from freshwater fish and *Thominx* from sun-fish, sea-pike and from tetraodontid spp.

The life cycles and modes of transmission of the capillarian worms are as yet incompletely known. Species of *Cyclops* and *Tubifex* are suspected to act as intermediate hosts.

We may here also mention the family Cystoopsidae, represented only by a single species *Cystoopsis acipenseris* Wagner, which lives in the Volga sturgeon *Acipenser ruthenus* L. Here, as in *Sphaerularia* (a rhabditoid worm parasitizing bumblebees), there seems to be no room for the profusion of eggs produced by the female. The uterus consequently is everted through the vulva together with part of the intestinal canal (Hyman, 1951) (Fig. 92). The worms produce pustules in the fish which develop into ulcers. Intermediate hosts are amphipod crustaceans.

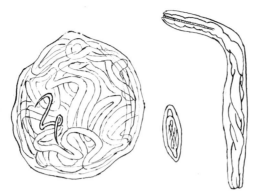

FIG. 92. *Cystoopsis acipenseris* Wagner. Left: gravid encysted female. Middle: egg. Right: male.

Order Oxyuroidea

Only a few species of this very large Order have been described from fish. Most of them belong to the family Kathlanidae. In barbels the genera *Spironoura* and *Monhysterides* have been seen on a few occasions only.

Order Spiruroidea

The Order is represented among the fish parasites by *Metabronema salvelini* Fujita, occasionally found in trout. The Gnathostomidae, worms belonging to an allied family, are of greater importance. The larvae parasitize several Asian freshwater fish like *Anabas, Clarias, Notopterus, Ophiocephalus* and *Glossogobius* (Africa *et al.*, 1936). First intermediate hosts are species of *Cyclops*; the fish serve as second intermediates. Final hosts for the two species *Gnathostoma spinigerum* Owen and *G. hispidum* Fedtschenko are cats, dogs and pigs. Humans have been attacked in regions where fish are eaten raw and have suffered oedematous swelling of the face and the extremities (Daensvang, 1946).

Order Camallanoidea

Many members of this multiform family have been found parasitizing fish. In the stomach and gut of heterosomata, salmonids and sturgeons the genera *Bulbodacnitis, Cucullanus* (Fig. 93), *Cucullanellus, Dacnitis* and *Dacnitoides* (Family Cucullanidae) have been found. The typical camallanid genera (*Camallanus, Procamallanus*) are frequently found

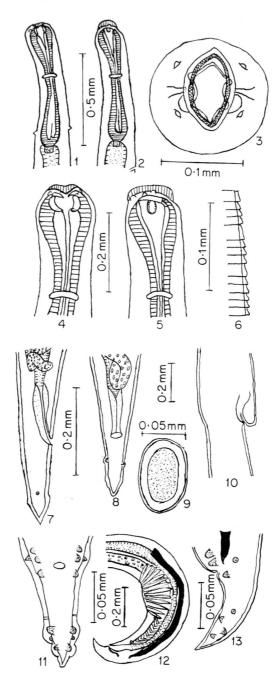

FIG. 93. *Cucullanus annulatus* Margolis from the gut of the flatfish *Parophrys vetulus* G. 1–5, Anterior end of male; 3, In anterior view; 6, Cuticula of ventral oesophageal region of female; 7, 8, Posterior part of female; 11–13, Posterior part of male; 9, Egg; 10, Vulva. (After Margolis.)

in tropical fish. Intermediate hosts for *Camallanus truncatus* Rud. are species of *Cyclops* and *Asellus* or insect larvae (*Agrion* spp.). In *Camallanus lacustris* Zoega, the first hosts are fish.

Gadids, eel and shark are infested by members of the families Rictulariidae and Physalopteridae. The first of these families includes *Spinitectus inermis* Zeder in the caeca of eel where, according to Schäperclaus (1954), they cause severe inflammation.

The *Cystidicola* species are of interest (Family Thelaziidae) because they are mainly found in the swim-bladder. Trout fisheries may be invaded by the much feared *Cystidicola farionis* Fischer (= *Ancyracanthus cystidicola*). The white worms, often several dozens of them, may be seen to crawl about in the swim-bladder. *Cystidicola impar* Schn. lives in the smelt (*Osmerus eperlanus* L.), *C. serrata* Wright in coregonids. In the same Family we find the genera *Rhabdochona* and *Haplonema*. *Rhabdochona denudata* Duj. is often found in the chubb (*Squalius cephalus* L.), *Haplonema* species in *Amia*.

Order Dracunculoidea

Members of this Order, which includes the well-known and spectacular guinea worm of human parasitology, have been found in cyprinid fish. *Philometra abdominalis* Nyb., for instance, occurs in the body cavity. The parasite, because of the red colour, goes by the name of "blood-worm". A similar species, *Philometra opercularis* Nyb., lives under the operculum and *P. sanguinea* Rud. on the fins of crucian carp (*Carassius carassius* L.). Primary hosts are again species of *Cyclops*. The rainbow trout (*Salmo irideus* Gibbons) of the American West has occasionally been found heavily infested by the dracunculid *Philometra oncorhynchi* Kuit.-Ekb. The worms live in the peritoneal cavity (Haderlie, 1953).

Class Nematomorpha

Members of the gordian worms or Nematomorpha, a Class including the peculiar long white freshwater worm known as the "Watercalf" (*Gordius aquaticus* L.), may also be found in various fishes. Nigrelli (1943) records the larvae as frequent parasites of aquatic animals, particularly insects. In the New York aquarium in 1942, he saw five cases of gordiid infection in cold-water fish. In one of these the worms had perforated the sinus venosus, thereby killing the fish. Heavier losses through gordiid worms occurred in tropical fish. Fourteen of these were lost from this cause in 1941 when their internal organs were completely destroyed by the worms. Their exact specific name was not ascertained and no further fatalities through gordiid worms have been recorded since.

4*

REFERENCES

Africa, C. M., Refuerzo, P. C. and Garcia, E. Y. (1936). Observations on the life cycle of *Gnathostoma spinigerum*. *Philipp. J. Sci.* **59**, 513–521.

Amlacher, F. (1961). "Taschenbuch der Fischkrankheiten." G. Fischer, Jena.

Baylis, H. A. (1921). On the classification of the Ascaridae. I. The systematic value of certain characters of the alimentary canal. *Parasitology* **12**, 253–264.

Bishop, Y. M. M. and Margolis, L. (1955). A statistical examination of *Anisakis* larvae (Nematoda) in herring (*Clupea pallasi*) of the British Columbia coast. *J. Fish. Res. Bd. Canad.* **12**, 571–592.

Campana-Rouget, Y. (1961). Nématodes de poissons. *Publ. K.E.A. Inst. Roy. Sc. Nat. Belg.* III. **4**, 1–57.

Ghittino, P. (1961). Su una Capillariosi epatica in trote di allevamento e in altri teleostei delle acque libere del bacino del Po, in Piemonte con descricione di una nova specie (*Capillaria eupomotis*). *Riv. Parasit.* **22**, 193–204.

Haderlie, E. C. (1953). Parasites of the freshwater fishes of Northern California. *Univ. Calif. Publ. Zool.* **57**, 303–440.

Heinze, K. (1933). Die Gattung *Capillaria* Zeder 1800 als Fischparasit. *Z. Parasitk.* **5**, 393–406.

Hyman, L. (1951). "The Invertebrates", Vol. III. McGraw-Hill, New York.

Kahl, W. (1938). Nematoden in Seefischen. *Z. Parasitk.* **10**, 415–431.

Margolis, L. (1960). A new nematode of the genus *Cucullanus* (Camallanata: Cucullanidae) from a flounder, *Parophrys vetulus* Girard 1854, with notes on the species from Pleuronectiformes. *Canad. J. Zool.* **38**, 839–849.

Nigrelli, R. F. (1943). Causes of diseases and death of fishes in captivity. *Zoologica* **28**, 203–216.

Reichenbach-Klinke, H. (1952). Beobachtungen an fischpathogenen Arten der Nematodengattung *Capillaria* Zeder. *Aqu. Terr. Z.* **5**, 68–70.

Schäperclaus, W. (1954). "Fischkrankheiten", 3rd edn., Akademie Verlag, Berlin.

Schuurmanns-Stekhoven, J. H. jr. (1935). Nematoda parasitica. *In* "Die Tierwelt der Nord- und Ostsee" (G. Grimpe and E. Wagler, eds.). Leipzig.

Skrjabin, K. J. (1960). " Ossnowy Nematodologii." Moscow.

Thiel, P. K. v., Kuipers, F. C. and Roskam, R. T. (1960). A nematode parasitic to herring causing acute abdominal syndromes in man. *Trop. Geogr. Med.* **2**, 97–113.

Travassos, L., Artigas, P. and Pereira, C. (1928). Fauna helmintholojica dos peixes do agua dolce de Brasil. *Arch. Inst. Biol. São Paulo* **1**, 5–68.

Yamaguti, S. (1961). "Systema Helminthum", Vol. III, I. The Nematodes of Vertebrates. II. The Nematodes of Vertebrates. Interscience, London and New York.

Yorke, W. and Maplestone, P. A. (1962). "The Nematode Parasites of Vertebrates." London.

K. LEECHES (HIRUDINEA) PATHOGENIC FOR FISH

Leeches, extracting their nourishment by powerful suction from their hosts, may cause widespread damage among fish populations. They belong to the segmented worms (Annelida), have suckers at both ends but usually no bristles, have a small body cavity, are hermaphrodite, usually dark in colour and are easily recognized by their size and shape.

On fish one of the most commonly encountered species is *Piscicola geometra* L. recognizable by its distinctively annulated body. The number of rings is ±14. *P. rapax* occurs on the summer flounder (*Pleuronectes flesus* L.), *P. funduli* on *Fundulus pisculentus*, one of the tooth carps (Cyprinodontidae). Leeches are very difficult to exterminate. The only means of cleaning a heavily infested pond consists in complete drainage, drying and the application of quicklime. Worms attached to fish may be induced to remove themselves in a very short (5 sec) bath of 2 g freshly made quicklime in 1 litre of water. A Lysol bath (1–2 g in 5 l of water) for 5–15 sec may also be tried. Apart from the direct damage it does, *Piscicola geometra* may also transfer to the fish certain blood parasites of the genus *Trypanoplasma* (= *Cryptobia*).

Less frequently seen are the barbel leech *Cystobranchus respirans* Troschel, the burbot leech *Cystobranchus mammillatus* Malm. and *Hemiclepsis* (= *Placobdella*) *marginata* Müller, recognized by dorsal rows of small warty irregularities of the skin. On the whole the latter genus limits itself to attack turtles, frogs or toads.

Large marine leeches like *Branchellion raveneli* Girard and members of the genus *Pontobdella* are found on rays and skates. The former is recognized by the presence of leaf-like gill appendages.

The Polychaeta, another Class of annelid worms, play a minor role in fish parasitology. The species *Ichthyotomus sanguinarius* Eisig is known to attack the conger eel where numerous individuals may be found attached to the skin and the fins. Most Polychaeta are free-living non-parasitic forms.

REFERENCES

Amlacher, E. (1961). "Taschenbuch der Fischkrankheiten." G. Fischer, Jena.
Autrum, H. J. (1936). Hirudineen, I. *In* "Klassen und Ordnungen des Tierreichs" (H. G. Bronn, ed.). Leipzig.
Duijn, C. v. (1956). "Diseases of Fish", publ. *Water Life*, London.
Hyman, L. (1951). "The Invertebrates", Vol. V. McGraw-Hill, New York.
Pratt, H. S. (1951). "A Manual of the Common Invertebrate Animals." Blakiston, Philadelphia.
Schäperclaus, W. (1954). "Fischkrankheiten," 3rd edn., Akademie Verlag, Berlin.

L. CRUSTACEANS PATHOGENIC FOR FISH

The Crustacea (Class I of the Arthropoda or jointed animals) and among them in particular the Orders Copepoda, Cirripedia and Isopoda play a major and double role in the science of parasitology. They not only act as intermediate hosts for a multitude of other parasites but are, in many cases, obligatory parasites themselves, changing their features in the process to such an extent so as to become almost unrecognizable. Crustacean species, looking totally different in the free-living and in the parasitic stage, have occasionally been described as different species before their identity was recognized.

The majority of forms which are of interest here belong to the Order Copepoda, small shield- or wormlike aquatic animals, most of them segmented into a head, a thorax, and an abdomen, inhabitants of all kinds of fresh and marine waters, where they live, in the free stage, on micro-organisms and form a conspicuous part of the plankton. Here they play a big role as staple food of many young fish, thereby atoning in part for the damage they do in transmitting parasites. The mouth of some species is fitted with a sucking stylet. Females are easily recognized by the ovisacs carried on both sides of the tail. Special organs of attachment are developed in the parasitic forms. The following Copepoda may assume importance in pisciculture.

Family Ergasilidae

Small white nodules on the gills of a fish usually indicate the presence of Ergasilidae. The commonest form, *Ergasilus sieboldi* v. Nordmann, attaches itself to the gills of many species of freshwater fish of the Northern Hemisphere. It resembles the well-known *Cyclops*, is 1·3–1·7 mm long and distinctly segmented (Fig. 94). The species has in some cases been found invading our aquaria. A new, as yet undetermined type of *Ergasilus* was recently found on the gills of freshly imported *Mollienisia petenensis* Val. We may always expect new parasitic arrivals among fish imported from the New World (Fig. 95). The latest arrival is conspicuous by the presence of some brilliantly blue pigment, typical of the Family. *Ergasilus*, whose second antenna has been changed into a stout prehensile claw, adheres firmly to the gills of the host, destroying and digesting the epithelial lining of these delicate organs. Its activity soon leads to secondary infection by bacteria and fungi and to the development of adhesions between the villi. Breathing is impaired, the fish refuse to feed, lose weight and their general health deteriorates seriously. Keys for the differentiation of the various members of this family may be found in Bychowsky (1962). *Thersitina gasterostei* Pagenstecher, an Ergasilid found on sticklebacks, is in some details aberrant. It measures only 0·8 mm. The head of the female is conspicuously spherical.

Schäperclaus (1954) suggested that Ergasilids might be killed by immersing the fish in DDT baths (concentrations from 1 : 50–1 : 100 million). The fish may remain in such baths for several days. Equally recommended is hexachlorocyclohexane (Gesarol), an insecticide.

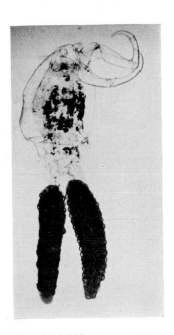

FIG. 94. *Ergasilus sieboldi* Nordmann. (Photo.: Amlacher.)

FIG. 95. *Ergasilus* sp. from a freshly imported *Mollienisia petenensis*. Left: Female with one egg sac. The chromatophores are sky-blue. Right: Female in between gill villi.

Family Sphyriidae

Sphyrion lumpi Kröyer, a crustacean which parasitizes perch, tunnyfish the sea wolf (*Anarrhichas lupus* L.) and *Cyclopterus lumpi* is one of the forms which, in adaptation to their parasitic mode of life, have changed their shape to such an extent that nobody would, at first sight, spot their relationship to the crabs or lobsters. The parasite has a head which is kept deeply buried in the host's muscle, a long and slender neck and a much expanded posterior end covered with branched processes to ensure gas exchange. Its common habitat is the Atlantic coast of N. America (Fig. 96).

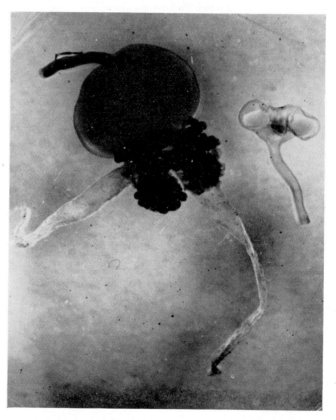

Fig. 96. *Sphyrion lumpi* Kröyer. Left: Body with egg sac. Right: Proboscis. (After Amlacher.)

Family Caligidae

The Caligidae are small copepods widely distributed among marine fish. They lead completely parasitic lives and some of the females can only be recognized for what they are by the paired ovisacs typical of the Order. Some of them have an anterior segment shaped like a shield, others have lost all similarity to the typical crustacean appearance (Figs. 97–99). They measure 3–20 mm in length. The posterior part of

FIG. 97. *Caligus lacustris* Steenstrup and Lütken.

FIG. 98. *Lernaea cyprinacea* L. (After Schäperclaus.)

FIG. 99. *Tracheliastes polycolpus* Nordmann. (After Vejdowskij.)

the body has only 2–3 segments. A few Caligids occur in fresh waters. *Caligus lacustris* Steenstrup and Lütken, for instance, has been found on the gills of freshwater fish in the Northern Hemisphere (Fig. 97). Other forms are widely distributed among marine fish, the majority belonging to the genus *Caligus*. *C. rapax* Milne Edwards, for instance, may be found on the skin, the gills, the fins, under the operculum or under the scales, while flatfish are often parasitized by members of the genus *Bomolochus*. (Expl. *B. soleae* Claus, Fig. 100). Other species have been reported from gadids and from the conger eel (*Conger conger* L.) (Stock, 1959). Another species, widely distributed throughout the Northern Hemisphere is *Lepeophtheirus*. *L. salmonis* Kröyer infects the whole skin of salmonid fish particularly preferring the circumanal region. It may equally be found on the gills of trout and salmon in the Pacific and in the N. Atlantic (Scott and Scott, 1913) and on *Oncorhynchus* spp.

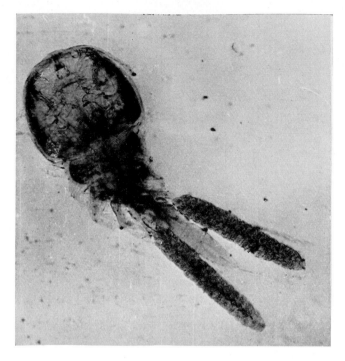

FIG. 100. *Bomolochus soleae* Claus. (Photo.: Reichenbach-Klinke.)

Family Lerneaidae (Anchor Worms)

There can hardly be a parasite which has lost its original marks of identity as a copepod more than the anchor worm. The first stage (nauplius) still shows that the animal belongs to the crustaceans, but when an individual has once settled on the gills or the skin of a fish it looses its locomotory organs and looks far more like a worm than a copepod. But the life cycle does not end here. The parasite regains its swimming appendages after a resting period and leaves the host. Fertilization takes place in the water and the males die. The females, however, attach themselves to the skin or the gills of a second fish and undergo, for the second time, a retrogressive process which completely changes their appearance. They again look like worms supplied with anchoring processes at the anterior end; the only reminders of the copepod stage are again the external ovisacs.

The Lerneidae are freshwater parasites, but they are not often seen in the aquarium. The commonest species, *Lernaea cyprinacea* L. (Fig. 98), *Lernaea esocina* Burm. and *Lernaea phoxinacea* Kröyer, are known from minnows (*Phoxinus phoxinus* L.) and may be recognized by their worm-like shape and the anterior branching processes which resemble antlers. These processes may be found deeply embedded, sometimes even invading blood vessels of the host. Only *Lernaea phoxinacea* is a gill parasite; the other two species named parasitize the skin.

These dermal anchor worms have been found especially on cyprinids like the goldfish (*C. carassius auratus* L.), the golden ide or orfe (*Idus idus* L. = *Leuciscus idus*) and on various tropical cichlids. *Lernaea carassii* Tidd appeared in N. American aquaria introduced from a pond in the neighbourhood of Cleveland, Ohio (Tidd, 1938). Morphologically *L. carassii* resembles the other species mentioned (Fig. 101). Fig. 102 shows the degree to which an infestation with

FIG. 101. *Lernaea carassii* Tidd. Adult female. × 6·8. (After Schlumberger.)

FIG. 102. Goldfish, infected with *Lernea carassii*. × 0·6. (After Schlumberger.)

Lernaeids may develop. The parasite has also been blamed for the development of dermal tumours in goldfish seen simultaneously with the lerneid infection. It was suspected that the worms transmitted a tumour-producing virus but the connection could not be proved experimentally (Schlumberger, 1952).

Salt baths (NaCl 0·76–1·1%) or DDT baths (see p. 202) serve for the eradication of lerneid infestation.

Family Lernaeopodidae

The females of this Family look, in their mature state, even less like copepods. All that remains is a worm-like body with the anchoring processes in front and a couple of ovisacs behind. Adaptation to parasitism

FIG. 103. Gill arch of giant pike-perch infested with *Achtheres percarum* v. Nordm.
Photo.: Amlacher.)

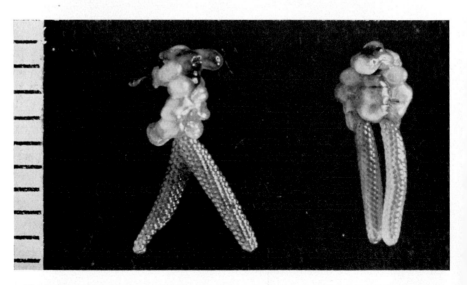

FIG. 104. *Basanistes huchonis* Schrank. (Photo.: *Bayr. exp. biol. Inst.*) mm scale.

could hardly go further. The species *Achtheres percarum* v. Nordm. and
Tracheliastes polycolpus v. Nordm. have occasionally been found in
European freshwater fish (Figs. 99, 103). *Brachyella thynni* Cuv.
parasitizes tunnyfish, another copepod, *Basanistes huchonis* Schrank
(Fig. 104) is found under the operculum of *Hucho hucho* L. Species of
Salmincola, an allied lernaeopodid, are found on salmonid and cottid
fish. The females are very similar to those of *Achtheres* and *Tracheliastes*
shown in Figs. 99 and 103.

Family Argulidae

In the Sub-class Branchiura of the crustaceans we find one of the
best known of all fish parasites in the Family Argulidae: the fish
louse (*Argulus* Müller). Of this genus the most widely distributed
species is the carp louse (*Argulus foliaceus* L.) (Fig. 105). The identity
of this parasite is easily recognized by the flat, leaf-like carapace which
covers the whole animal and has a heart-shaped incision posteriorly.
In front, two large compound dorso-laterally positioned eyes can be
seen. The various appendages are all on the ventral side. The two
antennae are fitted with small fixing hooks, the mandibles have dent-
ated edges and the maxillae are united to form a stiletto retractable
into a tube. The stiletto is fairly long and sharp, well capable of penetrating the skin of fish. On both sides of the stiletto we find two large
adhesive disks, probably modified maxillipeds. There follow a pair of
normal maxillipeds fitted with apical claws and finally four pairs of
swimming legs. The tail is bipartite and typical in its details for the
various species of the genus.

The eggs of the carp louse may be found in rows stuck on to aquatic
plants or to stones. In the aquarium the eggs may be stuck on to the
glass. They take 4 weeks to hatch and the young then swim about
until they have found a host. They attach themselves to the skin and
feed for 5–6 weeks before they become sexually mature.

The likelihood that *Argulus* is capable of transmitting other diseases
from one fish to another has lately been much discussed. Unfortunately,
the suspicion is well-founded. Fish infected with these parasites should
therefore be treated at once, and particular attention should be paid
to imports which may be infected with argulid species new to this
country. Hindle (1949) reported on extensive damage to fish by
Argulus in the London Aquarium.

Fish lice are not particular in their choice of hosts; they also attach
themselves to tadpoles. They adhere with their antennal hooks and
their adhesive disks and immediately introduce their sharp stylet as
deeply as they can to suck up tissue juice and blood. After a period of

feeding they release their host and swim about unattached. They are
not as completely dependent on the host as some other crustaceans,
which die if they do not find a host within a few days. Considering,
however, that argulids may survive for quite some time even in an
unoccupied tank, an aquarium, empty of fish for some time, cannot

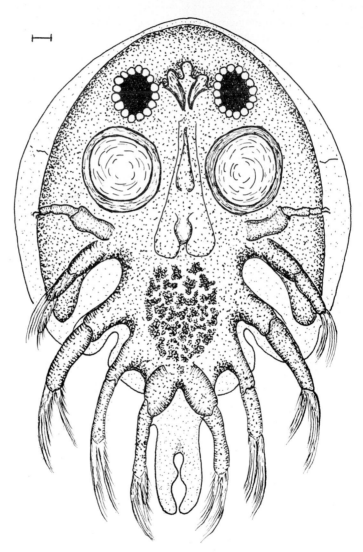

FIG. 105. *Argulus foliaceus* L. ♀. Note compound eyes, suctorial mouth parts with large
adhesive disks, one pair of maxillipeds and four pairs of swimming legs. Scale: 1/10 mm.
(Elkan.)

necessarily be relied on to be free from infection. On the contrary, perfectly healthy fish, introduced into a tank which had been unoccupied for some time, have been observed to become heavily infected within a few days after having been moved. According to Schäperclaus (1954) *Argulus* survives 3 weeks of starvation even at the height of summer. It depends, however, on vertebrates as hosts and is in so far an obligatory parasite.

Assuming the fish louse does not transmit other infections, the direct damage it does is tolerable. Like so many sucking parasites, however, it not only abstracts nutritive substance from the host, but it injects at the same time some kind of poison which irritates the tissues, causing oedema and inflammation. Small fish may not be able to tolerate even a few of these parasites. They loose consciousness and die even if attacked by a few fish lice only. Larger fish tolerate proportionally greater numbers of *Argulus*. These prefer for their attack those parts of the skin best supplied with blood vessels, like the circumoral region, the operculum and the base of the various fins. The penetration of the skin by the stylet causes much local irritation and the fish may be seen to become restless and to rub repeatedly against stones or branches. Even if they succeed in ridding themselves of the irritating parasites *Saprolegnia* may invade the wound and cause further damage.

Heuschmann (1953) and Wunder (1962) have drawn attention to the various infectious fish diseases which may be transmitted by the sting of *Argulus*. In particular it is held responsible for the distribution of the infectious ascites of cyprinids. *Trypanoplasma* may be transmitted in the same way. The deleterious activity of *Argulus* in pisciculture obviously deserves greater attention than it has received in the past.

The stimuli which determine the movements of fish lice have been studied by Herter (1927). They do not seem endowed with any very effective chemoreceptors to detect fish at a distance, but *Argulus foliaceus* was found sensitive to light and to water pressure. In the pond it preferred regions near the shore where fish fry were its habitual victims.

The following species of fish have been found particularly affected by *Argulus*:

Carp (*Cyprinus carpio* L.), tench (*Tinca tinca* Cuv.), bitterling (*Rhodeus amarus* Bloch), bream (*Abramis brama* L.), bleak (*Alburnus lucidus* Heckel), roach (*Rutilus rutilus* L.), minnow (*Phoxinus phoxinus* L.), trout (*Salmo trutta* L.), pike (*Esox lucius* L.), perch (*Perca fluviatilis* L.), two species of sticklebacks (*Gasterosteus aculeatus* L. and *Pygosteus pungitius* L.), eel (*Anguilla anguilla* L.)—all fish of temperate zones. Tadpoles of *Rana temporaria* have equally been found infested.

We know at present about fifty different species of *Argulus*. They are either marine or freshwater species and the majority are found in the U.S.A. from where they are occasionally imported to European aquaria. The tropical species, however, do not seem to acclimatize themselves over here.

Some *Argulus* species have been described from the Eurasian region. Martin (1932), Nettovich (1900), Thiele (1904) and Wagler (1935) describe the following types from Central European fresh waters:

Argulus coregoni Thorell from *Coregonus lavaretus* L., *Thymallus thymallus* L., *Salmo trutta* L., *Phoxinus phoxinus* L. and *Lucioperca lucioperca* L.

Argulus pellucidus Wagler from *Cyprinus carpio* L.

On Central American fish which are occasionally imported have been found:

Argulus funduli Kröyer on *Fundulus ocellaris* Jordan and Gilbert from Florida and Louisiana;
Argulus chromidis Kröyer on Central American cichlids;
Argulus indicus Weber from fighting fish (*Betta splendens* Regan);
Argulus cubensis Wilson on cichlids;
Argulus lunatus Wilson in the goldfish *C. carassius auratus* L;
Argulus japonicus Thiele and *A. trilineatus* Wilson equally from goldfish.

The various species are distinguished by the shape of the tail parts.

Among the tropical fish commonly kept in aquaria it is the guppy (*Lebistes reticulatus* Peters) particularly that may be attacked by *Argulus* when these are introduced together with live food.

The argulid genus *Chonopeltis*, which has no poisonous stylet, lives in E. Asia and E. Africa. Best known is the species *Chonopeltis inermis* Thiele which might be expected on African cichlids. The S. American genus *Dolops* has neither stylet nor suction disks. The most important species of this genus is *Dolops dorsalis* Cornalia which attacks the Central American catfish *Doras niger* Val. Other *Dolops* species have been found in Africa, particularly on eel, while one of the African argulids limits itself entirely to tadpoles (*Dolops ranarum* Stuhlmann). Any of these species may be expected as undesirable guests among tropical fish imports.

Eradication of *Argulus* may, according to Schäperclaus (1954), be attempted by Lysol baths (1 cm^3 : 5 l of water) or by a bath in a solution of potassium permanganate (1 g : 100 l of water). Meinken recommends an insecticide distributed by Höchster Farbwerke under the name of GIX. It was effective in a large ornamental basin. The pike kept in the aquarium had severely infected themselves with *Argulus* introduced with their food.

Order Cirripedia

This Order, which includes the well-known but non-parasitic barnacles also embraces a few parasitic species. *Sarcotaces arcticus* Collet, for instance, may be found on the fish *Molva byrkelange* Walb. The parasite is found deeply embedded in the dorsal muscle close to the spinal column, only the segmented posterior part protruding. It is assumed that *Sarcotaces* feeds on the host's blood (Fig. 106). It is often found surrounded by a cyst measuring 4–8 cm which is filled with ink-coloured blood (Amlacher, 1961). The same author mentions another cirripede *Anelasma squalicola* Lov. (Lepadidae) on shark.

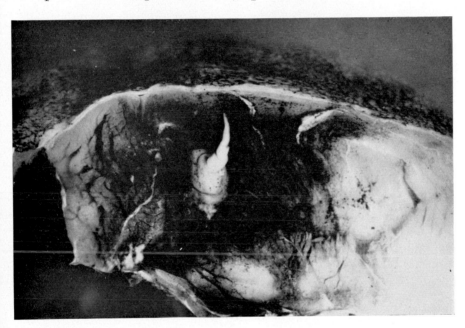

FIG. 106. *Sarcotaces arcticus* Collet in the abdominal muscles of *Molva byrkelange* Walb. (After Amlacher.)

Order Isopoda

Close relations of the Cirripedia are the Malacostraca which include the Order Isopoda among which we find the well known "pill-bug" of our gardens and the aquatic "sow-bug". The Family Cymothoidae counts about one hundred species many of which are fish parasites. One of the earliest forms known from marine fish is *Anilocra physodes* L.

Freshwater forms have only recently come to our knowledge. Most of these come from S. America. We discovered for instance *Livoneca symmetrica* van Name on the ventral aspect of the gastropelecid *Carnegiella strigata* Gthr. imported from Brazil (Fig. 107). The parasites are large and easily discovered. The average length of the mature individual is 24 mm. The fish are severely damaged by the infestation. The parasites can be removed with forceps. This has to be done carefully because the isopods are firmly anchored to the skin. The remaining break in the skin should be touched with an antiseptic.

Szidat (1955) reported on the genera *Braga, Conilera, Rocinela, Aega,*

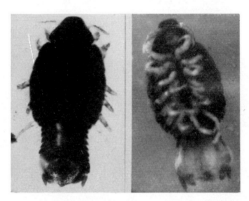

FIG. 107. An isopode, *Livoneca symmetrica* van Name. Left: Dorsal; right: Ventral view.

Livoneca, Ichthyoxenus and *Riggia,* some of which were found in pocket-like depression on the ventral aspect of fish. Wunder (1962) described the isopod *Nerocila orbignyi* Guérin-Ménéville from *Tilapia galilaea.* The parasitic isopods of the La Plata river system were described by Szidat (1955).

REFERENCES

Amlacher, E. (1961). "Taschenbuch der Fischkrankheiten." G. Fischer, Jena.
Baer, J. C. (1946). "Le Parasitisme." Masson, Paris.
Bychowsky, B. E. (1962). Opredelitel patasitow pressnowodnych ryb. SSSR, Moscow.
Herter, K. (1927). Reizphysiologische Untersuchungen an der Karpfenlaus (*Argulus foliacea* L.). *Z. vergl. Physiol.* **5**, 283–370.
Heuschmann, O. (1953). Zur Frage der Beteiligung von Hautparasiten an der Übertragung der ansteckenden Bauchwassersucht des Karpfens. *Allg. FischZtg.* **75**, 564–566.
Heuschmann, O. (1953). Teichversuche zur Frage der Bekämpfungsmöglichkeit der ansteckenden Bauchwassersucht des Karpfens. *Beitr. z. Abwasser-Fischerei und Flussbiologie,* Heft 1, 76–108.

Hindle, E. (1949). Notes on the treatment of fish infected with *Argulus*. *Proc. zool. Soc. Lond.* **119**, 79–81.

Jara, Z. (1961). *Sphyrion lumpi* Kröyer. *Windom. Parasyt.* **7**, 595–599.

Martin, M. F. (1932). On the morphology and classification of *Argulus*. *Proc. zool. Soc. Lond.* 771–806, 1932.

Meinken, H. (1954). *Aqu. Terr. Z.* **7**, 50–51.

Nettovich, L. v. (1900). Beiträge zur Kenntnis der Arguliden. *Arb. Zool. Inst. Wien* **13**, i-32.

Pratt, H. S. (1951). "A Manual of the Common Invertebrate Animals." Blakiston, Philadelphia.

Reichenbach-Klinke, H. (1955). Erstmalige Einschleppung einer amerikanischen *Livoneca* Art nach Europa (Isopoda, Crustacea). *Zool. Anz.* **154**, 318–320.

Schlumberger, H. G. (1952). Nerve sheath tumours in an isolated goldfish population. *Cancer Res.* **12**, 890–899.

Szidat, L. (1955). Beiträge zur Kenntnis der Reliktfauna des La Plata Stromsystems. *Arch. Hydrobiol.* **51**, 209–260.

Tidd, W. M. (1938). Studies on the Life History of a Parasitic Copepod *Lernaea carassii* Tidd. *Abst. Doc. Diss. Ohio State Univ.* **26**, 59–62.

Thiele, J. (1904). Beiträge zur Morphologie der Arguliden. *Mitt. Zool. Mus., Berlin*, **2**, 1–51.

Wagler, E. (1935). Die Deutschen Karpfenläuse. *Zool. Anz.* **110**, 1–10.

Wilson, C. B. (1903). North American parasitic copepods of the Family Argulidae with bibliography of the group and a systematic review of all known species. *Proc. U.S. Nat. Mus.* **25**, 635–742. Pl. 8–17.

Wilson, C. B. (1944). Parasitic copepods in the United States National Museum. *Proc. U.S. Nat. Mus.* **94**, 20–34.

Wilson, C. B. (1927). A copepod (*Argulus indicus*) parasitic on the fighting fish in Siam. *J. Siam. Soc. Nat. Hist.* Suppl. **7**, 1–3.

Wunder, W. (1962). *Nerocila orbignyi*, ein proterandrischer Hermaphrodit und parasitischer Isopode auf *Tilapia galilea* im See Borullus in Ägypten. *Zool. Anz.* Suppl. **25**, 140–151.

Wunder, W. and Dombrowski, H. (1951). Ergebnisse wissenschaftlicher Untersuchungen im Aischgrund. *Allg. FischZtg.* **76**, 159–163.

M. TONGUE WORMS (LINGUATULIDA)

These peculiar parasites are neither worms nor do they particularly affect the tongue. Systematically they are classified with the mites and spiders (Arachnida) and the name "tongue" worm refers to their shape. Their usual habitat is the naso-pharyngeal space of reptiles, birds and mammals. They and their larvae may also be found in the smaller carnivores, rodents, more rarely in reptiles, where they parasitize the lungs of crocodiles, amphibians and fish. The nymphs of the genera *Leiperia*, *Sebekia* and *Subtriquetra* have been found in the Congo basin (Fig. 108). The fish harbouring *Leiperia* belonged to the genera *Mastacembelus*, *Chrysichthys*, *Labes*, *Bathybates* and *Alestes* (Fain, 1961).

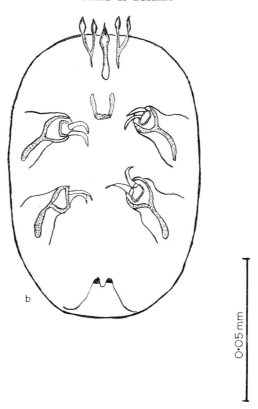

b

0·05 mm

FIG. 108. Larval stage of *Leiperia cincinnalis* Sambon. (After Fain.)

The mature linguatulids of these three genera live in crocodiles which feed on infected fish.

REFERENCE

Fain, A. (1961). Les Pentastomides de l'Afrique Centrale. *Mus. Tervuren Ann. Zool. Wetenschap.* **92**, 1–115.

N. MOLLUSCA

The phylum Mollusca includes three Families of freshwater clams, the Margaritiferidae, the Unionidae and the Mutelidae which, during one part of their life cycle, are parasitic on fish. The young larvae (Glochidia) first grow among the outer lamellae of the mussel's gills which specially adapt themselves for this reproductive period. The *Glochidia*, once they have hatched, sink towards the bottom and enter the mouth of fish either with the water these aspirate or in the course of feeding. The *Glochidia*, fitted with anchoring threads or hooklets, succeed in attaching themselves to the gills of a fish compressing the epidermis between the two halves of their shell. Stimulated by this assault the epidermis begins to proliferate and gradually more or less covers the young mussel completely (Fig. 109). A cyst forms and here the larva remains for 9–80 days. After this resting period the mussel, by way of histiolysis and active movements, frees itself and sinks to the ground.

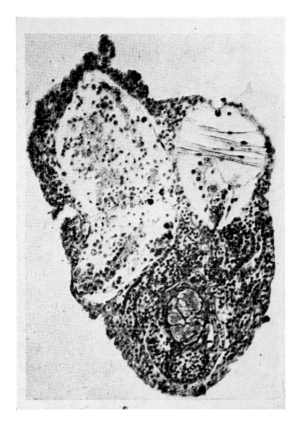

FIG. 109. Section through a normal (right) and degenerated (left) glochid *Lampsilis anodontoides* 15 h after fixation. × 167. (Photo.: Arey.)

The number of glochid larvae which may infest one fish is apparently limited. If this number is too large the majority degenerate and only a limited number of larvae survive to maturity. It has also been observed that fish which have survived previous attacks on glochids develop an immunity allowing them to repel the larvae before these have come to the end of their development (Arey, 1932; Faussek, 1855; Pflugfelder, 1951; Reuling, 1919).

REFERENCES

Arey, L. B. (1932). The nutrition of Glochidia during metamorphosis. A microscopical study of the sources and manner of utilization of nutritive substance. *J. Morph.* **53**, 201–219.
Arey, L. B. (1932). A microscopical study of Glochidia immunity. *J. Morph.* **53**, 367–377.
Faussek, V. (1855). Über den Parasitismus der *Anodonta* Larven in der Fischhaut. *Biol. Zbl.* **15**, 115–125.
Pflugfelder, O. (1951). Über das Parasit-Wirtsverhältnis von Anodontaglochidien und Spiegelkarpfen, *Cyprinus carpio* L. *Z. Parasitk.* **15**, 119–133.
Reuling, F. H. (1919). Acquired immunity to an animal parasite. *J. infect. Dis.* **24**, 337–346.

O. Fishes Damaged by Parasitic Algae

The question whether or not fishes could be damaged by parasitic algae has been debated for a long time. Exact data were lacking up to 1960, when Hoffman, Bishop and Dunbar reported on mass deaths among stock in a Florida fish farm. Examination of the casualties showed that the lamellae of the gills were bound together by adhesions and that the epithelial cells contained masses of green algae resembling *Mucophilus cyprini* Plehn, a globular type observed (1920) in the epidermis of several fish. It seems possible that there is a limit to the invasion with algae which the fish can tolerate. They may equally suffer from *Cladophora* if the long threads of this alga become enmeshed with their gills. Finally we may mention an observation by Kahls (1930) who found *Protococcaceae* (*Chlorochytrium piscicolens* Link) in the skin of young carps, tench and perch.

REFERENCES

Hoffman, G. L., Bishop, H. and Dunbar, C. E. (1960). Algal parasites in fish. *Progr. Fish Cult.* **22**, (4) 180.
Kahls, O. (1930). Uber das Vorkommen von Algen und Pilzen bei Fischen. *Z. Fischerei* **28**, 253–262.
Plehn, M. (1920). Neue Parasiten in Haut und Kiemen von Fischen. (*Ichthyochytrium* und *Mucophilus*). *Zbl. Bakt.* **85**, 275–281.

P. Fungi Pathogenic for Fish

Mycology, the science of fungi, is of only recent date both in human and animal pathology. A few fungal species like the well known genus *Empusa* (= *Entomophthora*) which attacks insects and various species of *Saprolegnia*, perhaps the most common of the undesirable guests in our aquaria, have been well studied, but there still exists great uncertainty with regard to the majority of fungal species we may meet on fish. Yet the importance of mycology for pisciculture can hardly be overrated, seeing that some marine species are infested by fungi of one sort or another by up to 15%. If such an infestation extends to the internal organs the fish die and this is bound to happen sooner or later to every fish infected.

Ichthyosporidium hoferi Plehn and Mulsow is one of the most widely distributed fungal species. It occurs both in fresh and marine waters and has recently been found to invade indoor aquaria. It has proved to be more lethal than even the ubiquitous *Saprolegnia* which prefers dead material. Other extremely lethal fungi invade the intestines of fish and give rise to tumours and a high mortality among the stock. Table 2 lists the species so far recorded. It is very likely that this list will be already incomplete by the time it appears in print. The determination of the exact species of a fungus which has—usually by mere chance—been found to parasitize a fish is notoriously difficult, and is frequently impossible if the fungus is discovered in the gut or the liver long after the animal has been killed and immersed in fixing fluid. Exact determination is, in most cases, made from fruiting bodies only. This means that the fungus must be cultured in specially equipped laboratories and on media suitable for the particular species. Even then, seeing how very similar many of the fungi are, only a specialist expert will be able to keep them apart. It is not surprising therefore that the favourable circumstances needed for the exact diagnosis of a fungal disease in fish are rarely available and that our knowledge of parasitic mycology is still in a state of indeterminacy and development. No observations are to date available about host specificity among fungi. As far as we know, any species may be expected to invade any kind of fish, a circumstance which does not help us in arriving at a diagnosis (Table 2).

Ichthyosporidium hoferi Plehn and Mulsow (= *Ichthyophonus hoferi* Plehn and Mulsow)

Caullery and Mesnil (1905) discovered a parasite in several marine fish which they took to be a Haplosporidium and they described it as *Ichthyosporidium gasterophilum*. Pettit (1911) showed this organism to be a fungus similar to another freshwater parasite described by Hofer in 1893. Hofer did not name the fungus but described the disease and particularly its leading symptom—loss of equilibrium—under the name of "the staggers". Plehn and Mulsow (1911) found the same parasite in freshwater fish, confirmed its nature as a fungus and, in honour of its original discoverer, described it as *Ichthyophonus hoferi*.

TABLE 2
Fungi Pathogenic for Fish

No.	Name	Host	Organs affected	Diagnostic characters	Authors
1	Phycomycetes: Zygomycetes: Entomophthoraceae: *Basidiobolus intestinalis* (Léger and Hesse)	*Salmo trutta f. fario* *Salmo gairdneri*	Intestinal epithelium	Hypha partly ramose with beak cells and formation of zygotes	Léger and Hesse (1923) Léger (1927) Léger (1929a, b)
2	*Basidiobolus lotae* (Léger)	*Lota vulgaris*	id.	id.	Léger (1924) Léger (1929a, b)
3	*Ichthyosporidium gasterophilum* (Caullery and Mesnil)	*Onos mustela* *Liparis vulgaris* *Salmo trutta* *Pleuronectes flesus*	Viscera	Large plasmodia up to 200 μ; thick hypha rich in cytoplasma	Caullery and Mesnil (1905)
4	*Ichthyosporidium hoferi* * (Plehn and Mulsow)	Freshwater and marine fish	Viscera; not epidermal	id.	Sproston (1947) Reichenbach-Klinke (1954) incl. older references
5	Oomycetes: Saprolegniaceae: *Lagenidium rabenhorsti* Zopf.	*Esox lucius* (in conjunction with algae)	Skin		Kahls (1930)
6	Several saprolegniaceae of the genus *Saprolegnia* Nees van Esenbeck and *Achlya* N. v. E.	Secondary parasites of freshwater fish	Skin		Hofer (1906)
7	Phycomycetes non certae sedis: *Ichthyochytrium vulg.* Plehn *Aphanomyces* sp.	Tropical river fish	Skin Skin; muscles	Globular plasmodia Diameter: 1–6 μ Mycelium	Schäperclaus (1954) Shanor and Saslow (1944)
8	*Branchiomyces sanguinis* Plehn	*Cyprinus carpio* *Tinca tinca* *Blicca björkna*	Gills	Syncytium, then 9–15 μ wide hyphae with spores	Schäperclaus (1929)
9	*Branchiomyces demigrans* Wundsch	*Tinca tinca* *Esox lucius*	Gills	id.	Wundsch (1929, 1930)

* The species *Ichthyosporidium phymogenes* Caull. and Mesn. and *I. hertwigi* Swarczewski have been found to be Microsporidia (Reichenow, 1952–53).

	Name	Host	affected	characters	Authors
10	Ascomycetes: Penicillium piscium (Reichenbach-Klinke)	Hyphessobrycon rosaceus, H. innesi, Carassius carassius, Lovicaria parva, Neolebias ansorgi	Ovary, Body cavity	Ramose threads 2–3 μ wide, acospores Resting spores	Reichenbach-Klinke (1956)
11	Fungae non certae sedis: "Nephromyces piscium" Plehn	Cyprinidae	Kidney	Septate, ramose threads, 5–3 μ wide, Conidia. Resting spores Mycelium	Hörter (1960)
12	Fusarium culmorum (W.G.Sm.) Sacc. var. cereale (Cke) Wr.	Cyprinus carpio	Skin	Mycelium	
13	Sp. indetermin. 1	Lucioperca sandra	Cornea Lens	Ramose threads 7–15 μ wide	Schäperclaus (1954)
14	Sp. indetermin. 2	Cyprinus carpio	Kidney	Mycelium. Hypha, septate, 2–3 μ wide	Verdun (1903)
15	Sp. indetermin. 3	Aphanius fasciatus	Pseudotumour of subcutis. (Sarcome lymphoblastique)	Ramose, septate mycelium 3 μ wide	Montpellier and Dieuzeide (1953)
16	Sp. indetermin. 4	Phoxinus phoxinus	Giant cell in abdominal tumour	Ramose septate mycelium 2 μ wide. Intercalary chlamydospores	Harant and Vernières (1933)
17	Sp. indetermin. 5	"Salmon" from Idaho	Granuloma of head	Ramose mycelium	Walker (1951)
18	Sp. indetermin. 6	Aphanius chantrei	Granuloma of collagen tissue	Sept. threads, 1·2–2·5 μ wide. No spores seen	Ermin (1952)
19	Sp. indetermin. 7	Salmo trutta	Skin	Non-septate threads 1–2 μ wide. Spores	Kahls (1930)
20	Sp. indetermin. 8 ("Fungus 'c'")	Xiphophorus helleri	Hypertrophic cells in muscle	Septate threads 4 μ wide Resting spores	Reichenbach-Klinke (1954)
21	Sp. indetermin. 9	Trichogaster leeri	Skin	Muriform spores	Reichenbach-Klinke (1956)
22	Sp. indetermin. 10	Gadus morrhua	Gills	Ramose sept. mycelium	Reichenbach-Klinke (1956).

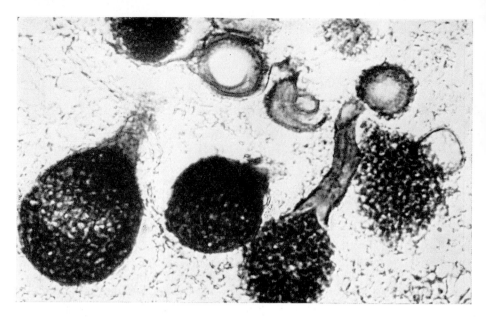

FIG. 110. *Ichthyosporidium* in the liver of a herring. Above right: several empty spores; from these issues a short mycelium ending in a large syncytial mass. Four other syncytia can be seen. × 500. Prepared by J. C. Sindermann. (After Schlumberger, 1958.)

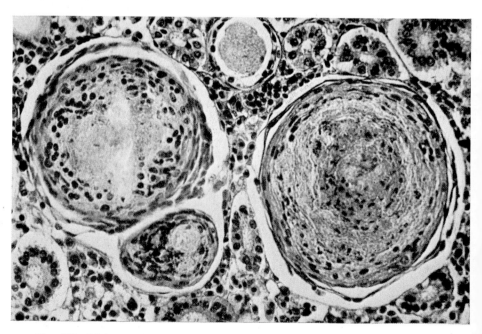

FIG. 111. *Ichthyosporidium* encysted by connective tissue in the kidney of a goldfish. × 300. (After Schlumberger, 1958.)

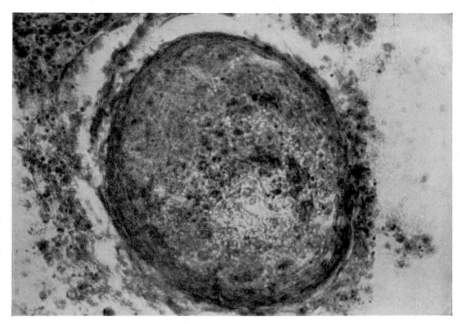

Fig. 112. *Ichthyosporidium*. Section through a single cyst from the liver of *Betta splendens*. Cytoplasm in the process of plasmotomy. Cyst wall of collagen tissue. Azan 462 : 1.

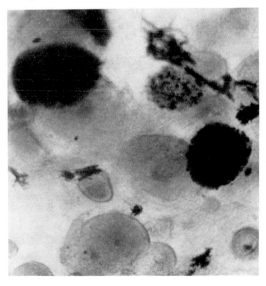

Fig. 113. Strongly pigmented plasmodia of *Ichthyosporidium hoferi* P and M. from the ovary of a fish.

5

Pettit (1913), who studied the parasite at about the same time, confirmed its identity with the one seen by Caullery and Mesnil but did not succeed in germination experiments. However, applying the rules of nomenclature, he changed the name to *Ichthyosporidium hoferi* Plehn and Mulsow, identical probably with *I. gasterophilum*, but as long as the identity has not been proved both names must persist. Equally the name *Ichthyophonus* is still used by authors who disagree with Pettit. The steps between the first appearance of the fungus on the skin of the host to the actual penetration into the tissues have been studied by Neresheimer and Clodi (1914). Further details of the biology and pathology were given by Schäperclaus in 1953.

The parasite is classed with the Phycomycetae. It is spherical or egg-shaped and has a diameter of 0·2–2·0 mm. There are several nuclei and pigmented bodies which increase with age. Development starts with the germination of the thallus. The originally undifferentiated cells grow either into broad non-septate hyphae of 7–15 μ width (macrohyphae) or into fine non-septate threads (microhyphae) of 2–3 μ width only. We have been able to confirm the findings of Neresheimer and Clodi (1914) who saw long macrohyphae in several marine fish. In ornamental tropical fish, however, the threads are short and divide into daughter bodies immediately on germinating. The picture, in tropical fish, is usually that of the first-generation parasite lying surrounded by numerous spherical daughter cells without the intermediate development of tubular hyphae. The daughter cells are plasmodia with a diameter of 18–150 μ. They grow rapidly and soon equal the mother body in size. In marine fish we have also seen oval conidia with brownish shells and a diameter of 10–20 μ as well as small endoconidia of 1·5–4 μ diameter. These conidia, which are themselves capable of germination, develop at the extremity of a hyphen or in chains on the surface. Chains of this kind were found in the cyst shown in Fig. 112. Apart from this type of reproduction the plasmodium may occasionally simply divide into many small daughter cells, all of which are then found lying together in a cyst. No signs of a typical sexual differentiation have so far been observed in this species.

The various stages of development of this fungus may be found in any organ of the fish. The liver is frequently attacked and may show many depots of closely packed plasmodia (Figs. 110–111). Such depots were equally seen in the spleen, the kidney the heart, the ovaries (Fig. 113), and in the connective tissue. They are also not infrequently seen in the optical tract of the brain, a location which produced protrusion of the eyeballs. Typically plasmodia are found within cysts in any of the organs listed, but free plasmodia may also occur in the

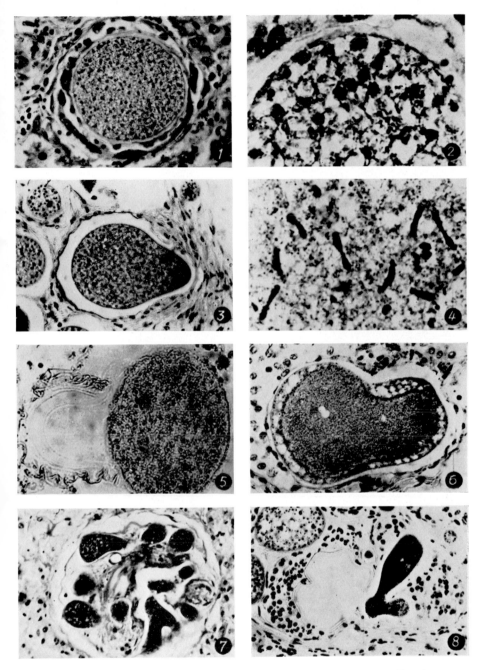

Fig. 114. *Ichthyosporidium hoferi* P. and M. from the rainbow trout. 1, Resting cyst in the liver. × 300. 2, The same. × 1250. 3, Germination. × 300. 4, Nuclei in division (heart, 40 days after infection). × 1 250. 5, Development of a plasmodium in the stomach of a trout 24 h after infection. 6–8, Further development. × 300. (After Dorier and Degrange.)

ovarian membrane or the intestinal epithelium (Fig. 114). As the infection advances, muscle and subcutis become involved and large bleeding wounds with ulceration may develop (Fig. 115). Direct observation of the invasion of the epidermis has so far not yet been possible. Sometimes the development of infectious foci can be observed in the mouth of a fish where tumours develop in the subcutis of the palate.

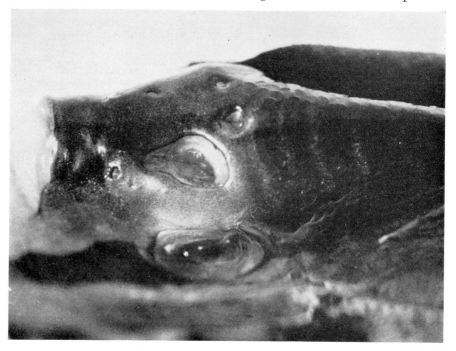

FIG. 115. Ichthyosporodiosis in *Symphysodon discus* H. with perforation of bone. (Photo.: Meyburg.)

The fish is infected by feeding on contaminated material and the first stages of the disease are seen in the gut. Digestive fluid dissolves the membrane; the parasite is freed and starts to germinate. Daughter cells invade the intestinal epithelium, penetrate into deeper layers and eventually into blood vessels. The general circulation then carries them to all other organs including the brain. Here they mature and eventually produce endoconidia which are only $1\cdot5\,\mu$ wide and easily carried to as yet uninfected parts of the body.

The fungus is protean in its adaptability to varying circumstances. In cold-water fish, whether freshwater or marine, long germinative tubular hyphae are produced, but we fail to see these in the tropical freshwater fishes. Concentrically laminated pigmentless capsules develop in cold-water fish whereas in tropical fish these capsules are heavily melanin-pigmented (Figs. 110, 113). These differences inclined authors to believe in the existence of two different species of this parasite (Schäperclaus, 1954; Reichenbach-Klinke, 1954), species which were temporarily designated as the "salmonid" and the "aquarium" forms. The type which produced the oral tumours seemed even to represent a third form of appearance whose details were different from the two others. Many attempts were made with the object of producing mixed infections of the three forms in one and the same fish. Neither of these was ever successful nor have such mixed infections ever been seen in freshly caught fish. We must therefore conclude that the varying aspects under which the parasite appears develop in response to environmental differences. Temperature and salinity may be the prime factors. There is room here for further investigations.

The original habitat of *Ichthyosporidium* was apparently the sea. Secondarily it was introduced into fresh waters. Up to the present it has been found on thirty-five marine and forty-eight freshwater fish (Reichenbach-Klinke, 1954, 1956), most of them Teleostei (bony fish). The distribution of the fungus includes so many different groups of fish as to make any specific host immunity or resistance very unlikely. The fungus has further been found in copepod crustaceans like *Calanus finmarchicus* Gunner, (Jepps, 1937, and Apstein, 1911 ("Parasit '6' ")), *Paracalanus parvus* Claus, *Clausocalanus arcuicornis* Dana and *Acartia clausi* Giesbr. (Chatton, 1920).

While we cannot, in the present state of our knowledge, definitely assert that the various fungi found in copepodes and those found in fish are all identical, preliminary feeding experiments made with infected crustaceans make this seem very probable indeed (Reichenbach-Klinke, 1956). One might even suggest that the copepodes should be regarded as the original hosts of the fungus. Since many of them represent the staple food of pelagic fish, the infection would easily spread to the latter. Freshwater copepods have so far not been found infected with *Ichthyosporidium*, but a discovery in this direction seems very likely if investigators once pursue the subject.

The appearance of the parasite is as varied as its effect on the infected fish. Infection of the liver goes parallel with loss of muscle substance, pallor of the skin, thrombosis of blood vessels and even total loss of fins. Infection of the brain causes loss of equilibrium, exophthalmus and staggering movements. Infection of the subcutis ends in inflammation and ulcerating skin defects. Wurmbach (1951) reports on sex reversal in guppies (*Lebistes reticulatus* Peters) whose ovaries were affected by the fungus.

Dorier and Degrange (1960–61) studied the effect of *Ichthyosporidium* in trout. They found differences between the modes of germination *in vivo* and *post mortem* (Fig. 114). Cysts which were swallowed formed so-called "amidoblasts" in the gut which divided first into multinuclear, and finally into mononuclear amoeboid parts. These free amoebulae remained active for several days and could be recovered, in the form of spherical cells, from the heart, the blood or the body cavity within 48 h after infection. In cultures the parasite remained alive for 2 months.

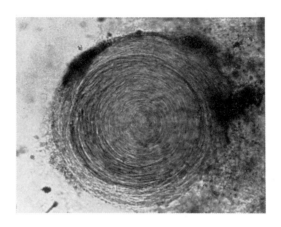

Fig. 116. Ichthyosporodiosis. A cyst from the bitterling (*Rhodeus amarus* Bloch).

An epizootic among herrings on the east coast of the U.S.A., caused by *Ichthyosporidium*, was studied by Sindermann and his colleagues (1954, 1956). Infected fish were recognized by the "sandpaper"-effect of their skins, which were rough and covered with small reddish pustules representing stages of the parasite encysted in the superficial parts of the muscle. Heart and liver were found affected at the same time (Fig. 110). Grown on Sabouraud dextrose the parasites remained alive over 14 months. During the first few days the fungus produced club-shaped buds analogous to those seen in freshwater cultures (Reichenbach-Klinke, 1956a) (Fig. 117).

In the fight against an invasion by *Ichthyosporidium* we are unfortunately confined to prophylactic measures. It is imperative to segregate or destroy every suspicious-looking fish as early as possible, for the smallest skin tag which may be eaten by other fish may teem with infectious stages of the parasite. Equally one fish disseminating material of this kind from a small external ulcer may infect the whole population. Partial successes with fungicidal drugs like phenoxctol and para-chloro-phenoxetol have been reported from America. They seem to be effective in the early stages only (Rankin, cited in Duijn, 1956).

The following mode of treatment is recommended: A stock solution of Phenoxetol is made by dissolving 1 cm³ in 99 cm³ of water; 10–20 cm³ of this stock solution per litre are added to the aquarium water. At the same time the fish are fed on dry fish-food soaked in the stock solution. The water in the aquarium must be changed after treatment. If para-chloro-phenoxetol is used the stock solution contains 1 cm³ : 1 litre of water and 50 cm³/litre are used in the aquarium, evenly

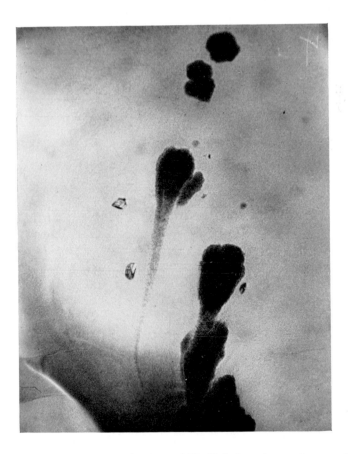

Fig. 117. *Ichthyosporidium hoferi* P. and M. Club-shaped parasites germinating on agar. (After Reichenbach-Klinke.)

distributed over 1–2 days. Here, too, the water has to be changed after treatment.

Two other hints may help in arresting an outbreak of ichthyosporodiosis. It has been found that fish are sometimes helped in encysting and killing the fungus if the water is slightly acidified and the temperature raised. It is, however, necessary to repeat this procedure several times since the thick-shelled endoconidia are unaffected by the treatment.

It is, of course, at the same time indispensable to pay the greatest attention to any outside source from which the stock may become re-infected again and again. This may happen by way of infected fish-food, through the aquarium soil and through any infected fish still in the tank with an open skin defect or ulcer. No infection has been reported through faeces. The parasite is firmly anchored in the gut epithelium and not excreted.

The minute size of the endoconidia (1–4 μ) makes it impossible to isolate them from the aquarium soil or to test their resistance to external influences experimentally. In trying to exterminate them we must rely on dry heat or boiling and on applying the usual disinfecting chemicals. We know of no such substances specifically lethal to *Ichthyosporidium*.

It is probably too much to hope that we shall ever be able to breed races of fish resistant to this dangerous infection, which is equally widely distributed in aquaria and in the normal habitat of fish. It must also be considered that *Ichthyosporidium* is particularly common in surface- and in plankton-feeding fish, i.e. in fish which either may continually reinfect themselves from contaminated copepods or which may ingest smaller fish already contaminated themselves. Bottom-feeding fish seem to be far less exposed to this danger, the deciding factor obviously being the mode of feeding.

Infection with *Basidiobolus*

Léger and Hesse (1923) found a fungus of the family Entomophthoraceae in the gut of trout. The fungus was determined as *Basidiobolus intestinalis*. It is closely related to the mould *Empusa muscae* Fres. often seen on dead house-flies. In the gut of the diseased trout the authors found long tubes and zygotes (fertilized ova) (Fig. 118) and a similar fungus was discovered in the burbot (*Lota lota* L.). Both parasites, described as *Basidiobolus intestinalis* and *B. lotae*, have not so far been seen again, but similar species are common in frogs and might easily gain access to collections.

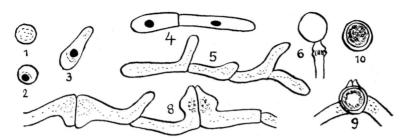

FIG. 118. *Basidiobolus intestinalis* Léger. 1, Spore. 2–4, germinating spores. 5, growth of branches. 6, conidium. 8 and 9, sexual stage. 10, mature zygote. (After Léger and Hesse.)

Saprolegniaceae

Saprolegnia, the most ubiquitous genus of aquatic fungus, commonly attacks fish. It must however always be regarded as a secondary parasite which establishes itself in a defect caused by another agent, either an injury or a primary parasite. Starting from such a focus *Saprolegnia* begins to cover the skin of the fish like a white mould. Under the microscope we see the mycelial threads bearing spores at the extremity. The spores are shed into the water and spread the infection. Gradually the whole fish is destroyed by the mould, which may belong either to the genus *Saprolegnia* or to the closely related *Achlya*. Initially the parasites infect only the very surface where they are accessible to topical treatment with disinfectants. Potassium permanganate baths (1 g in 100 l of water for 90 min) and salt baths (30 g of NaCl in 1 litre of water), further copper sulphate baths (5 g in 10 l of water); silver proteinate baths (0·00001 of collargol in 1 litre of water for 20 min) or painting with tincture of iodide have been recommended.

Saprolegnia develops in tanks lacking strict supervision. It thrives on unconsumed surplus food or any other dead protein matter, particularly in badly aerated tanks. Fish eggs are attacked at once if they are not viable, while live, developing eggs are resistant to infection. It is however very advisable to separate "mouldy" eggs as early as possible and to step up the aeration in tanks where the infection shows itself (Fig. 119).

Ichthyochytrium vulgare Plehn

Ichthyochytrium vulgare seems to be a fungus allied to the algae. It has been observed growing in the skin and on the gills of freshwater fishes. The spherical bodies of 5–20 μ diameter contain strongly refractive granules. The parasite is rare and has not been reported for several years.

5*

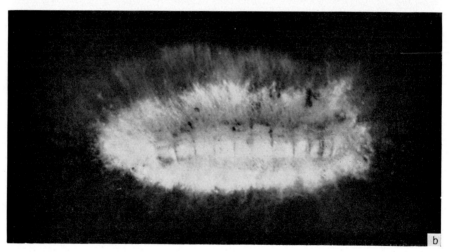

Fig. 119. *Saprolegnia ferax* growing on a mealworm (*Tenebrio* sp.). (a) In the clear water of an aquarium; (b) the same specimen after transfer for 12 h to a solution containing 5% sucrose.

Gill Rot

Two other fungi allied to the algae, *Branchiomyces sanguinis* Plehn and *B. demigrans* Wundsch, are known to invade the gills of European carp and pike, where they form long and wide ramose tubes

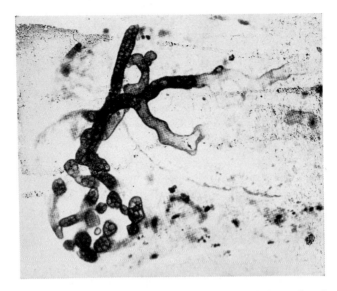

FIG. 120. *Branchiomyces sanguinis* Plehn. (After Schäperclaus.)

and cause a disease which goes by the name of gill rot (Fig. 120). Ornamental fish have so far not been attacked. The growth of the fungus on the gills leads to inflammation, thrombosis and the development of granulation tissue. As the disease develops, the gills are more and more put out of action. The disease is one of the greatest threats to commercial pisciculture.

Moulds (Ascomycetes) in Visceral Organs

Several years of observation have revealed the presence of moulds of the family Aspergillaceae in the peritoneum and the ovary of cyprinid fish (Reichenbach-Klinke, 1956a). Since the species observed seemed to be identical with *Nephromyces piscium* Plehn (Fig. 121) found in the kidney of carp, it was described as *Penicillium piscium*. Eggs and collagen tissue are found penetrated by septate ramose threads, 2–3 μ wide, and thallous, pseudoparenchymatous masses as well as thick-shelled resting and ovoid, mostly bipartite ascospores. The central fungal mass in the diseased organs is surrounded by a loose network of septate hyphae representing a reduced pericarp. At the further periphery typical *Penicillium* fructifications represented by long hyphae, branching out into metulae, daughter threads (phialids) and conidial chains, can be seen (Fig. 122).

The fungus seems to be widely distributed. It was found in *Loricaria parva* Boul., *Neolebias ansorgi* Boul. and others. In most cases the infection is not visible on the surface but occasionally it may cause large ulcerations (Fig. 123). In sections the most striking features are the oval spores (Fig. 124). Bipartite spores are seen in the body cavity of goldfish (*C. carassius auratus* L.), Neon fish (*Hyphessobrycon innesi* Myers) and *H. rosaceus* Durbin (Fig. 125). The disease is confined to the digestive system, and infection probably occurs with feeding. Excessive growth of the fungus kills the fish.

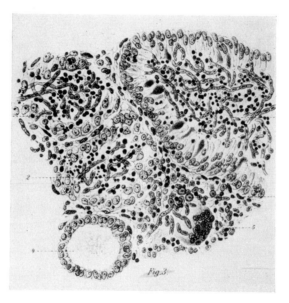

FIG. 121. *"Nephromyces piscium"* Plehn. (After Plehn.)

Aphanomyces

Shanor and Saslow (1944) reported a severe infection of guppies (*Lebistes reticulatus* Peters), *Anoptichthys jordani* Hubbs and Innes and *Xiphophorus helleri* Heckel with the fungus *Aphanomyces*. Apparently the fish had become infected through unobserved skin lesions. The disease manifested itself at first with dark patches in the dorsal muscle, which were caused by masses of hyphae. Later fungal threads, up to 2 mm long, broke through the skin and appeared on the surface. Every affected fish died within a week.

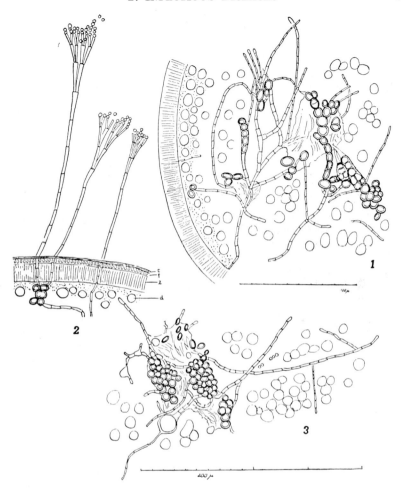

Fig. 122. *Penicillium piscium* (Plehn). 1, Endogenous ascogenous and nutritive hyphae with ascospores and chlamydospores. Parasite among the yolk globules of a maturing egg of *Loricaria parva* Boul. Left: egg membrane. 2, Fructification of the parasite with development of conidia. *d,* Yolk globules; *z,* zona radiata of egg; *f,* follicle epithelium. 3, Hyphae, ascospores and chlamydospores in the egg of *Loricaria parva* B.

Fusaria

A *Fusaria* infection of fish must be regarded as a rarity. Yet Hörter (1960) reported the case of a freshly constructed pond in which all the carp introduced died within a few weeks from blindness and fungal invasion of the whole skin. Apparently the pond was unsuitable for the accommodation of fish, the whole bottom being covered with beech leaves.

Tumours in Fish and Fungal Infection

It is of interest to observe that, just as in human pathology, fungi may provoke the development of tumours in fish, particularly if the same genera are responsible in both hosts as noted in the case of *Alternaria* (see Fig. 129).

One of the first cases of this kind was the "pseudo-tumour" or "sarcome lymphoblastique" found by Montpellier and Dieuzeide

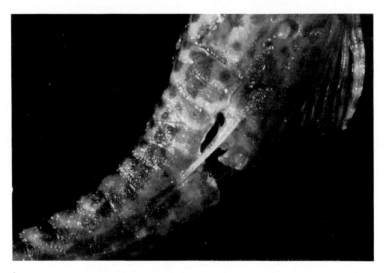

FIG. 123. *Penicillium* growing on a wound of *Loricaria parva* B.

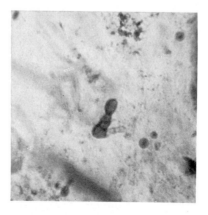

FIG. 124. *Neolebias ansorgi* Boul. Body cavity infected with *Penicillium*.

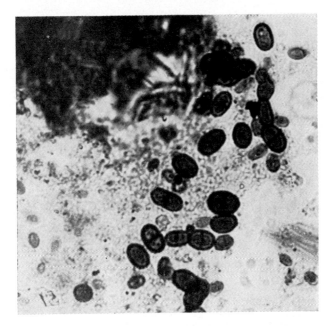

FIG. 125. Bipartite spores of an undetermined fungus (aspergillacea?) from a veil tail (*Carassius carassius* L.).

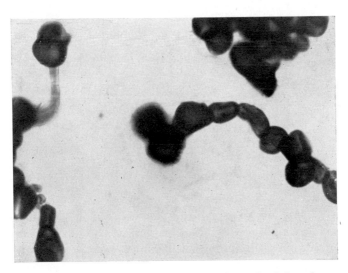

FIG. 126. Sclerotized hyphae and spores of an undetermined fungal tumour in the tail of a swordtail (*Xiphophorus helleri* H.) (After Reichenbach-Klinke.)

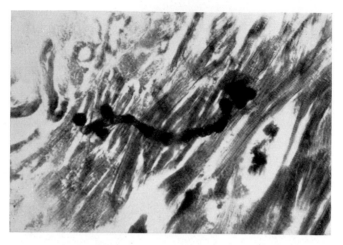

FIG. 127. Details of the fungus shown in Fig. 126.

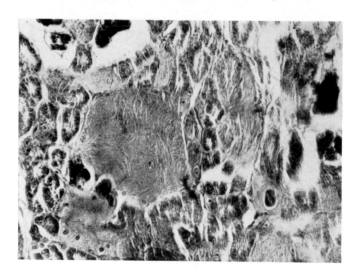

FIG. 128. Hypertrophic cells in the tumour of the tail of a swordtail, containing fungal hyphae, etc., as shown in Figs. 126 and 127.

(1933) in the subcutis of *Aphanius fasciatus* Val. At about the same time Harant and Vernières (1933) saw fungal threads in giant cells of an abdominal tumour in a minnow (*Phoxinus phoxinus* L.), and in 1952 Ermin described septate fungal threads from a connective tissue granuloma in *Aphanius chantrei* Gaillard. In these cases only isolated stages in the development of the fungi could be demonstrated. Finally numerous spore-chains of an undetermined fungal species could be demonstrated in a tumour from the tail of a *Xiphophorus helleri* Heckel ♀ (Figs. 126, 127). The hyphae were sclerotic and septate and contained numerous resting spores usually clumped together in groups. The fungus had invaded the muscles and the connective tissue. The most interesting feature was the relation of the parasite to the host cells. Every parasitized cell was hypertrophic. Fig. 128 show a hypertrophied cell from a section through the tumour. The cytoplasm

FIG. 129. Fungus resembling *Alternaria* from a superficial wound in *Trichogaster leeri* B.

contains sclerotic fungal threads. These threads were found in every hypertrophic cell. We have here a parallel to the effect of *Glugea anomala* M. on the cells of the stickleback. Since it was, at the time, not possible to culture this fungus, it was provisionally listed as "Fungal type C". A similar form was found in the gills of *Gadus morrhua* L. (Reichenbach-Klinke, 1956a, b).

REFERENCES

Apstein, C. (1911). Parasiten von *Calanus finmarchicus*. *Wiss. Meeresunters. Kiel.* N.F. **13**, 205–222.

Brown, G. T. (1932). Sensitization to fungi. *Ann. intern. Med.* **6**, 655–671.

Caullery, M. and Mesnil, F. (1905). Recherches sur les Haplosporidies. *Arch. Zool. exp. gén.* **4**, 101–180.

Chatton, E. (1920). Les Peridiniens parasites. *Arch. Zool. exp. gén.* **59**, 1.

Dorier, A. and Degrange, Ch. (1960–61). L'évolution de l'*Ichthyosporidium* (*Ichthyophonus*) *hoferi* (Plehn and Mulsow) chez les Salmonides d'élevage (Truite arc-en-ciel et Saumon de fontaine). *Trav. Lab. Hydrobiol. Grenoble* **52/53**, 7–44.

Duijn, C. v. (1956). "Diseases of Fishes", publ. *Water Life*, London.

Ermin, R. (1952). Fungus associated with a granuloma in a Turkish fish *Aphanius chantrei* Gaillard. *Zoologica* **37**, 1, 43–54.

Harant, H. and Vernières, P. (1933). Tumeur abdominale et complexe parasitaire chez le vairon (*Phoxinus phoxinus* L.) *Arch. Zool. exp. gén.* **75**, 255–266.

Hofer, B. (1906). "Handbuch der Fischkrankheiten." Stuttgart.

Hörter, R. (1960). *Fusarium* als Erreger einer Hautmykose bei Karpfen. *Z. Parasitk.* **20**, 355–358.

Jepps, M. W. (1937). On the protozoan parasites of *Calanus finmarchicus* in the Clyde sea area. *J. micr. Sci.*, N.S. **79**, 589–658.

Kahls, O. (1930). Über das Vorkommen von Algen und Pilzen bei Fischen. *Z. Fischerei* **28**, 253–262.

Léger, L. (1924). Sur un organisme du type Ichthyophone parasite du tube digestif de la Lote d'eau douce. *C.R. Acad. Sci., Paris* **179**, 785–787.

Léger, L. (1927). Sur la nature de l'évolution des "sphérules" décrites chez les Ichthyophones Phycomycètes parasites de la truite. *C.R. Acad. Sci., Paris* **184**, 1268–1271.

Léger, L. (1929a).Obstruction stomacale chez la truite par une formation mycétogène d'origine alimentaire. *Ann. Univ. Grenoble* N.S. Sci. Méd. VI, 79–85.

Léger, L. (1929b). Sur la nature et l'évolution des sphérules décrites chez les Ichthyphones phycomycètes parasites de la Truite. *Ann. Univ. Grenoble* N.S. Sci. Méd. VI, 133–137.

Léger, L. and Hesse, R. (1923). Sur un champignon du type *Ichthyophonus* parasite de l'intestin de la truite. *C.R. Acad. Sci., Paris* **176**, 420–422.

Montpellier, J. and Dieuzeide, R. (1933). Pseudo-tumeur mycélienne chez un Poisson (*Cyprinodon fasciatus* Val.). *Bull. Trav. Sta. Aqu. Pêche Castiglione* 1932, I. 551–557.

Neresheimer, E. and Clodi, C. (1914). *Ichthyphonus hoferi* Plehn et Mulsow, der Erreger der Taumelkrankheit der Salmoniden. *Arch. Protistenk.* **34**, 217–248.

Pettit, A. (1911). A propos du Microorganisme producteur de la Taumelkrankheit: *Ichthyosporidium* or *Ichthyophonus*. *C.R. Soc. Biol., Paris* **70**, 1045–1047.

Pettit, A. (1913). Observations sur l'Ichthyosporidium et sur la maladie qu'il provoque chez la truite. *Ann. Inst. Pasteur* **27**, 986–1008.

Plehn, M. (1916). Pathogene Schimmelpilze in der Fischniere. *Z. Fischerei* **18**, 51–54.

Plehn, M. and Mulsow, K. (1911). Der Erreger der Taumelkrankheit der Salmoniden. *Zbl. Bakt.* I. Abt. **59**, 63–68.

Reichenbach-Klinke, H. (1954). Untersuchungen über die bei Fischen durch Parasiten hervorgerufenen Zysten und deren Wirkung auf den Wirtskörper. I. *Z. Fischerei* N.F. **3**, 565–636.

Reichenbach-Klinke, H. (1955). Pilze in Tumoren bei Fischen. *Verh. dtsch. zool. Ges. Tübingen*, 1954, Leipzig, pp. 351–357.

Reichenbach-Klinke, H. (1956a). Eine Aspergillacee (*Fungi, Ascomycetes, Plectascales*) Endoparasit bei Süsswasserfischen. *Veröff. Inst. Meeresk. Bremerhaven* **4**, 111–116.

Reichenbach-Klinke, H. (1956b). Über einige, bisher unbekannte Hyphomyceten bei verschiedenen Süsswasser-und Meeresfischen. *Mycopathologia* **7**, 333–347.

Reichenbach-Klinke, H. (1956c). Augenschäden bei Meeresfischen durch den Pilz *Ichthyosporidium hoferi* (Plehn and Mulsow) und Bemerkungen zu seiner Verbreitung bei Mittelmeerfischen. *Pubbl. Staz. Zool. Napoli* **29**, *Festschr. R. Dohrn.* 22–32.

Reichenbach-Klinke, H. (1956d). Die Vermehrungsformen des zoophagen Pilzes *Ichthyosporidium hoferi* Plehn and Mulsow im Wirt. *Veröff. Inst. Meeresk. Bremerhaven* **4**, 214–219.

Reichenow, E. (1952–3). "Lehrbuch der Protozoenkunde," 6th edn., Jena.

Schäperclaus, W. (1929). Beiträge zur Kenntnis der Kiemenfäule des Karpfens. *Z. Fischerei* **27**, 271–286.

Schäperclaus, W. (1953). Fortpflanzung und Systematik von *Ichthyophonus*. *Aqu. Terr. Z.* **6**, 177–182.

Schäperclaus, W. (1954), "Fischkrankheiten", 3rd edn., Akademie Verlag, Berlin.

Schlumberger, H. G. (1958). Krankheiten dei Fische, Amphibien und Reptilien. *In* " Pathologie des Laboratoriumstiere " (Cohrs, Jaffé and Meesen, eds.), Vol, II. Springer, Berlin.

Shanor, L. and Saslow, H. B. (1944). *Aphanomyces* as a Fish Parasite. *Mycologia* **36**, 413–415.

Sindermann, C. (1956). Diseases of the Fishes of the Western North Atlantic. IV. Fungus disease and resultant mortalities of herring in the Gulf of St. Lawrence in 1955. *Res. Bull. Dept. Sea and Shore Fish. Augusta* **25**, 1–23.

Sindermann, C. and Rosenfield (1954). Diseases of Fishes of the Western North Atlantic. I. Diseases of the Sea Herring (*Clupea harengus*). *Res. Bull. Dept. Sea and Shore Fish. Augusta* **18**, 1–23.

Sindermann, C. and Scattergood, L. W. (1954). *Ibid.* II. Ichthyosporidium disease of the Sea Herring (*Clupea harengus*). *Res. Bull. Dept. Sea and Shore Fish. Augusta* **19**, 1–40.

Sproston, N. G. (1947). *Ichthyosporidium hoferi* (Plehn and Mulsow), an internal fungoid parasite of the Mackerel. *J. Mar. Biol. Ass. U.K.* **26**, 72–98.

Verdun, M. (1903). Mycose rénale chez une carpe commune. *C.R. Soc. Biol., Paris* **55**, 1313–1314.

Walker, R. (1951). Mycetoma in a landlocked salmon. *Anat. Rec.* Abstr. **111**, 531.

Wundsch, H. H. (1929). Eine besondere Art der "Kiemenfäule" bei Hechten und Schleien. *Z. Fischerei* **27**, 287–293.

Wundsch, H. H. (1930). Weitere Beobachtungen an *Branchiomyces demigrans* als Erreger der Kiemenfäule beim Hecht. *Z. Fischerei* **28**, 391–402.

Wurmbach, H. (1951). Geschlechtsunkehr bei Weibchen von *Lebistes reticulatus* Peters bei Befall mit *Ichthyophonus hoferi* Plehn-Mulsow. *Roux Arch.* **145**, 109–124.

Q. VIRUS DISEASES

Our knowledge of fish diseases caused by virus infection increases with the general rise of our knowledge in the field of virology. Virus-caused fish diseases are now known from both freshwater and marine fish.

The first viral condition described in fish is the *Lymphocystis* disease. The cells affected are first permeated with fine granules, later by a network of inclusion bodies (Fig. 130). The skin reacts to the presence of the virus by producing grape-like or raspberry-like growths, particularly on the fins. Sections show these growths to consist entirely of hypertrophic connective tissue cells. Details were recently described by Walker (1962). Zschiesche, who first saw these cells in 1910, mistook them for ova adhering to the skin.

Some European countries are plagued by the "Cauliflower Disease" of eel. Large epitheliomatous growths appear on the circumoral skin,

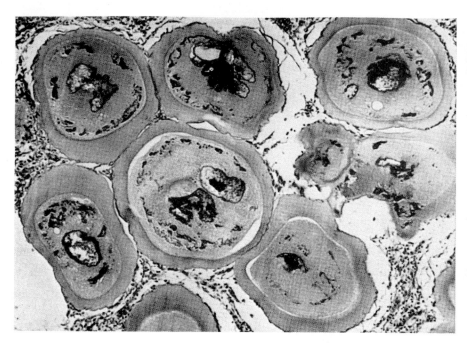

FIG. 130. Cells infected by *Lymphocystis*. The enlarged connective tissue cells are surrounded by thick hyaline capsules. (After Schlumberger, 1958.)

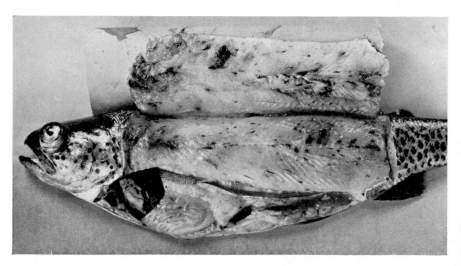

FIG. 131. Muscular haemorrhages in a trout suffering from a virus-septicaemia. (Photo.: Ghittino.)

the fins and elsewhere. The fish are listless, cannot feed and lose weight.

Another epidermal disease, this time of carp and tench, described as "Pox", is also thought to be of viral origin. In this case the epithelial plaques or growths may appear anywhere on the skin of the fish. They cannot be scraped off with a spatula and may be distinguished from local inflammatory foci by their grey-white colour. The fish affected display a subnormal growth rate but seem to be otherwise normal.

A greatly dreaded viral disease among freshwater fish is the "Virus-Septicaemia" of trout ("Trout-Pest", "New Trout-Disease", Egtved-Disease, or "INUL") (= Infektiöse Nierenschwellung und Leber-degeneration). The number of names shows the importance the disease has for those engaged in the rearing of trout. The disease is protean in its symptoms (Deufel, 1960; Tack, 1961). An acute attack produces comma-shaped haemorrhages in the muscles (Fig. 131), larger haemor-rhages in the liver, the swim-bladder, the gut and the swollen kidney. Externally exophthalmus and dermatitis may be noticed. In later stages fungi superinfect the skin. The disease may also manifest itself in the form of anaemia with an icteric-looking liver and exudation of bile into the peritoneal cavity (ascites of trout). While the two types of the disease described usually end with the death of the fish, a third type exists which mainly attacks the nervous system and causes staggering movements without, however, killing the fish.

The Infectious Pancreas Necrosis (IPN) of trout fry is also due to a viral infection (Wolf et al., 1960). The fish make corkscrew-like move-ments, their empty gut is filled with transparent mucus; the production of bile has ceased. Sections show necrotic foci in muscle and pancreas (Wood et al., 1955). The disease is highly lethal.

The causation of the ascites of carp is still under discussion. The protean nature of the disease induced authors to suspect a virus. On the other hand the bacterium Aeromonas punctatum may apparently cause the same clinical picture single or accompanied by a virus. The same situation exists in the case of the contagious epizootic of pike where, in most cases, no bacteria can be found. The disease produces multiple dermal ulcerations and is highly lethal.

Kryo-ichthyozoosis is the name given to a viral disease observed among freshwater fish in the Brazilian State of Sao Paulo (Pachecoe and Guimaraes, 1933). The base of the fins swells and the fish die within a few hours. The virus does not tolerate temperatures above 16°C.

Finally, we may mention a gular tumour described by Schäperclaus (1952) in Mollienisia, also apparently caused by a virus.

REFERENCES

Benisch, J. (1937). Über das Auftreten der Lymphocystis-Krankheit bei einigen Korallenfischen. Wschr. Aqu. Terrk. **34**, 380–382.

Deufel, J. (1958). Untersuchungen über den Erreger der "Infektiösen Nierenschwellung und Leberdegeneration" der Forellen. Arch. Fischereiwiss. **9**, 181–186.

Ghittino, P. (1962). L'ipertrofia renale e degeneratione epatica infettiva della trota di allevamento (Salmo gairdneri). Caratteristicha clinicha, eziologiche ed anatomo-isto-pathologiche. Vet. ital. **13**, 457–489.

Pachecoe, G. and Guimaraes, J. B. (1933). Ichthyozooties dans les eaux fluviales de l'Etat de Sao Paolo. C.R. Soc. Biol., Paris **111**, 1401.

Schäperclaus, W. (1952). Eigenartige Kehlgeschwülste beim schwarzen Molly. Aqu. Terr. Z. **5**, 154–155.

Schlumberger, H. G. (1958). Krankheiten dei Fische, Amphibien und Reptilien. In "Pathologie der Laboratoriumstiere" (Cohrs, Jaffé and Meesen, eds.), Vol. II. Springer, Berlin.

Tack, E. (1958). Beiträge zur Erforschung der Forellenseuche. Arch. Fischereiwiss. **10**, 20–30.

Walker, R. (1962). Fine structure of Lymphocystis virus of fish. Virology **18**, 503–505.

Wessing, A. and v. Bargen, G. (1959). Untersuchungen über einen virusbedingten Tumor bei Fischen. Arch. ges. Virusforsch. **4**, 521–536.

Wolf, K., Snieszko, S. F., Dunbar, C. E. and Pyle, E. (1960). Virus nature of infectious pancreatic necrosis in trout. Proc. Soc. exp. Biol., N.Y. **104**, 105–108.

Wood, E. M., Snieszko, S. F. and Yasutake, T. (1955). Infectious pancreatic necrosis in Brook Trout. A.M.A. Arch. Path. **60**, 26–28.

Zschiesche, A. (1910). Eizellen in der Haut von Macropoden. Zool. Anz. **36**, 294–298.

Chapter 3

Non-Infectious Diseases of Fish. Environmental Factors

A. Melanosis

Melanosis or total black discoloration occurs naturally in some hybrids. Some fish, which may otherwise have bright colours, are born with abnormal black patches. Just as in human pathology, the excessive appearance of melanin-bearing cells (melanophores) must be viewed with suspicion, since they may be the precursors of extremely malignant tumours (melanosarcoma).

Melanin-bearing pigment cells are much more widely distributed in all organs among the lower than in the higher vertebrates and the presence of some of these cells, even in visceral organs, is perfectly normal. In the subcutis they contribute to the normal pattern and coloration of the fish. In cases of melanosis, however, we may find dense strands of such cells invading the epidermis which is normally free from all chromatophores. The condition is particularly common among *Mollienisia*, *Xiphophorus* and *Platypoecilus* species. In black crosses of *Xiphophorus helleri* × *Platypoecilus maculatus* the subcutis is 5–10 times thicker than normal (Breider, 1956). In pure strains of platies which carry the factor "spotted", the brain is covered by macro-melanophores. In crosses between *P. maculatus* × *X. helleri*, bearing the factor "spotted", the melanophores invade the muscle, the brain, the spinal cord, the cartilage, the bone, the liver, the heart and the lateral trunk muscles. The whole fish is over-pigmented and very prone to develop malignant tumours (Breider, 1952).

Apparently it is particularly the genetic factor "spotted" which, in hybrids, predisposes to melanosis. The factor which incites the melanophores to invade the muscular system (normally free from chromatophores) also seems to shorten the life of the fish. We do not know yet whether the process is accompanied by other, metabolic disturbances, nor in which way the invaded tissues are damaged by the melanophores, nor can external examination reveal the boundaries between normal and excessive black pigmentation. The literature on melanomata and melanosarcomata is large but exact knowledge on the cellular pathology of these conditions has not yet been obtained.

In addition to genetically conditioned melanotic patches these may also arise in response to parasitic invasions or they may be caused by hormonal or nervous defects in the constitution of the individual fish. Such black patches arise, for instance, in the cysts walling off *Ichthyosporidium* or metacercaria (see pp. 8, 80, 278). Pigment cells may also appear in scars deriving from small injuries, and it should be stressed that most of the small black spots seen on otherwise normal-looking fish need give no cause for alarm.

REFERENCES

Breider, H. (1952). Über Melanome, Melanosarkome und homologe Zell-mechanismen. *Strahlentherapie* **88**, 619–639.

Breider, H. (1956). Farbgene und Melanosarkomhäufigkeit. *Zool. Anz.* **156**, 129–140.

Gordon, M. and Lansing, W. (1943). Cutaneous melanophore eruptions in young fishes during stages preceding melanotic tumour formation. *J. Morph.* **73**, 231–245.

Reichenbach-Klinke, H. (1954). Übermässige Pigmentbildung bei Fischen als Gradmesser einer Gewebsdegeneration. *Biol. Zbl.* **73**, 522–549.

B. Tumours Affecting Fish

In their natural habitat fish very rarely show externally visible tumours. Specimens affected with any debilitating condition do not survive long enough to present striking pathological pictures. Conditions are different in the aquarium where diseased fish can be isolated at an early stage. It is in many cases rewarding to keep such specimens in isolation either to observe the effects of therapeutic attempts or to obtain an impression of the morbid anatomy of the disease when it is fully developed. Many infections as well as tumours of all kinds develop extremely slowly in lower vertebrates. Equally, the power to survive if protected from predators is astonishing in these animals, many of which at first sight look rather frail. Yet, although they may survive for quite some time, once diseased they rarely recover and our skill to treat them is not commensurate with the number of mishaps that may befall them.

In the realm of tumours our knowledge is consequently mainly derived from specimens kept in aquaria. A first review of the widely dispersed literature on neoplastic disease in fish was made by Schlumberger and Lucké in 1948 and experimental observations, particularly on the pigment cell tumours of poeciliids, were published by Gordon and Lansing (1943), Gordon (1950) and Breider and Schmidt (1951).

The tendency of certain hybrids to develop melanotic tumours has already been mentioned. Large parts of the cytoplasm are in these cases devoted to nothing but an excessive formation of melanin and the chromatophore, far from fulfilling any useful function, may end up as a hypertrophied giant cell.

Analogous to the classification used in human pathology we may divide the fish tumours into the benign and the malignant. The benign tumours grow by expansion from one centre. They do not infiltrate neighbouring tissues but may damage adjacent organs by compression. They do not form new growths (metastases) in other parts of the organism. Malignant tumours on the other hand grow rapidly by infiltration and may produce metastases early in remote parts of the body. They are classified as carcinoma if they arise from the epithelium and

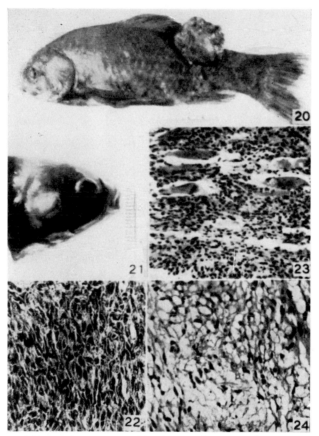

FIG. 132. Dermal fibrosarcoma of a goldfish (*C. carassius auratus* L.). (After Schlumberger and Lucké.)

as sarcoma if they arise from connective or other non-epithelial tissues. True sarcomata are rarely seen in fish but the pigmented variety or melanosarcoma is not so uncommon and represents one of the most malignant fish tumours. A carcinoma may, for instance, arise from a swelling and subsequent malignant degeneration of the thyroid gland, become very malignant and produce numerous secondary depots.

FIG. 133. Oral tumours in *Sphaerichthys osphromenoides* Canestrini. (Orig.)

To begin with, the skin, or any other epithelial structure may, either spontaneously, or as a response to stimulation by injury or parasites, produce epitheliomata, harmless tumours which, all the same, may grow to a considerable size. The centre of the epithelioma shown (Fig. 147) was taken up by the mycelium of a fungus. Mulberry-like epitheliomata may be found around the mouth, on the back and on the fins of fish. Sometimes, when these growths become more prominent, they resemble a cauliflower and are then called papillomata. They are still benign tumours consisting of a much folded epithelial surface and a core (stroma) of connective tissues nerves and blood vessels (Fig. 133).

Tumours consisting solely of connective tissue are called fibromata, if benign; fibro-sarcomata if malignant. A lymphosarcoma consists of cells resembling lymphocytes; a myxosarcoma is a connective cell tumour the cells of which are filled with excessive amounts of a mucoid substance. The variety of tumours is as great as that of the tissues.

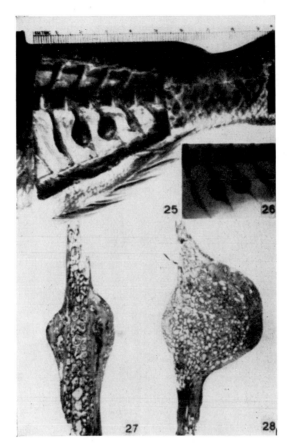

FIG. 134. Bony tumours in *Pagrosomus major*. No. 27 × 5·4; No. 28 × 4. (From Schlumberger and Lucké.)

FIG. 135. Myofibroma changing into melanosarcoma in a swordtail. × 37.

Bony tumours are among the rarest of all but occasionally osteomata or osteosarcomata may be seen. A case of this kind is shown in Fig. 134. If the tumour contains only cartilage it is called a chondroma or a chondro-sarcoma respectively.

Tumours arising in the muscle are rarely pure myomata but more usually mixed growths of the fibromyoma type (Fig. 135). Where there is much cell degeneration they may change into myxofibromata.

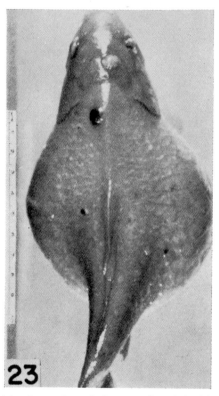

Fig. 136. Goldfish with advanced cystic degeneration of the kidneys, a neurilemmoma between the eyes and three pigmented neurofibromata. (After Schlumberger.)

Adenomata are tumours arising from glandular tissue. Here again the tumours are as different as the glands from which they arise. They may be solid or, as in the case of the cystadenomata, consist of nothing but large cystic spaces with narrow septa of connective tissue. Such cystadenomata are most commonly seen in the kidneys of fish where they may grow to such a size as to deform the whole body of the fish (Fig. 136). Stolk (1954) has described several cases of this kind from ornamental fish.

Hepatomata (tumours of the liver) have lately been reported from trout. Ghittino and Ceretto (1961) see the cause of these tumours in unsuitable nutrition. Severe cases lead to complete lipoid degeneration of the liver with local hyperplasia or cirrhosis. American authors blame artificial fish food as causative agent of these tumours. Our knowledge in this direction is as yet incomplete.

Thyroid Tumours

Thyroid tumours are the commonest adenomata in fish. They may start as harmless hyperplasias but may, in the end, become extremely malignant. Apparently the particular structure of the thyroid predisposes it to carcinomatous degeneration. A few thyroid cells, transported to remote parts of the body by the blood stream, can start a

FIG. 137. Two specimens of *Xiphophorus montezumae* with goitre. (Photo.: Gorbman and Gordon.)

new malignant growth. Most of these growths occur in the head region, sometimes in the floor of the mouth or in the gills. If the tumours grow they interfere with the breathing movements and eventually kill the fish. The pathology of these tumours has been described in detail by Gorbman and Gordon in 1951. Fig. 137 shows two of their diseased fish (*Xiphophorus montezumae* J. and S.) with tumours of the gular region and the operculum. Histological investigation showed a tumour originating in the thyroid gland which had grown into the mouth and had also displaced the upper abdominal viscera (Fig. 138). The bones visible in this figure were infiltrated by cells and partly eroded. It is remarkable to note that the advancing thyroid cells were found in the company of macromelanophores.

If a thyroid tumour is diagnosed in a very early stage of development an attempt might be made at treating it with iodine and potassium iodide. The prescription would be: R Iodine 1 part; Potassium iodide

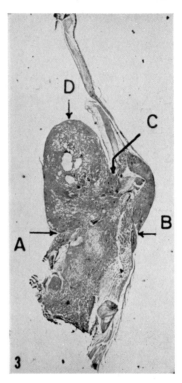

FIG. 138. Malignant thyroid tumour in *Xiphophorus montezumae* J. and S. *A*, Tumour invading bone; *B*, protusion of gular region; *C*, *D*, tongue displaced by advancing tumour. (Photo.: Gorbman and Gordon.)

100 part. Add to the fish food 1 part of this mixture : 2 500 l of water. If potassium iodide is to be added to the water directly, this should be done in a dilution of 1 part : 5 million parts of water.

Berg and Gordon (1953) treated specimens of *Xiphophorus* suffering from goitre with thyroid tablets which they dissolved in the water of the aquarium together with potassium iodide carbonate (10 μg : 1 cm^3 water). Some fishes recovered on being injected once weekly with 30 μg of thyroxin dissolved in 0·05 cm^3 of 0·65% saline.

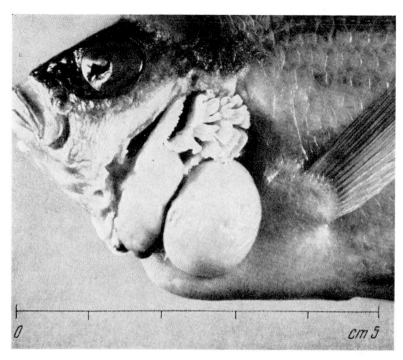

FIG. 139. *Lepomis megalotis*, the sun fish. Gills obstructed by a thyroid tumour. Gill cover removed. (After Schlumberger, 1958.)

FIG. 140. Eye tumour in *Mollienisia sphenops* C. and V. (Orig.)

Analogous to the thyroid other glands may show malignant degeneration. Stolk (1954) described a pituitary tumour. Pflugfelder (1953) observed the effect of a removal of the epiphysis in the guppy. The operation caused a rapid growth of the thyroid follicles, enlargement of the pituitary and spinal curvature.

Diseases of the eyes are almost entirely confined to the exophthalmic types of highly inbred goldfish, true ophthalmic tumours being rarities. One case was described by Levine and Gordon (1946) (Fig. 140). The malignant tissue consisted almost entirely of connective tissue cells which had grown all round the eyeball and caused extreme exophthalmus.

Neurilemmoma

Neurilemmoma (tumours arising from the connective-tissue sheath of peripheral nerves) were described by Schlumberger in 1952. They occurred in a population of goldfish. Fig. 141 shows a tumour of this kind in the body cavity which had compressed the other viscera and distended the abdominal wall. In sections masses of rod-shaped nuclei

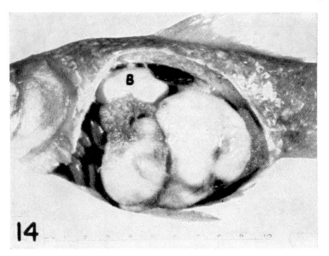

Fig. 141. Goldfish with two large neurilemmomata in the body cavity. *B*, Swimbladder. (After Schlumberger.)

could be seen in palisade formation (Fig. 142). Higher magnification (Fig. 143) reveals long rows of black granules in the neurilemmal cells. Accumulation of melanin always seems to herald malignancy, at least in the fish. Fig. 136 shows, between the eyes, a second small colourless neurilemmona and behind it another button-shaped pigmented neurofibroma, also blackened by the presence of melanophores.

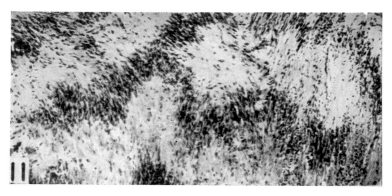

Fig. 142. Neurilemmoma of a goldfish showing palisade arrangement of nuclei. v. Gieson stain. × 105. (After Schlumberger.)

Fig. 143. Part of Fig. 142 at higher magnification showing the neurilemmoma cells. (After Schlumberger.)

6

Coloured Tumours

According to the pigment cells from which they derive, coloured tumours are described as melanomata (black), erythromata (red) or xanthoerythromata (yellow-red). Factors favouring the appearance of benign black pigmented tumours in *X. helleri* × *P. maculatus* hybrids have been described as "fuliginosus", "nigra" and "seminigra". If the tumours appear in the caudal fin some of the rays may be missing. Figs. 144 and 145 show further examples of these tumours (Breider,

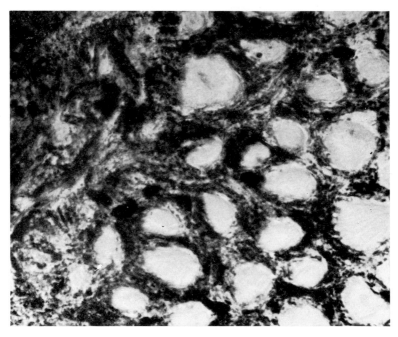

Fig. 144. Section through a melanoma in *Platypoecilus variatus* Meek. Pigment free and in melanophores. (After Reichenbach-Klinke.)

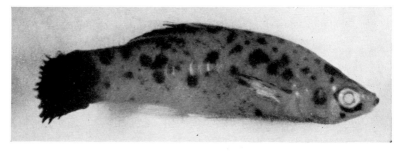

Fig. 145. Melanosarcoma in *Platypoecilus variatus* Meek. (After Reichenbach-Klinke.)

1938, 1939, 1956; Breider and Schmidt, 1951; Gordon, 1950; Kosswig, 1929).

The erythroma or xanthoerythroma with red or yellow chromatophores is a great rarity compared with the melanoma. After early descriptions by Smith *et al.* (1936), Kosswig (1938), and Nigrelli *et al.* (1951), Ermin (1953) gave a detailed account of the histology of a xanthoerythrophoroma in a specimen of *Platypoecilus maculatus* Gthr. Even in this mainly red-yellow tumour some macromelanophores could be seen, the latter cells giving the tumour a sarcomatous character. As the tumour grows the red-pigmented cells degenerate and the tumour develops into the more commonly seen erythromelanoma (Nigrelli *et al.*, 1951).

The causation of all these pigmented tumours lies most probably in some kind of genetic imbalance, an assumption made more likely by the preponderance of the chromatophoroma in hybrids. Alternative causes may be seen in local metabolic disturbances (cystadenomata) or in hormonal imbalance (thyroid tumours).

Fig. 146. A copepode (*Lernaea carassii*) penetrating into a neurilemmoma of a goldfish. ×10. (After Schlumberger.)

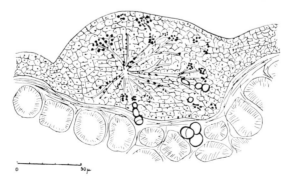

Fig. 147. A parasitic fungus with hyphae and spores in an epithelioma of the swordtail (*Xiphophorus helleri* H.).

Pseudotumours

It is as yet uncertain whether the ability of parasites to produce skin tumours is due to chemical or physical irritation or to both. The tumours they produce must be distinguished from the true tumours since they disappear with the disappearance of the noxious agent. They may be classed as pseudotumours or hyperplastic growths. As in the case of the parasitic crustacean *Lernaea carassii* Tidd (Fig. 146), it is not always possible to say with certainty whether the parasite alone produced the tumour or whether microsporidia, fungi and viruses (lymphocystis) took part in the pathological growth (Fig. 147). Giant cells of the foreign-body type may be caused by all these agents.

Granulomata

Some simple, harmless and entirely undifferentiated tumours which sometimes seem to present a process of regeneration after an injury or after loss of some tissue are described as granulomata. In some cases they have been found permeated by fungi; in others not. A fungal granuloma was described by Ermin (1952) from *Aphanius chantrei* G. Equally Walker (1951) reported on a granuloma of the head in a salmonid fish from Idaho, U.S.A. The tumour was permeated by a ramose fungal mycelium.

REFERENCES

Aronowitz, O., Nigrelli, R. F. and Gordon, M. (1951). A spontaneous epithelioma in the platy fish *Xiphophorus* (*Platypoecilus*) *variatus*. *Zoologica* **36**, 239–242.

Berg, O. and Gordon, M. (1953). Thyroid drugs that control growth of goitres in xiphophorine fishes. *Proc. Amer. Ass. Cancer Res.* **1**. Abstr. 5.

Breider, H. (1938). Die genetischen, histologischen und cytologischen Grundlagen der Geschwulstbildung nach Kreuzungen verschiedener Rassen und Arten lebendgebärender Zahnkarpfen. *Z. Zellforsch.* **28**, 784–828.

Breider, H. (1939). Über die Pigmentbildung in den Zellen von Sarkomen albinotischer und nicht albinotischer Gattungsbastarde lebendgebärender Zahnkarpfen. *Z. wiss. Zool.* **152**, 107–128.

Breider, H. (1952). Über Melanome, Melanosarkome und homologe Zellmechanismen. *Strahlentherapie* **88**, 619–639.

Breider, H. (1956). Farbgene und Melanosarkomhäufigkeit. *Zool. Anz.* **156**, 129–140.

Breider, H. and Schmidt, E. (1951). Melanosarkome durch Artkreuzung und Spontantumoren bei Fischen. *Strahlentherapie* **84**, 498–523.

Ermin, R. (1946). Histologie und Zytologie von Melanomen und Erythrophorengeschwülsten. *Rev. Fac. Sci. Univ. Istanbul*, sér. B. **14**, 147–180.

Ermin, R. (1952). Fungus associated with a granuloma in a Turkish fish, *Aphanius chantrei* Gaillard. *Zoologica* **37**, 1, 43–54.

Ermin, R. (1953). On a case of xantho-erythrophoroma formation in *Platy-poecilus maculatus* var. *fuliginosus*. *Rev. Fac. Sci. Univ. Istanbul*, sér. B. **18**, 301–314.

Ghittino, P. and Ceretto, F. (1961). Studio istologico ed ezio-patogenetico dell' epatoma della trota iridea di allevamente (*Salmo gairdneri*). *Atti Soc. ital. Sci. vet.* **15**, 579–585.

Gorbman, A. and Gordon, M. (1951). Spontaneous thyroid tumours in the swordtail *Xiphophorus montezumae*. *Cancer Res.* **11**, 184–187.

Gordon, M. (1950). Die Vererbung von Pigmentgeschwülsten bei Fischen. *Endeavour* **9**, 26–34.

Gordon, M. and Lansing, W. (1943). Cutaneous melanophore eruptions in young fishes during stages preceding melanotic tumour formation. *J. Morph.* **73**, 231–245.

Kosswig, C. (1929). Zur Frage der Geschwulstbildung bei Gattungsbastarden der Zahnkarpfen *Xiphophorus* und *Platypoecilus*. *Z. Abstammungslehre* **52**, 114–120.

Kosswig, C. (1938). Über einen neuen Farbcharakter des *Platypoecilus maculatus*. *Rev. Fac. Sci. Univ. Istanbul*, sér. B. **3**, 359 402.

Levine, M. and Gordon, M. (1946). Ocular tumours with exophthalmia in xiphophorine fishes. *Cancer Res.* **6**, 197–204.

Nigrelli, R. F., Jakowska, S. and Gordon, M. (1951). The invasion and cell replacement of one pigmented neoplastic growth by a second and more malignant type in experimental fishes. *Brit. J. Cancer* **5**, 54–68.

Pflugfelder, O. (1953). Wirkungen der Epiphysektomie auf die Postembryonalentwicklung von *Lebistes reticulatus* Peters. *Roux' Arch.* **148**, 115–136.

Schlumberger, H. G. (1952). Nerve sheath tumours in an isolated goldfish population. *Cancer Res.* **12**, 890–899.

Schlumberger, H. G. (1958). Krankheiten dei Fische, Amphibien und Reptilien. *In* " Pathologie der Laboratoriumstiere " (Cohrs, Jaffé and Meesen, eds.), Vol. II, Springer, Berlin.

Schlumberger, H. G. and Lucké, B. (1948). Tumours of fishes, amphibians and reptiles. *Cancer Res.* **12**, 657–754.

Smith, G. M., Coates, C. W. and Strong, L. G. (1936). Neoplastic diseases in small tropical fishes. *Zoologica* **21**, 219–224.

Stolk, A. (1953–54). Tumours of fishes. I-IV. *Proc. Koninkl. Ned. Akad. Wetensch.* C. **56**, 28–33; 34–38; 143–148; 149–151; 152–156; 57, 652–658.

Stolk, A. (1954). Polycystic kidneys in the viviparous Cyprinodonts *Lebistes reticulatus* Peters, *Xiphophorus helleri* Heckel and the hybrid *X. helleri* Heckel × *P. maculatus* Günther. *Proc. Koninkl. Ned. Akad. Wetensch.* C. **57**, 659–665.

Stolk, A. (1955). Polycystic kidneys in the characid *Hyphessobrycon callistus callistus* (Boulenger). *Proc. Koninkl. Ned. Akad. Wetensch.* C. **58**, 63–69.

Walker, R. (1951). Mycetoma in a landlocked salmon. *Anat. Rec.* **111**, 531.

C. Diseases due to Faulty Nutrition

Faulty or deficient nutrition in combination with or without simultaneous parasitic damage may by slow accumulation lead to a situation where the fish is unable to maintain its normal metabolism. We may notice the advent of such an emergency under the guise of a skin disease, listlessness, loss of weight or bony deformities. In some cases, as demonstrated by Liebmann (1956), the collapse of the defences against parasites is not the primary cause of disease but is secondary to an avitaminosis or a lack of other nutritional constituents. A metabolic disturbance may also open the doors to bacterial invasion, but as far as we know it is particularly the protozoa which take advantage of any breach in the defence of the fish.

Cases due to a shortage of the vitamins A and D have been observed in fishes kept in indoor aquaria where they were out of reach of any u.v. irradiation. It is not surprising to hear that in such tanks the fish die particularly in the winter months. As to vitamin A, the normal fish, particularly those breeds kept in ornamental aquaria, rely in their natural habitat largely on small crustaceans rich in carotene, a precursor of vitamin A (Mann, 1950). In captivity this source of a necessary vitamin may be lacking.

The same may be true of trace elements like copper, cobalt and magnesium, all of which are, if only in minute quantities, necessary to maintain the normal health of the fish. None of these substances should be supplied by adding it even in soluble form to the water. The dose would always be excessive. What is required is a "healthy" environment well-stocked with suitable plants which grow in a healthy soil and varied food, preferably live, chosen according to the natural requirements of the species kept. Even the best aquarium will not remain suitable for ever, though it may look ever so "balanced". From time to time it will have to be completely cleaned out, freed from algae, supplied with new soil and restocked with fresh plants, imitating thereby a seasonal renewal lacking in the indoor tank.

Lipoidosis

Unfortunately, where animals are kept as pets, they are as much in danger of being under- as being overfed with an abundance of one and the same monotonous food. They may accept this but their body will answer with the development of large masses of fat which displace vital viscera and particularly with fatty degeneration of the liver (Lipoidosis). The captured fish has no choice and when given the wrong food it may react with enteritis, oedema and liver cirrhosis as well as with fatty degeneration. The condition has particularly been studied in the rainbow trout, which develops a pale brown to yellow liver and shows histologically the typical picture of fatty degeneration. The disease is purely nutritional and not infectious. It should not be confused with the viral epizootic of trout which produces a similar affection of the liver. Ghittino (1961) noticed the disease among fish fed on slaughterhouse offal and dry food concentrates. The feeding of raw ox-liver had a good balancing effect.

Blue- Sac Disease

Another disease, due apparently to metabolic disturbances, is the so-called Blue-Sac Disease of fish fry. Since the fish affected often show the presence of bacteria like *Diplobacillus liquefaciens piscium* Betegh, the existence of two types of the disease, one constitutional, the other infectious, was at first suspected. Wolf (1957) investigated the condition, which is characterized by an enlargement of the yolk sac (Fig. 148). He could find proof neither of bacterial nor of viral infection

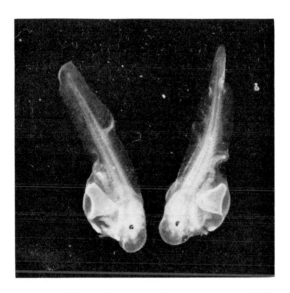

FIG. 148. Hydrops of yolk sac in young *Phractura ansorgei*. (Photo.: Foersch.)

and concluded that the disease developed in consequence of a number of simultaneously arising noxious factors like faulty nutrition of the parent stock, forced premature hatching, constituents of artificial food and the composition of the water.

Rucker *et al.* (1952) suggested similar causes for the otherwise bacterial dietary gill disease. Wolf (1957) agreed, and suggested, on the strength of experimental investigation, that the cause of the disease lies in a shortage of pantothenic acid. According to this view the appearance of myxobacteria of the genus *Cytophaga* is only accidental.

Soft Egg Disease. White Spot Disease

Two types of non-parasitic conditions which affect fish eggs, the Soft Egg Disease and the White Spot Disease were studied by Davis (1956). In the case of the Soft Egg Disease the eggs become soft, porous and lose their turgor. The White Spot Disease produces white spots on the yolk or on the embryos of salmonid fish. We do not as yet understand the causation of either of these diseases.

Hormonal Disturbances

With the exception of the hypertrophy or carcinomatous degeneration of the thyroid which has already been mentioned, hormonal imbalance in a fish is difficult to ascertain. The word imbalance indicates that over- or underproduction in one gland may affect other hormonal systems. Hypertrophy of the thyroid for instance stimulates the pituitary and the gonads, but cases of this kind are rare in fish compared with other classes of animals and have never been seen to cause appreciable losses of stock.

Bone Diseases

Like other vertebrates fish may occasionally suffer from bone diseases. Softening of the bone (osteomalacia; ricketts) or bony tumours (osteoma; osteosarcoma) may occur. Mann (1940) demonstrated that

Fig. 149. Perforation of the operculum in a marine pike (*Merluccius merluccius* Flemming).

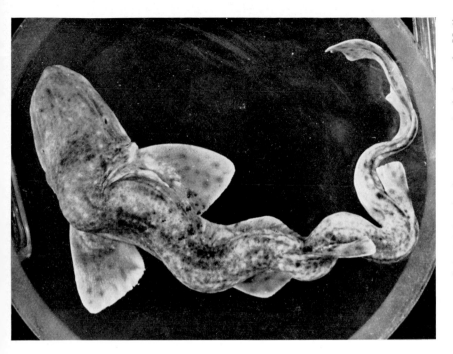

FIG. 152. Spinal deformity in a young shark from the Mediterranean. (Orig.)

FIG. 150. Guppy (*Lebistes reticulatus* Peters) ♀ with deformity of spine. (Photo.: Kramer.)

FIG. 151. Rainbow trout with spinal deformity and infestation with *Acanthocephala*. (Radiograph: Kramer.)

any of these conditions is accompanied by an increase in acid phosphatase an enzyme increasing the removal and mobilization of calcium from the bones. The bones become soft and fragile, the surface flaky and the whole bone may be deformed. We see such deformations in the mandible and in the operculum which may become perforated or atrophy completely. A condition of this nature is illustrated in Fig. 149. Some fish, which also lack the power of walling off invading parasites, seem to be more prone to skeletal deformities than others. Abnormal curvature of the spinal column (Figs. 150, 152) has been seen in: (a) hormonal imbalance (removal of the epiphysis; Pflugfelder, 1953); (b) faulty genetic factors; (c) chronic parasitic infestation with *Ichthyosporidium hoferi* (P. and M.), mycobacteria (Figs. 11, 12), bacteria causing ascites, Acanthocephala (Fig. 151). The cause of the development of true bony tumours is as yet unknown.

Any serious disturbance of the health of a fish may have a deleterious effect on its skin where we may observe general pallor, loss of gloss, inflammation with local hyperaemia or even small haemorrhages (petechiae). Dissection and investigation of the first fish affected may sometimes allow us to indicate the way in which further losses may be avoided.

Blue Disease

Authors have described "Blue Disease" in *Hyphessobrycon heterorhabdus* Ulrey and in *Rasbora heteromorpha* Duncker, a skin disease characterized by the appearance of white spots which gradually change to blue. The cause is as yet unknown. Duijn (1956) recommends treatment with a double strength solution of methylene blue. (Make a 2% stock solution. Add to this 1 cm³ to each gallon of water and repeat this in 1–2 days time.)

REFERENCES

Davis, H. S. (1956). "Culture and Disease of Game Fishes." Berkeley and Los Angeles.
Duijn, C. v. (1956). "Diseases of Fishes", publ. *Water Life*, London.
Ghittino, P. (1961). Eziologia, Patogenesi e Tentativi di Trasmissione della "Degenerazione lipoidea epatica" nella trota iridea (*Salmo gairdneri*). *Vet. Ital.* **12**, 3–16.
Liebmann, H. (1956). Ernährungsstörung und Degeneration als primäre Ursache der Bauchwassersucht bei Fischen. *Tierärztl. Wschr.* 1956, 21–34. Berlin and Munich.
Mann, H. (1940). Knochenweiche und Wirbelsäulenverkrümmung bei Karpfen nach Erkrankung an ansteckender Bauchwassersucht. *Zool. Anz.* **131**, 228–238.

Mann, H. (1950). Über die Bedeutung der Karotine für die Ernährung bei Fischen. *Wschr. Aqu. Terrk.* **44**, 122–124.

Mann, H. (1951). Chemische Untersuchungen über Knochenweiche bei Karpfen. *Arch. Fisch. Wiss.* **3**, 103–113.

Pflugfelder, O. (1953). Wirkungen der Epiphysektomie auf die Postembryonalentwicklung von *Lebistes reticulatus* Peters. *Roux' Arch.* **148**, 115–136.

Rucker R. R., Johnson, E. H. and Kaydas, G. M. (1952). An interim report on gill disease. *Progr. Fish. Cult.* **14**, 10–14.

Wolf, K. (1957). Blue-sac disease investigations: microbiology and laboratory induction. *Progr. Fish. Cult.* **19**, 14–18.

D. ENVIRONMENTAL FACTORS

Environmental factors include oxygenation, hydrogen ion concentration, salinity, temperatures, electricity, trauma, chemicals, detergents, pest control drugs and poisoning by flagellates.

Lack and Superabundance of Oxygen

Lack of oxygen (anoxia) is one of the commonest causes of death in fishes. As soon as the oxygen concentration in the water sinks, the rate of gill motion rises, the fish moves to the region which still has the highest oxygen concentration and eventually "hangs" on the surface in an obviously distressed condition. This may happen in ponds polluted with decomposing organic matter, where bacteria use up all the available oxygen or, more frequently, in overstocked or otherwise badly arranged aquaria. The maintenance of a good balance between the number of fish per litre of water, the plants, the soil, the illumination and the amount of food to be given, is of paramount importance but not always easy to achieve. Where, for instance, oxygenation by plants and illumination is impracticable, artificial aeration must take its place. The smaller machines offered for this purpose are, however, not very sturdy and often in a bad state of repair, and many an aquarist has suffered the shock of finding all his fish dead after a hot summer night with the aerator emitting nothing but a sad low hum.

The accumulation of organic matter on the aquarium floor is unavoidable but in the aquarium, whatever its size, we cannot rely on the forces of disposal which operate in lakes, rivers and the sea. Bacterial decomposition proceeds the quicker the more oxygen is available, and in the summer the plants may be able to produce the amount of O_2 needed. In the winter, however, aeration is indispensable.

Superabundance of oxygen, though a much more unlikely event, is equally dangerous for the fish. It leads to the development of the "Gas Bubble Disease" where gas accumulates in small depots under the skin or between the viscera. If such bubbles cause air embolism in major blood vessels the fish can hardly survive. Gas may even accumulate on or in the eyeball. The gas need not necessarily be oxygen. Sulphuretted hydrogen (H_2S), developing under the influence of intense sunlight on decomposing mud, may perhaps produce similar symptoms. This gas is, in its pure state, strongly poisonous and, whatever the cause for its appearance, affected fish should immediately be transferred to another tank before they are killed by suffocation, poisoning or gas embolism. With regard to aquaria it must be considered that a stream of rising "aerating" air bubbles not only helps in the mixing of the various strata of the water and in the introduction of O_2: it will also remove any gas present in an abnormal concentration in the water. Kühl and Mann (1955), for instance, showed that an oversaturation with O_2 of 216% could, by way of aeration, be reduced to 113% in 50 min. In the aquarium where the healthy influence of wind, weather and water current is absent, the maintenance of efficient aeration is almost indispensible, particularly if the fish population, as is so often the case, is denser than it would be in normal circumstances.

Hydrogen Ion Concentrations

Correct hydrogen ion concentration (pH) in the aquarium is of great importance to the health of the inhabitants. Ladiges (1950) takes values of pH 6–8 as being optimal for ornamental fish, although different species may have their preferences for small deviations from these figures. Fish also vary in their tolerance of temporary pH variations. Perch seem to prefer values of 7–8·5, i.e. a slightly greater alkalinity than, for instance, *Rasbora maculata* which prefers a pH of 5–6. Most fishes develop skin degeneration if the acidity rises to pH 5·5 or more. On the other hand, excessive alkalinity, which may start with values of 8–9, is always fatal if allowed to rise above pH 9.

Parallel with variations in the hydrogen ion concentration a state of "biogenic calcium deficiency" may develop in overplanted and overilluminated aquaria. The condition has been seen to cause sudden seemingly inexplicable losses among otherwise healthy stock. It can easily be remedied by the introduction of some lime-stones to the aquarium furniture.

Other salts may be of importance in the maintenance of a healthy aquarium balance. Potassium salts, even at 3%, corrode the gill epithelium. Ordinary salt (sodium chloride, NaCl) is harmless at 1%, but small fish may be killed in 3 h by a 2% solution. Larger freshwater fish tolerate temporary salt baths in concentrations approaching their blood salinity $\pm$ 0·6%. Lime has already been mentioned as necessary in small quantities. Some fish definitely prefer soft water, which may be obtained by collecting rain or by using a water softener.

Excessive Temperatures

It is not surprising to learn that excessive temperatures may do considerable damage to fish, and here as in all other aquatic animals, high temperatures are far more dangerous than cold ones. Temperatures below 6°C may produce shock and haemolysis (destruction of the red blood corpuscles), even in cold-water fish. Though many species may survive even lower temperatures for short periods, their skin may be damaged if the exposure lasts too long. This should particularly be remembered where fish are sent by rail during the cold season. A night in an unheated railway-shed has killed more than one consignment. Fish exposed to excessive cold react by becoming listless, holding their fins close to the body, becoming pale, and making slow rocking movements.

Light

The effect of light on a fish population is more indirect than direct. Obviously a fish relying on its eyes for finding or catching its food will be hampered by darkness and insufficient illumination which will directly injure the plants and lead to a shortage of oxygen in the water, but darkness as such does not seem to harm the fish. Basically light, and particularly the u.v. part of the spectrum, is necessary for the maintenance of all forms of life, and where an approximation to natural conditions is desired, daylight is superior to any artificial source. At the same time, daylight encourages not only the growth of desirable plants but also that of undesirable algae. A purely ornamental aquarium is therefore easier to maintain under electrical illumination which contains more light in the yellow-red bands than on the blue side. Consideration of the choice of illumination for an aquarium emphasizes the fact that it may often be impossible to keep together in the same tank fish of widely varying habitat. Unless, for instance, an aquarium has sufficient depth, bottom-living and surface-living fish will not happily live in the same tank. In this respect, as in so many others, the fitting-out of the aquarium will have to be done according to the fish intended to live in it. The "community tank" is a most unbiological invention.

Electricity

Even electricity may nowadays come to play a role—usually a lethal one—in the life of fish, either because it is—legally or illegally—

used for fishing, or because a badly insulated wire drops into the tank. In the latter case the effects may be as lethal for the owner of the aquarium as for the fish, which may even survive while their owner is killed. It seems that those species which have the highest oxygen consumption are most sensitive to electric shocks. It would be interesting to know something about the sensitivity of those fish which produce electricity in their own bodies. Small subcutaneous haemorrhages registering as dark patches on the surface have been ascribed to electric shocks, but there will not be many who have seen this condition.

Mechanical Injury

Though to some extent well protected by the water, fish are not entirely safe from mechanical injury. In their natural surroundings they may be bitten by larger fish, shrews, rats, crayfish, crabs or birds, and lampreys may leave their circular marks on the skin of their victim. Eel have been found cut and even bisected by propellers; larger fish have died from the rupture of their swim-bladder induced by a nearby detonation. Even the wakes of ships on lakes can damage fish-fry swimming about close to the shore.

The interaction of the many factors which influence the life of fish both in natural and artificial surroundings has been studied by Kühl and Mann (1952). So far as the daily changing rhythm in the pH is concerned the fish are quite capable of adapting themselves, and it is not advisable to add buffering substances which may damage the plants. The right pH quickly re-establishes itself when the water is changed; if the tank is replanted this may take 3–4 days. It is, for this reason, inadvisable to introduce sensitive fish into an aquarium which has just been set up. A well-established tank in which the plants are rooted and growing is the best habitat we can produce for captive and particularly for tropical fish. Special rules apply in this respect to the marine aquarium which cannot be run without permanent aeration and filtration if creatures used to clear, constantly moving and highly oxygenated water are to thrive in it.

REFERENCES

Kühl, H. and Mann, H. (1952). Rhythmische Veränderungen im Chemismus von Aquarienwässern. Z. *Fischerei* N.F. **1**, 7–27.
Kühl, H. and Mann, H. (1955). Über unperiodische Veränderungen im Chemismus von Süsswasseraquarien. Z. *Fischerei* N.F. **4**, 223–234.
Kühl, and Mann, H. (1956). Über den Stickstoffkreislauf im Aquarium. *Aqu. Terr. Z.* **9**, 99–102; 125–129.
Ladiges, W. (1950). Die Bedeutung der pH-Werte für die Fische. *Taschenkal. Aqu. Terr. Fr.* 34. Jahrg., 109–115.

E. Poisons Affecting Fish

Among chemical poisons which may affect fish we name particularly iron, which is dangerous in the form of its hydroxide. The amount tolerable to fish is, according to Schäperclaus (1954), 1·9 mg/l. Manganese compounds are tolerated in solutions of less than 0·5 g/l. One of the most potent fish poisons is copper sulphate, which should not be present in amounts exceeding 0·5 mg/l. Zinc and its compounds must also be avoided and fish cans plated with zinc should be painted before use. All metal compounds, including those of nickel and aluminium, and particularly ammonia, should be avoided. In case of doubt *Daphnia* or *Cyclops* should be introduced to test the water. This seems particularly advisable in those frequent cases where the urban taps produce heavily chlorinated water. Free chlorine ruins the gills, the skin, the eyes and generally paralyses the fish. Where no chlorine-free water is obtainable Mann (1955) recommends the addition of 1 g of sodium thiosulphate : 10 l of water to inactivate the free chlorine.

Equally poisonous to fish are tar products, in particular phenol and its compounds. According to Czensny (1943) 5 mg of phenol/l killed carp after 20 h. The phenols are typical nerve poisons. The fish react with highly increased frequency of breathing, growing restlessness and wild aimless swimming movements. Spastic staggering movements and death soon supervene. Only in the very first stage is a recovery likely. Tar products are frequently discharged by factories and may, like the equally poisonous hydrocarbons, be widely distributed in our rivers. Creosote, lysol and similar substances can usually be spotted by their smell. Schäperclaus (1954) has some maximum figures at which substances may be tolerated: anilin 100 mg/l; petrol 100 mg/l; benzol 10–20 mg/l; carbolineum 10 mg/l; dinitrotoluene 1·5–2 mg/l. (Further details may be found in the original publication.)

Even where the water pollution with any of these substances remains below the lethal level the taste of fish grown in such waters may suffer appreciably. It can even be transferred to poultry if fish taken from polluted rivers are used as food. The tolerance of fish to these substances is even lower if the waters are at the same time polluted with detergents, which remove the protective mucus from the skin and in addition may give rise to the production of highly poisonous chlor-phenol compounds. All detergents are strong fish poisons and lethal doses affect the taste of the fish. Ingestion of fish killed by detergents causes a burning sensation in the lips.

Fish even enter the smoking controversy. Mann (1951) found that nicotine may be absorbed by the water of an aquarium not protected by a well-fitting lid. Ten mg/l kill adult guppies within 5 min. Smaller doses are reported to produce infertility, abortion and malformation of the young fish. In an atmosphere heavily laden with tobacco smoke Mann found guppies killed after 70 min. If tobacco smoke is directly blown into the water the fish die in 3–5 min with spasm of the pectoral fins, pallor and sinking to the bottom. Nicotine does not remain active and, though immediately poisonous, does not leave behind any deleterious effects in the aquarium.

While pure nitrogen would not affect fish very much, its compounds are variously poisonous. We have mentioned ammonia and its salts which corrode the gills, produce spastic movements with extended fins and end in a general state of tetany. A state of this kind may arise where artificial fertilizers containing ammonia salts are used to increase the growth of aquatic plants. Krauss (1936) ascertained that $0\cdot05\%$ of ammonium chloride kills fish within 6 h. Fertilizers of unknown composition should not be used at all. Urea is tolerated in levels below 3%. Above this level it kills in 6 h. Nitrates and nitrites are less dangerous. They may accumulate as end-products of the decomposition of protein. If not too excessive these products, derived from decaying plant or animal matter, are quickly used again by bacteria or plants, and the resistance of various breeds of fish to water polluted by protein derivatives is very unequal. Mann (1955) found the presence of more than 150 mg/l of nitrites noxious to guppies. There are as yet no exact data available on nitrates. On the whole the earlier products of protein decomposition, particularly ammonia, are more poisonous than later stages. The poisonous undissociated $NH_3 \cdot H_2O$ changes into more harmless dissociated ions $NH_4 + OH$ at a speed dependent on the amount available, the temperature and the prevailing pH value. The greater the alkalinity and the higher the temperature the more free NH_3 may dissolve in the water. At 17°C and pH 9 this may be 25%. Young trout do not tolerate values above $0\cdot2$ mg/l, minnow tolerate $0\cdot6\%$, larger fish 1% and more. It must not be forgotten that plant activity may, in the summer, raise the pH in ponds considerably. The poisonous effect of ammonia would thereby be enhanced.

Pest Control Insecticides

None of the Pest Control Insecticides should be used where there may be a danger that they might come in contact with fish. Adlung and Müller-Bastgen (1957) and Lüdemann and Neumann (1960) as well as Bandt (1959) and Bauer (1961) have warned against their use. The following values were found to represent maximum concentrations tolerated by young carp (Lüdemann and Neumann, 1960).

Insecticide	mg/l
DDT	0·057
Lindan	0·28
Toxaphen	0·056
Chlordan	1·16
Heptachlor	0·38
Aldrin	0·165
Dieldrin	0·067
Endrin	0·004
Thiodan	0·011
Parathion	3·5
Chlorthion	4·1
Diazinon	5·2
Malathion	29·4
Systox	15·2

The poisonous effect of these substances seems to exert itself particularly on the brain where they cause histological changes in the cytoplasm of the ganglion cells (Kayser et al., 1962).

Accidents have also been reported when attempts were made to exterminate mice with chemical substances either in rainy weather or in conditions of frozen ground. Pesticides of any description should not be used where there is any likelihood of even a minute drainage of the treated soil towards the nearest fishpond.

Dinoflagellates

In unusually warm water fish may be poisoned by dinoflagellates. Reports of this kind have come from the Near East where Sklower (1950/51) reported on the lethal activity of *Prymnesium parvum* Carter, first observed in Israel in 1945. It caused heavy losses among carp, 50% of which died. Attempts to eradicate the flagellate with ammonium sulphate were unsuccessful. The death of whole fish populations is also occasionally reported from tropical coasts where the fish are killed by red-coloured planktonic protozoans (Red Tide). In California the offending organisms were determined as *Gonyaulax polyedra* and *Gymmodinium flavum*. Riegel et al. (1949) isolated a toxic substance from *Gonyaulax catenella* W. and K., 0·6 μg of which were lethal to mice. The authors counted 20–40 million dinoflagellates per cm³ of sea-water in Monterey bay. In 1948 Gunter *et al.* gave an account of a Red Tide on the coast of Florida caused by *Gymmodinium brevis*, which killed thousands of fish, turtles, crabs and molluscs.

REFERENCES

Adlung, K. G. (1957). Zur Toxizität insektizider und akarizider Wirkstoffe für Fische. *Naturwissenschaften* **44**, 471–472.

Adlung, K. G., Bodenstein, G. and Müller-Bastgen, G. (1957). Uber die Toxizität einiger Pflanzenschutzmittel für Fische. *Aquaristik* **3**, 44–51.

Adlung, K. G. and Müller-Bastgen, G. (1957). Ergebnisse über die Toxizität von Pflanzenschutzmitteln auf Fische. *Aquaristik* **3**, 88–92.

Bandt, H. J. (1959). Chemische Pflanzenbekämpfungsmittel (Herbizide) und Fische. *Dtsch. Fischereiztg.* **6**, 241–244.

Bauer, K. (1961). Studien über Nebenwirkungen von Pflanzenschutzmitteln auf Fische und Fischnährtiere. *Mitt. Biol. Bundesanst. Land-u. Forstwirtschaft* **105**, 1-72.

Czensny, R. (1943). "Untersuchungsverfahren zur chemischen Wasseranalyse." Stuttgart.

Gunter, G., Williams, R. H., Davis, C. C. and Smith, F. G. W. (1948). Catastrophic mass mortality of marine animals and coincident phytoplankton bloom on the west coast of Florida, Nov. 1946 to Aug. 1947. *Ecol. Monogr.* **18**, 310–324.

Ivlev, S. (1934). Die giftige Wirkung der Stoffwechselprodukte der Fische. *Z. Fischerei* **32**, 661–674.

Kayser, H., Lüdemann, D. and Neumann, H. (1962). Veränderungen an Nervenzellen nach Insektizidvergiftung bei Fischen und Krebsen. *Z. angew. Zool.* **49**, 135–148.

Krauss, O. (1936). Über die Wirkung verschieden gelöster Düngemittel und von K-, Na-, und Ca-salzen auf Haut und Kiemen von Fischen. *Z. Fischerei* **34**, 787–817.

Lüdemann, D. and Neumann, H. (1960). Versuche über die akute toxische Wirkung neuzeitlicher Kontaktinsektizide auf einsömmerige Karpfen (*Cyprinus carpio* L.). *Z. Fischerei* **47**, 11–33.

Mann, H. (1950). Die Einwirkung von Chlor auf Fische und Fischnährtiere. *Aqu. Terr. Z.* **3**, 119–120.

Mann, H. (1951). Ist Tabakrauch für Aquarienfische giftig? *Aqu. Terr. Z.* **4**, 98–99.

Mann, H. (1955). Die Einwirkung von grenzflächenaktiven Waschmitteln auf Fische und Fischnährtiere. *Arch. Fischereiwiss.* **6**, 131–137.

Riegel, B., Stanger, D. W., Sommer, H., Wikholm, D. and Mold, J. D. (1949). Paralytic shellfish poison. V. The primary source of the poison, the marine plankton organism *Gonyaulax catenella*. *J. biol. Chem.* **177**, 7–71.

Schäperclaus, W. (1954). "Fischkrankheiten." 3rd edn., Akademie Verlag, Berlin.

Sklower, A. (1950–51). Carp breeding in Palestine. *Arch. Fischereiwiss.* **2**, 80–119; **3**, 42–54.

Wurtz-Arlet, J. (1959). Toxicité des détergents anioniques vis-à-vis des alevins de truite commune. *Bull. franç. Pisc.* **31**, 41–45.

CHAPTER 4

Healing of Wounds and Regeneration

The epithelium of fish has a good power of regeneration and super-ficial wounds heal quickly while foreign bodies are walled off by connective tissue. Artificial implantations have shown the speed of the healing process to depend on the nature of the foreign body used (Figs. 153, 154). In the gills the process of healing may leave structural changes behind. Granulocytes and lymphocytes take part; there may be a local hyperaemia and vesicular histiocytes may participate (Wunder, 1941). Remaining scar tissue may be recognized by melanin laid down during the healing process.

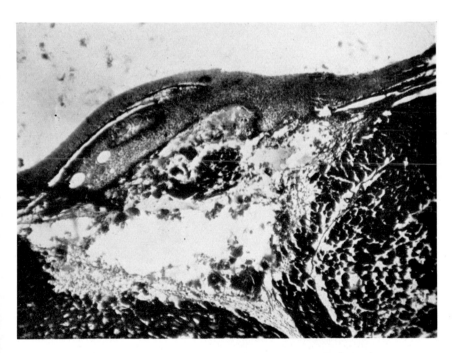

FIG. 153. Wound healing after implantation of pith. (Orig.)

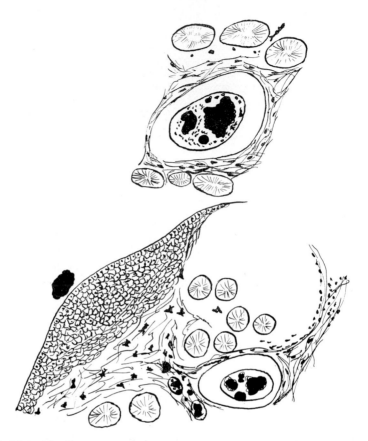

FIG. 154. Wound healing after implantation of soot. The particles are surrounded by the connective tissue. (Orig.)

The regeneration of lost scales takes some time and the original pattern may often remain disturbed. New scales may be smaller than normal and of irregular shape.

Korschelt (1932) studied the healing process of fractures in fish. Fractures of ribs, for instance, heal well by a process of development of osteoid tissue between the fractured ends of the bones. Contrary to what we are used to see in higher vertebrates there is in fish no deposition of temporary cartilage around fractures.

Fins lost in fights are usually well regenerated. Sometimes the new fins exceed the original ones in size (Schäferna, 1934; Schnakenbeck, 1952). Goldfish whose pectoral fins were amputated produced abnormally long new fins (Hase, 1935).

REFERENCES

Hase, A. (1935). Über ein hypertrophisches Flossenregenerat beim Goldfisch (*Carassius auratus* L.). *S.B. Ges. naturf. Fr. Berl.* 1935, 283–289.

Korschelt, E. (1932). Über Knochenbruchheilung bei Fischen. *Z. wiss. Zool.* **142**, 624–635.

Korschelt, E. (1938). Über einen Wirbelsäulenbruch bem Hecht und die Widerstandsfähigkeit der Fische gegen Verletzungen. *Anat. Anz.* **85**, 284–292.

Sauter, V. (1935). Regeneration und Transplantation bei erwachsenen Fischen. *Roux' Arch.* **132**, 1–41.

Schäferna, K. (1934). Karpfen und Barsch mit abnorm verlängerten Flossen. *Z. Fischerei* **32**, 375–379.

Schnakenbeck, W. (1952). Ein besonderer Fang. *Fischwaid* **7**, 48.

Reichenbach-Klinke, H. (1955). Untersuchungen über die bei Fischen durch Parasiten hervorgerufenen Zysten und deren Wirkung auf den Wirtskörper. *Z. Fischerei* N.F. **3**, 565–636 and **4**, 1–52.

Wunder, W. (1941). Die Veränderungen an der Karpfenkieme bei Kiemenfäule. *Allg. Fisch. Ztg.* **44**, 200–202.

Wunder, W. (1951). Ungewöhnliche Verletzungen bei Karpfen und ihre Verheilung. *Verh. dtsch. zool. Ges. Wilhelmshaven* 1951, 110–130.

CHAPTER 5

Abnormalities

True abnormalities are due either to faulty genetic combination or to disturbances in the early development of the embryo. Most commonly seen are double or multiple monsters, particularly the former. Two individuals may be completely or partly united or one fish may develop with an annex representing part of a twin from which it is not wholly separated. Such monsters derive from one and the same egg cell and are comparable to "Siamese Twins". They have been described from sharks, trout, *Mollienisia latispina* Les., from guppies (Schnaken-beck, 1953; Geus, 1961) and from *Haplochromis multicolor* (Bath, 1956). The partial unification may involve any part of the fish (Fig. 155). The exact mechanism by which these eggs are prevented from developing normally is as yet unknown. Attempts to produce the effect by

FIG. 155. *Lebistes reticulatus* ♂ with abdominal twin.

subjecting just fertilized eggs to some kind of trauma like either a single knock or repeated shaking always resulted in the death of the eggs (Thumann, 1953).

Other abnormalities occur in the form of excessively long or split fins (veiltails) or colour variations like albinism, melanism, or xanthorism. Albinotic specimens have been seen in eel, catfish, trout and flatfish. Among perch (*Perca fluviatilis* L.), tench (*Tinca tinca* L.), crucian carp (*Carassius auratus gibelio* Bloch, the original form of the goldfish) and the golden orfe (*Idus idus* L.), a red-golden variety is occasionally seen.

FIG 156. *Chondrostoma nasus* L. × *Idus idus* L. hybrid with abnormally long fins.

Ten per cent of American pike may present themselves in a blue variety caused by a lack of guanidine in the chromatophores. The condition, described as alampia, also occurs in carp.

Figure 156 shows a cross between *Idus idus* L. and *Chondrostoma nasus* L. with abnormally long fins.

Distortions of the tail, the skull or the operculum usually occur in consequence of diseases or avitaminosis.

One of the most extraordinary abnormalities seen in fish is that of sex reversal. It is usually the female which changes into a male. The opposite process has been observed but it occurs much more rarely.

Sex reversal has so far been observed in Salmonidae, Anabantidae, Poeciliidae and Cyprinodontidae, in particular in the following species:

Family Salmonidae:
  Oncorhynchus keta (Walbaum) (Usmann and Hesselholt, 1958)
  Salmo gairdneri Rich (Gibbs, 1956)
Family Anabantidae:
  Betta splendens Regan (Kaiser and Schmidt, 1954)
  Macropodus opercularis L. (Schmidt, 1930)
  Colisa labiosa Day (Schmidt, 1930)
Family Poeciliidae:
  Xiphophorus helleri Heckel (Schmidt, 1930)
  Xiphophorus helleri × *Platypoecilus maculatus* Gthr. (Schmidt, 1930)
  Mollienisia velifera Regan (Schmidt, 1930)
  Heterandria formosa Agassiz (Schmidt, 1930)
  Lebistes reticulatus Peters (Reichenbach-Klinke)
  Glaridichthys spp. (Philippi, 1904)
  Limia melanogaster Gthr. (Unger, 1956)
Family Cyprinodontidae:
  Fundulus majalis Walbaum (Newman, 1908)
  Fundulus heteroclitus L. (Chidester, 1917)

Fig. 157. *Xiphophorus helleri* ♀ during sex reversal. Gonopodium almost fully developed. Tailfin "sword" growing. (Photo.: Schmidt.)

Fig. 158. *Xiphophorus helleri*. Right: ♀ after sex reversal into ♂. Left: Fish from the same spawn showing early differentiation. (Photo.: Schmidt.)

Sex reversal is most commonly seen in the swordtail (*Xiphophorus helleri* H.). The reversal is so complete that fertile females change into fertile males. The ovary is replaced by a testicle and, in fish with internal fertilization, gonopodia, the copulative organs of the male, are developed. The growth of these gonopodia allows us to study the gradual change of the anal fin into an organ of copulation and the development of this organ is a measure of the degree of sex reversal that has been reached by an individual fish (Schmidt, 1930).

The stimulus which initiates this process is as yet unknown. The injection of male testicular extract into females is without effect (Hild, 1948). On the other hand ova develop in males treated with oestrogenic extracts. It looks as if the females turn into males when their gonads cease producing female hormone. This suggestion is supported by experiments made by Kaiser and Schmidt (1951). They removed the ovaries from adult females and observed the sexual regeneration which took place. Back, tail, anal and ventral fins began to grow, the female sexual papilla was reduced to that of a male, the small female upper lip grew into the bulky size typical of the male. Gradually the fish also developed the typical male aggressiveness and one of the castrated females copulated with a normal female and produced six young, thereby proving the completeness of the reversal. Dissection confirmed the presence of a mature testis instead of the ovary. These experiments were made on fighting fish (*Betta* sp.) which in their natural habitat do not reverse their sex very often.

An interesting case of sex reversal in *Heterandria formosa* was described by Schmidt (1930). A mature female developed a long male gonopodium but continued to give birth to young fish even after the copulatory organ was fully developed.

We owe another interesting observation to Wurmbach (1954) who reported on a specimen of *Xiphophorus helleri* infected with *Ichthyosporidium*. The fungus had affected the ovary to such a degree that no ova could be produced any more. The fish thereupon developed testicles and became a fertile male. In this case again, the exhaustion of the source of female hormone seems to have stimulated the growth of a male source.

REFERENCES

Anonymous (1951). Real Siamese twins. *The Aquarium*, p. 71.
Bath, H. (1956). "Siamesische Zwillinge" beim "Kleinen Maulbrüter". *Aqu. Terr. Z.* **9**, 284–286.
Chidester, F. E. (1917). Hermaphroditism in *Fundulus heteroclitus*. *Anat. Rec.* **12**, 389–396.
Duijn, C. v. (1956). "Diseases of Fishes", publ. *Water Life*, London.

Essenberg, J. N. (1923). Complete sex-reversal in the viviparous teleost *Xiphophorus helleri.* *Biol. Bull.*, *Woods Hole* **45**, 46–96.

Geus, A. (1961). Über eine siamesische Zwillingsbildung bei einem Männchen von *Lebistes reticulatus* Peters. *Aqu. Terr. Z.* **14**, 217–219.

Gibbs, E. D. (1956). A bisexual steelhead. *Calif. Fish & Game* **42** (3), 229-231.

Hild, S. (1948). Versuche über die Geschlechtsumkehr beim Schwertfisch. *Wschr. Aqu. Terrk.* **42**, 54–59.

Kaiser, P. and Schmidt, E. (1951). Vollkommene Geschlechtsumwandlung nach Kastration beim weiblichen siamesischen Kampffisch *Betta splendens.* *Zool. Anz.* **146**, 66–73.

Newman, H. (1908). A significant case of hermaphroditism in fish. *Biol. Bull.* **15**, 207–214.

Philippi, E. (1904). Ein neuer Fall von Arrhenoidie. *S. B. Ges. naturf. Fr. Berl.* **104**, 196–197.

Schmidt, H. (1930). Geschlechtsumwandlungen bei tropischen Zierfischen. *Züchter*, **2**, 297–305.

Schnakenbeck, W. (1953). Eine Zwillingsbildung bei *Lebistes reticulatus.* *Zool. Anz.* **151**, 1–5.

Thumann, M. E. (1953). Ein goldgelber Aal aus der Havel. *Z. Fischerei* N.F. **2**, 321–324. Ein gelber Kaulbarsch aus dem Müggelsee. **2**, 325–326.

Unger, F. (1956). Bei *Limia melanogaster* beobachtete Geschlechtsumwandlung. *Aqu. Terr. Z.* **9**, 308.

Uzmann, J. R. and Hesselholt, M. N. (1958). Teratological hermaphroditism in the chum salmon, *Oncorhynchus keta* (Walbaum). *Progr. Fish Cult.* **20**, 191-192.

Wurmbach, H. (1954). Geschlechtsumkehr bei Weibchen von *Lebistes reticulatus* Peters bei Befall mit *Ichthyophonus hoferi* Plehn-Mulsow. *Roux' Arch.* **145**, 109–124.

CHAPTER 6

Lampreys (Cyclostomata) and their Diseases

Fishes of the Sub-phylum Agnatha (fish without jaws) which includes the Class Cyclostomi (fish with circular mouth parts) deserve special attention for their own diseases and for those they cause to other fish. This Class embraces the true lampreys (Petromyzontia) and the hagfishes (Myxinoidea). In the place of jaws and teeth these fish have developed an extremely effective boring and sucking outfit which allows them to adhere firmly even to fast swimming victims, to abrade their protective surface, to penetrate—either by way of the gill chamber or directly through the skin—into the body and gradually to consume their prey from the inside. Lampreys attach themselves not infrequently to migrating species like salmon, and this mode of life has helped them to a considerable distribution. They may attack free swimming fish as well as those already caught on the line of a fisherman who may find half his fish eaten away when he pulls in the line the next day. Indeed lampreys are so voracious as to attack even dead fish already in the process of decomposition. Where they become too numerous they may interfere severely with the local fishing industry. Meyer (1951) reports a depression in the trade in sea-trout in the big lakes of N. America caused by the depredations of sea-lampreys. One-third of all the trout caught were so badly mutilated that they could not be sold.

With regard to their own ailments, the lampreys are prey to the same diseases, infections and parasites as other fish. The bacteriology of lampreys has so far attracted no attention (there is no reference to them in Bergey's standard manual). More, however, is known of their helminthology, where we find the following worms listed for lampreys:

Trematoda:

    Hemiurus appendiculatus (Rud.) Occurs in the intestinal tract of *Lampetra fluviatilis* L.

    Diplostomulum petromyzi fluviatilis Diesing parasitizes the cranial cavity of lampreys (Hoffman, 1960).

Cestoidea:

    Ligula intestinalis Goeze occurs in the peritoneal cavity of *Lampetra planeri* Bloch (Sprehn, 1960).

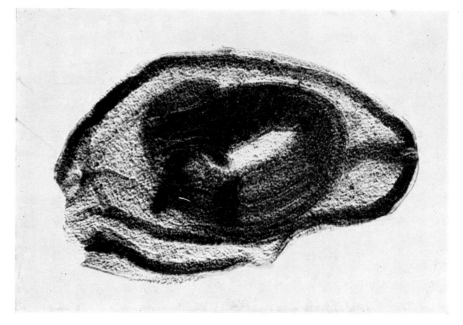

Fig. 159. Trypanorhynchid larva from *Petromyzon* sp. × 40. (After Emschermann.)

Scolex pleuronectis Müller was found in the gut of *Lampetra fluviatilis* L. by Joyeux and Baer (1936).

Trypanorhyncha sp. see Fig. 159.

Acanthocephala:

Corynosoma strumosum Rud. occurs in the gut of *Lampetra fluviatilis* L. and *Caspiomyzon wagneri*.

Corynosoma semerme Forsell has been found in the gut of *Lampetra japonica* by Petrotschenko (1956–1958).

Echinorhynchus salmonis Müller inhabits the intestine of *Lampetra fluviatilis* L. (Sprehn, 1960).

Nematoda:

Cucullanus stelmoides Vessichelli from *Lampetra planeri* Bloch (Yorke and Maplestone, 1962).

The lampreys seem to play no part in human hygiene either as intermediate hosts or as transmitters of infectious disease and we have no data to show how many may be consumed at one meal with impunity. Wunder (1936), however, found that the mucus produced by the lamprey's skin is poisonous. It is the practice to remove the mucus by placing the fish into common salt, after which they are quite suitable for human consumption.

REFERENCES

Bahr, K. (1933). Das Flussneunauge (*Lampetra fluviatilis*) als Urheber von Fischverletzungen. *Mitt. dtsch. Seefischereiver.* **49**, 3–8.

Joyeux, C. and Baer, J. G. (1936). Cestodes. *In* "Faune de France." Paris.

Hoffman, G. L. (1960). Synopsis of *Strigeoides* (*Trematoda*) of fishes and their life cycles. *Fish. Bull.* **60**, 437–469.

Meyer, P. F. (1951). Massenauftreten von Neunaugen in den grossen Seen Nordamerikas. *Natur u. Volk* **81**, 180–186.

Petrotschenko, W. J. (1956–58). "Akantocefaly domashnich i dikich shivotnych." Moscow.

Sprehn, C. (1960). *Trematoda* and *Cestoidea*. *In* "Die Tierwelt Mitteleuropas." I. (P. Brohmer, P. Ehrmann and G. Ulmer, eds.)

Wunder, W. (1936). Physiologie der Süsswasserfische Mitteleuropas. *In* "Handbuch der Binnenfischerei Mitteleuropas." II. B. (Demoll-Maier, ed.) Stuttgart.

Yorke, W. and Maplestone, P. A. (1962). "The Nematode Parasites of Vertebrates." Churchill, London.

CHAPTER 7

Fish as Carriers of Human Diseases

Since fish, with or without the consent of those who construct reservoirs, inhabit waters used to supply distant populations of cities, some knowledge of their capacity to transmit diseases may be desirable. In any case, the assumption that the fish-tapeworm represents the only danger that may threaten us from that direction is erroneous, even if we strictly exclude all those cases arising from the consumption of poisoned or decomposed fish.

We have seen that many fish play the part of intermediate host to a number of worms which will welcome the opportunity to mature in any warm-blooded vertebrate; the fish may also act as a simple carrier, neither helping nor hindering the parasite but transporting it without any bad effect to its own health.

It has been known for some time that workers habitually handling fish may become infected by a type of *Corynebacterium* if small cracks or abrasions of the skin allow these germs to obtain a foothold. The guilty species is *Erysipelothrix insidiosa* Langford and Hensen (= *E. murisepticus* Rosenbach) a bacillus known to cause the disease of "Red Murrain" or erysipelas in pigs. In humans it produces an erysipeloid condition known as "Fish Rose", which begins with a burning and itching sensation of the skin, and lasts for up to 3 weeks. For those habitually handling fish it may be regarded as an occupational disease, because the guilty bacteria may always be found on the skin of dead fish. They never, however, have any bad effect on the fish themselves, so that it is impossible to detect their presence with the naked eye. *Erysipelothrix* has been found on freshwater and on marine fish and has on occasion caused severe inflammation when wounds were infected with the mucus of dead fish.

Escherichia coli Castellani and Chalmers may be transmitted by salmonid fish without doing any harm to the fish themselves. It is possible to infect such fish experimentally with this bacillus, but only if very heavy doses are used will develop a purulent enteritis. Such cases, and also the occasional appearance of *paracolon* bacilli in fish, are rare.

As may be expected, the carriers of bacteria dangerous to humans are nearly always freshwater fish, particularly when they are taken from waters hardly deserving the euphemistic adjective of "fresh". Shewan (1962), reviewing the pathogenic bacteria carried by fish lists, apart from *Escherichia coli*, *Shigella* spp., Streptococci, *Clostridium botulinum* type E Gunnison *et al.*, *Clostridium tetani* Flügge-Holland and *Staphylococcus aureus* Rosenbach. The last named bacillus has been found responsible for cases of poisoning from badly manufactured fish preserves. Equally *Clostridium botulinum* has been transmitted by insufficiently sterilized tins of preserved fish.

"Red Feed" is a form of oedema and dermatitis which occurs in fishermen who, with bare hands, handle the red-coloured contents of the gut of herrings and mackerels which (between June and September) feed on red-pigmented copepods of the genus *Calanus*.

Fortunately, few helminths, which use the fish as intermediate host, rely on the human race for final development. All the same, such infections are possible where raw or insufficiently cooked fish is consumed. The best known of these infections is that with the broad fish tapeworm *Diphyllobothrium latum* L. (formerly *Bothriocephalus latus*). The first intermediate host of this worm is a crustacean of the genus *Cyclops* or *Diaptomus* where the larva develops in the body cavity. The small crustaceans commonly serve as the staple food of pelagic fish. The larvae penetrate into the muscles of the fish and develop there into the second larval form, the Plerocercoid (Sparganum of older authors). The disease spread from the shores of the eastern Baltic Sea, where up to 78% of the fishing population was affected, to other parts of Europe, S. Canada and the U.S.A. In man it causes a severe anaemia, the haemoglobin values sometimes reaching levels as low as 25% (Musser, 1938). Eggs of the intestinal worm are soon found in the stools and treatment follows the lines laid down for ordinary tapeworm infestation. The disease has also been reported from western Alpine lakes where pike, perch and ruff have been found infected. A complication arises from the fact that, apart from man, dogs and pigs may serve as final hosts and such lateral chains of infestation may remain unobserved for long periods.

A closely related tapeworm, *Diphyllobothrium cordatum* Leuckart, affects inhabitants of Greenland and Iceland. The other members of the genus, all of which are very similar in appearance, use birds, rarely mammals, as final hosts but are harmless to humans.

The cat liver-fluke *Opisthorchis felineus* Rivolta plays a similar part in E. Asia where it uses fish as intermediate hosts and gains access to consumers of raw fish. The mature worms live mainly in the bile ducts shedding their eggs and mature proglottids into the duodenum. The worm has spread to northern Asia and northern Europe as far as the Baltic.

Opisthorchis tenuicollis (Rud.) Stiles and Hassall (= *O. viverini* Poirier), a digenetic trematode, uses fish as intermediate hosts and may affect man; the closely allied *Clonorchis*—now *Opisthorchis sinensis* Cobbold—is a widely distributed human parasite in E. Asia from Japan to Indo-China where it may be found in the liver of cats, dogs, and man. The infection is usually acquired through the consumption of raw or badly smoked cyprinid fish. The metacercariae they contain are distinguished by the possession of eye spots.

A closely allied trematode, *Heterophyes heterophyes* Stiles and Hassall, is usually found mature in cats, dogs and foxes, but may also infect man. The infection is acquired by the ingestion of mullets (*Mugil cephalus* L.) when these fish are eaten without having been properly cooked.

Finally, we may mention another digenetic trematode, *Metagonimus yokogawai* Katsurada, which may be encountered in E. Siberia and in the Balkans, where it is a common parasite of dogs and cats but may also gain access to humans where it lives in the duodenum. The first intermediate hosts are molluscs (Thiaridae; Melanidae); in the fish the larvae encyst beneath the scales. Vojtkowa (1959) found the species for the first time in Central Europe.

Nematodes too, have recently been reported to have reached human hosts via ingested fish, where they caused a phlegmonous enteritis accompanied by eosinophilia. The suspected worm was *Eustoma rotundata* Rud., acquired by way of eating lightly salted herrings. It seems that, while a first infection with these worms is tolerated without reaction, the intestine becomes sensitized and reacts to the challenge of a second assault. The normal final hosts of this worm are seals (Thiel *et al.*, 1960).

An epidemic of an otherwise inexplicable type of meningitis which occurred among the inhabitants of Tahiti after the consumption of Bonito (*Katsuwonus pelamis*) was described by Rosen *et al.* (1961). The leading symptoms were headaches and rigidity of neck and back. Neither bacteria, viruses nor worms could be found but the disease was accompanied by an intense eosinophilia and the suspicion remained that it was caused by nematodes.

The Gnathostomidae are nematodes with two obligate intermediate hosts, the first of which is a crustacean, the second a fish, frog or aquatic snake. It is again the consumption of raw fish which transfers the parasites to human beings. The worm, which has its main distribution in Indo-China, is *Gnathostoma spinigerum* Owen. The normal final hosts are cats, dogs, mink and other carnivorous mammals.

The question as to whether fungi, pathogenic to man, can be transmitted by fishes, has as yet not found an unequivocal answer. Examples of aspergillous and imperfect fungi have been seen in fish. Workers have also succeeded in transmitting strains from human patients to fish, and in growing them on the fish skin for short periods. Generally, however, fish do not enter the ranks of transmitters of fungi pathogenic for humans.

The same dictum applies to viruses. No case in which viruses pathogenic in man have been transmitted by fish has as yet been reported.

It must, however, never be forgotten that, in spite of appearances to the contrary, fish do not always live in the healthiest of mediums, and that they may be carriers of bacteria or poisons harmless to themselves but dangerous to man. Sometimes such a danger can be spotted by a change in the smell, taste or colour of the fish and it should be a strict rule never to release fish collected after mass deaths which may have occurred in polluted waters.

In a few fish only particular organs are unsuitable for human consumption at some particular time of the year. The ovaries of the bream (*Abramis brama* L.) and the barbel (*Barbus barbus* L.) cause indigestion at spawning time. This has led to the promulgation in some areas of regulations prohibiting the sale of these fish unless they are cleared. The serum of eel, catfish, moray and conger is poisonous when taken from live fish. Small doses kill minor mammals quickly. The active substance is described as "Ichthyotoxin". It has an inflammatory effect on the conjunctiva; the eyes therefore should be especially protected from contact with the serum of these fish. Since the poison decomposes at 60–70°C, the fish are harmless when properly cooked. Equally the sera of the small N. American catfish (*Ameiurus nebulosus* Le Sueur), the giant pike-perch, the common perch, the ruff, the tench and the bream have proved mildly toxic (Wunder, 1936).

In some regions the fish-eating population suffers from some well-defined diseases caused by their diet (Shewan, 1962). In Japan, for instance, certain Tetraodontids are eaten though they are known to be poisonous. In countries bordering the Eastern Baltic a condition locally known as "Haff-Disease" (Haff = local name of inland sea) is caused by the consumption of fish containing a factor inhibiting thiamin (vitamin B_1). The patient complains of muscular pain in arms, legs and back, the skin is extremely sensitive to touch and the urine brown to black.

7

"Minimata" (so called after a local bay in Japan) is thought to be due to pollution. It causes numbness of the skin in the circumoral region and the extremities as well as visual disturbances.

The disease "Ciguatera" of tropical bays is probably due to the consumption of fish which have fed on poisonous algae (Halstead, 1962).

Only the fish tapeworms and perhaps some nematodes are of general practical importance and nearly everything poisonous a fish may contain is destroyed by boiling. Care, however, is needed where fish are only salted or smoked or where they are preserved in tins. Fish should never be taken from polluted inland waters, particularly in the hot season where there is an enhanced danger of contamination with staphylococci or *Clostridium botulinum*.

REFERENCES

Halstead, B. W. (1962). Biotoxications, allergies and other disorders. *In* "Fish as Food" (G. Borgstrom, ed.), Vol. II, pp. 521–542. New York and London.

Hyman, L. H. (1951). "The Invertebrates", Vol. III. McGraw-Hill Book Co., New York.

Kuipers, F. G. (1962). Eosinofiele Flegmone van de dünne Darm. *Tijdschr. Gastro-enterol.* **51**, 320–327.

Musser, J. H. (1938). "Internal Medicine." H. Kimpton, London.

Rosen, L., Laigret, J. and Bories, S. (1961). Observations on an outbreak of eosinophilic meningitis on Tahiti, French Polynesia. *Amer. J. Hyg.* **74**, 26–42.

Shewan, J. M. (1962). Food poisoning caused by fish and fishery products. *In* "Fish as Food" (G. Borgstrom, ed.), Vol. II, pp. 443–466. New York and London.

Thiel, P. H. van, Kuipers, F. G. and Roskam, R. T. (1960). Nematode parasitic to herring causing acute abdominal syndromes in man. *Trop. Geogr. Med.* **2**, 97–113.

Wunder, W. (1936). *In* "Handbuch der Binnenfischerei" (Demoll and Maier, eds.), Vol. II, B. Schweizenbarth, Stuttgart.

CHAPTER 8

Review of the Main Symptoms and Localization of Fish Diseases

The diagnosis of the cause of death in a fish or of the disease it may have spread and caused to other inhabitants of its environment or even to man is by no means always obvious. It is, in fact, often so difficult that only a laboratory specializing in veterinary diseases has any chance of arriving at a satisfactory result. One of the greatest problems lies in getting the extremely perishable material to the laboratory in time and, if possible, without the use of fixatives like alcohol or formaldehyde, which make most further bacteriological investigations impossible. Skin smears, too, should always be examined on the spot, since it is very much easier to recognize Protozoa when they are alive and display all their natural features than when they are fixed, shrunk and shrivelled. Blood smears should be taken and dried as soon as the fish is dead, for no part of the fish changes quicker *post mortem* than the blood. Once dry, the smears can be put aside, but they must be carefully protected from flies, which like to make a meal of them. Where no facilities to investigate exist at all, the best method remains to freeze the fish hard and to send it off packed in ice or, better, solid CO_2.

It may occasionally be possible to prepare blood smears from freshly killed fish and in such circumstances it may be useful to compare the results of blood counts with some of the normal values available. The following figures taken from Grodzinski and Hoyer (1925) followed by data from Schlicher may serve as a guide:

Erythrocytes	per mm3	Leucocytes per mm3	Authors
Mustelus canis	393 000	97 000	Reznikoff and Reznikoff
Raia sp.	230 000	?	Schulz and Krüger
Acipenser sturio	771 600	19 170	Babudieri
Acipenser ruthenus	1 500 000	?	Zwetkow
Cyprinus carpio	2 000 000	90 000	Stolz
Platessa platessa	1 875 000	9 580	Babudieri
Salmo trutta	1 140 000	25 500	Schlicher
Salmo gairdneri	1 100 000	34 000	Schlicher
Tinca tinca	1 400 000	52 000	Schlicher
Anguilla anguilla	1 425 000	90 000	Schlicher
Esox lucius	1 900 000	37 500	Schlicher

Obviously these figures can only serve as a very rough guide since even within one species there is bound to be a considerable fluctuation in the number of blood cells according to the age and the state of health of the particular fish.

The following list, which makes no claim to completeness, may serve as a rough guide in the examination of fish received:

Skin conditions	Possible causes
Deposits resembling cotton wool	*Saprolegnia*
Velvety surface	*Oodinium*
Blueish-white membrane	*Costia* *Chilodonella* *Trichodina* *Gyrodactylus* Hyperacidity of the water
Blue patches	"Blue disease"
Pale spots	Damage through cold Microsporidia Acid-fast bacilli, tuberculosis Various infections Virus septicaemia of trout Renal diseases
Red spots	Ascites Tuberculosis Virus-septicaemia of trout Furunculosis Kidney disease Septic dermatitis
Small white pustules	*Ichthyophthirius*
Pin-head size white dots	Dermal cercariae
Larger compound knots	*Lymphocystis* disease
Bleeding ulcerations	*Ichthyosporidium* Fish tuberculosis Ascites Furunculosis Sepsis of pike Bacterial septic dermatitis Sepsis of eel
Round, red-walled defects	*Argulus* stings
Swelling without discoloration	Tumours of various kinds Sporozoa
Swelling with melanism	Melanosarcoma, metacercariae
Cutaneous air bubbles	Hyperoxygenation
Blisters filled with fluid	Infectious ascites

Skin conditions	Possible causes
Red discoloration of anus	Infectious ascites *Eimeria* enteritis Nephritis Virus septicaemia of trout
Black spots	Reaction to cercarial invasion
Partial black discoloration	Staggers
Roughness of scales	Ascites Bacterial infections
Oval or cylindrical white cysts	*Dermocystidium*
Red boils and ulcerations	Sepsis of marine eel
Round white cysts	*Glugea anomala*

Fins	Possible causes
Loss of substance	*Ichthyosporidium* Fights Nephritis Alkalosis of water Virus septicaemia
Whirring of pectoral fins	Excessive cold
Stiffness of pectoral fins	Nicotine poisoning Excessive cold *Ichthyophthirius* *Ichthyosporidium*

Head	Possible causes
Turbidity of pupil, blindness	Metacercariae
Exophthalmus	*Ichthyosporidium* Bacterial infection Virus septicaemia Fish tuberculosis *Trypanoplasma*
Eyes sunk in	Excess of chlorine in water Ascites
Operculum permanently open	*Oodinium* Goitre Oedema. Parasites of gills
Operculum perforated	Shortage of lime Avitaminosis
Mandible shortened	Osteomalacia
Mouth permanently open	*Ichthyosporidium* Thyroid tumour
Mandibular growths	Cauliflower disease of eel

Gills	Possible causes
Loss of substance, partial destruction	Excess of acid or alkali in water Damage through chlorine or salts
Small knots	*Ichthyphthirius* *Oodinium*
General swelling	*Diplozoon* Sporozoa *Ichthyophthirius* *Ergasilus* *Dactylogyrus* Avitaminosis Bacterial infections
White turbidity	*Costia, Chilodonella, Trichodina*
Whitish spots	Gill crustaceans
Yellow-brown discoloration	Gill sepsis
Tumours at base of gills	Thyroid tumours *Dermocystidium, Dermosporidium*

Skeleton	Possible causes
Deformity of spine	Osteomalacia, rickets, avitaminosis Staggers Lack of calcium phosphate *Ichthyosporidium* Fish tuberculosis, ascites Acanthocephala

Viscera	Possible causes
Small, dark foci in liver, kidney, heart, spleen, gut, ovary or testis	*Ichthyosporidium*
Yellow-white discoloration of liver	Lipoid degeneration Nephritis, ascites Virus septicaemia of trout
Yellow knots in the liver	Fish tuberculosis Cestodes, trematodes *Ichthyosporidium*
Green discoloration of liver	Obstruction of bile ducts Necrosis of pancreas
Swelling of liver with knots	*Triaenophorus* Hepatoma

Viscera	Possible causes
Necrosis of pancreas	Viral infection
Oedema of kidney	Viral septicaemia Bacterial nephritis and congestion
Enteritis	*Eimeria* and other gut parasites Faulty nutrition, avitaminosis Necrosis of pancreas Virus septicaemia of trout Ascites, nephritis Water pollution of any kind
Small knots in the gut	*Eimeria*
Yellow knots on the outside of gut	*Acanthocephala*

Muscular system	Possible causes
Comma-shaped haemorrhages	Ascites, virus septicaemia of trout
Knots	Sporozoa Old encysted parasites Septicaemia of eel, ascites
Abscess	Furunculosis, tuberculosis Pike-pest *Ichthyosporidium*

Peritoneum and swim-bladder	Possible causes
Burst swim-bladder	Decompression, detonations
Haemorrhage of swim-bladder	Virus septicaemia of trout Ascites
Fluid in body cavity	Sepsis of any kind, enteritis Ascites Heart and liver conditions with general congestion

Eggs, ovaries, embryos	Possible causes
Unusual size of yolk sac	Yolk sac ascites
Perforated eggs without turgor	"Soft egg disease"
Death of eggs with white spots on embryos	Fungus infection
Discoloration of eggs	Bacterial infection

Disturbances of motility	Possible causes
General unrest	Phenol poisoning, anoxaemia Hyperoxaemia Ammonia poisoning Various parasites
Rising for air	Anoxaemia, water pollution Various diseases and parasites
Sluggishness	Cold, hyperoxaemia Metal poisoning
Loss of balance	*Ichthyosporidium* Poisoning Damage of labyrinth by parasites Damage to swim-bladder Cold
Staggering or spinning motion	"Staggers" Virus septicaemia of trout *Hexamita* Necrosis of pancreas

REFERENCES

Grodzinski, Z. and Hoyer, H. (1925). Das Blutgefässsystem. *In* Bronn, H. G.
"Klassen und Ordnungen des Tierreichs", vol. VI, pt. 1, chap. IX, p. 65.
Schlicher, J. (1927). Vergleichend-physiologie Untersuchungen der Blutkörper-
chenzahlen bei Knochenfischen. *Zool. Jahrb.* **43**, 121-200.

Chapter 9

Treatment

A. Treatment by Means of Drugs and Chemical Substances

Since new drugs and chemical compounds are invented every day it is with regard to these that this book will most quickly be outdated. On the other hand we have recently learnt some sharp lessons both in human pathology and in pest control. These will make us wary in trying out new compounds on a large scale before they have been thoroughly tested in experimental stations, both in their effects on the fish they are supposed to protect or heal and on the ecological balance in general. In the aquarium mistakes can easily be corrected; in lakes and rivers the consequences of hazardous chemical experiments may be far reaching and economically painful.

Meanwhile here is a list of means of treatment which have been used with success and which are safe if used carefully. Most of them are in the form of baths, a few are used as paints or as food additives. Trade names, which usually only cover mixtures of well known chemicals, have been avoided as far as possible.

Names of chemical substances in alphabetical order	Method of use	For use against
Acetic acid	2 tablespoonfuls : 25 l water	Turbellaria
Acriflavin *see* Trypaflavin		
Ammonium nitrate	1 g : 20 cm³ of water	*Hydra*, Turbellaria
Aquarol	2 g : 25 l of water	*Ichthyophthirius*
	Repeat bath in 3 days	*Hydra, Saprolegnia*, Fin rot
Ammonia	10–25 cm³ : 1 l of water 10–15 min	*Gyrodactylus*
Atebrine	1 g : 100 l of water	Skin parasites
Aureomycin	13 mg : 1 l of water	Bacteria, *Oodinium Ichthyophthirius*
Calomel	2 g : kg as food additive for 4 days	*Hexamita*
Chloramine	1 g : 15 l of water 2–4 h bath	Turbellaria, skin parasites

Names of chemical substances in alphabetical order	Method of use	For use against
Calcium nitrate, hydrated	1 kg/cbm³	Disinfestation of ponds
Chestnut decoction	Flour from one chestnut stirred in 5–15 l of water, poured into a cheesecloth bag and suspended in the water	*Hydra* *Turbellaria*
Collargol	0·1 mg/l water. Bath for 20 min	*Saprolegnia*
Copper sulphate	1 g : 10 l of water. Bath 10–30 min *Application.* Stock solution: 1 g : 1/1 water. Of this 2 cm³ : 1 l of aquarium water. Leave for 7–10 days. If required, repeat in a fresh tank. Before application remove sand, gravel and shells of molluscs	*Oodinium*
Chloromycetin	0·1 mg : 0·1 l of water as injection intraperitoneally 80 mg : 1 l of water for fih of 10 g weight as bath for 8 h. Not to be added to the aquarium water. 1 mg : 1 g flour as food additive, 1 or 2 doses	*Aeromonas punctata*
DDT	1 : 50–100 million	*Lernaea, Argulus, Ergasilus*
Formaldehyde	20–50 cm³ of the 40% commercial solution : 100 l of water. Bath 30–45 min	*Costia, Trichodina Gryodactylus*
Gantrisin	*See* Sulphamerazin	
GIX (an insecticide)	1–2 drops : 1 l of water (1 : 10 000). Short bath	*Argulus*
HTH (calcium hypochlorite)	10 mg/l for external parasites. 100–200 mg/l for disinfection	Skin parasites General disinfectant
Iodine in alcohol	10% for painting	Wounds, injuries
Lysol	1 cm³ : 5 l of water. Bath	Disinfection
Malachite green	1 g : 10 m². Bath every 2nd day up to 0·15 mg/l	External parasites
Methylene blue	3 cm³ of a 1% solution to 10 l of water. Bath 3–5 days	*Chilodonella* *Gyrodactylus*
Para-chloro-phenoxetol	Of a stock solution (1 cm³ : 1 l of water) add 50 cm³ in the course of 2 days	*Ichthyosporidium*
Penicillin	40 000 Units : 100 l of water. Bath	*Ichthyophthirius* Dermatitis. Gill infections
Phenoxetol	Stock solution 1%. Of this 10–20 cm³/ 1 of water	*Ichthyosporidium*
Plasmoquine	1 g : 100 l of water. Bath	Skin parasites
Potassium iodide	1 part of iodine+ 100 parts Pot. iodide. Food additive 1 : 2 500	Thyroid tumours

Names of chemical substances in alphabetical order	Method of use	For use against
Potassium permanganate	1 g : 100 l of water. 30 min bath	*Saprolegnia, Costia, Chilodonella, Trichodina,* bacteria, ext. lesions
PMA (pyridylmercuroacetate)	1 : 500 000	External parasites
Quicklime	0·1–0·15 kg/cbm³ of water	Disinfection of ponds
Quinine hydrochloride or sulphate	1 g : 75–100 l of water. Bath	*Ichthyophthirius* Skin parasites
Rivanol	1 g : 400 l of water. Bath	Skin parasites
Roccal (10% alkyl-dimethyl benzylammonium-chloride)	1 : 50 000	Bacteria
Sodium chloride (common salt)	10–15 g : 1 l of water. 20 min bath	*Costia, Chilodonella, Trichodina, Gyrodactylus, Dactylogyrus, Saprolegnia*
Sod. thiosulphate	1 g/10 l of water	Dechlorination
Sulphadiazine	100–250 mg/l water	Bacteria
Sulphaguanidine	*See* Sulphamerazin	
Sulphamerazin	100–200 mg/kg fish as food additive every 3rd day to daily	Furunculosis, ulcers, nephritis
Sulphanilamid	100–250 mg/l water	Fungi, bacterial infections
Streptomycin (1/33 of activity of chloromycetin. Schäperclaus, 1956)	*See* Chloromycetin	*Aeromonas punctata*
Terramycin	3 mg/150–400 g weight of fish as injection. Also as food additive in the same dose	Bacterial infection
Trypaflavin (acriflavin)	1 g : 100 l of water	Skin parasites, infected wounds, ulcers
Zephirol	1 : 2 000–4 000. 30 min bath	*Costia, Trichodina, Gyrodactylus*

B. PHYSICAL AND BIOLOGICAL MEANS OF TREATMENT

In the normal habitat of fish physical measures of treatment are by and large impossible; in the tank or aquarium they are of the greatest importance because they are milder in action, reversible and easier graded than chemical means. Not every fish adapts itself to captivity and where the fish suffers from nothing but claustrophobia, either because the tank is too small or because it is overcrowded and filled with stale water, the remedy is obvious. Like other animals, fish born in captivity adapt themselves better than those caught as adults, but even this method has its limit because many open waters, and particularly streams, have features which are difficult to imitate even in the best-run aquarium. Even from the point of view of the fish, however, the medal has its reverse side. We need not, in the aquarium, tolerate the many parasites which shorten the life of free-living fish; we can protect them from starvation and, most important, from ending up playing their part in the great feeding cycle where every fish is in continual danger of ending up in the stomach of the one that is just a little larger. Hence the presence, in many an aquarium, of fish of astonishing size and venerable old age, which are a credit to their keepers.

Parasites are often strictly adapted to certain temperatures and a temporary raising of the temperature may well be tried as a first approach. For tropical fish Stolk (quoted from Duijn, 1956) recommends 6 h at 33°C during the day with a drop to 21°C in the night; this to be repeated three to five times. The method is recommended against *Costia* and *Plasmodia*; it may at least slow down the spreading of *Ichthyosporidium*.

It is, however, of the greatest importance to remember that the general decomposition of organic matter is speeded up parallel with the temperature rise, that this means a growing shortage of oxygen in the water, and that this must be balanced by increased aeration. Fish should be carefully watched while their normal temperature is raised.

Fish may survive a change in the pH, while this means death to parasites. Slight acidification has been found useful in the fight against *Ichthyosporidium*.

Light and water circulation play a great part in the maintenance of healthy aquarium conditions. The installation of green-coloured glass panes prevents the development of algae, but is badly tolerated by the other plants growing in the aquarium. Water circulation which can be combined with filtration (particularly essential in marine aquaria) and aeration is welcomed by every kind of fish and a high O_2 content of the water inhibits the growth of bacteria.

Unsuitable nutrition has caused the death of many a fish. Like other imports from distant countries, tropical species may be highly specialized in their requirements. Geisler and Bolle (1954) pointed out how dependent such fish may be on certain food plants and insects. This is particularly true in respect of South American species imported as tropical ornamental fish. They may not always adapt themselves to the food we can offer them.

Where it is possible to breed fish in captivity, the rules governing all animal breeding should be followed. The best specimens of each generation should be selected and tested for their resistance and adaptability. Only those found most suitable should be selected for further breeding.

Just as in the realm of pest control elsewhere, the ideal would be to apply biological methods, i.e. to support the growth of such protozoa or metazoa which destroy parasites but are harmless to fish. Schäperclaus (1955, 1956) reported successes in the establishment of virus cultures which destroyed *Aeromonas punctata*, the cause of ascites of fish. Bacteriophages, too, can be filled into ampules and sent by post. It remains to be seen how far methods of this kind can be developed.

A great help in the establishment of a healthy aquarium is the growing of plants selected for the desired temperature range. A tank in which plants grow rapidly will usually be found healthy in other respects as well. The following list may sum up the requirements for the maintenance of healthy conditions in the aquarium:

Suitable water (correct pH: O_2 concentration)

Optimal food (live wherever possible; vitamins as required; live food from unpolluted waters)

Correct amount of food

Correct furnishing of the habitat with stones and plants

Careful choice of species chosen to share the same tank.

REFERENCES

Duijn, C. v. jr. (1956). "Diseases of Fishes", publ. *Water Life*, London.
Geisler, R. and Bolle, S. (1954). Nahrungsuntersuchungen bei nordargentinischen Wildfischen. *Aqu. Terr. Z.* **9**, 208–213.
Schäperclaus, W. (1955). Die Rolle der Bakteriophagen im Stoffhaushalt der Gewässer und bei der Entstehung der Fischkrankheiten. *Arch. Hydrobiol.* Suppl. **22**, 488–493.
Schäperclaus, W. (1956). Neue Möglichkeiten zur Bekämpfung von Infektionskrankheiten bei Aquarienfischen. *Aqu. Terr. Z.* **9**, 213–215.

Part II

Amphibia

CHAPTER 10

Technique of Investigation

A. WHEN SHOULD AN INVESTIGATION BE CARRIED OUT?

Like many other living creatures, the Amphibia present a variety of diseases, some of which announce themselves by external, easily observable symptoms, while nothing abnormal can be noticed in others. In such cases the only leading signs may be apathy and refusal to feed.

Initially an attempt will be made to ascertain whether the case is caused by infection or injury or whether it may not be due to an unsuitable and damaging environment. One would, in this case, check the natural habits and ecological conditions of the species and adjust the conditions under captivity accordingly as far as this is possible. This should include a check on temperature, humidity of the air, composition and pH of the soil, supply and growth of plants, illumination and food. The last of these factors may be the most difficult one to assess. Failure to keep the animal under conditions as close to the optimal as possible often favours a parasitic origin of the disease. Diseases of the skin may be amenable to topical treatment. Internal diseases can rarely be treated because their true nature can only be ascertained after the death of the victim. If an epidemic breaks out in a population of animals, the specimens showing most pronounced symptoms should be killed and dissected as early as possible.

In assessing the nature of a disease or the cause of death of an animal it must be considered whether the symptoms observed may not be due to *age*. It is therefore important to know something about the natural *life span* of the animals in question. In the case of the Amphibia the information at our disposal is as yet unfortunately scanty. Hesse and Doflein in their textbook on animal life and structure (1935) give some figures as follows:

Species	Life span (years)
Hyla arborea	10
Bombina sp.	19
Triturus alpestris	20
Salamandra salamandra	40

The smaller the species the shorter, on the whole, is their life span. Noble (1931), in stating this rule, quotes the length of life of the following Amphibia kept in captivity:

Species	Life span (years)
Pleurodeles waltli	20
Cynops pyrrhogaster	25
Siren sp.	25
Amphiuma sp.	26

As the maximal life span observed in an amphibian, he quotes 52 years for a specimen of *Megalobatrachus maximus* kept in the aquarium of the Amsterdam zoological gardens.

B.   Killing and Dissection of Specimens

External parasites of the skin which can easily be detached may usually be diagnosed from swabs and treated with disinfecting baths or by painting the affected part with a suitable lotion (see Chap. 7). Where internal disease is suspected or where specimens are seriously ill, killing and dissection cannot be avoided, particularly if the health of many animals is endangered. In such a case it is indispensable to have a correct diagnosis of at least two specimens. Dead animals are subject to rapid changes. Fresh material only is suitable for any investigation. This is particularly true in the case of bacterial infection where early putrefaction masks and obliterates the original invaders.

Many considerations enter into the decision when to kill a diseased animal. In the case of unique or valuable specimens every attempt will of course be made to cure them. Where, however, an epidemic breaks out among stock of less valuable animals, it is imperative to isolate and kill several of them as early as possible to arrive at an explanation for the losses. Lower vertebrates manage on the whole to survive for surprisingly long periods with the most crippling diseases, particularly if they are kept at low temperatures. This ability is related to the fact that amphibians, and reptiles particularly, can starve for many weeks if no food is available and can in many instances hibernate with an almost completely suspended metabolism. If an animal refuses to feed and starts losing weight during the summer months, it should in any case be isolated at once, since diseased or disabled animals are often attacked by the fellow-inhabitants of their cage. If it can be assumed that the disease must cause considerable discomfort and pain, we shall be more inclined to kill the specimen early. Where this is not the case, we may be inclined to wait, so as to obtain an unmistakable picture of the disease at the post-mortem dissection. This applies particularly to cases of internal malignant tumours which can sometimes be felt by palpation of the live animal. They do not occur very often and our knowledge of the pathology of such tumours is as yet insufficient. Material of well-developed cases of this kind is therefore of great interest to the animal pathologist.

Since it cannot be foreseen which part of the animal will be needed for more detailed investigation, the method of killing should not involve any "surgical" operation, nor should it incite the outpouring of large quantities of sticky mucus from the animal's skin, which makes handling awkward and difficult. We have at our disposal several methods which entirely avoid these snags. One of the easiest to apply is the placing of the animal into a 5% solution of urethane, which slowly anaesthetizes and kills the animal without causing any violent reaction on its part. It must, however, be remembered that urethane is a bone marrow poison and that it should not be used where this is to be studied.

An equally good method, which, however, involves the use of a syringe, is the injection of a small dose of one of the many preparations of soluble barbitone (e.g. "Nembutal" = pentobarbitone sod., Abbott Laboratories) under the skin or, for quicker action, into the peritoneal cavity. For tadpoles and fish-fry urethane is the method of choice. Should this not be available chloroform–water can be used but it must be remembered that the use of chloroform may affect the blood picture. The use of inflammable substances like ether and chloroform is on the whole obsolete and should be avoided.

The preparation Metacain (Sandoz MS. 222) has been found useful for the purpose of immobilizing or killing both larval and adult batrachians. The concentration of the solution used varies according to the size and age of the animal. Tadpoles of anurans and urodeles will be anaesthetized in 5–30 min by concentrations of 1 : 1 000– 1 : 10 000. Adult specimens react in 30–180 min to concentrations of between 1 : 1 000 and 1 : 3 000.

For the purpose of dissection the animal, if of suitable size, is placed on its back and fixed to a cork mat or in a dish with a $\frac{1}{2}$ in (1·3 cm) layer of hard paraffin by non-rusting needles pushed through the extended hands and feet. In some cases it may be advisable to fix the head by placing additional needles in the angle behind the mandible so that no part of the body can move during further manipulation. If weight and measurements are to be recorded this should be done as soon after death as possible. Specimens found dead, as often happens, at times when immediate dissection is impossible, can be kept in the ice box of any household refrigerator, but it must be remembered that this procedure will also kill any parasites which may be present, some of which are better studied alive than dead.

We can never know at the outset, when dealing with herpetological material, whether we shall be presented with a common condition which we have often seen before, or with one that is very rare or new to us. It is therefore of utmost importance to record, by way of drawing or photography, those steps in the dissection that reveal anything striking. The least time-consuming procedure is the taking of close-up photographs with a miniature camera permanently set up for this purpose, and a good array of dishes, Perspex containers, lamps and filters will be required to adapt each case according to its requirements. Some specimens are best photographed under water, thereby avoiding excessive highlights; others need every shade of contour we can make visible and must be taken dry with the most oblique lighting we can devise. Colour photographs are always superior to black and white for the purpose of recording, but it must be remembered that they are rarely welcomed as illustrations by the scientific journals. Wherever possible, a photograph should show conditions undisturbed entirely. A diseased animal should be photographed before it is killed; an organ before it has been removed from its natural situs and before pieces have been removed for further study. Failure to do this places insuperable difficulties into the path of the reader who eventually tries to reconstruct the case as it was seen during dissection.

The dissection starts by a division of the skin in the ventral mid-line. In most amphibians the skin is not attached to the body but separated from it by large lymphatic spaces. It can therefore be lifted with forceps and cut with sharp scissors. Once it has been incised from the anus to the shoulder girdle it can be flattened out by means of further cuts at right angles. Further steps depend on the condition suspected. If it is desired to obtain a good view of the abdominal wall this can be distended and, if so desired, fixed in distension by injecting the abdominal cavity with saline or a fixative. If fluid contained in the peritoneal cavity is to be examined for bacteria it should, at this stage, be aspirated with a sterile syringe. Once the peritoneal cavity is opened the fluid escapes and will become secondarily contaminated. A mid-line incision through the abdominal wall, continued by splitting the sternum with stout scissors and where necessary combined with additional cuts at

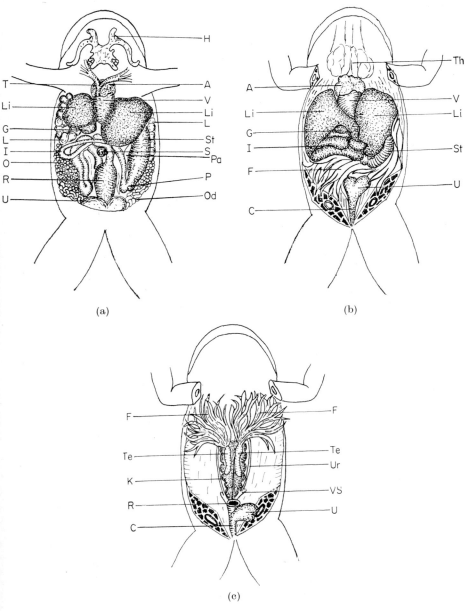

(a)

(b)

(c)

Fig. 160. (a) Viscera of a female frog, diagrammatic. *A*, Auricles; *G*, gall bladder; *H*, hyoid cartilage; *I*, small intestine; *L*, lungs; *Li*, liver; *O*, ovary; *Od*, oviduct; *P*, pylorus; *Pa*, pancreas; *R*, rectum; *S*, spleen; *St*, stomach; *T*, truncus arteriosus; *U*, urinary bladder; *V*, ventricle.

(b) Viscera of male frog, ventral layer, diagrammatic. *A*, Auricles; *C*, cloaca; *F*, fat body; *G*, gall bladder; *I*, small intestine; *Li*, liver; *St*, stomach; *U*, urinary bladder; *V*, ventricle.

(c) Viscera of male frog, dorsal layer, diagrammatic. *C*, Cloaca; *F*, fat body, *K*, kidney, *R*, rectum; *Te*, testis; *U*, urinary bladder; *Ur*, ureter; *VS*, seminal vesicle.

right angles, gives us a good view of most of the intestines (Fig. 160a–c).
Such a cut may, however, easily injure the urinary bladder and to
preserve this organ it is preferable to cut from the xiphoid process in the
direction of both legs, leaving the central area of the abdomen intact.
If, in this way, the urinary bladder is left undisturbed, parasites can
often be seen in it with the naked eye or with a hand lens.

The only organs not easily approached by ventral dissection are the
retroperitoneally situated kidneys, and these are much better approached
by dorsal dissection. This involves division and removal of the spinal
column and the iliac bones, a procedure which can easily be carried
out with stout scissors once the animal has been turned over. In cases
of renal tumours this dissection from the back may produce interesting
pictures conveying more information than can be obtained from
ventral dissection.

C. FURTHER INVESTIGATION

It must be remembered at the outset that bacteriological and virological examinations can only be carried out on fresh, unfixed and un-
contaminated material. For bacteriological examination swabs should
be taken or fluid should be sent in sterile containers. Material for virological study should be sent immersed in glycerine. In either case such
samples should reach the laboratory as quickly as possible. Further
details will be found in textbooks on histology and laboratory procedure.

Skin lesions are examined by making smears on glass slides which are
then inspected, stained or unstained, for bacteria or parasites as the
case may be. In the case of large ulcers or cysts, smears made from the
contents may be suitable for microscopical examination but fixed
material should always be preserved for sectioning either with the
freezing or the paraffin microtome. It is often advisable to examine a
piece of skin by transillumination. In cases of tubercular infection, for
example, the skin may look like a moth-eaten carpet.

Cysts and tumours of the muscular system are easily seen with a
hand lens, particularly in the anterior abdominal wall which, in emaciated animals, becomes as thin as paper (Fig. 185, 186).

The *investigation of the intestinal canal* involves the opening of this
canal by longitudinal section from beginning to end. In the case of
the smaller amphibians the intestinal canal must first be straightened
out by removing all the other organs to which it is adherent. It must
then be floated in a Petri dish placed on black paper and filled with
water or, better, amphibian Ringer solution. The intestinal canal can
then be split with fine scissors, when any parasites present escape into

the fluid and are immediately seen against the black background. In the case of the lungs the same procedure is adopted. The urinary bladder, frequently inhabited by parasites, must be inspected before it is destroyed by the later steps of the dissection. The solid organs (liver, spleen, kidney) are inspected from outside and are then sliced with a sharp scalpel or a razor blade. The gall bladder, very frequently inhabited by sporozoans, may deserve special attention. The larger nematode and trematode worms, so frequently seen in amphibians, can usually be spotted without the aid of a microscope. The diagnosis of the very much smaller blood parasites is much more difficult and cannot be made without the aid of special staining methods and high magnification. It is useful, on such occasions, to have some knowledge of the normal shape and size of the amphibian red blood corpuscles (erythrocytes). In the amphibians these are nucleated and of larger size than in man (Fig. 161). They number, in frogs, 400 000–600 000 per mm^3,

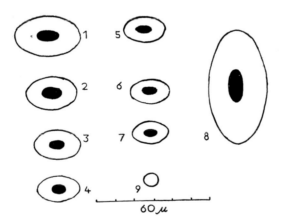

FIG. 161. Erythrocytes of amphibians compared with a human red blood cell.
1, *Salamandra salamandra* L. (Diam. 36 : 21·5 μ).
2, *Triturus vulgaris* L. (Diam. 29·9 : 19·8 μ).
3, *Rana esculenta* L. (Diam. 24·4 : 17·6 μ).
4, *Rana temporaria* L. (Diam. 22·3 : 15·7).
5, *Bufo bufo* L. (Diam. 24·4 : 12·7 μ).
6, *Pelobates fuscus* Laur. (Diam. 21·0 : 15·0 μ).
7, *Bufo calamita* L. (Diam. 20·0 : 14·0 μ).
8, *Proteus anguineus* L. (Diam. 58·0 : 34·0 μ).
9, *Homo sapiens* L. (Diam. 7–7·4 μ). (After Jung.)

in tailed amphibians from 50 000–140 000 per mm^3. About 15% of the white blood corpuscles are granulocytes. Some of the large monocytes found in amphibian blood may contain melanin or iron (haemosiderin). The blood should be scrutinized for the presence of bacteria, flagellates

TABLE 3*

Blood Corpuscles and Haemoglobin in *Rana temporaria*, *R. esculenta* and *Xenopus laevis*

Blood constituents	Rana temporaria	Rana esculenta	Xenopus laevis
Erythrocytes (mm³)	460 600 ±21 350	307 700 ±14 220	565 800 ±13 100
Leucocytes (mm³)	14 400 ± 1 620	6 050 ± 510	8 150 ± 950
Thrombocytes (mm³)	20 800 ± 1 880	16 300 ± 1620	17 100 ± 950
Haemoglobin (g%)	14·34± 0·29	9·7± 0·51	14·86± 0·45

TABLE 4*

Differential Blood Pictures of *Rana temporaria*, *R. esculenta* and *Xenopus laevis*

%	Rana temporaria	Rana esculenta	Xenopus laevis
Early stages	1·5	1·0	0·7
Neutrophile juveniles	1·5	1·4	1·1
Neutroph. granulocytes	5·0±1·0	7·4±2·1	6·9±1·1
Eosinophile juveniles	0·1	0·7	0·1
Eosinoph. granulocytes	14·4±2·9	18·7±1·3	0·5
Basophile juveniles	0·1	0·1	0·7
Basoph. granulocytes	24·1±2·2	16·5±1·3	7·8±1·4
Monocytes	0·8	1·3	0·5
Plasmocytes	0·4	1·0	0·2
Lymphocytes	68·5±2·9	52·0±3·3	65·3±2·7

* From Fey (1962).

or microfilaria and a blood count should be made. Finally the erythrocytes themselves should be examined for intracellular Protozoa.

In an amphibian like the frog which is host to so many parasites and symbionts, all of which may permanently or temporarily influence the blood picture, it is not easy to establish what the "normal" values are. Ideally these could only be taken from laboratory-bred and parasite-free frogs, but it might be objected that such frogs would not be "normal" because they do not exist in nature. We have to content ourselves, therefore, with figures derived from the average frog as we find it, bearing in mind that only gross deviations from the figures obtained are significant in the interpretation of pathological changes. Excellent starting figures were given by Fey (1962) working on *Rana temporaria, Rana esculenta* and *Xenopus laevis*, three of the batrachian species most commonly used in the laboratory. Tables 3 and 4 are quoted from Fey's paper.

Further observations, particularly on bufonids, would be of interest in view of the remarkable difference observed between the reaction of these toads to bacterial and microsporidian infections (Canning *et al.*, 1964). Whereas in bacterial infection we see the classical picture of intense eosinophilia with abscess formation, not a single eosinophile cell appears in even the heaviest microsporidian infection where the defence is entirely left to the monocytes. These, however, do not form abscesses and do not appear in sufficient numbers to save the toad. The relative impotence of these defences and the absence of a temperature-raising mechanism presents a very weak spot in the amphibian's defence against infectious diseases.

The *reproductive organs* should be examined with a hand lens. A detailed examination can be made from sections only.

Parasites may occasionally even invade the central nervous system. In the absence of any lesions in other organs it may therefore be necessary to examine the brain and the spinal column. Parasites of this kind, which occur, for example, in the axolotl, are however motile and can usually be found in swabs taken from brain tissue.

Of the *nervous receptor organs* the eyes, the ears, and the lateral line system should be considered. The eyes may be the seat of nematode larvae, but blindness can be due to many other causes as well, and the determination of its cause may require a very detailed investigation.

True *tumours*, which may be found in any organ, can never be diag-nosed without fixation, embedding and sectioning, but it must again be remembered that virological investigation can only be done on fresh, unfixed material.

It should finally be remembered that not every foreign inhabitant found in the amphibian intestine is to be regarded as a harmful parasite. Few frogs and toads are ever found entirely free of intestinal worms, yet these only kill their hosts if they become unusually abundant. Flagellates of the Family Opalinidae abound in most amphibians, but as far as we know they never cause greater damage than that due to abstracting a small part of the host's food.

D. DESPATCH OF AMPHIBIANS TO THE LABORATORY

If animals die from causes which cannot de determined on the spot and which may well be new to science, they should be sent to a laboratory equipped for dealing with animal pathology. The laboratory will be most grateful if the animal is sent while still alive, packed in wet moss or leaves and enclosed in a box with a perforated lid to avoid suffocation. The specimen can then be kept at the laboratory until it dies a natural death or it can be painlessly killed and fixed immediately so as to avoid any deterioration of the tissues. Live animals should never be posted during a heat-wave, however well-packed, as they are very likely to die from lack of oxygen.

The sending of heavy glass containers can be avoided by the use of polythene bags. It has even been found quite feasible to send live fish in a pint or two of water contained in such a bag without any air being included. Water plants should be used to prevent excessive shaking and it is a special refinement to blow some oxygen through the water before despatch. In the case of amphibians and reptiles this is not necessary. While amphibians must be protected from desiccation, reptiles are best sent in boxes with dry leaves or wood shavings, not in airtight bags or containers.

Dead animals or parts of them can be sent accompanied by a well-closed ice bag if the distance to the laboratory is not too great. If the parcel has to travel far it should be sent by airmail. Bacteriological and virological examination can only be carried out on unfixed material.

E. FIXATION

The two most easily available and generally satisfactory fixatives obtainable at any chemist's are alcohol and formaldehyde.

Surgical spirit can be used in dilutions of 50–70%. In the case of formaldehyde concentrations of from 4 to 6% are satisfactory. Only in the case of very small specimens like tadpoles is it sufficient simply to place the animals in the fixing solution. The skin of amphibians, which would, of course, fix first, becomes very tough and impermeable, and in larger specimens fixation of the skin can be complete while the viscera are found to be completely useless through putrefaction. It is therefore imperative either to open the peritoneal cavity or to inject a sufficient amount of fixing solution so that every part of the specimen is penetrated. As soon as the injection is completed, the animal should be fixed with pins and straightened out on a cork mat. The mat is then turned over and floated on a dish filled with the fixing solution. After 24–48 h the animal can be detached, wrapped in cotton wool moistened with the fixing solution, placed in a polythene bag, sealed with Cellophane strip and packed. It is very difficult to examine animals which arrive coiled up or in distorted shape because they have simply been dropped into fixing solution and left there to harden. They cannot be softened again and the natural relation of the organs, once distorted through fixation in unnatural positions cannot be restored. To sum up: no method of despatching such material is better than that of sending either live animals or dead ones accompanied by an ice bag. Fixation, if attempted, must be done carefully. A "pickling jar" serving as a dump for any animal that may die is useless.

REFERENCES

Canning, E. U., Elkan, E. and Trigg, P. I. (1964). *Plistophora myotrophica* spec. nov. causing high mortality in the Common Toad *Bufo bufo* L., with notes on the maintenance of *Bufo* and *Xenopus* in the laboratory. *J. Protozool.* **11**, 157–166.

Fey, F. (1962). Haematologische Untersuchungen an *Xenopus laevis* Daudin I. *Morph. Jahrb.* **101**, 9–20.

Hesse, R. and Doflein, T. (1935). "Tierbau und Tierleben", 2nd edn. Fischer, Jena.

Noble, G. K. (1931). "Biology of the Amphibia." Reprinted by Dover Publications, 1934.

CHAPTER 11

Infectious Diseases

A. DISEASES DUE TO BACTERIAL INFECTION

TUBERCULOSIS IN AMPHIBIANS

The discovery that, analogous to the well-known tuberculous disease of man and the warm-blooded animals, there exists a similar infection in amphibians, goes back to the year 1905 and the extensive investigations of Küster, and Weber and Taute, who reported the first cases of tuberculosis in frogs. A further case was reported by Lichtenstein in 1921, and in 1930 Scott and Griffith confirmed the occasional occurrence of a disease, clinically indistinguishable from human tuberculosis, in frogs, the only difference being that the causative organism, acid-fast like *Mycobacterium tuberculosis*, would not grow at temperatures above 28°C. In 1941 Griffith made a further detailed study of the acid-fast bacteria of cold-blooded animals and showed that they could be split up into several groups. Whether the designation of these types, e.g. *Mycobacterium ranae* Bergey *et al.*, *Mycobacterium piscium* and *Mycobacterium ranicola* I and II Haag, is justified, is still doubtful. Darzins (1952) investigated the Smoky Jungle frog (*Leptodactylus pentadactylus* L.) from the neighbourhood of Bahia, Brazil, and found that they suffered from tuberculous lesions of the liver, the lungs and the intestinal canal. From these he isolated an acid-fast Gram-positive bacillus of 3–5 μ length and a width of 0·4–0·5 μ, and described it as *Mycobacterium giae*. This investigation was continued by Stuckrad (1955).

The development of our knowledge of any animal disease runs parallel with the importance the animal concerned has for us, either as food or in the laboratory. Since Hogben (1930) discovered that frogs could be used for pregnancy tests, *Xenopus*, *Bufo* and *Rana* have gained entry into the clinical laboratories of the world. No wonder, therefore, that their diseases, too, have become better known. In 1959 Schwabacher reviewed the history of our knowledge of the occurrence of acid-fast bacilli in poikilothermic animals and described as *Mycobacterium xenopei* a strain cultured from skin lesions of *Xenopus laevis*, the South African clawed toad. Some of the clinical manifestations of an attack on an amphibian by these acid-fast cold-water bacilli were described by Elkan (1960).

The natural histories of tuberculosis in cold- and warm-blooded animals differ in some fundamental aspects. Whereas among man and the higher vertebrates tuberculosis may affect any animal, whether weak or strong, it is in amphibians mainly debilitated or injured specimens which are predominantly attacked; and while, in the warm-blooded animals, the disease, once introduced, may spread rapidly among the stock, this does not necessarily occur in amphibians, whose natural resistance against these bacilli seems to be much higher than that of the homoiothermal animals. Like that of fish, amphibian tuberculosis is a secondary disease, arising among animals weakened by other

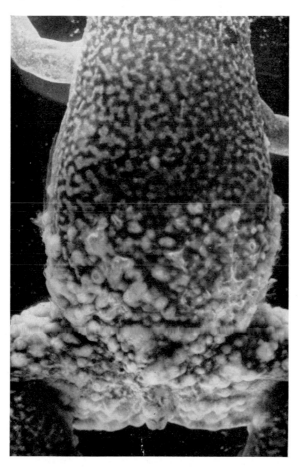

Fig. 162. *Xenopus laevis*. Adult female with dermal tuberculosis. (Photo.: Elkan.)

Normal skin   Stage I   Stage II   Stage III

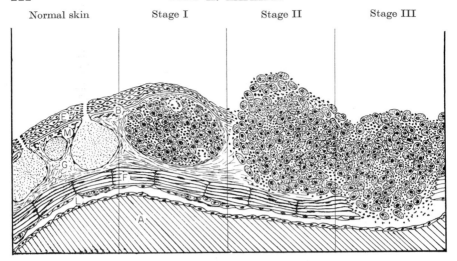

FIG. 163. Progress of dermal tuberculosis in *Xenopus laevis* D. (semi-diagrammatic). Stage I. Abscess formation in the glandular layer of the dermis. Stage II. Epidermis destroyed by granulation tissue. Stage III. Destruction of all dermal layers and perforation of skin. Monocytes crammed with acid-fast bacilli are seen in Stages I and II. There is no formation of adhesions, no reaction to the inflammatory process on the part of the endothelial cells and no attempt at defence or repair in Stages II and III.

A, Body of toad; *B*, basal membrane; *E*, epidermis; *F*, fibrous layer of dermis; *G*, glandular layer; *L*, lymph sac; *M*, melanophores. (Del. Elkan.)

FIG. 164. *Xenopus laevis* D. Tuberculous ulcer of the leg. (Photo.: Elkan.)

conditions, injuries or adverse environmental circumstances like unsuitable nutrition (too little or too much food), chemically unsuitable water or soil, or cages stocked with unsuitable plants. Illumination and temperature, too, play an important part. The presence of acid-fast bacteria in our cages and aquaria cannot be avoided, but if all the above-mentioned factors are carefully considered they will do little harm to our stock. How great the immunity against these bacteria is in the average healthy amphibian can be seen in a grossly overcrowded tank, where, for example, *Xenopus* may be kept for pregnancy diagnosis, one animal out of sixty contracts the disease and dies of it, while all the others remain entirely unaffected. The immunity of the healthy animal goes further than that. Normal tadpoles of *Rana temporaria* were kept in a small glass jar together with a *Xenopus* toad whose skin was heavily inflamed and ulcerated by dermal tuberculosis. Although the tadpoles had no other food than the detritus shed by the tuberculous toad and although many acid-fast bacilli could be seen in sections through their intestines, they grew happily and completed their metamorphosis even in this most unsuitable environment, while the infected *Xenopus* died when the greater part of its skin had been destroyed by tuberculous ulceration.

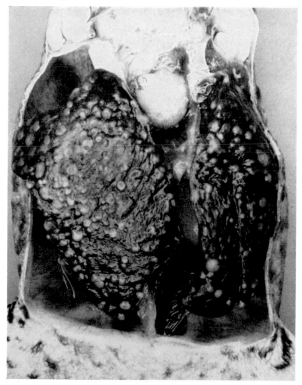

FIG. 165. (a) *Bufo bufo* L. Tuberculosis of the liver. (Photo.: Elkan. Courtesy Zool. Soc. Lond.)

Fig. 165. (b) Miliary tuberculosis in a male adult specimen of *Bufo bufo* L. Tubercles disseminated throughout the visceral organs, particularly in the liver. ×2. (Photo.: Elkan. Courtesy Zool. Soc. Lond.)

It is not possible to describe any form of amphibian tuberculosis as "typical" since either the skin, the respiratory or the intestinal system may become affected (Fig. 165). The only definitely typical aspect of the disease must be looked for in sections, where the presence of tubercles confirms the diagnosis. They differ slightly from those seen in the higher vertebrates in the fact that giant cells are very rarely seen and central caseation is not usually pronounced. Acid-fast bacilli are usually abundant in the peripheral parts of the tubercle. The exotoxins produced by these bacteria cannot be very harmful since more than half of a vital organ can be destroyed before the animal dies of the disease.

Since the most frequent cases of amphibian tuberculosis seen are those of the intestinal and respiratory tracts, one would conclude that infection usually occurs by way of the mouth. This, of course, does nothing to explain why one of sixty animals, all fed with the same food, should contract the disease. Though the mouth may be the common port of entry, the disease is not usually found in the stomach or the intestine but in the liver, the spleen, the kidney and the testes, all of which may become almost completely destroyed by the tubercular process before the animal dies. In cases where the liver is first affected, it may either be riddled with small, grain-like tubercles (Fig. 165a, b) or it may be the seat of a few large ones. In either case, if much liver parenchyma is destroyed by the tubercular process, melanin, much of which is normally stored in the amphibian liver, enters the blood stream, is eliminated by the renal glomeruli, and found reabsorbed by some of the cells lining the proximal uriniferous tubules. While some of these cells fill themselves to capacity with the dark pigment, others absorb none at all although both types of cells may lie side by side (Fig. 166). The reason for this selectivity among the cells

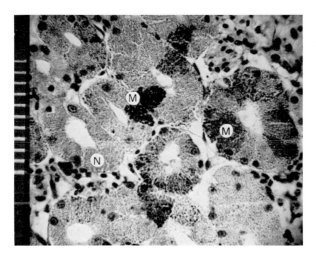

Fig. 166. *Xenopus laevis*. Kidney in a case of advanced destruction of the liver by tuberculosis. The liberated melanin is readsorbed by some of the cells lining the proximal uriniferous tubules. *N*, Normal proximal uriniferous tubule; *M*, epithelial cells filled with reabsorbed melanin. (Photo.: Elkan.)

in the proximal sector of the nephron is still unknown (Frontispiece, Fig. 2). Alongside liberation of melanin, haemosiderin also enters the blood stream and can be demonstrated in the basal membrane of the glomerular capillaries. Visceral tuberculosis, the commonest type in amphibians, does not usually spread to the lungs. On the other hand the pulmonary type usually leads to the death of the animal before other organic systems are affected. It would appear from the results of dissections that the tubercular process starts at the bifurcation of the main bronchus and spreads slowly towards the caudal extremity of the lungs. Gradually both lungs become completely solidified by this process but even where it has transformed the whole lung into one massive, sausage-shaped piece of lobar tuberculous pneumonia the process does not necessarily break through the pleura, the lungs are not found adherent to the pleuro-peritoneal cavity, and there is usually little if any true caseation even at the centre of the diseased organ (Fig. 167a, b). The number of acid-fast bacilli in sections made of this kind of tissue is so great that the sections remain uniformly red after "decolorization" with hydrochloric acid so that the diagnosis can be made without the aid of the microscope (Figs. 169, 170). No

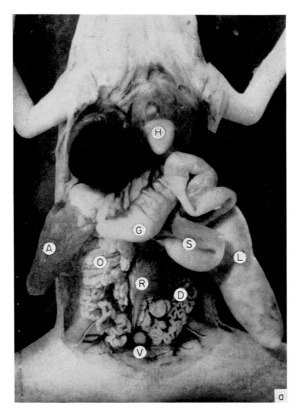

Fig. 167. *Xenopus laevis*. Adult female with lobar tuberculous pneumonia. (Photos.: Elkan, cf. Frontispiece, Fig. 4.) (a) View of the viscera after removal of abdominal wall. For further explanation, see (b).

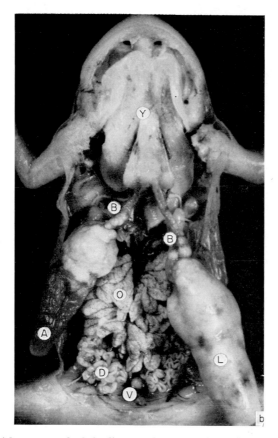

FIG. 167. (b) After removal of the liver to show the affected bronchi. A, Right lung, B, bronchus; D, oviduct; G, stomach; H, heart; L, left lung; O, ovary; R, rectum; S, small intestine; V, bladder; Y, hyoid.

animal but an amphibian whose gas exchange is partly dermal and which needs its lungs only partly for breathing and partly for the control of buoyancy, could live while a pathological process destroys three-quarters of its lungs, and observations of this kind again emphasize that the amount of exotoxin produced by these cold-water acid-fast bacteria must be very small.

Equally, their small power of penetration was emphasized by the case of a toad (X. laevis D.) in which the tuberculous process, starting probably again at the bronchial bifurcation, had not affected the lungs but produced large globular masses entirely enveloping and obscuring the atria and the truncus arteriosus. Apart from a few small tubercles in the visceral ventricular pericardium the ventricle was not affected. The animal probably died when the atria were completely immobilized by the spreading tubercular masses (Fig. 170).

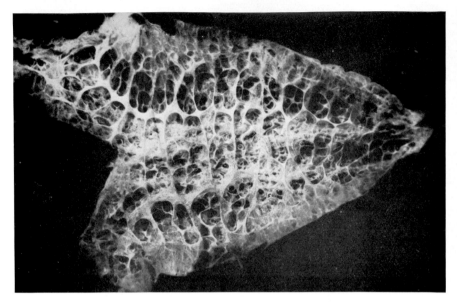

FIG. 168. *Xenopus laevis*. Normal lung. Interior aspect. cf. Fig. 169. (Photo.: Elkan.)

The tuberculous affection of the skin may appear either in the form of an ulcer which gradually erodes the dermis and then spreads out, destroying the muscles (Fig. 164), or it may take the shape of a verrucous inflammation which may start in one or several places at the same time and gradually affect large areas of the skin (Fig. 162). For a reason which we do not understand the destructive process in such a case limits itself to the perforation of the dermis and does not breach the super-ficial fascia. The skin, inspected *post mortem* in transillumination, looks like a severely moth-eaten carpet. The animal probably dies from the loss of fluid caused by the multiple drainage of all its sub-cutaneous lymph sacs.

In the Amphibia tuberculosis may be suspected if, when the body cavity is opened, a large white tumour comes into view which is smooth on the surface, not adherent to neighbouring structures and in many cases not accompanied by similar deposits in other organs. Examples have already been shown (Figs. 167a, b, 168, 170) where a primary tubercular lesion grew to a considerable size yet remained limited by a thin serous membrane like the pleura or the pericardium. The same

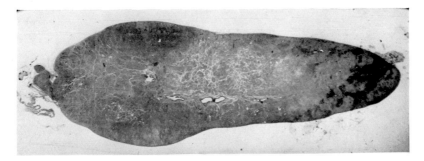

Fig. 169. *Xenopus laevis*. Longitudinal section through lung. Lobar tuberculous pneumonia. Cf. Fig. 168. (Photo.: Elkan.)

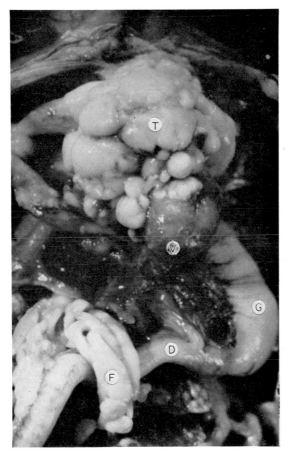

Fig. 170. *Xenopus laevis*. Adult female. Viscera after removal of the liver. Tuberculous pericarditis. Tuberculous infection of the fat bodies. *D*, Duodenum; *F*, fat body; *G*, stomach; *T*, tubercular masses obscuring the view of the atria and the truncus arteriosus; *V*, ventricle. (Photo.: Elkan.)

process has been observed in the case of a claw-footed toad (*Xenopus laevis*) where the acid-fast bacilli invaded the wall of the rectum. The resultant tumour grew to a size of 2·5×4 cm, yet not only did the peritoneal surface of the rectum remain intact, the tuberculous process also stopped sharply at the ileo-rectal junction. It extended only in the direction of the anus where it finally presented in the shape of a large polypus (Figs. 171a, b, 172). Tumours of this size naturally grow slowly and the affected toad must have suffered from complete intestinal obstruction for weeks before it died. Thus the case again demonstrates the incredible resistance of amphibians to crippling injuries and diseases

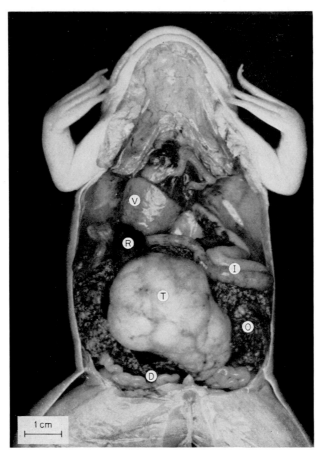

FIG. 171. (a) *Xenopus laevis* D. Adult female with tuberculosis of the rectum. *D*, Oviduct; *I*, small intestine; *O*, ovary; *R*, ileo-rectal junction distended by faecal matter; *T*, tuberculous mass obstructing the rectum; *V*, ventricle. Cf. Frontispiece, Fig. 3. (Photo.: Elkan.)

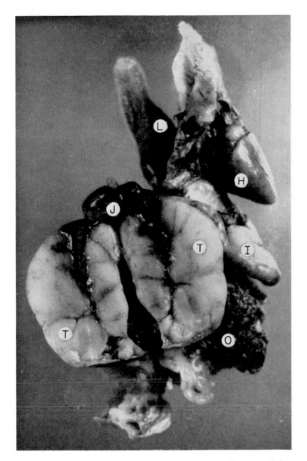

Fig. 171. (b) *Xenopus laevis*. Tuberculosis of the rectum. Tumour bisected longitudinally. *H*, heart, *I*, small intestine; *J*, ileo-rectal junction; *L*, right lung; *O*, ovary; *T*, tuberculous tumour. (Photo.: Elkan.)

which would have killed warm-blooded animals at a much earlier stage.

We may also mention a case of tuberculosis observed in another claw-footed toad (*Xenopus laevis* D.). This toad, a fully grown ♀ specimen, developed small tumours in one finger and in the web of one foot. While the finger lesion grew to the size of a peppercorn the foot tumour, during 4 months of observation, grew to the size of a hazelnut. The toad, which had previously been one of sixty kept in one tank, was isolated as soon as the disease was discovered. None of the other inmates of the tank fell ill. The isolated toad continued feeding for 3½ months while the tumour gradually grew to its final size. After refusing to feed for a fortnight the toad eventually died spontaneously. Of the viscera only the spleen and the ovary were affected and were heavily invaded by acid-fast bacteria. Since these do not seem to produce any

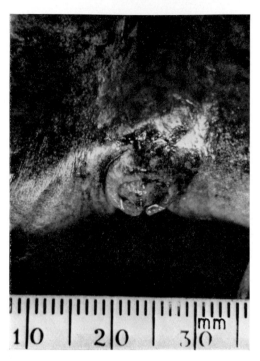

FIG. 172. *Xenopus laevis*. D. Adult female with tuberculosis of the rectum. Part of the tuberculous mass is seen protruding at the anus in form of a polyp. (Photo.: Elkan.)

exotoxins the cause of death remains doubtful. Sections through the foot lesion showed a tumour entirely made up of epithelioid cells all crammed to capacity with acid-fast bacteria. Since authors have recorded difficulties in applying the Ziehl-Neelsen staining method to tubercle bacilli derived from fish (Parisot and Decker, 1960), it might here be mentioned that this *Xenopus* strain could easily be demonstrated by the standard Z–N technique. The remarkable feature of the case is the size to which the foot tumour grew without ever causing ulceration. Sections showed that the mass of epithelioid cells and the bacteria are arrested by the zona compacta of the dermis. This layer which consists of dense strands of collagen fibres is very tough in *Xenopus* and the bacteria obviously find it easier to spread up the leg and to invade visceral organs rather than to break through to the immediately adjacent surface.

With regard to amphibian tuberculosis we are at present still at the fact-finding stage. It remains to be determined whether the various clinical pictures produced by acid-fast bacteria in poikilotherm animals are due to differences in the bacteria or in the defensive powers of the hosts. Only extensive experimental work can elucidate these points.

Amphibian tuberculosis thus presents a number of interesting pictures and problems. Fortunately it is not of very great importance to those who keep these animals either in laboratories or as pets because, though single cases may appear in any collection, the disease never assumes the extent of an epizootic and the natural immunity of the Amphibia against these bacilli must be reassuringly high. Even with the best intentions we cannot hope to keep our tanks and aquaria free from the ubiquitous *Mycobacterium*; equally we cannot hope to cure an amphibian by treatment once it has developed the disease to such a degree that it can be diagnosed *in vivo*.

INFECTION BY PSEUDOMONADS

Collections of frogs are often invaded by bacteria of the type *Aeromonas* which causes a disease similar to the much-dreaded infectious ascites of carps. The bacteriology of these invasions has not yet been investigated in every detail. In most cases we see a reddening of the skin, particularly in the abdominal and the flexor region of the legs. The skin, particularly the webbed skin of the feet, is affected by haemorrhagic inflammation, later by ulceration. The animals rarely survive.

Emerson and Norris (1905) described an epidemic disease of frogs spread all over North America and Europe and caused by *Aeromonas hydrophila*. Because of the main symptom the disease has since been known as " Red Leg", but the pink to deep red discoloration of the skin need not be confined to the legs. The diseased animals are listless and fail to react to the usual stimuli. The skin, where not affected directly by the inflammation, is pale, the lymph sacs are filled with a turbid serous effusion giving the animals an oedematous appearance. At least 50% of the affected animals are killed by the disease which is most common in September and October.

The causative organism, now called *Aeromonas hydrophila*, appeared first under the name of *Bacillus hydrophilus fuscus* and is similar to *Aeromonas punctata*, which is pathogenic in fish. Sanarelli (1891) reported the natural occurrence of this bacillus in wells.

Accounts of epidemics caused by *Aeromonas* have appeared repeatedly, not only among stock held in laboratories but also in the

8*

natural habitat of the affected animals when conditions became unsatisfactory.

The disease known as "Red Leg" is probably the most important infection to which frogs are subject. It is widely distributed in Europe and N. America. The organism responsible for the majority of outbreaks is *Aeromonas hydrophila*, but it should be noted that other organisms are capable of bringing about this disease. Miles (1950), for instance, has described a typical outbreak of "Red Leg" in tree frogs which was caused by *Bacterium alkaligenes*.

One of the first reports on the pathogenic effect of *Aeromonas hydrophila* (formerly known as *Bac. hydrophilus fuscus*) is that of Russell (1898). In his opinion the infection was brought about by the passage of pathogenic organisms through skin lesions.

A further and very good description of the symptoms shown by infected frogs was given by Kulp and Borden in 1942. Their report was based on the study of 130 frogs suffering from "Red Leg", including both naturally infected animals and others infected experimentally with *A. hydrophila*. They noted that, at first, the frogs became sluggish and that, a day or two later haemorrhagic areas appeared on the ventral surface. The final stage was accompanied by extreme oedema of the thighs and the abdominal region.

Autopsy of the animals revealed the presence of blood-stained fluid in the lymph sacs with petechiae present on the abdominal and thigh muscles. Haemorrhages of varying extent may also be seen on the tongue and the mouth may be filled with a blood-tinged exudate. In severe cases dermal ulcers may form and extend to the underlying muscle. The heart muscle was found pale and flaccid, the lungs highly congested and the peritoneal cavity filled with haemolized blood and exudate.

Stomach and intestine were seen to be distended and the associated blood vessels congested. The liver was mottled and of a dark brown colour and the spleen greatly enlarged. These authors noticed furthermore that the fluid contained in the gall bladder varied from light-yellow to dark-green and that bacteria could easily be isolated from the former but not from the latter variety. The kidneys, in this series, were apparently not affected.

The term "Red Leg" therefore describes a form of severe generalized sepsis caused by haemolytic bacteria easily transferred from one animal to the next. It is one of the most dangerous epizootics that can affect collections of aquatic or semi-aquatic amphibians.

Dusi (1949) observed a population of about three hundred American toads (*Bufo americanus* Lec.) in a small pond during the breeding season. The next day all but a few of the toads were found dead. Blood and tissue cultures revealed the causative organism which, when reinjected into healthy frogs, caused the typical symptoms of "Red Leg" with ulcerations and haemorrhages of the legs and the abdominal skin.

Apart from *Aeromonas hydrophila*, *Pseudomonas fluorescens granulata* Brunner and Striegel-Jaxtheimer and *Aeromonas punctata* Zimmermann can affect frogs, the latter two species being equally pathogenic for fish (Junghaenel, 1953). Frogs therefore must be regarded as potential carriers of bacteria which can become lethal to fish in streams and lakes. In the laboratory every specimen showing the slightest inflammatory discoloration of the abdominal skin combined with general listlessness and refusal to feed should at once be isolated. The cage or tank should then be emptied of animals and a thorough disinfection should be carried out while general conditions (overcrowding, lack of light, infected soil, etc.) should be improved as far as possible. In the laboratory, where overcrowding is often difficult to avoid, it has been found extremely useful to raise the salinity of the water in which the Amphibia are kept. This, of course, applies in particular to those which are completely aquatic, e.g. the South African clawed toad (*Xenopus laevis* D.) which is not gregarious naturally and has to be kept under very unnatural conditions in captivity. The salinity to which such aquaria may be adjusted is not critical but it must not exceed that of frog saline (0·6%). Experience has shown that in aquaria so adjusted, limphibians can be safely kept, even when grossly overcrowded, and that the distressing epidemics of the past which sometimes wiped out the whole stock of such collections can be avoided. Frequent examination of each single specimen kept in such tanks is nevertheless advisable because even in "salted" tanks single specimens may be attacked. If they are promptly removed, however, no epidemic need develop. If necessary the percentage of the salt level can be temporarily raised above 0·6%.

OTHER BACTERIAL INFECTIONS

In 1890 Ernst described a fatal epidemic among frogs and called it the "Spring Plague". It was caused by a Gram-negative short, rod-like bacillus of 1–3 μ length which was isolated from various organs of the common frog (*Rana temporaria*). The bacteria grew optimally at 30°C but died off at 37°C. The main symptoms observed were yellow-green discoloration and general lassitude with much yawning ending with the death of the frog. Ernst called the organism responsible *Bacterium ranicida* (Fig. 173).

Pettenkofer and Kaufmann reported in 1951 on an epidemic in frogs caused by a Gram-negative diplobacillus (*Diplobacterium ranarum*). The animals suffered from exudations, ulcerations, intestinal inflammation, oedema and increasing lassitude culminating in death. The intestine was found distended by gas and blood-stained mucus. Haemorrhagic exudates filled the lymph sacs. The causative organism

Fig. 173. *Bacterium ranicida* Ernst among red blood corpuscles of the grass frog. (After Ernst.)

could be grown on any medium and it liquefied gelatine, but its growth seemed to be very dependent on the correct temperature. Artificially infected animals died when kept at 20°C and above, but they survived at 10°C. Apart from frogs the organism was found to be pathogenic for white mice.

Urbain (1944) reported on a single case of an infection of *Rana esculenta* with *Salmonella paratyphi* B. which caused paralysis and ecchymosis of the abdominal skin.

It may finally be mentioned that Galuso and Remenzowa (1957) reported on the occurrence of *Brucella* in frogs. The importance of this report has not as yet been assessed.

BARTONELLAE AND SPIROCHAETAE

East Canadian bullfrogs (*Rana catesbeiana* Shaw) were repeatedly found to harbour spirochaetes which were described as *Spirochaeta manitoni* Fantham, Porter and Richardson (1942). The length of these spirochaetes varied between 12·5 and 16·5 μ, their width between 0·2 and 0·3 μ. Scharrer (1935) found similar parasites in Europe.

Zavattari (1931) reported on a severe infection of the frog spleen with *Bartonella ranarum*. The organism was found in erythrocytes from the spleen, the liver, the lungs and the kidneys. Infected animals died after 160–180 days.

EFFECTS OF CHRONIC INFLAMMATION

It might be mentioned here that, just as in higher vertebrates, chronic inflammation can induce the formation of heterotopic tissue, i.e. tissue which would normally not be found at the place where it occurs. A specimen of *B. bufo*, for example, was, on dissection, found

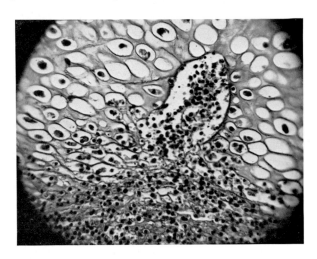

FIG. 174. *Bufo bufo.* Heterotopic cartilage from an inflammatory abdominal mass which had destroyed one kidney. (Photo.: Elkan. Courtesy Zool. Soc. Lond.)

to have died from a large inflammatory tumour which had gradually destroyed one kidney. It was not attached to any part of the toad's skeleton, yet in the centre of the mass an islet of well-formed cartilage was seen, derived probably from the numerous fibroblasts present in the inflammatory mass (Elkan, 1960) (Fig. 174).

REFERENCES

Ambrus, J. L., Ambrus, C. M. and Harrison, J. W. F. (1951). Prevention of *Proteus hydrophilus* infections (red leg disease) in frog colonies. *Amer. J. Pharm.* **123**, 129.

Breed, R. S., Murray, E. G. D. and Hitchens, A. P. (1957). "Bergey's Manual of Determinative Bacteriology", 7th edn., Baillière, Tindal and Cox, London-Baltimore.

Darzins, E. (1950). Tuberculose das Gias. Sep. *Arch. Inst. Brasil. Invest. Tubercul.* **9**, 1.

Darzins, E. (1952). The epizootic of tuberculosis among the Gias in Bahia. *Acta tuberc. scand.* **26**, 170. Abstr. in *Vet. Bull.* **22**, 444.

Dusi, J. L. (1949). The natural occurrence of "red-leg". *Pseudomonas hydrophila* in a population of American toads, *Bufo americanus. Ohio J. Sci.* **49**, 70–72.

Elkan, E. (1960). Some interesting pathological cases in amphibians. *Proc. zool. Soc., Lond.* **134**, 375–396.

Emerson, H. and Norris, C. (1905). "Red-leg", an infectious disease of frogs. *J. exp. Med.* **7**, 32–58.

Ernst, P. (1890). Die Frühjahrsseuche der Frösche und ihre Abhängigkeit von Temperatureinflüssen. *Beitr. path. Anat. allg. Path.* **8**, 203–220.

Fantham, H. B., Porter, A. and Richardson, L. R. (1942). Some Haematozoa observed in vertebrates in Eastern Canada. *Parasitology* **34**, 199–226.

Fey, F. (1962). Hämatologische Untersuchungen an *Xenopus laevis* Daudin I. Die Morphologie des Blutes mit einigen vergleichenden Betrachtungen bei *Rana esculenta* und *R. temporaria. Morph. Jahrb.* **101**, 9–20.

Francis, J. (1958). "Tuberculosis in Animals and Man." Cassel, London.

Friedmann, F. F. (1903). Der Schildkrötentuberkelbazillus, seine Züchting, Biologie und Pathogenität. *Dtsch. med. Wschr.* No. 26. Also *Zbl. Bakt.* Abt. I, **24**, 647.

Galuso, J. G. and Remenzowa, M. M. (1957). Les réservoirs et les vecteurs de l'infection brucellique dans la nature. Ref. in *Bull. Inst. Pasteur* **55**, 1139.

Griffith, A. S. (1930). Tuberculosis in cold-blooded animals. "A System of Bacteriology in Relation to Medicine", Vol. 5, 326–332.

Griffith, A. S. (1930). Infections of wild animals with tubercle bacilli and other acid-fast bacilli. *Proc. roy. Soc. Med.* **32**, 1405.

Griffith, A. S. (1941). The susceptibility of the water (or grass-) snake (*Tropidonotus natrix*) to the avian tubercle bacillus and to reptilian strains of acid-fast bacilli. *J. Hyg., Camb.* **41**, 284.

Jacob, E. (1909). Zur Pathologie der Urodelen und Anuren. *Zool. Anz.* **34**, 628–638.

Jung, T. (1955). Zur Kenntnis der Ernährungsbiologie der in dem Raum zwischen Harz und Heide vorkommenden Hirudineen. *Zool. Jb. Phys.* **66**, 79–128.

Junghaenel, H. (1953). Die pathogene Wirkung verschiedener Bakterien der Gattung *Pseudomonas* auf Wasserfrösche. (*Rana esculenta*). Diss. München.

Küester, E. (1905). Ueber Kaltblütertuberkulose. *Münch. med. Wschr.* No. 2.

Küester, E. (1928). Die Kaltblütertuberkulose. *In* "Handbuch der pathogenen Mikroorganismen" (Kolle and Wassermann, eds.), 3rd edn. Vol. V, pt. 2, p. 1037. G. Fischer, Jena.

Kükenthal-Matthes, W. (1953). "Leitfaden für das Zoologische Praktikum", 13th edn. Fischer, Stuttgart.

Kulp, W. L. and Borden, D. G. (1942). Further studies on *Proteus hydrophilus*, the etiological agent in "red-leg disease" of frogs. *J. Bact.* **44**, 673.

Ledoux-Lebard (1900). Le Bacille pisciaire et la tuberculose de la grenouille due à ce bacille. *Ann. Inst. Pasteur* **14**, 535–554.

Lichtenstein, S. (1921). Ein Fall von spontaner Froschtuberkulose. *Zbl. Bakt. Parasitol.* **85**, 249–252.

Miles, E. M. (1950). "Red-leg" in Tree Frogs caused by *Bacterium alkaligenes. J. gen. Microbiol.* **4**, 434.

Parisot, Th. J. and Decker, A. H. (1960). A comparative study of the causative agent of a mycobacterial disease of salmonid fishes. I. *Amer. Rev. resp. Dis.* **81**, No. 1, 59–67.

Parisot, Th. J. and Wood, E. M. (1960). A comparative study of the causative agent of a mycobacterial disease of salmonoid fishes. II. *Amer. Rev. resp. Dis.* **82**, No. 2, 211–222.

Pettenkofer, H. and Kaufmann, F. (1951). Zur Immunität der Kaltblüter. *Arch. Hyg. Bakt.* **134**, 300–313.

Reed and Toner (1942). *Proteus hydrophilus* infections in pike, trout and frogs. *Canad. J. Res.* 20 D. 161–166.

Russell, F. H. (1898). An epidemic septicemic disease among frogs due to the *Bacillus hydrophilus fuscus*. *J. Amer. med. Ass.* **30**, 1442.

Sanarelli, G. (1891). Uber einen neuen Mikroorganismus des Wassers welcher für Tiere mit veränderlicher und konstanter Temperatur pathogen ist. *Zbl. Bakt.* **9**, 193–199; 222–228.

Scharrer, B. (1935). Über Spirochaeta (*Treponema minutum* Dobell) bei Amphibien. *Zool. Anz.* **111**, 1–7.

Schwabacher, H. (1959). A strain of *Mycobacterium* isolated from skin lesions of a cold-blooded animal, *Xenopus laevis* and its relation to typical acid-fast bacilli occurring in man. *J. Hyg., Camb.* **57**, 57–67.

Scott, H. (1926). A mycotic disease of batrachians. *Proc. zool. Soc. Lond.*, pt. II., 683–692.

Stuckrad, J. v. (1955). Untersuchungen eines Kaltblütertuberkuloseerregers *Mycobacterium giae*. Diss. Munich.

Urbain, A. (1944). La paratyphose des grenouilles. (*Rana esculenta*). *C.R. Soc. Biol., Paris* **183**, 458–459.

Vallé, H. and Panisset, L. (1920). "Les Tuberculeuses Animales." Doin fils, Paris. cf. for further literature.

Weber, A. and Taute, M. (1905). Die Kaltblütertuberkulose. Tuberkulosearbeiten aus dem kaiserl. Gesundheitsamt, Berlin. H.3.

Zavattari, E. (1931). Bartonellosi nelle rane smilzate. *Bull. Soc. ital. Biol. sper.* **6**, 120–122.

B. DISEASES CAUSED BY PROTOZOA

MASTIGOPHORA

Unicellular animals bearing flagella have a wide distribution both as free-living forms and as parasites. It is not surprising, therefore, that a considerable number have been found inhabiting amphibians. They can be found in various humoral fluids (blood, intestinal), in the skin of aquatic caudates, mostly as harmless guests (commensals), in some cases of doubtful benefit to the host. Only *Oodinium* is known to be definitely harmful.

These flagellates belong to the Orders Protomonadina, Polymastigina Rhizomastigina, Dinoflagellata and Opalinida (Protociliata). Those occurring in amphibians will be dealt with in this order (Fig. 175).

A number of Protomonadina can be found in the blood of amphibians. They are in most cases slender flagellates, equipped with a varying number of flagella. The best-known among them are the *Trypanosoma*, inhabitants of the blood and distinguished by possessing an undulating membrane. Their presence is usually discovered because of their rapid wavy motion. *Trypanosoma rotatorium* Mayer is frequently found in the blood of *Rana esculenta*. This is one of the largest species of *Trypanosoma*. It has a comparatively broad body. Repeated investigations have shown that a leech, *Hemiclepis marginata* L., functions as intermediate host and that the infection is acquired in the tadpole stage. The species observed in the tree frog (*Hyla arborea*) is probably identical with the one described. There is no proof so far that it causes any disease. *Trypanosoma inopinatum* Sergent, found in the blood of Algerian frogs and equally transmitted by a leech, has a slightly narrower body. *Trypanosoma bocagei* Franca has been found in African and East Asian toads. The intermediate host is, in this case, a mosquito sucking blood from the toads.

Recent investigations on specimens of *Rana esculenta* in Upper Bavaria showed these to be parasitized not only by *Trypanosoma rotatorium* of 60–90 μ but also by a much smaller and slenderer species of 20–30 μ length. It has not been possible yet to establish whether the latter belongs to a separate species or not.

This does not exhaust the list of flagellates which may be found in amphibians. Fantham, Porter and Richardson (1942) discovered in the N. American toad *Bufo americanus* Lec. the following *Trypanosoma*:

(1) *Trypanosoma lavalia* F., P. and R.: a protozoon with the impressive length of 31–35·5 μ and a width of 3·9–4·4 μ equipped with a free flagellum 1·5–2·6 μ long.

(2) *Trypanosoma gaumontis* F., P. and R.: smaller than the previous form, with two variants of 15–15·8 μ and 19·7–20·7 μ length and 1·3–1·85 μ and 1·5–1·85 μ width respectively.

(3) *Trypanosoma montrealis* F., P. and R.: one of the largest trypanosomes of 45–68 μ length, 1·9–6 μ width and a long free flagellum of 3–5·5 μ.

The same authors reported the presence of the ubiquitous *Trypanosoma rotatorium* Mayer in Canadian frogs.

If the infections with these flagellates become very heavy the host animals suffer. They become listless, refuse food and are eventually killed by the parasites.

Apart from frogs, North American newts have also been found to harbour haemoflagellates. *Trypanosoma diemyctyli* Tobey has been found in *Diemyctylus viridescens* Raf., *Trypanosoma tritonis* Ogawa in the Japanese newt *Cynops pyrrhogaster* Boie.

The Polymastigina appear as a very varied group embracing several species of amphibians. They are all either harmless commensals or they may be found in debilitated animals. They belong to the genus

Hexamita (= *Octomitus*) (*Diplomonadina*) and most of them live in the intestinal fluid.

One of the commonest Polymastigina is *Hexamita intestinalis* Duj. with a slender pear-shaped body, equipped with eight flagella, two of which act as drag lines. The length of this protozoon varies between 4–10 μ. The intestine and the gall bladder of *Rana esculenta* L. are often found inundated by these creatures which, notwithstanding their enormous number, do not seem to interfere with the normal life of the frog. Some of them were even seen in the blood, swimming about among the erythrocytes and immediately attracting attention by their rapid movement. As they swim, their shape varies between square and slender.

Frandsen and Grundmann (1951) reported *Hexamita pulcher* Becker from Utah, U.S.A.

Some of the rarer multiflagellate forms appear occasionally as harmless inhabitants of the intestine, e.g. *Giardia agilis* Künstler can be found in the tadpoles of frogs and toads. This species has a slightly more elongated body and attaches itself to the intestinal wall after the manner of *Lamblia*.

Chilomastix caulleryi Alexeieff, a form equipped with three flagella, may be found in the intestine of frogs, toads, salamanders and axolotls. It has a finely drawn-out posterior end and may reach a length of 20–25 μ.

The last two flagellates mentioned do not seem to be definitely pathogenic to their hosts and this also holds for the following species which are occasionally encountered without assuming a great significance. *Retortomonas dobelli* Bishop, for example, and *Retortomonas rotunda*, a species related to *Chilomastix* and armed with three flagella, have been found in frogs, toads and salamanders often in company with *Monocercomonas batrachorum* Dobell and species of the genus *Tritrichomonas*, e.g. *Tritrichomonas batrachorum* Perty and *Tritrichomonas augusta* Alexeieff. The various shapes of these species are best seen in the illustrations (Fig. 175). While *Hexamastix batrachorum* Alexeieff, encountered in newts, is comparatively rare, *Trichomonas prowazeki* Alexeieff is frequently seen (cf. André, 1913; Odening, 1955) in the intestine of several amphibians.

The Order Rhizomastigina is distinguished by a reduction in the number of the flagella and an amoeboid body. Like the previously mentioned Protozoa they occur in the intestine of frogs and toads. They have been investigated by Becker (1925). He described a peculiar protozoon, *Mastigina hylae* Frenzel (Fig. 176), about 100 μ long and 28 μ wide, which lived in the rectum of the tadpoles of the South American

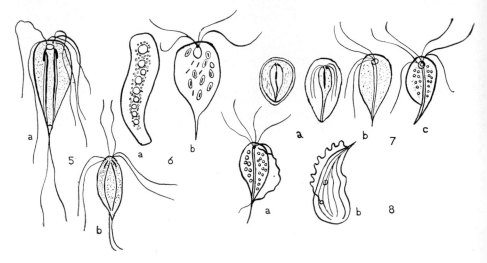

FIG. 175. Flagellates and rhizopodes found in amphibians.
5. *Hexamita intestinalis* Duj. × 3 000. a, Nach Doflein-Reichenow; b, drawn from life.
6. a, *Vahlkampfia ranarum* Epst. and Ilowaisky. × 600; b, *Chilomastix caullery* Alexeieff. × 1 000. (Both after Doflein-Reichenow.)
7. a, *Retortomonas dobelli* Bishop × 1 800; b, *Monocercomonas batrachorum* Dobell. × 1 000; c, *Hexamastix batrachorum* Alexeieff. × 1 000. (All after Doflein-Reichenow.)
8. a, *Trichomonas prowazeki* Alexeieff. × 1 000; b, *Trypanosoma rotatorium* Mayer. × 850. (All after Doflein-Reichenow.)

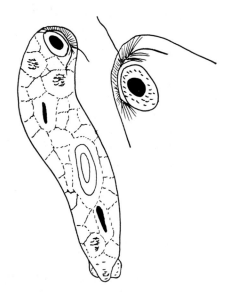

FIG. 176. *Mastigina hylae* Frenzel. × 690. Right: Anterior extremity enlarged. × 1 200. (After Becker.)

Hyla raddiana Fitzinger as well as in North American species of *Rana* and perhaps also in the European species *Alytes obstetricans* Laur. and *Bufo calamita* Laur. It is often seen in enormous numbers but it has not been held responsible for any particular disease.

Of the "armoured" Dinoflagellata, *Oodinum pillularis* Schäperclaus has been familiar as a parasite on the skin of fish but it has lately repeatedly been reported from aquatic amphibians. Geus (1960) found *Oodinum* on axolotls and tadpoles (Fig. 177). The Oodinia are true

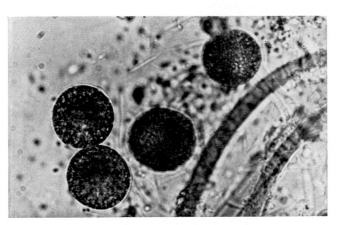

Fig. 177. *Oodinium pillularis* Schäperclaus. Free-swimming stages before settling down. × 750. Photo.: Matthes. (After Geus.)

parasites which anchor themselves in the skin and in the gills of the host by protoplasmic pseudopodia. Externally the pear-shaped animals are protected by a cellulose membrane. Their size varies between 40–80 μ. They often populate the host epithelium in such density that it seems to be covered by a fine grey deposit. Their life cycle includes a free-swimming stage. The parasitic stage develops into free-swimming forms, the so-called dinospores, which have the shape of free-living dinoflagellates equipped with one longitudinal trailing flagellum and another placed around the equator of the body. These dinospores multiply by continued fission and live free in the water. If within 24 h they have not reached their specific host they perish. Otherwise they adhere to the skin of the host and change again into the parasitic shape. Geus warns of epidemics of this kind which must be expected to break out among aquatic newts. Copper sulphate (2 mg/l of water) and trypaflavin (10 mg/l of water) have been found useful in fighting the epidemic.

Opalina, another type of multiflagellate Protozoa, can be said to be almost ubiquitous in the amphibian intestine. It can be found in every single specimen unless this has been brought up under sterile conditions in the laboratory. These Protozoa are always harmless. They do not even compete in the consumption of food since they occur in the rectum where digestion has, in any case, finished and no absorption of useful material takes place.

Because of their uniform ciliation *Opalina* has previously had its place among the ciliates. It is now counted among the flagellates because the individuals are multi-nucleate and because their plane of cleavage in cell division is that characteristic of the latter.

The species most commonly seen is *Opalina ranarum* Ehrenberg, a flat oval shape moving with a continual spiral movement (Fig. 178).

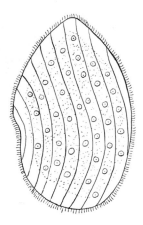

Fig. 178. *Opalina ranarum* Ehrenberg. × 100. (After Doflein-Reichenow.)

Hundreds of specimens are often seen in the intestine of all sorts of frogs and toads. Similar but slightly rarer are the species *Opalina obtrigona* Stein, *Cepedea dimidiata* Stein and *Protoopalina intestinalis* Stein. All these types are of a remarkable size. *Opalina ranarum* may grow to 0·3 mm and can, placed against a dark background, be seen with the naked eye. *Cepedea* and *Protoopalina* have an almost circular shape.

Opalina ranarum inhabits mainly species like *Rana* and *Bombina*; it has also once been reported from *Triturus alpestris*, whereas *Opalina obtrigona* is found in *Hyla arborea*. *Protoopalina intestinalis* inhabits mainly *Bombina*, probably also *Pelobates fuscus*, other frogs and newts. A very rare species, *Protoopalina mitotica* Metcalf, is found in the axolotl (*Siredon mexicanum* Say); *Cepedea dimidiata* in the gut of frogs and toads. It is recognized by its almost circular shape.

RHIZOPODA (SARCODINA)

Of the parasitic rhizopodes only the amoebic *Entamoeba ranarum* (Grassi) is of pathological importance. It is reported to occur frequently in the gut and the liver of larvae of frogs and toads. In the encysted state it is almost indistinguishable from similar species.

Reichenow found in the rectum of frogs another amoeba, *Vahlkampfia ranarum* Epstein and Ilowaisky, which reaches a length of up to 50 μ. No details are known as yet about this species (Fig. 175, 2).

Other amoeboid Protozoa which may be seen in amphibians are *Entamoeba pyrrhogaster*, *Copramoeba salamandrae* and *Vahlkampfia salamandrae*. For details the original communication by Lobeck (1940) should be consulted.

Another type of rhizopode occurring in amphibians is mentioned by Frandsen and Grundmann (1961) who describe *Cytamoeba bacterifera* from the axolotl (*Ambystoma tigrinum*) in which, however, it is not seen very frequently.

SPOROZOA

The Sporozoa are unicellular organisms, all of them of parasitic habits, which reproduce by forming spores. In contrast to the Mastigophora, whose presence cannot be detected with the naked eye, the Sporozoa produce easily visible small cysts and tumours in the skin or in the muscular system of amphibians. In the case of a dermal lesion a dignosis may therefore be made while the "patient" is still alive.

Those belonging to the Sub-order Eimeridea (Order Coccidia) (Fig. 179) parasitize the digestive system where they live in the gut, the bile duct and the liver. *Eimeria salamandrae* Steinhaus produces spherical cysts in the intestine of the salamander which may contain either the female oocysts, male microgametes or fully formed spores. The species may live both in the nucleus and in the cytoplasm of the intestinal epithelium. *Eimeria grobbeni* Rudovsky, however, lives exclusively in the nuclei of the intestinal epithelium of *Salamandra atra* L. Some Eimeriae, living in the gut of newts, produce oblong oocysts, e.g. *Eimeria propria* Schneider and *Eimeria canaliculata* Lavier. In others, as in *Eimeria tertia* Lavier and *Eimeria spherica* Schneider, the oocysts are of spherical shape. Two species of *Eimeria* have been found in frogs: *E. ranarum* Labbé in the gut of *Rana esculenta*, and *E. neglecta* in the tadpole of the same species. As for toads, *Eimeria laminata* Ray has been found in the Indian *Bufo melanostictus*. Details of these infections are given in the original publications (Fig. 180).

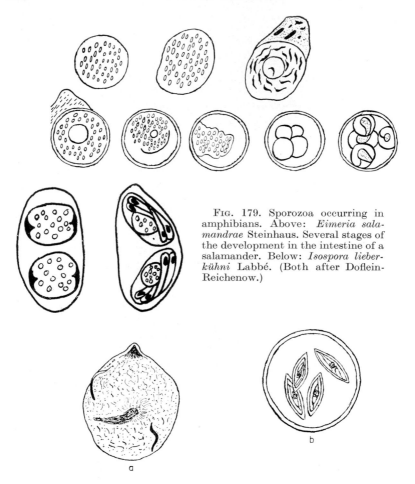

Fig. 179. Sporozoa occurring in amphibians. Above: *Eimeria salamandrae* Steinhaus. Several stages of the development in the intestine of a salamander. Below: *Isospora lieberkühni* Labbé. (Both after Doflein-Reichenow.)

Fig. 180. *Eimeria laminata* Ray from *Bufo melanostictus* Schneider. (a) Macrogamete with two microgametes; (b) mature oocyst. × 3500. (After Ray, 1935.)

The allied genus *Isospora*, distinguished from *Eimeria* by the fact that each cyst produces two instead of four spores and which occasionally parasitizes higher vertebrates as well, is also occasionally met with in amphibians. *Isospora lieberkühni* Labbé may occur in the kidney of *Rana esculenta, R. temporaria* and toads. *Isospora*, discovered in tree frogs, are *Isospora hylae* Mesnil; in Brasilian hylids *Isospora cruzi* Pinto and Vallin, *Isospora wenyoni* Ray and Das Gupta from the Indian *Bufo melanostictus* and *Isospora brumpti* Lavier from a Syrian *Bufo viridis*. Because of the rarity of these infections we again refer for details to the original publications.

The Haemosporidia which, like those causing malaria, parasitize the red blood corpuscles of amphibians, are of great interest and importance (Fig. 181). Most of them are small organisms which are

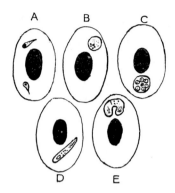

FIG. 181. Blood parasites occurring in amphibians. A–C, *Dactylosoma ranarum* Hintze in erythrocytes. D, E, *Lankesterella minima* Chaussat in erythrocytes of the grass frog. (After Hintze.)

transmitted by blood-sucking animals. Among these the leeches are under particular suspicion (Nöller, 1920). Having gained admittance, the early stages of the parasite penetrate the erythrocytes, where they grow and multiply by division. The blood corpuscles are consumed and finally exploded. The liberated organisms enter new erythrocytes and repeat the process. Eventually a sexual generation with female macro- and male microgametes arises. The host eventually dies of the progressively increasing anaemia.

These blood parasites seem to be widely distributed among frogs. Privora (1948) found *Lankesterella minima* Chaussat in 60% of a N. E. Bohemian population of *Rana esculenta*, in one case associated with the related protozoon *Dactylosoma ranarum* Kruse. The *Lankesterella* are ovoid structures, approximately of the size of an erythrocyte nucleus. In the case reported these intranuclear parasites had affected the eye, detached the retina and destroyed the ciliary body. *Dactylosoma* also invade the erythrocytes but can easily be distinguished from *Lankesterella* because of this curved shape and smaller size. The author mentions that 1–7% of the red cells were affected in his specimens. He was the first (1948) to try treatment of this condition with Atebrin, a drug active in malarial infection in man, but he could not observe any beneficial results in frogs.

Lehmann (1959) reported finding a peculiar blood parasite, *Haemo-gregarina boyli* Lehmann, in the Californian yellow-legged frog *Rana boyli boyli*. The following other blood parasites have been found in North American amphibians (Fig. 182):

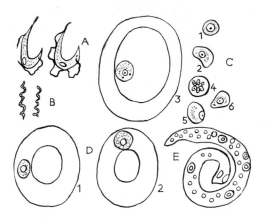

Fig. 182. Blood parasites occurring in Canadian amphibians.
  A, *Trypanosoma gaumontis* Fantham, Porter and Richardson. × 900.
  B, *Spirochaeta manitoni* F., P. and R. × 1 200.
  C, *Plasmodium catesbeiana* F., P. and R. × 900. 1, 2, 3 and 4 drawn without erythro-
    cytes.
  1–3, Trophozoit; 4, schizont; 5, macrogamete; 6, microgamete. (After Fantham,
    Porter and Richardson.)
  D, *Dactylosoma silvatica* F., P. and R. × 900. 1, Amoeboid stage; 2, multinuclear
    schizont.
  E, "*Microfilaria ranae sylvaticae*" F., P. and R. (After Fantham, Porter and Richard-
    son.)

(1) *Lankesterella canadensis* Fantham, Porter and Richardson in the blood of the bull frog *Rana catesbeiana* Shaw. Length: 10·6–19·2 μ; width: 3·7–7·8 μ.

(2) *Plasmodium catesbeiana* F. P. and R. in the blood of the same host.

(3) *Plasmodium bufonis* F. P. and R. in the N. American toad *Bufo americanus*.

(4) *Haemoproteus laurentiae* F. P. and R. ⎫
(5) *Haemoproteus lavalis* F. P. and R.   ⎬ in the same species.
(6) *Haemoproteus lanoraica* F. P. and R. ⎭

(7) *Dactylosoma silvatica* F. P. and R. in *Rana sylvatica* Le Conte.

The Myxosporidia are predominantly parasites of fish. *Myxobolus hylae* Johnston and Nancroft was however found in the Australian Golden Tree frog (*Hyla aurea*) parasitizing testes and ovaria. Equally Guyénot and Naville (1922) described *Myxobolus ranae* from *Rana temporaria* (Fig. 183). *Myxobolus* is rarely seen in amphibians. It may be recognized from the relatively large size of the spores (length 8–12 μ) with their two typical pear-shaped polar capsules.

Guyénot and Naville (loc. cit.) reported on a specimen of *R. temporaria* in which they found a double infection of *Myxobolus* and a microsporidian. The latter they thought to be identical with *Glugea danilewskyi*

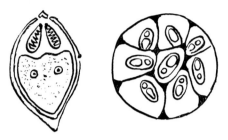

FIG. 183. Left: Mature spore of *Myxobolus ranae* Guyénot and Naville from a dermal tumour of *Rana temporaria* L. × 2 160. (After Guyénot and Naville.) Right: Pansporoblast of *Plistophora bufonis* Guyénot and Ponse with macrospores. From Bidder's organ of a common toad. × 2 250. (After Guyénot and Ponse.)

FIG. 184. *Bufo bufo* L. Adult males. Both specimens came from the same habitat and were caught at the same time. A, Toad infected for 2 months with *Plistophora myotrophica* Canning & Elkan. B, Toad infected for 2 years. Specimen B died shortly after this photograph was taken. (Photo.: Elkan. Courtesy *J. Protozool.*)

Pfeiffer, a parasite found by Danilewsky in frogs and turtles in the Ukraine (1891). Unfortunately the descriptions of these earlier authors are not definite enough to allow for an exact evaluation of this parasite. It would have been interesting to see their material because a similar

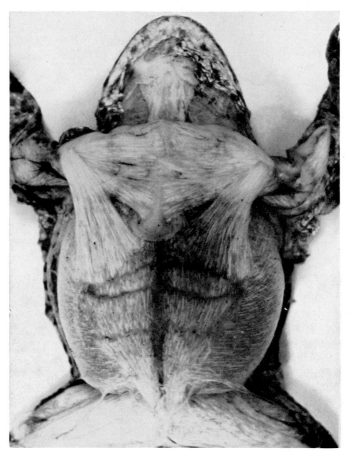

FIG. 185. *Bufo bufo* L. Adult ♂ heavily infected with *Plistophora myotrophica* Canning & Elkan. Abdominal wall expanded to show the numerous depots of spores (white lines) between the muscle fibres. All skeletal muscles are affected. × 4. (Photo.: Elkan Courtesy *J. Protozool.*)

infection has recently been observed among large numbers of common toads (*B. bufo* L.) obtained for pregnancy tests from the neighbourhood of Hemel Hempstead (Hertfordshire, England). It was noticed that, in spite of meticulous husbandry and regular feeding, the mortality among the *Bufo* stock was very much higher than that among the stock of *Xenopus* kept for the same purpose. About one-third of the toads refused to feed after having been in captivity from 3 to 12 months. They became emaciated and died (Figs. 184–6). It was at first thought that this high mortality could be explained by the presence of the usual multitude of helminths in the toad's intestine. In this respect the toad is the stickle-back of the amphibian world: no other amphibian is as abundantly infested with parasites of all kinds, and large clumps of nematodes certainly may cause intestinal obstruction and death. It was found, however, that many toads, found dead and emaciated, had very few worms and the cause of death was not ascertained until their muscular system was examined. It was then found that every striated muscle with the exception of the heart was infected by a microsporidium The fusiform depots follow the direction of the muscle fibres and, where these cross, as in the lateral abdominal wall, the white lines, representing the microsporidian depots, cross as well (Fig. 186). The parasite, which

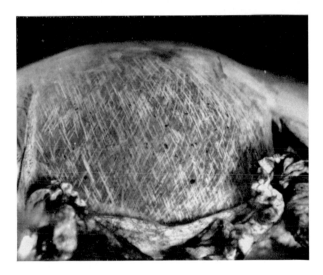

FIG. 186. *Bufo bufo* L. Adult ♂ heavily infected with *Plistophora myotrophica* Canning & Elkan. Lateral abdominal wall, expanded to show the depots of spores in the muscle fibres. As the Mm. obliqui int. and ext. cross so do the *Plistophora* depots. × 3. (Photo.: Elkan. Courtesy *J. Protozool.*)

was found to produce 60–100 spores from one sporoblast, was deter-mined as a *Plistophora*. Though similar in its clinical manifestation to the one described by Danilewsky, it could not be identical because the earlier parasite produced only two spores per sporoblast and was therefore assigned to *Glugea*. The establishment of the rather complicated chain of development of this parasite was only possible from experi-mentally infected toads obtained from a different source and known to

be uninfected. The hatching of the amoebula in the stomach of the
toads could not be observed. The first sign of infection was the appearance
of fusiform bodies in muscular capillaries on the eighteenth day after
infection (Fig. 187. 2a). It was impossible to treat the disease and toads

FIG. 187. *Plistophora myotrophica*. Life cycle in skeletal muscle of *Bufo bufo* L.
1, Emergence of sporoplasm; 2, granular body (2a) in capillary at 18 days; 3, 3a,
binary fission leading to chain formation; 4, 4a, 5, multiple fission of tetranucleate
schizonts; widening depot; 6, 6a, plasmotomy of octonucleate schizonts; 7–11, sporont
formation; 12, group of sporoblasts; 13, group of spores; 14, mature spore. Courtesy
J. Protozool.)

died at between 3 and 12 months after infection. Transmission to toad
tadpoles failed. In one case a specimen of *R. temporaria* could be infected. On the whole the parasite seemed to be host-specific.

In specimens where parts of the femoral muscle were in an advanced state of disorganization long chains of sarcoblasts appeared (Fig. 188). Their identity was established by Giemsa and Feulgen staining. The chains were often over 30 nuclei long and were similar to those seen by Godman (1957) in experimental rabbits, only very much longer. They obviously represented an attempt at muscle regeneration which failed, just like the simultaneous feeble attempt on the part of monocytes to phagocytize spores. The defensive powers of the toad are not equal to cope with an infection of this severity.

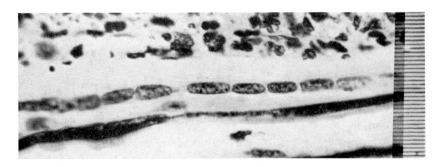

FIG. 188. Chain of sarcoblasts in skeletal muscle of *Bufo bufo* L. heavily infected with *Plistophora myotrophica* Canning & Elkan. These chains, often found over 30 nuclei long, represent a last desperate attempt at muscle regeneration. Stain: Giemsa. Scale 1·7 μ. (Photo.: Elkan. Courtesy *J. Protozool.*)

It is interesting to speculate on the source which infected these toads. Experiments showed that they could not have been infected in the larval stage. Toads feed only on land, after the breeding season. Slugs, worms, beetles and other insects are their staple food but none of these are known to be carriers of this parasite. A toad which died from a *Plistophora* infection might infect an area of soil but it is difficult to see how so many toads (we examined about 150) could have become infected. The infection was first seen in 1961 and again, on a smaller scale, in 1962. It seems to be endemic in the area where the toads were caught.

Plistophora, otherwise mainly a parasite of fishes and insects, was also found in Bidder's organ (Guyénot and Ponse, 1926). On the whole its appearance in an amphibian must be regarded as very exceptional. The new species, affecting *Bufo bufo* only, was described as *Plistophora myotrophica* Elkan (1963). Experiments are now being carried out to show whether the infection can be transmitted by *Lucilia* maggots feeding on dead infested foods. This possibility, if confirmed, would explain the sudden outbreak of the disease in a local toad population.

Nosema balantidii Lutz and Splendore may be mentioned as a secondary amphibian parasite. It occurs in *Balantidium*, a ciliate which inhabits the intestine of frogs and toads. The sporont of *Nosema* produces one spore only.

The commonest Sporozoa found in amphibians are probably the Haplosporidia and some related groups whose systematic determination is as yet uncertain. All Haplosporidia produce dermal cysts, easily visible without detailed examination. They have no polar capsule; the spore, which is round, opens by way of a lid. A genus commonly seen in amphibians and occasionally also in fish is *Dermocystidium* (Fig. 189).

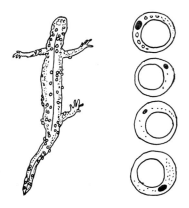

Fig. 189. Newt heavily infected with *Dermocystidium pusula* Pérez. The left leg has been amputated. (After Moral.) Right, above: Spores of *D. pusula*. (After Pérez, and Moral.) Below: Spores of *Dermocystidium ranae*. (After Guyenot and Naville.) × 1 830.

The spores of *Dermocystidium* have an eccentrically situated nucleus and mostly a large vacuole. The parasite starts as a multinuclear plasmodium which eventually divides into numerous spherical spores. In newts *Dermocystidium pusula* Pérez produces numerous pinhead-sized dermal tumours whose presence greatly debilitates the host. Moral (1913) suggested that the newts contracted the disease from eating small parasitized crustaceans. This, however, has not yet been proved experimentally.

Dermocystidium ranae Guyénot and Naville (Fig. 190a, b) produces U-shaped dermal cysts in anurans. It has been found in *Rana temporaria*, *R. esculenta* and *Alytes obstetricans*. The frogs are, however, never as intensely affected as by *D. pusula*, and the number of cysts remains

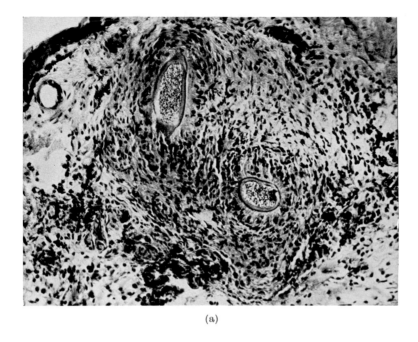

(a)

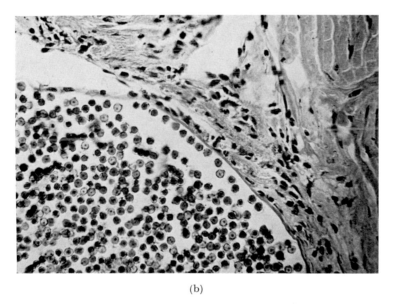

(b)

FIG. 190. *Dermocystidium ranae* Guyénot and Naville. (a) Section showing two cysts; (b) cortex of cyst with sporoblasts. × 200. (After Broz and Privora.)

small. Recently this parasite has been reported from Northern Bohemia (Broz and Privora, 1952).

A few further forms which are more rarely seen and whose systematic place is as yet uncertain must here be mentioned. *Dermosporidium*

(a)

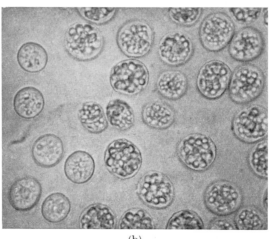

(b)

FIG. 191. *Dermosporidium granulosum* Broz and Privora. (a) Naked eye view of cyst; (b) spores. × 2 000. (After Broz and Privora.)

hylae Carini produces spherical tumours in the subcutis of the tree-frog *Hyla rubra* Daudin, from S. America. The cysts are usually found filled with innumerable spherical spores. A similar species is *Dermosporidium granulosum* (Fig. 191a, b) described by Broz and Privora in

1952. This parasite produces semispherical tumours in the subcutaneous tissue of *Rana temporaria*, considerably larger (4–8 mm diameter as against 0·4–0·5 in *D. hylae*) than those of the former. It is remarkable to note that this parasite which, on the whole, is rarely seen, infected about 30% of a frog population in an area of Bohemia.

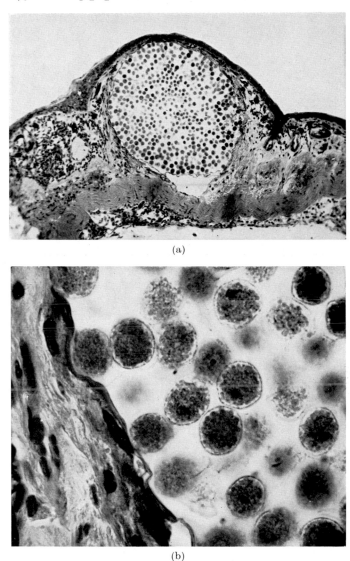

(a)

(b)

FIG. 192. *Dermosporidium multigranulare* Broz and Kulda. (a) Section through a dermal cyst; (b) cortical area of cyst. × 1 000;

9

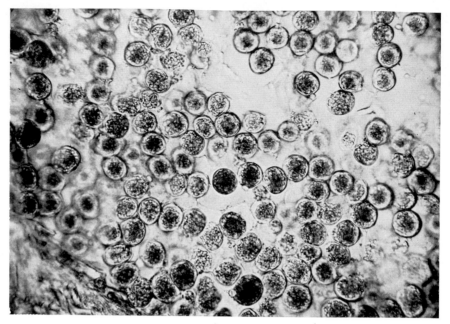

FIG. 192. (c) Central area of cyst. × 333. (After Broz and Kulda.)

Broz and Kulda have recently described a third species, *Dermosporidium multigranulare*, occurring in the skin of *Rana esculenta* of the same area, where it produces cylindrical cysts in the skin of the frogs. The spores have twice the size of *D. granulosum* (18 μ). The cysts measure about 0·35–2 mm. Fig. 192c shows a section through a whole cyst and spores at higher magnification.

We should here like to mention *Dermomycoides* although some authors (Poisson) hold this organism to be a fungus and not a protozoon. Here again we find spherical cysts filled with small round corpuscles. Two species are known: *Dermomycoides armoriacus* Poisson (Fig. 193) and *Dermomycoides beccari* Granata. Poisson, who found this parasite in the skin of *Triturus helveticus* in France, described it in detail in 1937. The external appearance of the diseased newt is very similar to the one infected by *Dermocystidium pusula* Pérez. Sections through the cysts also look very similar to those of *Dermocystidium* or *Dermosporidium*. Fig. 193 shows two stages in the growth of this organism. Pathologically the genus does not seem to be of great importance since it has not so far been seen to cause any epidemics. This also holds good for *Dermomycoides beccari* Granata, which is even rarer than the former organism.

As to the Gregarinae they are, by nature, parasites of annelid worms and arthropods, occasionally also of echinoderms, molluscs, tentaculates and tunicates. They do not, usually, occur in vertebrates. Amphibia, however, feed on many of the lower orders, and their

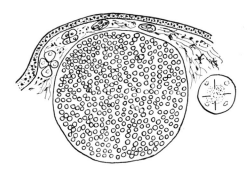

FIG. 193. Section through a subcutaneous cyst of *Dermomycoides armoriacus* Poisson from *Triturus helveticus*. About × 35. (After Poisson.)

parasites, having in this way gained entrance, may stay alive for some time and may even spread to organs distant from the digestive tract. This kind of parasitism has been observed in *Lacerta agilis* (quoted by Reichenow, 1953). Nöller even found spores in the liver and the gut of young specimens and tadpoles of *Rana temporaria* very similar to *Nematopsis*. He therefore called them *Nematopsis temporariae*. We have ourselves found spores, probably of Gregarinae, in a specimen of *Pleurodeles waltli* kindly sent in by A. Kleinschmidt, Stuttgart.

CILIATA

The ciliated Protozoa associated with amphibians live, like the Opalinidae, mostly in the rectum, nourishing themselves from what remains of the digestive process. Numerically *Balantidium* is by far the most commonly encountered species (Fig. 194a).

Like the other members of this genus *Balantidium entozoon* Ehrenberg has an oval, anteriorly blunt body, and a well-visible deep oral funnel. It grows to a length of 0·1–0·6 mm.

Much smaller forms are *Balantidium duodeni* Stein (0·075 mm) and *Balantidium ranarum* Ghosh (6·5 μ), a little more slender is *Balantidium elongatum* Stein (0·1–0·3 mm long). All these species are mainly inhabitants of anurans but they can also be encountered in newts and axolotls. In these, Jirovec (1930) found a new species, *Balantidium amblystomatis* of only 43·5 × 33 μ, one of the smallest Balantidia known.

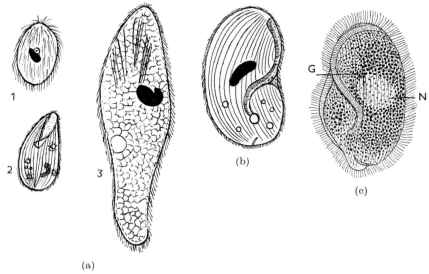

(a)

FIG. 194. (a) Ciliates occurring in amphibians.
1, *Balantidium amblystomatis* Jirovec. × 340. (After Jirovec.) 2, *Balantidium entozoon* Ehrenberg × 150. (After Doflein-Reichenow.) 3, *Balantidium elongatum* Stein. × 340. (After Doflein-Reichenow.)
(b) *Nyctotherus cordiformis* Ehrenberg. × 240. (After Kükenthal-Matthes.)
(c) *Nyctotherus* from the cloaca of a frog. Stained to show the glycogen granules. G, Glycogen granules; N, nucleus. (From Hyman after Barfurth.)

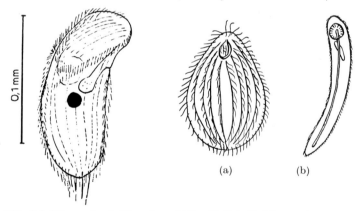

FIG. 195. *Colpidium colpoda* Ehrenberg.(After Doflein-Reichenow.)
FIG. 196. (a) *Tetrahymena pyriformis* Ehrenberg. × 550; (b) *Haptophrya gigantea* Maupas. × 40. (Both after Doflein-Reichenow.)

Bhatia and Gulati (1927) discovered several species in Indian anurans and reviewed those known up to that time.

In the company of *Balantidium* we often find *Nyctotherus* (Fig. 194b, c). This ciliate, heart- or kidney-shaped, has a convex dorsal and concave abdominal shape. The commonest species is *Nyctotherus cordiformis* Ehrenberg, widely distributed among frogs, toads and their larvae. Bhatia and Gulati *loc. cit.* described further species from Indian frogs.

While all these ciliates may be regarded as harmless commensals, others must be listed as definitely harmful parasites. Of those devoid of adhesive organs we must mention the genera *Glaucoma*, *Tetrahymena* and *Colpidium* (Fig. 195), all grouped together as Tetrahymenidae (Fig. 196). These forms seem inclined to change from free-living organisms to saprophytes and eventually to definite parasites. *Colpidium colpoda* Ehrenberg may be found in waters somewhat dirty and putrid and on the surface of fish eggs, where it seems to feed, executing circular movements.

Another frequent inhabitant of putrefying water is *Tetrahymena pyriformis* Ehrenberg, a species which has also been found in human faeces. This ciliate has recently been used as a test organism in physiological investigations, particularly on the efficacy of antibiotic drugs. Occasionally this protozoon may also be found in the coelomic cavity of insect larvae (McArthur). This tendency towards endoparasitism is also shown by *Glaucoma*, only distinguished from *Tetrahymena* by the fact that the long axis of the oral funnel lies, not parallel to that of the body, but at an angle to the main axis. Epstein (1926) described an infection of the nervous system of fish (*Abramis brama*) by organisms of *Glaucoma* type. Shumway (1940) discovered in the brain and the connective tissue of axolotls (*A. texanum*) forty-two specimens of some type of *Glaucoma*, 60 μ long, 25 μ wide and 17 μ thick, whose body was covered with twenty rows of cilia. The exact species was unfortunately not determined. It remains doubtful whether the two parasites discovered by Epstein and Shumway respectively belong to the genus *Tetrahymena* since these were only separated from *Glaucoma* by Furgeson in 1940. The genus is not often seen in amphibians, but we must keep in mind that specimens may be transferred from insect larvae. Experimental documentation of this possibility would be desirable.

Two further ciliates, distinguished by the possession of more developed adhesive organs, must be mentioned. They are *Haptophrya* and *Trichodina*.

The Haptophrydae may be found in the gut of turbellarians and of anurans. Their anterior end is armed with an adhesive disk. The largest species, *Haptophrya gigantea* Maupas, occurs in the gut of *Bufo regularis* and *Discoglossus pictus*, where it reaches a length of up to 1 mm. *Haptophrya michiganensis* Woodhead is commonly seen in the

gut of the axolotl (*Siredon mexicanum*), and in that of the salamander
Hemidactylium scutatum. *Triturus alpestris* harbours another species,
Haptophrya tritonis Certes. It is not known as yet whether these invaders
are harmful to the hosts or not.

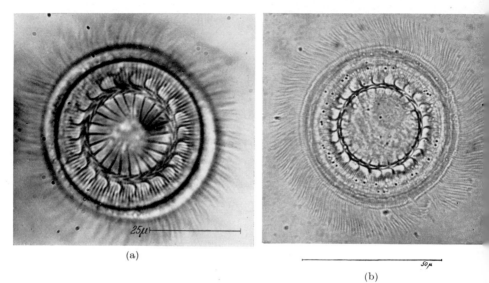

(a)

(b)

Fig. 197. (a) *Trichodina domerguei* Wallengren. (After Hirschmann and Partsch.).
(b) *Trichodina pediculus* Ehrenberg. (Photo.: Löfflath.)

Trichodina (Fig. 197), a common parasite of the skin in fish, is also
found on the skin of aquatic amphibians. The genus inhabits a great
variety of freshwater hosts. *Trichodina domerguei* Wallengren, for
example, which is commonly seen in fish, has been seen in the axolotl
and in frog tadpoles, as well as in *Triturus cristatus carnifex*. Zick (1928)
discovered the parasite in the urinary bladder of this newt. This
observation, however, must be met with suspicion since it is known
that the urinary bladder of toads and of *Necturus* may be the domicile
of another type of *Trichodina*, *T. urinicola* Fulton. *Trichodina* from
the skin and the gills can be transferred to *Hydra*, but not those taken
from the urinary bladder (Kahl, 1935). The small form *Trichodina
pediculus* Ehrenberg (the "polyp louse") attaches itself to hydra and to
tadpoles. Reports that this species too has been found in the urinary
bladder of *Rana esculenta* and *Triturus cristatus* must be regarded
sceptically.

Investigation into the classification and specificity of *Trichodina*
forms is still proceeding. Lom, who carried out extensive transfer

experiments in 1960, showed that neither *Trichodina pediculus* Ehrenberg nor *T. steini* Clap. and Lachm. would leave their hosts (*Hydra* or *Planaria*) for tadpoles, while *Trichodina reticulata* Hirschmann and Partsch and a *Trichodinella* sp. did so. Lom suggests that all species of *Trichodina* parasitizing fish will equally invade amphibians, whereas those at home on crustaceans, bivalves and planarians will not. It remains therefore to be seen if *Trichodina pediculus* Ehrenberg really occurs on amphibians.

The safest measure against these annoying skin parasites is a bath in a solution of trypaflavin 1 : 1 000–1 : 100, according to the size of the "patient".

REFERENCES

André, E. (1913). Recherches parasitologiques sur les Amphibiens de la Suisse. *Rev. suisse Zool.* **20**, 471–485; **21**, 179–200.

Becker, E. R. (1925). The morphology of *Mastigina hylae* Frenzel from the intestine of the tadpole. *J. Parasit.* **11**, 213–216.

Bhatia, B. L. and Gulati, A. N. (1927). On some parasitic ciliates from Indian frogs, toads, earthworms and cockroaches. *Arch. Protistenk.* **57**, 85–120.

Bishop, A. (1931). A description of *Embadomonas* n. sp. from *Blatta orientalis*, *Rana temporaria*, *Bufo vulgaris* and *Salamandra maculosa* with a note upon the "cyst" of *Trichomonas batrachorum*. *Parasitology* **23**, 286–300.

Bishop, A. (1932). A note upon *Retortamonas rotunda* n. sp., an intestinal flagellate in *Bufo vulgaris*. *Parasitology* **24**, 233–237.

Bishop, A. (1935). Observations upon *Chilomastix* from *Bufo vulgaris* with notes on *Chilomastix aulastomi*. *Parasitology* **27**, 507–518.

Borradaile, L. A. *et al.* (1959). "The Invertebrata", 3rd. edn. Cambridge University Press.

Broz, O. and Kulda, J. (1954). *Dermosporidium multigranulare* n. sp. parasit z kuze *Rana esculenta*. *Vestn. ceskosl. zool. spol.* **18**, 91–97.

Broz, O. and Privora, M. (1952). Two skin parasites of *Rana temporaria*: *Dermocystidium ranae* Guyénot and Naville and *Dermosporidium granulosum* n. sp. *Parasitology* **42**, 65–69.

Canning, E. U. and Elkan, E. (1964). *Plistophora myotrophica* spec. nov., causing high mortality in the common toad *Bufo bufo* L. with notes on the maintenance of *Bufo* and *Xenopus* in the laboratory. *J. Protozool.* **11**, 157–166.

Danilewsky, B. (1891). Über die Myoparasiten der Amphibian und Reptilien. *Zbl. Bakt.* **91**, 9.

Doflein, F. and Reichenow, E. (1953). "Lehrbuch der Protozoenkunde", 6th edn. G. Fischer (3 vols.).

Elkan, E. (1963). A microsporidium affecting the common toad (*Bufo bufo* L.). *Brit. J. Herpet.* **3**, No. 4, June 1963.

Epstein, H. (1926). Infektion des Nervensystems von Fischen durch Infusorien. *Arch. Russ. Prot.* **5**, 169.

Fantham, H. B., Porter, A. and Richardson, L. R. (1942). Some Haematozoa observed in vertebrates in Eastern Canada. *Parasitology* **34**, 199–226.

Frandsen, J. C. and Grundmann, A. W. (1951). The Parasites of some Amphibians of Utah. *J. Parasit.* **46**, 678.

Geus, A. (1960). Nachträgliche Bemerkungen zur Biologie des fischpathogenen Dinoflagellaten *Oodinium pillularis* Schäperclaus. *Aqu. Terr. Z.* **13**, 306.

Godman, G. C. (1957). On the regeneration and redifferentiation of mammalian striated muscle. *J. Morph.* **100**, 27–82.

Guyénot, E. (1922). Sur une Myxosporidie (*Myxobolus ranae* sp. nov.) et une Microsporidie, parasites de *Rana temporaria. Rev. suisse Zool.* **29**, 413–425.

Guyénot, E. and Naville, A. (1922). Un nouveau Protiste du genre *Dermocystidium*, parasite de la grenouille: *Dermocystidium ranae* n. sp. *Rev. suisse Zool.* **29**, 133–145.

Guyénot, E. and Ponse, K. (1926). Une Microsporidie, *Plistophora bufonis*, parasite de l'organe de Bidder du Crapaud. *Rev. suisse Zool.* **33**, 213–350.

Hyman, L. H. (1940). "The Invertebrates", Vol. I. McGraw-Hill, New York.

Jirovec, O. (1930). Ueber ein neues *Balantidium* aus dem Darmtraktus von *Amblystoma tigrinum. Z. Parasitk.* **3**, 17–21.

Kifer, W. (1933). Studies on populations of infusoria of the genus *Nyctotherus* Stein in the intestine of native frogs. *Acta parasit. polon.* **1**, 291–312.

Kudo, R. (1924). A biologic and taxonomic study of the Microsporidia. *Illin. Biol. Monographs* **9**, Nos. 2 and 3, 7–268.

Kudo, R. (1960). "Protozoology", 4th edn. C. Thomas, Springfield, Ill. U.S.A.

Kükenthal, W. and Matthes, D. (1953). "Leitfaden für das zoologische Praktikum", 13th edn. Fischer, Stuttgart.

Lavier, G. (1936). Sur la structure des Flagelles du genre *Hexamita. C. R. Soc. Biol., Paris* **121**, 1177.

Lavier, G. (1936). Recherches sur les Coccidies des Tritons. *Ann. Parasit. hum. comp.* **14**, 150.

Lobeck, E. A. (1940). *Entamoeba pyrrhogaster* n. sp. with notes on other intestinal amoebae from salamanders. *J. Parasit.* **25**, 243–272.

Lom, J. (1958). A contribution to the systematics and morphology of endoparasitic Trichodinids from amphibians, with a proposal of uniform specific characteristics. *J. Protozool.* **5**, 251.

Lom, J. (1960). *Trichodina reticulata* Hirschmann and Partsch, 1955 from Cruzian Carp, and *Trichodina domerguei* f. *latispina* Dogiel, 1940 from *Diaptomus. Vestn. ceskosl. zool. spol.* **24**, 246–257.

Moral, H. (1913). Ueber das Auftreten von *Dermocystidium pusula* Pérez einem einzelligen Parasiten der Haut des Molches *Triton cristatus. Arch. mikr. Anat.* **81**, 381–393.

Nöller, W. (1913). Die Blutprotozoen des Wasserforsches und ihre Uebertragung. *Arch. Protostenk.* **31**, 169–240.

Nöller, W. (1920). Kleine Beobachtungen an parasitischen Protozoen. *Arch. Protostenk.* **41**, 169–189.

Odening, K. (1955). Ueber die Parasitenfauna des Wasserfrosches *Rana esculenta* L. in einigen mitteldeutschen Biotopen. *Wiss. Z. Schiller Univ. Jena. Math. Nat. Wiss. Reihe* **4**, 487–508.

Pérez, C. (1913). *Dermocystidium pusula*, parasite de la peau des tritons. *Arch. Zool. exp.* **52**, 343–357.

Poisson, R. (1937). Sur une nouvelle espèce du genre *Dermomycoides* Granata 1919: *Dermomycoides armoriacus* Poisson 1936, parasite cutane de *Triturus palmatus* Schneider. *Bull. biol.* **71**, 81–116.

Pratt, H. S. (1951). "A Manual of the Common Invertebrate Animals." Blakiston, Philadelphia.

Privora, M. (1948). Sporozoa z krve *Rana esculenta*. Sporozoa from the blood of *Rana esculenta*. *Vestn. zool. spol.* **12**, 141–149.

Ray, H. (1935). On a Coccidian, *Eimeria laminata* n. sp. from the intestine of an Indian toad, *Bufo melanostictus*. *Parasitology* **27**, 369–373.

Reichenbach-Klinke, H. (1949). Ueber eine Hautkrankheit unserer Lurche. *Wschr. Aqu. Terrk.* **43**, 21–23.

Reichenbach-Klinke, H. (1956). Knochendegeneration beim Rippenmolch (*Pleurodeles waltli* Michahelles in Zusammenhang mit intermuskulärer Melanophorenanreicherung). *Biol. Zbl.* **75**, 407–416.

Shumway, W. (1940). A ciliate protozoan parasitic in the central nervous system of larval *Ambystoma*. *Biol. Bull.* **78**, 283–288.

Sorowiak, A. (1937). Ueber *Nyctotherus* aus *Hyla arborea*. *Zool. polon.*, *Lemberg* **2**, 1.

Wach, T. (1953). Investigations on the population of *Opalinata* in the intestine of the native frogs. *Acta parasit. polon.* **1**, 259–290.

Zick, K. (1928). *Urceolaria korschelti*, eine neue marine Urceolarine nebst einem Ueberblick über die Urceolarinen. *Z. wiss. Zool.* **132**, 355.

The following Protozoa are commonly found in amphibians:

Host	Parasite
Caudata and Salientia generally	*Nyctotherus cordiformis* Stein (Ciliophora)
Alytes obstetricans	*Dermocystidium ranae* Guyénot and Naville (Haplosporidia)
Ambystoma tigrinum	*Protoopalina mitotica* Metcalf (Flagellata)
Bombina spp.	*Protoopalina intestinalis* Stein
Bufo bufo	*Opalina ranarum* Ehrenberg (Flagellata)
	Glugea danilewskyi Pfeiffer (Sporozoa)
	Plistophora bufonis Guyénot and Ponse (Sporozoa)
	Plistophora myotrophica Elkan
Bufo lentiginosus	*Wardia ohlmacheri* Gurley (Myxosporidia)
Bufo marinus	*Cystodiscus immersus* Lutz (Myxosporidia)
	Superinfection in a *Balantidium*: *Nosema balantidii* Lutz and Splendore
Bufo melanostictus	*Cystodiscus sauerbachi* Weill (Myxosporidia)
	Eimeria laminata Ray (Coccidia)
	Isospora wenyoni Ray and Das Gupta (Coccidia)
Bufo spp. generally	*Lankesterella minima* Labbé (Coccidia)
Bufo valliceps	*Zelleriella brasiliensis* Pinto (Ciliophora)
Bufo viridis	*Isospora brumpti* Lavier (Coccidia)
Discoglossus fasciatus	*Plasmodium discoglossi* Aragao and Neiva (Haemosporidia)
Hyla arborea	*Isospora hylae* Mesnil (Coccidia)
	Opalina obtrigona Stein (Flagellata)
Hyla spp.	*Isospora cruzi* Pinto and Vallim (Coccidia)

9*

Host	Parasite
Hyla aurea	*Myxobolus hylae* Johnston and Bancroft (Cnidosporidia)
Leptodactylus ocellatus	*Cystodiscus immersus* Lutz (Myxosporidia)
	Zelleriella brasiliensis Pinto (Flagellata)
Pelobates fuscus	*Protoopalina intestinalis* Stein (Flagellata)
Proteus anguineus	*Chloromyxum protei* Joseph (Myxosporidia)
Rana esculenta	*Lankesterella minima* Nöller (Coccidia)
	Paracoccidium prevoti Laveran and Mesnil (Coccidia)
	Eimeria ranarum Labbé
	Eimeria neglecta Nöller (Coccidia)
	Wardia ohlmacheri Gurley (Myxosporidia)
	Dermocystidium ranae Guyénot and Naville (Haplosporidia)
	Protoopalina intestinalis Stein (Flagellata)
Rana pipiens	*Myxidium serotinum* Kudo and Sprague (Myxosporidia)
Rana temporaria	*Isospora lieberkühni* Labbé (Coccidia)
	Wardia ohlmacheri Gurley (Myxosporidia)
	Myxobolus ranae Guyénot and Naville (Myxosporidia)
	Glugea danilewskyi Pfeiffer (Microsporidia)
	Dermocystidium ranae Guyénot and Naville (Haplosporidia)
	Opalina ranarum Ehrenberg (Flagellata)
Salamandra atra	*Eimeria grobbeni* Rudovski (Coccidia)
Salamandra spp.	*Dactylosoma ranarum* (Haemosporidia)
Siphonops annulatus	*Zelleriella siphonopsi* Carini (Ciliophora)
Salamandra salamandra	*Eimeria salamandrae* Steinhaus (Coccidia)
Triturus spp.	*Eimeria propria* Schneider
	Eimeria canaliculata Lavier
	Eimeria tertia Lavier
	Eimeria spherica Schneider (Coccidia)
	Dermocystidium pusula Pérez (Haplosporidia)
	Protoopalina intestinalis Stein (Flagellata)
Triturus alpestris	*Opalina ranarum* Ehrenberg (Flagellata)
Triturus cristatus	*Chloromyxum caudatum* Thélohan (Myxosporidia)
	Trichodina domerguei Wallengren (Ciliophora)

C. Diseases Caused by Worms

The number of helminths found in amphibians is smaller than that found in either reptiles or fish. Yamaguti (1961) lists: 13 families of digenetic Trematodes; 4 families of cestodes; 20 families of nematodes. The nematodes embraced 53 genera with 201 species.

The trematodes, small worms armed with a sucking disk, are common parasites of the Amphibia. Odening (1957) in his investigation of the parasites of *Rana esculenta* lists thirteen adult and three larval species of trematodes. Bailenger and Chanseau (1954) found ten species of trematodes in the same host in the neighbourhood of Bordeaux.

How much the host animals suffer from such an invasion depends on the number of the parasites and on their distribution in the various organs and tissues. The most commonly seen trematode is *Opisthio-glyphe ranae* Frölich. Parasites which invade the cerebrospinal fluid and those which spend their larval stages in the muscular tissue seem to impair the health of the host far more than those living in the lungs or the intestine where considerable numbers of worms may be present without, apparently, shortening the life of the host very much.

Trematoda monogenea

The Monogenea (Figs. 198, 199), sometimes also called Heterocotylea, embraces small worms which live only on one host, usually on the gills, of fishes. The species most frequently met with in amphibians is *Poly-stoma integerrimum* Rud., a parasite of the urinary bladder of frogs. The worm grows to a size of 10 mm and is easily recognized by the group of six sucking disks at the posterior end. The eggs of *Polystoma* hatch when shed into the water. The larvae, propelled by groups of cilia, have to attach themselves to a tadpole within 24 h. Unattached, they cannot survive any longer. They prefer to attach themselves to small tadpoles with external gills. As the external gills shrink, the larvae enter the opercular cavity and continue to feed on the internal gills. Some of them, the neotenic larvae, maturing rapidly, produce only one or two eggs by way of self-fertilization. These eggs give rise to a second generation of *Polystoma* capable of infecting large tadpoles with internal gills. The remaining larvae are not neotenic. They grow slowly, and at the time of the frog's metamorphosis, when the gills disappear, they migrate down the intestinal canal, eventually reaching the bladder, where they remain until they become sexually mature. They feed during this period on blood abstracted from the vesicular blood vessels of the frog. In the third year the larvae become sexually mature and lay their first eggs simultaneously with the spawning of the frogs.

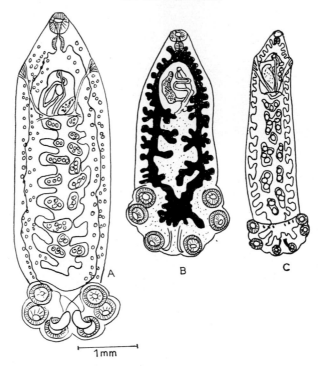

FIG. 198. Monogenetic trematodes occurring in amphibians. A, *Polystoma rhacophori* Yamaguti. (After Yamaguti.) B, *Polystoma africanum* Szidat. (After Szidat.) C, *Polystoma integerrimum* Rud. (After Dawes.)

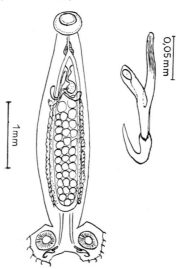

FIG. 199. *Sphyranura osleri* Wright. (After Price.)

They may, after this, continue to live in the same habitat for another 3 years.

An allied species, *Polystoma gallieni* Price, is a parasite of the mediterranean tree-frog *Hyla arborea meridionalis*.

A further species, *Polystoma africanum* Szidat (1932), inhabits *Bufo regularis* in Liberia. While *P. integerrimum* is armed with eight posterior hooks this species has nine. It reaches a size of up to 4·8 mm length and 2·2 mm width. A *Polystoma* species from the Far East is *P. rhacophori* Yamaguti, from the urinary bladder of *Rhacophorus schlegeli* Gthr., a species supplied with a rather more prominent main hook than the others.

Two different types of *Polystoma* have been reported from Cuba. Vigueras (1955) discovered *P. stellai* in the local tree frog *Hyla septentrionalis*, Caballero and Cerecero found *P. naevius* in *Hyla daudini*. For details in the structural differences between these species, distinguishable to the specialist only, the original publications should be consulted.

A more definite deviation from the usual pattern is seen in a North American species, *Sphyranura osleri*, which has been assigned to a separate genus. As shown in our illustration (Fig. 199), this species has only two posterior disks. The two main types are *Sphyranura osleri* Wright and *S. oligorchis* Alvey. They do not, like the other *Polystoma* types, live in the urinary bladder of tree frogs but are found on the skin of the N. American newt *Necturus maculosus*, the "mudpuppy". Both types are about 3 mm long.

Related types like *Polystomoides*, *Parapolystoma*, *Polystomoidella* and *Neopolystoma* may be found in the amphibians of East Asia, India and North America. Details have been reported by Price (1939).

One rather deviating type, *Diplorchis ranae* Ozaki, is reported from the urinary bladder of *Rana rugosa* Schlegel, a frog found in N. America and Japan.

Trematoda digenea

The digenetic trematodes change their host once or several times in the course of their larval stages, some of which may include generations with parthogenetic reproduction. In the bodies of amphibians either encysted larvae (Metacercariae) or mature worms may be found. The latter mainly inhabit the intestinal canal, where they develop after the host has fed on larval stages which had parasitized an intermediate host.

In the order of the frequency of their appearance trematodes may

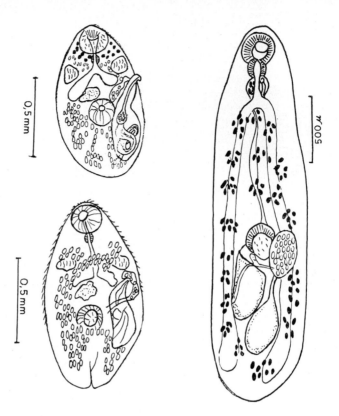

Fig. 200. Left above: *Prosotocus fülleborni* Travassos. (After Bailenger and Chaseau.) Left below: *Prosotocus sigalasi* Bailenger and Chanseau. Right: *Haematoloechus complexus* Seely. (After Krull.)

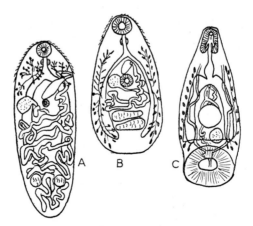

Fig. 201. A, *Pleurogenes claviger* Rud. (After Dawes.) B, *Opisthioglyphe ranae* Frölich. (After Dawes.) C, *Diplodiscus subclavatus* Pallas. (After Dawes.)

be found in the following organs: small intestine, rectum, pylorus sector, oral cavity, urinary bladder, lungs, cerebrospinal fluid, skin, muscular system, other viscera and eye.

The *small intestine* of frogs is particularly inhabited by the genus *Prosotocus*. The worms are of oblong oval shape and about 1 mm long. The commonest European species are *Prosotocus fülleborni* Travassos, *P. confusus* Loos and *P. sigalasi* Bailenger and Chanseau. Our illustrations (Fig. 200) show the main features of these worms. The first intermediate hosts are snails and the second vectors are insects, particularly the nymphs of dragonflies.

A slightly more slender form is *Pleurogenes claviger* Rud. (Figs. 201, 206c). It is about 3 mm long and differs from the other forms mentioned by being cylindrical.

Opisthioglyphe ranae Frölich is one of the commonest intestinal trematodes of *Rana esculenta* on the continent of Europe. It is not, however, very frequently seen in specimens of *R. temporaria* in the British Isles, where it is replaced by *Dolichosaccus rastellus* Travassos. It reaches a length of 1·5–2·5 mm. The first intermediate hosts are again snails, particularly *Limnaea stagnalis* L. or *Galba palustris* Müll. The secondary vectors are caddis flies (Order Trichoptera). It is remarkable that the larvae of this parasite also occur in tadpoles.

The commonest inhabitants of the gut of newts are *Brachycoelium salamandrae* Frölich (length 3–5 mm), which occurs in *Salamandra salamandra* and in toads in Europe and *Cercorchis necturi* Perkins from N. American newts. A rarer type is the Liberian *Monocoelium monodi* (length 2·8–3·5 mm) (Fig. 205).

The *rectum* of amphibians may be found infested with *Diplodiscus subclavatus* Pallas which may become up to 6 mm long and which, after Odening (1959), is often confused with the similar *Opisthodiscus nigrivasis* v. Méhely. *Diplodiscus amphichrus japonicus* Yamaguti, a smaller worm, is found in the rectum of frogs in the Far East. In Japan it is the commonest trematode in amphibians (Figs. 201, 206).

The development of these species is similar to that of those already mentioned. Of particular interest is the genus *Diplodiscus* (Fig. 201c). The intermediate generation of *D. subclavatus* which multiplies by asexual parthenogenesis lives in snails of the genus *Planorbis*, that of the N. American *D. temperatus* lives in the red snail *Helisoma trivolvis* Say. The cercariae of *D. temperatus* are known to encyst in the skin of frogs and probably those of *D. subclavatus* follow the same pattern. These worms require two intermediate hosts before they get into the frog, where they become sexually mature. They may possibly also encyst in tadpoles.

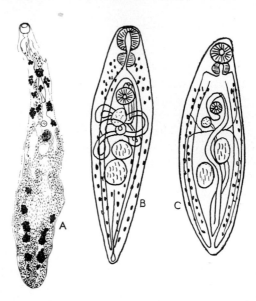

Fig. 202. A, *Haematoloechus variegatus* Rud. (After Odening.) B, *Dolichosaccus rastellus* Travassos. (After Dawes.) C, *Plagiorchis mentulatus* Stossich. (After Dawes.)

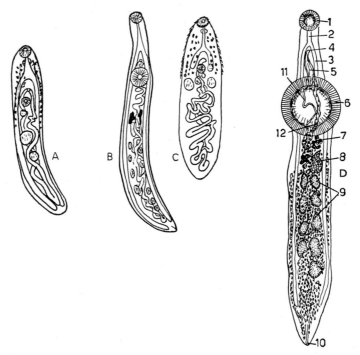

Fig. 203. A, *Haplometra cylindriace* Zeder. (After Dawes.) B, *Gorgodera cygnoides* Zeder. (After Dawes.) C, *Brachycoelium salamandrae* Frölich. (After Dawes.) D, *Gordodera*, frog rectum, from life. 1, Oral sucker; 2, oesophagus; 3, intestine; 4, gonopore; 5, cirrus sac; 6, acetabulum; 7, yolk glands; 8, ovary; 9, testes; 10, nephridiopore; 11, sperm duct; 12, uterus.

Amphistoma subclavatum Rud., which has been found in *Triturus alpestris*, should, after Odening (1959), be included with *D. subclavatus*.

The *oral cavity* of amphibians, too, is often the seat of trematode worms. In frogs, for example, we may find *Halipegus ovocaudatus* Vulpian (Fig. 204). The first intermediate host of this worm is the snail

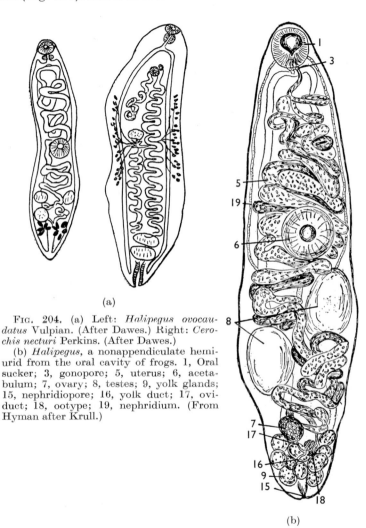

(a)

(b)

FIG. 204. (a) Left: *Halipegus ovocaudatus* Vulpian. (After Dawes.) Right: *Cerochis necturi* Perkins. (After Dawes.)

(b) *Halipegus*, a nonappendiculate hemiurid from the oral cavity of frogs. 1, Oral sucker; 3, gonopore; 5, uterus; 6, acetabulum; 7, ovary; 8, testes; 9, yolk glands; 15, nephridiopore; 16, yolk duct; 17, oviduct; 18, ootype; 19, nephridium. (From Hyman after Krull.)

Planorbis, the second the nymph of the dragonfly *Calopteryx virgo*. Frogs which feed on these nymphs allow the worms to reach their oral cavity where they adhere and become sexually mature.

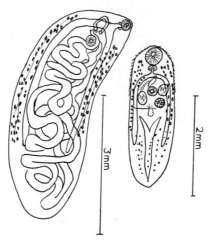

Fig. 205. Left: *Haplometroides rappiae* Szidat. Right: *Monocoelium monodi* Dollfus (After Szidat.)

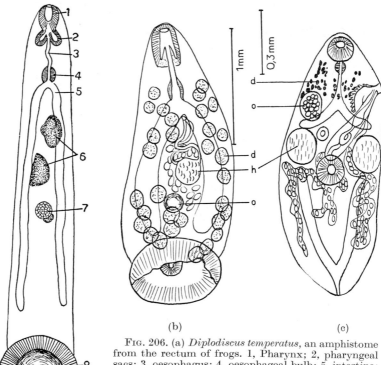

(b)

(c)

Fig. 206. (a) *Diplodiscus temperatus,* an amphistome from the rectum of frogs. 1, Pharynx; 2, pharyngeal sacs; 3, oesophagus; 4, oesophageal bulb; 5, intestine; 6, testes; 7, ovary; 8, acetabulum. (From Hyman.) (b) *Diplodiscus amphichrus japonicus* Yamaguti. (c) *Pleurogenes japonicus* Yamaguti. d, Yolk granules; h, Testis; o, Ovary.

(a)

The *urinary bladder* is parasitized by several trematodes, the commonest being *Polystoma integerrimum* (Fig. 198c) Rud. and *Gorgodera cygnoides* (length up to 10 mm) (Fig. 203b).

Infestation of the *lungs* with trematodes occurs only in frogs, the commonest on the European continent being *Haematoloechus variegatus* Loos (Fig. 202a) and *Haematoloechus complexus* Seely. The latter has a length of up to 1·5–5·2 mm and lives in N. American species of *Rana* (Fig. 200, right).

In Great Britain the lungs of *Rana temporaria* may be inhabited by *Haplometra cylindrica* Loos, of 10–20 mm length (Fig. 203a).

Krull (1933) published extensive studies on the pulmonary trematode *Haematoloechus complexus* Seely. The main sufferers from this parasite are *Rana pipiens* and *Rana clamitans*. A snail, *Pseudosuccinea columella*, terrestrial but living near water courses, functions as first, some dragonfly nymphs of the genera *Sympetrum, Pachydiplax* and *Holotaenia* as second intermediate hosts. Metacercariae may be found encysted in the muscles, the fat body or free in the head, the rest of the body or in the first segments of the legs of the dragonfly nymphs. The cerebrospinal fluid of aquatic frogs is sometimes invaded by the free swimming metacercaria of the strigeid trematode *Tylodelphis excavata* Rud. which lives in the intestine of the stork. The cercaria has been described as *Tylodelphis rhachiaea*.

Nobody has as yet devised a mode of treatment against trematode infestation likely to be successful. In small numbers the worms do little harm to their hosts, even when located in the lungs. Only a mass invasion would endanger the life of a frog or a newt.

Far more frequent than the mature worms of the digenetic trematodes are their larvae, the metacercariae which, encysted, pass a stage of rest in various organs, preferably in the skin or the muscle. They are liberated when the host is eaten and digested by another animal, in which case the amphibium serves as the second intermediate host for the parasite. These encysted larvae are in many cases harmless, but they may more severely interfere with the life of the host when they invade vital organs like the eyes, the heart, liver, lung, central nervous system or the lateral line system.

The following species of trematode larvae (metacercariae) may commonly be found in the *skin* of amphibians: in Europe *Cathaemasia hians* Loos, *Codonocephalus urnigerus* Rud. and others (Fig. 207a); in N. America *Euryhelmis squamula* Poche and *Fibricola cratera* Barker and Noll, the latter of which limits itself entirely to the hind legs of *Rana pipiens*. The cysts harbouring these larvae are often detected because of the dark pigment deposited around them.

Snails of various descriptions function as first intermediate hosts for these worms. In the case of *Cathaemasia hians* it is *Planorbis planorbis* L. or *Galba palustris* L., in the case of *Fibricola cratera* specimens of the genus *Physa* in N. America. It follows that Amphibia can only become

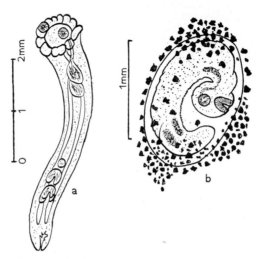

FIG. 207. Trematodes occurring in frogs. (a) Metacercaria of *Codonocephalus urnigerus* Rud. (After Lühe.) (b) Metacercaria of *Cotylurus variegatus* Creplin from the liver of *Rana esculenta*. (Orig.)

infected when living in company with snails of their normal environ-ment. The final hosts of these larvae may be either other frogs as in *Dolichosaccus rastellus* (Fig. 202b), snakes, as in *Encyclometra japonica* and *Proalarioides serpentis*, birds or mammals. Storks and herons are the final hosts for *Cathaemasia hians*. *Euryhelmis squamula* reaches sexual maturaity in the polecat (*Putorius putorius* L.).

The larvae may be found in small round or oval cysts not only in the skin but in the *eye or in other organs* where they are not immediately visible as in the case of:

    Cotylurus variegatus Creplin (= *Tetracotyle ovata* v. Linstow (Fig. 207b); *Encyclometra japonica* Yoshida and Ozaki: abdominal muscles; *Diplostomulum xenopi* Nigrelli and Maraventano: peri-cardium; *Proalarioides serpentis* Yamaguti: thoracic muscles; *Tylodelphys excavatum* Rud.: spinal cord of frogs.

We have, on several occasions, seen the first of these species in the *liver* of frogs. It is also interesting to see *Diplostomulum*, usually an inhabitant of the pericardium of fish, produce a very heavy infestation of the *pericardium* of the S. African clawed toad *Xenopus laevis* Daudin.

The authors (Nigrelli and Maraventano, 1944) report that out of fifty-five toads forty-three were infested, each with from 25 to 100 cercariae of 0·2–0·76 mm length. Those animals which were only mildly parasitized did not seem to suffer from the infestation (Fig. 208).

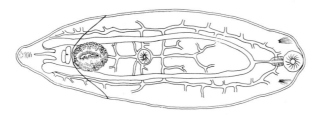

FIG. 208. *Diplostomulum xenopi*. Composite figure from stained preparations. (From Nigrelli and Maraventano, 1944.)

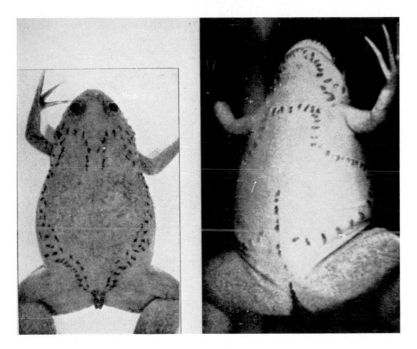

FIG. 209. *Xenopus laevis*. Adult female with cercarial infestation of the lateral line system. Cercarial cysts below each neuromast with intense melanosis. Left: dorsal; right: ventral view. (Photo.: Elkan. Courtesy Zool. Soc. Lond.)

It cannot surprise that a permanently aquatic species like *Xenopus laevis* should be almost universally parasitized by trematodel arvae which may be found encysted in any part of the body without, in most cases, doing much harm to the toad. Sometimes, however, a massive attack by cercariae is more than the toad can stand. The effect of such a mass invasion was described by Elkan and Murray in 1952. It occurred not in S. Africa but in England among toads which had been in captivity for well over a year. Normally these toads are of a dark mottled brown colour while their neuromasts—sensory patches analogous to the lateral line system—stand out like white "stiches". In the infected toads this

Fɪɢ. 210. Cercarial cysts surrounded by melanophores in a case of infestation of the lateral line system of *Xenopus laevis*. Low magnification. Unstained preparation. (Photo.: Elkan. Courtesy Zool. Soc. Lond.)

colour scheme was reversed (Fig. 209a, b). The "patients" became pale, the neuromasts darker and darker—so much so that a ventral median line of neuromasts, up to then not located, was discovered. Eventually, when the whole toads were pale grey while every neuromast stood out coal black, the animals died. It could then be shown that the entire lateral line system had been undermined by cercarial cysts which had, in their turn, caused a local proliferation of melanophores (Fig. 210). The metacercariae were strigeids of the *Neascus* group. It is not clear why they killed the infected toads so long after the original infection which, in the absence of intermediate hosts, could not have occurred after the toads left their native country.

Another interesting observation on the finding of trematode larvae (metacercariae) in the skin of ranid tadpoles comes from Cort and Brackett (1938) who describe their cases as "vesicular" disease of tadpoles, because the encysted trematodes produced prominent vesicles in the skin of the froglets. The metacercariae were 0·12–0·2 mm long. They came from snails of the species *Galba palustris*.

Dollfus and Timon-David (1960) describe similar cysts with cercariae of 0·3–0·4 mm length whose intermediate host could not be determined. The mature worms (*Massaliatrema gyrinicola* Dollfus and Timon-David) have been found in the intestine of cats and pigeons. The damage they cause does not seem to be extensive.

Some of the catastrophes described probably occur when cercariae invade the "wrong" host, i.e. an unusual host which is outside their normal adaptive range. The exact determination of a given species depends on structural differences which can only be seen by the specialist (cf. Dawes, 1946 and others). Both fish and Amphibia often react to a cercarial invasion by an abundant deposition of melanophores around the cysts. These can often be seen to have a double wall, the inner layer being produced by the parasite, the outer, much thicker one, by the host.

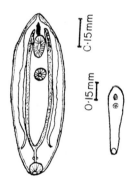

Fig. 211. Cercaria of *Diplostomulum scheuringi* Hughes from *Notophthalmus viridescens* Raf. (From Etges.)

Kelley (1934) described injuries to the eye and the brain of American newts (*Notophthalmus viridescens* Raf.) caused by cercarial infection. Etges (1961) identified these as *Diplostomulum scheuringi* Hughes, parasites common in various N. American types of perch (*Lepomis gibbosus* and *Micropterus salmoides*). The intermediate host is the snail *Helisoma anceps* Menke (Fig. 211).

It may also be mentioned that frogs and toads in the Far East may act as second intermediate hosts to two species of trematodes which may attack man. They are *Haplorchis microrchis* Katsurada and *Centrocestus armatus* Tanabe (cf. Piekarski, 1954).

Only massive invasions or invasions which include vital organs are dangerous to the hosts. With the aid of a hand lens it is quite possible to remove larvae from dermal cysts with a needle.

Trematode cysts are usually larger and more raised than those caused by *Dermocystidium* or *Dermosporidium;* they are mostly round and never U-shaped and they contain the larva, mostly curled up, which can best be manipulated with a needle with a curved tip.

REFERENCES

Ameel, J. D. (1938). The morphology and life cycle of *Euryhelmis monorchis* n. sp. (Trematoda) from the mink. *J. Parasit.* **24**, 219–224.

Bailenger, J. and Chanseau, J. (1954). Étude des vers parasites des amphibiens anoures de la région de Bordeaux. Nouvelles espèces. *Ann. Parasit. hum. comp.* **29**, 546–560.

Borradaile, L. A. *et al.* (1959). "The Invertebrata", 3rd edn. Cambridge University Press.

Caballero, C. E. and Cerecero, C. (1941). Una nueva especie de *Polystoma (Trematoda, Polystomatidae)*, parasito de la vejiga de *Hyla daudini* (Dum. and Bibr.). *Ann. Inst. Biol.* **12**, 615–621.

Cort, W. W. and Brackett, S. (1938). A new strigeid cercaria which produces a bloat disease of tadpoles. *J. Parasit.* **24**, 263–271.

Dawes, B. (1946). "The Trematoda. With Special Reference to British and other European forms." Cambridge University Press.

Dollfus, R. and Chabaud, A. G. (1953). *Distomum musculorum suis* Duncker 1896, Mésocercaire d'*Alaria alata* Goeze 1782. (Trematoda Strigeata) chez un sanglier (*Sus scrofa* L. *fera*). *Ann. Parasit. hum. comp.* **28**, 252–264.

Dollfus, R. P. and Timon-David, J. (1960). Sur une larve de Distome, parasite de têtards de *Rana esculenta* L., devenant adulte chez le Chat Domestique *Felis catus* L. domest. et le Pigeon domestique *Columba livia* Gmel. domest. *C.R. Acad. Sci., Paris* **250**, 1909–1911.

Elkan, E. and Murray, R. W. (1952). A larval trematode infection of the lateral line system of the toad *Xenopus laevis* D. *Proc. zool. Soc., Lond.* **122**, 121–126.

Etges, F. T. (1961). Contributions to the life history of the brain fluke of newts and fish, *Diplostomulum scheuringi* Hughes 1929 (Trematoda. Diplostomatidae). *J. Parasit.* **47**, 453–458.

Hoffman, G. (1955). Notes on the life cycle of *Fibricola cratera* (Trematoda: Strigeida). *J. Parasit.* **41**, 327.

Hyman, L. H. (1940). "The Invertebrates." Vol. II. McGraw-Hill, New York.

Kelley, R. S. (1934). The trematode parasites of *Triturus v. viridescens* Raf. *Univ. Bull.* **31**, 201–210.

Krull, W. H. (1933). Studies on the life history of a frog lung fluke *Haematoloechus complexus* Seely. Krull n. comb. *Z. Parasitk.* **6**, 192–206.

Lopez-Neyra, C. R. (1952). *Polystoma palancai* n. sp. (Monogenea, Polystomatida) parasita de la vejiga urinaria de la rana de San Anton. *Rev. Iber. Parasit.* **12**, 289–295.

Lühe, M. (1911). Trematodes. *In* "Süsswasserfauna Deutschlands." Brauer, Jena.

Nigrelli, R. F. and Maraventano, L. W. (1944). Pericarditis in *Xenopus laevis* caused by *Diplostomulum xenopi* sp. nov., a larval Strigeid. *J. Parasit.* **30**, 184–190.

Odening, K. (1954). Über die Parasitenfauna des Wasserfrosches (*Rana esculenta* L.) in einigen mitteldeutschen Biotopen. *Wiss. Z. Schiller Univ. Jena. Math. Naturw. Reihe* **4**, 487–508.

Odening, K. (1957). Die Helminthenfauna ostthüringischer *Rana esculenta esculenta* L. *Zbl. Bakt. I. Abt.* **169**, 288–304.

Odening, K. (1958). Die Zooparasiten der Frösche Deutschlands. *Wiss. Z. Schiller Univ. Jena. Math. Naturw. Reihe* **5**, 179–215; Suppl. *id.* **8**, 37–44.

Odening, K. (1959). Über die *Diplodiscidae* der einheimischen Frösche. (Trematoda Paramphistomata.) *Z. Parasitk.* **49**, 54–66.

Piekarski, G. (1954). "Lehrbuch der Parasitologie." Springer, Berlin-Goettingen-Heidelberg.

Pratt, H. S. (1951). "A Manual of the Common Invertebrate Animals." Blakiston, Philadelphia.

Price, E. W. (1939). North American Monogenetic Trematodes. IV. Polystomatidae: Polystomatoidea. *Proc. hel. Soc., Wash.* **6**, 80–92.

Sandner, H. (1949). Contribution à la connaissance de la faune parasitaire des Batraciens des environs de Varsovie. *Act. Zool. Oec. Unov. Lodziensis*, **3**, 2 (12).

Sevcenko, N. (1956). Die Parasitenfauna verschiedener Arten von Amphibien und Wasserreptilien im Gebiet des mittleren Laufes des nördlichen Don. (In Russian). "Arb. II. wiss. Konf. d. Parasitologen d. Ukrain. S.S.R." pp. 117–118 (E. Markevic, ed.).

Skrjabin, K. J. (1947 *et seq.*). Trematody shiwotnych i tscheloweka. Moskow.

Southwell, T. and Kirshner, A. (1937). On some parasitic worms found in *Xenopus laevis*, the South African clawed toad. *Ann. trop. Med. Parasit.* **31**, 245–265.

Szidat, L. (1932). Parasiten aus Liberia und französisch Guinea. II. Teil. Trematoda. *Z. Parasitk.* **4**, 506–521.

Szidat, L. (1935). Warum wirft der Storch seine Jungen aus dem Nest? *J. Ornithol.* **83**, 76–87.

Szidat, L. (1939). Beiträge zum Aufbau eines natürlichen Systems der Trematoden. I. Die Entwicklung von *Echinocercaria choanophila*. U. Szidat zu *Cathaemasia hians*. *Z. Parasitk.* **11**, 239–283.

Vigueras, J. P. (1955). Contribucion al conocimiento de la fauna helminthologica cubana. *Mem. Soc. cubana Hist. nat.* **22**, 21–71.

Yamaguti, S. (1936). Studies on the helminth fauna of Japan, pt. 14. Amphibian trematodes. *Jap. J. Zool.* **6**, 551–576.

Yamaguti, S. (1958). "Systema Helminthum." Interscience, London.

TAPEWORMS (CESTOIDEA)

Eleven species of tapeworms are at present known to occur in amphibians in the sexually mature state. The best-known piecses is

Nematotaenia dispar Goeze, a tapeworm found in the intestine of various amphibians in Europe, the Channel Islands (Baylis), Africa, N. America and India (Fig. 212). It has been found in *Bufo bufo, B. viridis, Hyla arborea, Pelobates fuscus, Rana esculenta, Rana temporaria, Salamandra salamandra* and *Salamandra atra*. The distribution of this worm seems to indicate that it prefers a warm climate, hence its particular distribution in the Southern Swiss Alps, Southern France and Italy. *Nematotaenia dispar* is 5–22 cm long, cylindrical and of 0·5–0·6 mm diameter. The scolex is unarmed, the rostellum absent or rudimentary. Segmentation can only be seen externally in the last segments. These can live free in the intestine. A particular characteristic of the Nematotaeniae are the so-called intrauterine organs. It is not known yet

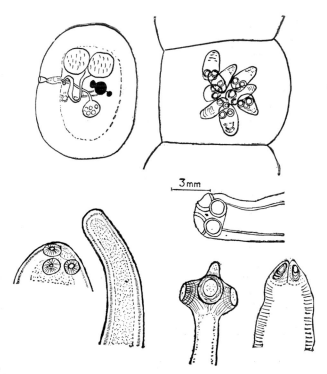

FIG. 212. Tapeworms (cestodes) occurring in amphibians. Above: *Nematotania dispar* Goeze. Left, longitudinal section, segment with genital organs. Right, segment with parauterine organs. (After Joyeux and Baer.) Middle: *Ophiotaenia saphena* Osler. (After Osler.) Below: Left, *Baerietta baeri* Hsü. (After Hsü.) Right, *Cylindrotaenia quadrijugosa* Lawler. (After Lawler.)

how the species develops and whether it makes use of an intermediate host or not. Joyeux and Baer (1936) incline to the view that no such host is employed. The mere presence of this parasite does not seem to inconvenience the host much. Elkan (1960), however, reported about repeated cases where, in *Bufo bufo*, the worms had multiplied to such an extent as to cause intestinal obstruction, gangrene and death. Commensalism between the worm and the host therefore seems to be far from well-established. The worm, though unarmed, presents a potential danger, particularly to small amphibians.

Cylindrotaenia americana Jewell and *C. quadrijugosa* Lawler (Fig. 212, below, right) differ from *Nematotaenia dispar* in the fact that in the former we find only one testicle per segment whereas there are two in *Nematotaenia*. The genus *Cylindrotaenia* occurs mainly in N. America, *americana* in *Bufo*, *Hyla* and *Rana* species, *quadrijugosa* in *Rana pipiens*.

Distoichometra bufonis Dickey occurs in U.S.A. bufonids, *D. kozloffi* Douglas (length 2·5 cm) in *Hyla regilla* Baird and Girard.

The genus *Baerietta* may be found in the Old and the New World. *Baerietta baeri* Hsü occurs in E. Asian toads (Fig. 212, below, left) *B. jägerskiöldi* Janicki in Africa, *B. japonica* Yamaguti in Japanese anurans and *B. diana* Helfer in the N. American newt *Batrachoseps attenuatus*.

The intestines of N. American and E. Asian amphibians sometimes harbour the flat and very long *Ophiotaenia*, worms of the family Protocephalidae whose final hosts are poikilothermic vertebrates. The intermediate hosts are not known. Larvae of *Ophiotaenia saphena* have been found in small crustaceans (Copepola). The Ophiotaeniae occurring in amphibians have a scolex armed with four round adhesive disks. They can be distinguished from the *Nematotaeniae* by the shape of the segments which are usually longer than wide, have a lateral

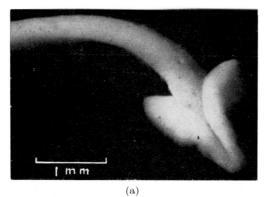

(a)

Fig. 213. (a) *Cephalochlamys namaquensis* Cohn. Scolex. (Photo.: Elkan. Courtesy Zool. Soc. Lond.)

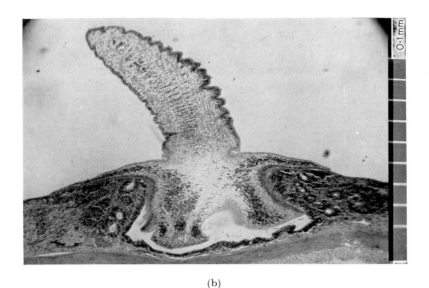

(b)

Fig. 213. (b) *Xenopus laevis* female. Jejunum with *Cephalochlamys namaquensis* invading the mucosa. (Photo.: Elkan.)

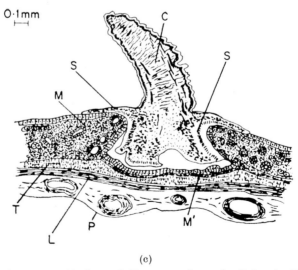

(c)

Fig. 213. (c) As Fig. 213(b) above. *C*, Free part of cestode; *L*, longitudinal muscular coat of jejunum; *M*, *M'*, intestinal mucosa; *P*, peritoneum; *S*, scolex, the rim is partly spread over the surface; *T*, transverse muscular intenstinal coat. (Del. Elkan.)

sexual pore and no intrauterine organs (Fig. 212, middle). *Ophiotaenia saphena*, which reaches a length of up to 28 cm, is found in N. American frogs (Fantham, 1948); more rarely *O. magna* Hannum (60–100 cm); in the axolotl *O. filarioides* La Rue (8–11 cm) and in newts *O. loennbergii* Fuhrmann (17–19 cm long). The difference between these various cestodes, which lie in the number of testes and uterine branches, are disputed and not easily ascertained.

Xenopus laevis, the S. African clawed toad, now widely kept in laboratories for the purpose of pregnancy tests, often arrives infected with a tapeworm, *Cephalochlamys namaquensis* Cohn (Fig. 213). The toads are cured of this infection by the use to which they are put. At one stage of the preparation of the urinary extract, bromphenol is used as an internal indicator and, while this substance has no deleterious effect on the frogs, it acts as an unfailing vermifuge, so that no worms are ever seen in toads that have once been used for a pregnancy test (Elkan, 1960).

In 1957, L. J. Thomas found a mature specimen of the pseudophyllean *Bothriocephalus rarus* Th. in *Triturus viridescens* (Fig. 214b).

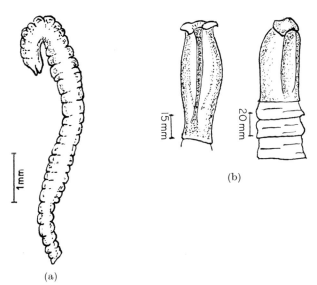

(a)

(b)

FIG. 214. (a) Plerocercoid of *Diphyllobothrium latum* L. (After Vergeer from Wardle and MacLeod.) (b) *Bothriocephalus rarus* Thomas from *Triturus viridescens*. (After Thomas.)

Amphibia may not only suffer from the presence of sexually mature worms; their larval stages as well can do considerable harm to the hosts. The mature worms abstract some of the nutritive value from the intestinal fluid. The rapidly growing larvae are probably even more harmful and interfere even more with the nutrition of the host.

Aquatic amphibians may be found to function as second intermediate hosts of tapeworms whose earlier stages they take up by feeding on crustaceans. Many tadpoles and fully grown fish are infested by the plerocercoid stage of *Diphyllobothrium mansoni* Cobbold which comes to maturity in the dog. Frogs, newts and tadpoles have occasionally been found to harbour the plerocercoids of *Diphyllobothrium latum* L. (Fig. 214a), the broad fish tapeworm which becomes sexually mature in man. Ghittino (1958) found this parasite when dissecting specimens of *Rana esculenta* from the neighbourhood of Turin. Up to that time this tapeworm had, in Europe, only been found in the countries bordering the Baltic Sea and in Ireland with some small endemic foci in Switzerland, mentioned by Wardle and McLeod (1952). Recently the worm has made such frequent appearances among N. Italian fish that the authorities are considering sale restrictions (personal communication).

Apart from *Diphyllobthrium latum* Ghittino found plerocercoids of another tapeworm, probably *Diphyllobothrium ranarum*, a species which Fantham (1948) found in N. American frogs. It is, however, possible that these larvae were those of *Spirometra*, a worm which normally comes to maturity in members of the cat tribe but which occasionally infects the dog and man. The first intermediate hosts of these worms are small crustaceans and it is difficult to see how they could transfer to frogs unless the frogs fed on fish fry (the second intermediate host) and thereby became vectorial intermediate hosts after the manner of predaceous fish and birds.

Sparganosis, an ophthalmic disease of S.E. Asia, is also caused by such larvae. The transmission of the larva from frog to man is made possible by the local custom of applying parts of frogs to sores or inflamed eyes. This allows the larva to invade the diseased tissue, where it forms a suppurating abscess. Apart from surgery no treatment of the disease is known.

It may finally be mentioned that amphibians may occasionally act as second intermediate hosts to the tapeworm *Mesocestoides variabilis* Mudler, a rare worm which matures in the fox, the skunk, the dog and the racoon.

REFERENCES

André, E. (1913). Recherches parasitologiques sur des Amphibiens de la Suisse. *Rev. suisse Zool.* **20**, 471–485.

Douglas, L. T. (1958). The taxonomy of the nematotaeniid cestodes. *J. Parasit.* **44**, 261–273.

Elkan, E. (1960). The common toad (*Bufo bufo* L.) in the laboratory. *Brit. J. Herpet.* **2**, 177–181.

Elkan, E. (1960). Some interesting pathological cases in amphibians. *Proc. zool. Soc. Lond.* **134**, 275–296.

Fantham, H. B. (1948). The parasitic fauna of vertebrates in certain Canadian fresh waters. With some remarks on their structure and importance. *Proc. zool. Soc., Lond.* **117**, 609–649.

Ghittino, P. (1958). L'ispezione sanitaria delle Rana. *Progresso veter.* **13**, 808–814.

Hsü, H. F. (1935). Contribution à l'étude des Cestodes de Chine. *Rev. suisse Zool.* 42, 477–570.

Joyeux, C. and Baer, J. G. (1936). Cestodes. *In* "Faune de France." Paris.

Lawler, H. J. (1939). A new Cestode, *Cylindrotaenia quadrijugosa* n. sp. from *Rana pipiens*. With a key to Nematotaeniidae. *Trans. Amer. micr. Soc.* **58**, 73–77.

Lühe, M. (1910). Parasitische Plattwürmer. II. Cestodes. *In* "Die Süsswasserfauna Deutschlands" (Brauer, ed.), Heft 18. Jena.

Osler, C. P. (1931). A new cestode from *Rana clamitans* Latr. *J. Parasit*, **17**, 182–185.

Thomas, L. J. (1937). *Bothriocephalus raries* n. sp., a cestode from the newt, *Triturus viridescens* Raf. *J. Parasit.* **23**, 119–123.

Wardle, R. A. and McLeod, J. A. (1952). "The Zoology of Tapeworms." University of Minnesota Press, Minneapolis, U.S.A.

THE ACANTHOCEPHALA

The name of these worms is descriptive of their main feature: their cephalic end, or rather their proboscis, is lined with rows of backward-curving spines. Once these spines have penetrated the intestinal mucosa of the host the worm is firmly anchored and cannot detach itself. In this respect therefore the Acanthocephala must be regarded as a more

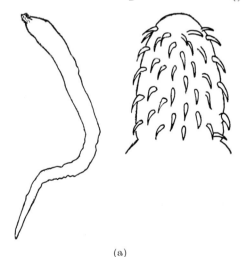

(a)

Fig. 215. (a) *Acanthocephalus ranae* Schrank. (After Lühe.)

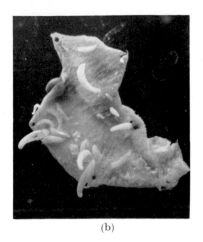

(b)

(c)

(d)

FIG. 215. (b) *Bufo bufo*. Adult male. Died shortly after being caught. Stomach heavily infested with *Acanthocephalus ranae*. (Photo.: Elkan.)

(c) Proboscis of *Acanthocephalus ranae* (from *B. bufo.*) Scale: 0·1–01 mm. Dark field illumination. (Photo.: Elkan. Courtesy *J. Protozool.*)

(d) *Acanthocephalus ranae* in the intestine of *Bufo bufo*. The worm, in retracting the proboscis, has pulled out a fold of the intestinal mucous membrane causing infection and inflammation in the area. (Photo.: Elkan. Courtesy Zool Soc. Lond.)

serious menace than other worms merely equipped with adhesive disks. They may anchor themselves deeply in the intestinal wall and may even cause a perforation, thereby causing a lesion much more serious to the

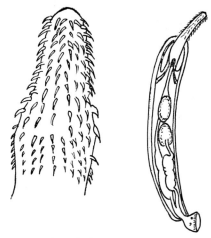

FIG. 216. *Acanthocephalus anthuris* Duj. (After Lühe.)

FIG. 217. *Corynosoma inerme*. (After Lühe.)

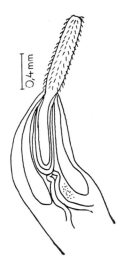

FIG. 218. As yet undetermined *Acanthocephalus* from Rana esculenta. (After Bailenger and Chanseau.)

host than any that could be set up by cestodes or trematodes. In addition to this the Acanthocephala are suspected of excreting toxic metabolic products interfering with the host's metabolism.

10

Among the amphibians Acanthocephala have mainly been found in frogs. There are few observations on urodeles. The following species of Acanthocephala may be found:

Acanthocephalus ranae (Schrk.) (Fig. 214a–d); *Acanthocephalus anthuris* Duj. (Fig. 216); *Corynosoma inerme* Forsell (Fig. 214), an as yet undetermined species (Bailenger and Chanseau) which occurs in *Rana esculenta* (Fig. 218); and the larval stage of *Centrorhynchus aluconis* Müller.

The commonest of these is *Acanthocephalus ranae,* an inhabitant of the stomach and the intestinal canal of frogs and toads, particularly of *Rana esculenta* and *Bufo bufo.* In one case (Elkan, 1960) fifteen of these worms were found attached to the gastric mucosa of the common toad. In another case it could be shown in sections that on retracting the proboscis, the worm cannot detach the barbed hooks from the mucosa, part of which is thereby drawn out and comes to lie "inside" the worm. Although it cannot be digested—the worm has no digestive system— the pull on the delicate mucous membrane sets up an injury leading at least to inflammation if not to the death of the host (Fig. 215d). The female worm may reach a length of 6 cm and a width of 2 mm, the male remaining smaller. Apart from the two species mentioned *A. ranae* may be found in *Bufo viridis* Laur.; *Bombina bombina* L.; *Salamandra atra* Laur.; *Triturus cristatus* L., *Triturus vulgaris* L. Infection probably takes place by way of ingestion of aquatic crustaceans, hosts of the larva.

Newts may be found infected with *A. ranae* and *A. anthuris* but few cases have been described, mainly from *Triturus cristatus* and *T. vulgaris* of Northern France and N. Italy. The cylindrical body of *A. anthuris* reaches a length of 8·5 mm in the female, 4·5 mm in the male (Fig. 216).

Yamaguti (1935) described another type, *Acanthocephalus artatus* van Cleave, from the intestine of the Japanese frog *Rana rugosa.* The female has a length of 15 mm, the male of 10 mm; the length of the proboscis is 0·3 mm. It has fourteen to fifteen rows of hooks, five hooks in each row.

The same author found *Acanthocephalus nanus* van Cleave in the small intestine of the newt *Cynops pyrrhogaster* in Japan. The female worm reaches a length of 6·2–10 mm, the male of 3·8–5·3 mm; proboscis 0·3–0·5 mm carrying eleven to fourteen rows of hooks with seven hooks in each row. The intermediate host is a crustacean, *Asellus aquaticus* L.

The exact species of the *Acanthocephalus* described by Bailenger and Chanseau (1954) could not be determined due to the immaturity of the generative organs. The other organic systems were described in detail. Length of the worm: 5·4 mm; width: 0·3 mm (Fig. 218).

Larvae of an *Acanthocephalus, Centrorhynchus aluconis* Müller may be found in frogs. The final hosts are birds of prey. The larvae reach a length of 3–9 mm.

Finally we may mention *Corynosoma inerme* Forsell, a club-shaped parasite found in *Rana esculenta*, of length 5 mm. The final host of this species is the seal (Fig. 217). Frogs cannot be regarded as normal intermediate hosts of these worms and they do not allow the parasite to develop to sexual maturity.

REFERENCES

Bailenger, J. and Chanseau, J. (1954). Études des vers parasites des amphibiens anoures de la région de Bordeaux. Nouvelles espèces. *Ann. Parasit. hum. comp.* **29**, 546–560.
Baylis, H. (1951). The parasitic worms of British reptiles and amphibia. *In* "The British Amphibians and Reptiles" (Smith, M., ed.), pp. 267–284. Collins, London.
Elkan, E. (1960). Some interesting pathological cases in amphibians. *Proc. zool. Soc., Lond.* **134**, 275–296.
Elkan, E. (1960). The common toad (*Bufo bufo* L.) in the laboratory. *Brit. J. Herpet.* **2**, No. 10, 177–182.
Lühe, M. (1911). Acanthocephalen. *In* "Süsswasserfauna Deutschland" (Brauer, ed.). Jena.
Meyer, A. (1933). Acanthocephala. *In* "Die Tierwelt Mitteleuropas" (Brohmer, ed.). Leipzig.
Odening, K. (1954). Ueber die Parasitenfauna des Wasserfrosches (*Rana esculenta* L.) in einigen mitteldeutschen Biotopen. *Wiss. Z. Schiller Univ. Jena Math. Naturw. Reihe* **4**, 487–508.
Yamaguti, S. (1935). Studies on the helminth fauna of Japan. 8. Acanthocephala I. *Jap. J. Zool.* **6**, 247–278.

ROUND WORMS (NEMATODA)

The *Nematoda* are long, thin worms with unsegmented bodies. They have a digestive system on the usual plan and no adhesive disks. Most of the reports on the infestation of amphibians with nematodes deal with their occurrence in frogs, but the reason for this may again lie in the fact that insufficient attention has been paid to the urodeles.

Nematodes are, above all, inhabitants of the intestinal canal; they are also, with great regularity, encountered in the lungs. Some of them are so ubiquitous in frogs that they may be regarded as symbionts rather than as parasites, but they may endanger the life of the host at any time if they become too numerous. The most serious nematode infection of frogs is that of the frog filaria, where the frog acts as second

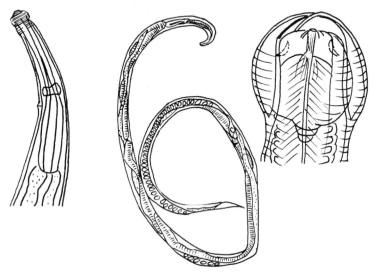

Fig. 219 (left). *Oswaldocruzia subauricularis* Rud. Anterior extremity. × 80. (After Yorke and Maplestone.)

Fig. 220 (centre and right). *Oswaldocruzia leidyi* Travassos. Whole worm and oral region. (After Steiner.)

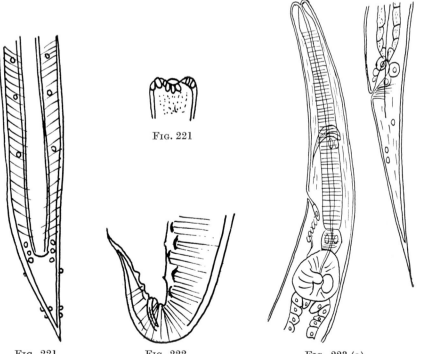

Fig. 221

Fig. 221   Fig. 222   Fig. 223 (a)

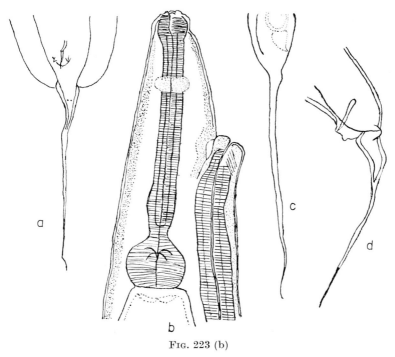

FIG. 223 (b)

FIG. 221. *Oxysomatium acuminatum* Schrank. Oral and anal region. × 56. (After Yorke and Maplestone.)
FIG. 222. *Cosmocerca ornata* Duj. Anal region. × 100. (After Yorke and Maplestone.
FIG. 223. (a) *Cosmocercella haberi* Steiner. Oral region of a ♀ and anal region of a ♂. (After Steiner.)
  (b) *Parathelandros mastigurus* Baylis from *Hyla coerulea*. (a) and (d) Anal region of male; (b) pharyngeal region; (c) anal region of female. (After Baylis.)

intermediate host. The filarial larvae invade the muscles and the blood vessels and may cause serious haemorrhages, killing the host.

We shall describe the various nematodes and their development in the order of frequency in which they appear in the small intestine, the rectum, the lungs, the peritoneal cavity, the liver and the blood vessels.

Nematodes of the Small Intestine

The number of different nematodes that may be found in the amphibian gut is great, and since only the trained specialist can with certainty distinguish the various species, we shall confine our description to those most commonly seen. Descriptions of the rarer species may be found in the original publications (see also Yorke and Maplestone, 1926, and Skrjabin, 1960).

Our illustrations show the main features of the commoner European species. They are: *Oswaldocruzia filiformis* Goeze (length: 10–20 mm),

Oswaldocruzia subauricularis Rud. (♀ 10 mm, ♂ 6–7 mm) (Fig. 219), *Oswaldocruzia leidyi* Travassos (♀ 9·9 mm, ♂ 5·2 mm) (Fig. 220), *Oxysomatium acuminatum* Schrk. (Fig. 221) and *Cosmocerca ornata* Duj. (Fig. 222). Fig. 223a shows *Cosmocercella haberi* Steiner (♀ 1·9 mm, ♂ 0·7 mm) parasitic in the American tree-frog *Hyla carolinensis*

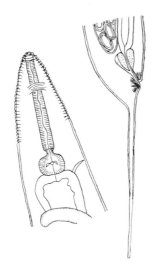

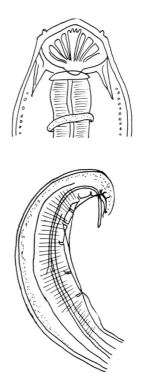

Fig. 224. *Pharyngodon batrachiensis* Walton from *Rana pipiens*. Left, Pharyngeal region; right, anal region of female.

Fig. 225. *Camallanus kachugae* Baylis and Daubney. Anterior and posterior region. × 120 and × 48. (After Yorke and Maplestone.)

Pennant. A rarer species is *Camallanus nigrescens* v. Linst. from the intestine of Indian frogs (Fig. 225).

Amongst the longest nematodes infesting Amphibia we find *Orneoascaris chrysanthemoides* Skrjabin (length up to 85 mm) and *Amplicaecum brumpti* Khalil, up to 80 mm long. Of the latter genus Fig. 226 shows the species *Amplicaecum africanum* Taylor.

Meteterakis japonica Wilkie, a worm of 5–6 mm length, may be recognized by the sharp caudal spine of about 0·54 mm length (Fig. 221).

The genus *Hedruris* may be distinguished by the presence of complicated folds and dermal warts at the posterior extremity (Fig. 228a–c).

Capillaria (Class I. Aphasmidia. Order I. Trichurata) are, as indicated by their name, as thin as hairs (Fig. 229). The eggs have an opercular plug. The commonest species is *Capillaria bufonis* Morishita. Others have been seen in salamanders (Müller, 1932).

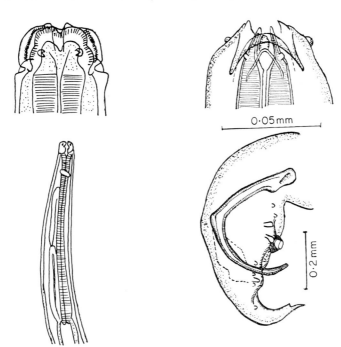

FIG. 226. *Amplicaecum africanum* Taylor. Oral and anterior region. × 48 and 18. (After Yorke and Maplestone.)

FIG. 227. *Meteterakis japonica* Wilkie, Oral and anal extremity. (After Wilkie from Skrjabin.)

Apart from those species which live in the amphibian gut as sexually mature worms we find, in the same habitat, larval (rhabdiform) stages of the genus *Rhabdias* (Fig. 230). For a more detailed description, see p. 296 f.

The effect of these worms on the host lies on the whole only in the fact that they abstract part of the nutritional value of the intestinal contents, but if they become too numerous they may not only starve the host but cause intestinal obstruction, peritonitis and death.

One further species, *Spiroxys japonica* Morishita (Fig. 231) may be mentioned here. It occurs in the pyloric region of the Japanese frog *Rana rugosa* Schlegel.

Nematodes inhabiting the Rectum

Spinicauda bufonis Yamaguti has been found in the rectum of toads on Formosa. The length of the female is 4–4·9 mm; that of the male 5–6·4 mm. The length of the spicula differs from that of *S. japonica*. It is given as 0·18–0·21 mm.

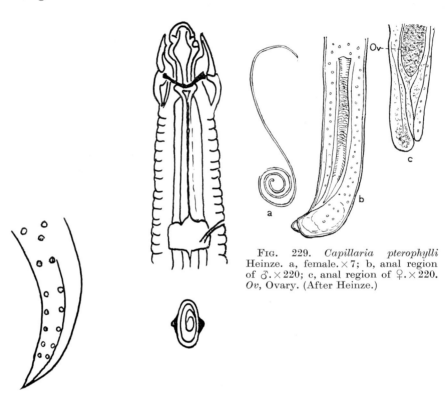

Fig. 229. *Capillaria pterophylli* Heinze. a, female. × 7; b, anal region of ♂. × 220; c, anal region of ♀. × 220. *Ov*, Ovary. (After Heinze.)

Fig. 228. Right above: *Hedruris siredonis* Baird oral region. × 100. Below: *Hedruris androphora* Nitzsch. Anal region of ♂. × 120; with egg. × 235. (All after Yorke and Maple-stone.)

Other species, for example *Aplectana*, which normally inhabit the small intestine, may be found in the rectum, and *Rhabdias* larvae may be found in any part of the gut.

Pulmonary Nematodes

It is a rare event indeed if, on dissecting the lungs of a frog or a toad one does not find it inhabited by one or, mostly, by several round worms. These are invariably nematodes of the Order Rhabdiasoidea. The

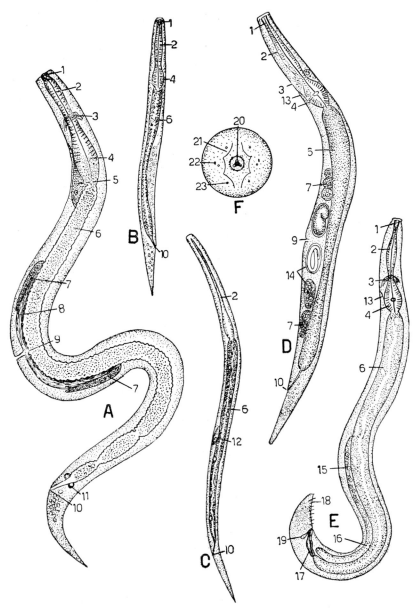

Fig. 230. Rhabdiasoidea, *Rhabdias*. A–E, *Rhabdias bufonis*. (After Metschnikoff, 1865.) A, Parasitic female; B, Rhabdiform young; C, filariform young; D, freeliving female; E, freeliving male; F, scheme of the anterior end. (After Chu, 1936.) (A should be twice as large relative to the others.)

1, Buccal capsule; 2, pharynx; 3, nerve ring; 4, end bulb; 5, renette cell; 6, intestine; 7, ovary; 8, uterus; 9, vulva; 10, anus; 11, anal glands; 12, primordium of reproductive system; 13, excretory duct; 14, embryos in uteri; 15, testis; 16, sperm duct; 17, spicules; 18, genital papillae; 19, gubernaculum; 20, mouth; 21, lips; 22, amphids; 23, external circlet of papillae. (From Hyman, 1951.)

10*

name derives from the Gk *rhabdion*: a small rod, because of the sclerotic, i.e. stiffened, portion of the pharynx of these worms. An excellent detailed description of the order can be found in Hyman (1940). The order is composed of two families: the Rhabdiasidae found in amphibian lungs and the Strongyloidae found in the intestine of mammals. Seven different species of the genus *Rhabdias* have been found in the lungs of amphibians, the commonest being *Rhabdias bufonis* Schrank and *Rhabdias fülleborni* Travassos (Fig. 232). Occasionally the infestation can be extraordinarily heavy.

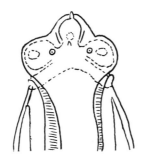

FIG. 231. *Spiroxys contortus* Rud. Anterior region. (After Yorke and Maplestone.)

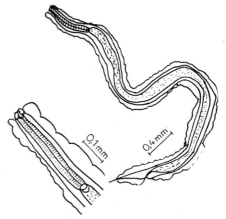

FIG. 232. *Rhabdias fülleborni* Travassos. Parasitic stage and oral region. (After Travassos.)

Williams (1959) found fifty specimens of *Rhabdias sphaerocephala* Goodey in the lung of one single *Bufo marinus*.

The extremely complicated life cycle of these worms was first investigated by Metschnikov and Leuckart in 1865, later by Fülleborn (1928) and Travassos (1926). The following picture has crystallized from these and other investigations:

The worms we find in the amphibian lung are "protandric hermaphrodites" which means that they are bisexual worms in which the male products (sperms) mature before the female ova. The sperms, when produced, are stored in a receptaculum. They fertilize the eggs, produced by the same worm, later on. The fertilized eggs, probably moved by ciliary motion, travel from the lungs through the bronchus towards the frog's oral cavity, where they are swallowed, thus obtaining access to the intestinal canal. Here the eggs develop into the "rhabdiform" young, many of which can easily be found when the intestinal content of frogs or toads is microscopically examined. The second part

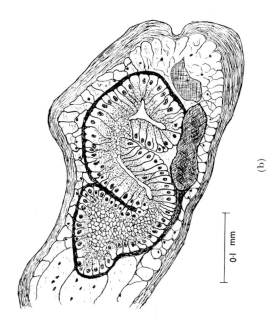

0·1 mm

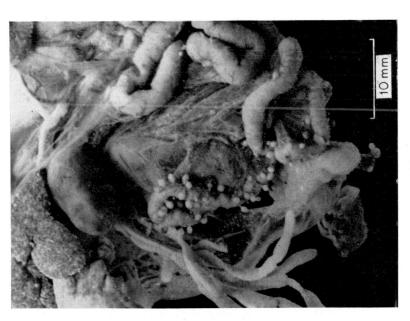

(a)

(b)

Fig. 233. (a) *Pipa pipa*. Intestinal canal of adult male with nematode infection. (b) Nematode larva. From a cyst attached to the small intestine of a specimen of *Pipa pipa*. (Del. Elkan. Courtesy Zool. Soc. Lond.)

10 mm

of the life cycle of these worms takes place in the soil. The rhabdiform young leave the frog with the excreta. They are of both sexes and in the soil copulation takes place. The females, when fertilized, produce a number of "filariform" young which are only liberated after having lived on the contents of the mother's body. These "infective juveniles" now disperse in the soil. They can be distinguished from the "rhabdi-form" young by the absence of the pharyngeal bulb. To complete the cycle, they must enter the body of a frog. They may achieve this either by adhering to an animal eaten by the frog (e.g. snails) or by directly penetrating the skin. On the whole infection per os seems to play a very minor part compared with entry through the skin (Schaake, 1931). Only those worms which, in their migration through the frog's body, finally reach the lungs, will develop to sexual maturity and repeat the cycle. Encysted and walled-off nematodes can frequently be found in other organs where they may give rise to tumours interfering with the health of the host even after the original parasite has died and disappeared (Elkan, 1960).

Apart from the species mentioned, the nematode *Cosmocerca tri-spinosa* Raillet and Henry may be found in the lungs of frogs. Some rare species also inhabit the peritoneal cavity.

An instance of nemode infestation was seen in a consignment of Surinam water toads (*Pipa pipa*) which did not seem to acclimatize themselves in captivity and died one by one within a few weeks. Dissection revealed that the toads were heavily infected with nematode larvae which had penetrated the intestinal wall and encysted themselves under the peritoneum. Since no mature worms were found the exact species could not be determined (Fig. 233a, b).

Nematodes in the Blood Vessels and the Lymphatic System

Another Order of nematodes which may infect amphibians is that of the Filarioidea (L. *filum*: a thread) representatives of which may be found in the blood vessels and in the lymphatic system of fish, warm-blooded vertebrates and man. A frog infected with microfilariae will appear generally listless, but the infection can reach considerable severity before the life of the host is endangered. As far as we know the frogs are infected by mosquitoes which act as intermediate hosts for some stages in the development of the worm. The mosquitoes suck up the microfilaria with the frog's blood. The worm, once inside the mosquito, probably sheds its skin, reaches the coelomic cavity and eventually matures in the muscles. From here it wanders towards the sheath of the proboscis, thereby gaining access to another frog which may be stung by the mosquito.

Extensive investigations of these parasites have been carried out by Wittenberg and Gerichter (1954). They found 50% of a population of *Rana ridibunda* of northern Palestine infected by the nematode *Foleyella duboisi* Yorke and Maplestone (Fig. 234). These frogs had

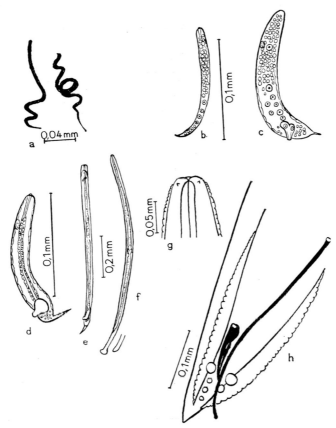

Fig. 234. The haemofilaria *Foleyella duboisi* Yorke and Maplestone. a, Microfilariae; b, first; c, second; d, third larval stage; e, pre-infectious; f, infectious larval stage; g, anterior region of a fully grown worm; h, posterior region of ♂. (After Wittenberg and Gerichter.)

not only a heavy microfilarial infection of the blood but 1–34 fully grown worms were found in the lymphatic system. The authors were successful in transmission experiments with the mosquito *Culex molestus* Forsk, a close relation if not a subspecies of our mosquito *Culex pipiens*. Transmission experiments with leeches which had been suggested as intermediate hosts were not successful.

The authors review the bibliography on filaria so far encountered in amphibians. They maintain twelve species of the genus *Foleyella* but leave another thirty-one species as undetermined because immature larvae only were available for examination. Of the remaining species the following are the more commonly seen and most completely described:

Species	Host and location
1. *Foleyella duboisi* Yorke and Maplestone	(*Rana*)
2. *F. americana* Walton	(*Rana*, N. America)
3. *F. brachyoptera* Wehr and Causey	(*Rana*, N. America)
4. *F. dolichoptera* Wehr and Causey	(*Rana*, N. America)
5. *F. leiperi* Yorke and Maplestone	(*Bufo*, Africa)
6. *F. ranae* Walton	(*Rana*, N. America)
7. *F. striata* Ochoterena and Caballero	(*Rana*, N. America)
8. *F. vellardi* Travassos	(*Bufo*, S. America)
9. *Icosiella kobayasii* Yamaguti	(*Rana*, Japan)
10. *I. neglecta* Seurat	(*Rana*, Europe, Asia, Africa)
11. *I. quadrituberculata* Walton	(*Rana*, N. America)

Foleyella helvetica Kreis is admitted but it remains doubtful whether the species should be placed into *Foleyella*.

It is extremely difficult if not impossible to distinguish between all these larval forms. We have not even a book giving a reliable key for the determination of all the adult worms. The genera *Foleyella* and *Icosiella* are distinguished as follows:

Icosiella	*Foleyella*
Oral aperture with chitinous reinforcement or denticles	Oral aperture simple, without lips
Oesophagus long	Oesophagus short
Cuticle smooth	Cuticle with lateral and caudal alae
Male without anal papillae	Male with anal papillae

Various stages in the development of *Foleyella* have been recognized: microfilariae with blunt caudal tip; a type showing the beginning of caudal elongation; a type bearing a spur; a pre-infective and an infective type, the latter occasionally showing an apical dilatation (Fig. 234a–h).

The infection is probably always transmitted by mosquitoes. In the case of *Icosiella neglecta* Seurat, *Forcipomyia velox* Winn. is held responsible. The "*Filaria rubella* Rud." found by Pflugfelder and Eilers (1959) possibly belongs to the same species. It must always be remembered that microfilariae may produce dermal tumours in amphibians. For further details on the development of the anuran filariae the papers by Causey (1939) and Kotcher (1941) should be consulted.

It is by no means a rare event to find frogs infected by haemofilariae. A population of *Rana esculenta* in Upper Bavaria, for example, showed an infection figure of nearly 100%.

Side by side with the microfilariae the lymphatics of frogs may be inhabited by the juvenile forms of *Rhabdias* species, progeny of mature worms inhabiting the lungs. The two species may be mistaken for one another because *Foleyella* too may be found in the lungs. *Foleyella* is recognized by the presence of the lateral folds or alae which extend along the whole length of the worm.

REFERENCES

Bailenger, J. and Chanseau, J. (1954). Études des vers parasites des amphibiens anoures de la région de Bordeaux. Nouvelles espèces. *Ann. Parasit. hum. comp.* **29**, 546–560.

Baylis, H. A. (1930). Some Heterakidae and Oxyuridae (Nematoda) from Queensland. *Ann. Mag. Nat. Hist.* ser. 10, **5**, 354–366.

Baylis, H. A. (1951). The parasite worms of British reptiles and amphibians. *In* "The British Amphibians and Reptiles", (Smith, M., ed.). Collins, London.

Causey, O. R. (1939). The development of frog filaria larvae, *Foleyella ranae* in *Aëdes* and *Culex* mosquitoes. *Amer. J. Hyg.* **29**, D. 131–132.

Causey, O. R. (1939). Development of the larval stages of *Foleyella brachyoptera* in mosquitoes. *Amer. J. Hyg.* **30**, D. 69–70.

Elkan, E. (1960). Some interesting pathological cases in amphibians. *Proc. zool. Soc., Lond.* **134**, 275–296.

Elkan, E. (1960). The common toad (*Bufo bufo* L.) in the laboratory. *Brit. J. Herpet.* **2**, No. 10, 177–182.

Ernste, L. (1954). Beiträge zur Kenntnis der Filarie *Icosiella neglecta* Diesing 1851 in Blut und Cowobe von *Rana esculenta* L. *Z. Parasitenk.* **16**, 126–144.

Fantham, H. B., Porter, A. and Richardson, L. R. (1942). Some Haematozoa observed in vertebrates in Eastern Canada. *Parasitology* **34**, 199–226.

Fülleborn, F. (1928). Über den Infektionsweg bei *Rhabdias bufonis* (*Rhabdonema nigrovenosum*) des Frosches. *Zbl. Bakt.* Abt. I. **109**, 444–462.

Heinze, K. (1933). Die Gattung *Capillaria* Zeder 1800 als Fischparasit. *Z. Parasitenk.* **5**, 393–406.

Hyman, L. H. (1940). "The Invertebrates", Vol. III. McGraw-Hill, New York.

Kotcher, E. (1941). Studies on the development of frog filariae. *Amer. J. Hyg.* **34**, D. 36–65.

Metschnikov, E. and Leuckart, K. G. F. (1865). Ueber die Entwicklung von *Ascaris nigrovenosa. Arch. Anat. Physiol.* 641. ·

Odening, K. (1954). Ueber die Parasitenfauna des Wasserfrosches (*Rana esculenta* Linné) in einigen mitteldeutschen Biotopen. *Wiss. Z. Schiller Univ. Jena. Math. Naturw. Reihe* **4**, 487–508.

Pflugfelder, O. and Eilers, W. (1959). Auslösung von Adenomen in der Epidermis von *Rana temporaria* durch "*Filaria*" *rubella* Rudolphi. *Z. Parasitenk.* **19**, 101–110.

Piekarski, G. (1954). "Lehrbuch der Parasitologie." Springer, Berlin-Göttingen-Heidelberg.

Schaake, M. (1931). Infektionsmodus und Infektionsweg der *Rhabdias bufonis* Schrank (*Angiostomum nigrovenosum*) und die Metamorphose des Genitalapparates der hermaphroditischen Generation. *Z. Parasitenk.* **3**, 517–648.

Steiner, G. (1924). Some nemas from the alimentary tract of the Carolina tree frog. *J. Parasit.* **11**, 594–602.

Thomas, L. J. (1957). *Bothriocephalus rarus* n. sp. a Cestode from the newt *Triturus viridescens* Raf. *J. Parasit.* **23**, 29–42.

Travassos, L. (1926). Entwicklung des *Rhabdias fülleborni* n. sp. *Arch. Schiffs-u. Tropenhyg.* **30**, 594–602.

Walton, A. (1929). Studies on some nematodes of North American frogs. I. *J. Parasit.* **15**, 227–240.

Walton, A. (1933). The Nematoda as parasites of Amphibia. II. *J. Parasit.* **20**, 1–32; **21**, 27–50.

Wilkie, J. S. (1930). Some parasitic nematodes from Japanese amphibians. *Ann. Mag. Nat. Hist.* ser. 10. **6**, 608–611.

Williams, R. W. (1959). Some nematode parasites of tree frogs, toads, lizards and land crabs of the Bermuda Islands. *J. Parasit.* **49**, 239.

Wittenberg, G. and Gerichter, C. (1944). The morphology and life history of *Foleyella duboisi* with remarks on allied filariids of Amphibia. *J. Parasit.* **30**, 245–256.

Yamaguti, S. (1935). Studies on the helminth fauna of Japan 10. Amphibian nematodes. *Jap. J. Zool.* **6**, 387–392.

Yamaguti, S. (1961). "Systema Helminthum", Vol. III (Pt. 1 The Nematodes of Vertebrates. Pt. 2 The Nematodes of Vertebrates). Interscience, London-New York.

Yorke, W. and Maplestone, P. A. (1926). "The Nematode Parasites of Vertebrates." Churchill, London.

THE GORDIAN WORMS (NEMATOMORPHA)

The mature worms are not parasitic but live in any kind of freshwater habitat. The larvae however parasitize various water insects. In 1943 Nigrelli made the remarkable discovery that gordian worms may infect fish and there are similar findings by Schreitmueller and Lederer (1930) who found gordiid worms in urodeles. Details of these observations are unfortunately not available (Fig. 235).

REFERENCES

Hyman, L. H. (1940). "The Invertebrates", Vol. III. McGraw-Hill, New York.

Nigrelli, R. F. (1943). Causes of diseases and death of fishes in captivity. *Zoologica* **28**, 203–216.

Schreitmueller, W. and Lederer, G. (1930). "Krankheitserscheinungen an Fischen, Reptilien und Lurchen." Berlin.

D. Leeches (Hirudinea) Parasitic in Amphibia

Toads and frogs are not infrequently found attacked by the leeches sharing their habitat. The leeches are not known to transfer any diseases and the frogs seem to be none the worse for the temporary visitation.

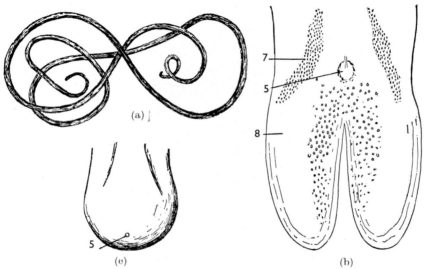

Fig. 235. (a) A Gordian worm (after Janda, 1893); (b) Posterior end of male *Gordionus* (after Heinze, 1937); (c) Posterior end of female *Gordius*. 5, anus; 7, pre-anal tracts and thorns; 8, caudal lobes. (From Hyman, 1951.)

It is, however, a very different matter with a frog-leech relation reported by Mann and Tyler (1963). The frogs in question were: *Rana grisea* van Kampen; *Hyla becki* Loveridge, *Hyla* n. sp. Tyler; *Nyctimystes kubori* Zweifel, and *Nyctimistes narinosa*, all from the central mountains of the Australian Trusteeship Territory of New Guinea, living at 4 600–10 500 ft altitude.

The leech, probably *Philaemon grandidieri* Bl., was not found externally attached as usual but had penetrated into the dorsal lymph sac. In about one-third of the specimens examined leeches were even found in the muscular body wall and in the body cavity. The leech—there seems to have always been only one per frog—is so large that it could take the whole of the frog's blood in one meal. It does not, however, do this but gives the frog time to regenerate its depleted supply. In this way the leech lives with the frog for a lengthy undetermined period. As an ectoparasite *Philaemon* is known from Madagascar, Australia, the Samoan Islands and Juan Fernandez, but it had not previously been registered for New Guinea (Fig. 236).

FIG. 236. A leech (Genus *Philaemon*) in the dorsal lymph sac of a small frog of New Guinea. (Courtesy B. N. Douetil, Esher, Surrey.)

Richardson (1949) found in Canada two specimens of *Rana catesbeiana* whose dorsal lymph sac was invaded by the leech *Batracobdella picta* Verrill. He regarded the invasion as accidental but in view of the findings by Mann and Tyler further attention will have to be paid to this question. Leeches may after all not be as harmless to frogs as we have previously thought. *Batracobdella algira* (Mocquin-Tandon) attacks

Discoglossus pictus and *Hydromantes g. genei* (Mertens, 1929). Autrum nominates further species of *Batracobdella, Oligobdella, Hemiclepsis* and *Haementeria*.

REFERENCES

Autrum, H.-J. (1936). Hirudineen. I. *In* "H. G. Bronns Klassen und Ordnungen des Tierreichs". Leipzig.
Mann, K. H. and Tyler, M. J. (1963). Leeches as endoparasites of frogs. *Nature, Lond.* **197**, 23 March.
Mertens, R. (1929). *Glossosiphonia algira* Mocquin-Tandon als Parasit von *Hydromantes genei genei* Schlegel. *Bl. Aqu. Terrk.* **40**, 206–207.

E. PARASITIC CRUSTACEANS

Small crustaceans lead parasitic lives on many aquatic hosts. It is therefore not surprising that occasionally they also infest amphibians. The most commonly seen crustacean parasite is the European fish louse *Argulus foliaceus* L. (Fig. 73). This small, flat and leaf-like crustacean is mainly an inhabitant of the skin of various freshwater fish, notably the carp and the trout, but it may also be found on *Rana*

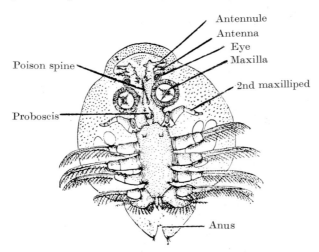

FIG. 237. *Argulus americanus*, the "fish louse" ♀. (From Borradaile.)

tadpoles. Armed with a sharply pointed proboscis it penetrates the skin. This blood-sucking can only have an extremely serious effect on hosts if they are as small as tadpoles, the more so since the parasite is suspected of injecting at the same time a poisonous and paralysing substance.

Argulus americanus Wilson, a N. American species has been found on tadpoles of frogs and newts (Goin and Ogren, 1956) (Fig. 237).

Baldauf (1961) reported on interesting cases where tadpoles of the N. American bull-frog (*Rana catesbeiana* Shaw) were attacked by *Lernaea cyprinacea* L. a fish louse not usually known to attack amphibians. Six parasites were found attached to the posterior part of the lips of a tadpole. The long, filiform crustaceans produced the effect as if the tadpole had been equipped with feelers. The parasites had a branching proboscis and were firmly and deeply anchored in the skin of the host.

REFERENCES

Baldauf, R. J. (1961). Another case of parasitic copepods on amphibians. *J. Parasit.* **47**, 195.
Duijn, jr. C. v. (1956). "Diseases of Fishes", publ. *Water Life*, London.
Goin, C. J. and Ogren, L. H. (1956). Parasitic copepods (*Argulidae*) on amphibians. *J. Parasit.* **42**, 172.
Reichenbach-Klinke, H. H. (1957). "Krankheiten der Aquarienfische." Kernen, Stuttgart.

F.   ARACHNOIDEA AND INSECTS

PARASITIC MITES (ACARINA)

It is not a rare event to find larval mites in the skin of frogs. Treefrogs in particular seem to be exposed to such infestations. We saw a case of this kind in a specimen of *Hyla arborea* L. The mite had burrowed into the skin of the host and was gradually surrounded and walled off by the surrounding tissue so that eventually it disappeared from view, hardly projecting above the surface. It was unfortunately impossible to determine the species.

We owe details about mites affecting amphibians to the work of Hyland (1950, 1956) who reports on the infection of both urodeles and anurans by mites of the genus *Hannemania*. He found *Hannemania dunni* Sambon in the northern dusky salamander (*Desmognathus fuscus*) in E. N. America, *H. penetrans* Ewing in the bronze frog (*Rana clamitans*) of Virginia, *H. eltoni* Sambon and *H. hegeneri* Hyland in *Rana pipiens* (Texas and Florida) and *H. hylae* Ewing in *Hyla arenicolor* (California). Hyland admits that, with the exception of *H. hylae* and *H. hegeneri* the determination of the acarine species remains doubtful (Hyland, 1956). *H. hegeneri* measured $278 \times 165 \mu$ when starved, $0 \cdot 8 \times 0 \cdot 5$ mm when well-fed. He succeeded in keeping the parasites in the laboratory. The larval Acarina fed on urodeles and anurans; the post-larval stages were fed on insect (collembola) eggs. Schlumberger mentions the genus *Hylodes* (= *Pseudacris*) as a possible host for Acarina.

Fain (1962) reports on Acarina found in the nasal cavities of frogs and toads. They are of the Family Ereynetidae which are more commonly found in the nasal passages of birds, more rarely in rodents and lemurs. The genera found in Salientia were *Lawrencarus* and *Batracarus* (Subfamily: Lawrencarinae).

Species of *Hannemannia* and the related genus *Schöngastia* which may infect frogs are described by Sambon (1928) (Fig. 238).

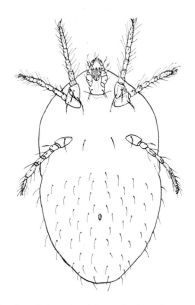

Fig. 238. *Hannemannia edwardsi samboni* from *Bufo variegatus* (Gthr.). (After Sambon.)

REFERENCES

Fain, A. (1962). Les acariens parasites nasicoles des batraciens. Revision des *Lawrencarinae* Fain 1957 (*Ereynetidae: Trombidiforme*). *Bull. Inst. R. Sci. Nat. Belg.* **38**, No. 25, 1–69.

Hyland, K. E. (1950). The life cycle and parasitic habit of the Chigger Mite *Hannemania dunni* Sambon 1928, a parasite of amphibians. *J. Parasit.* **36**, 32–33.

Schlumberger, H. G. (1958). Krankheiten der Fische, Amphibien und Reptilien. *In* "Pathologie der Laboratoriumstiere", Vol. II (Cohrs, Jaffe and Meesen, eds.). Springer, Berlin.

Sambon, L. W. (1928). The parasitic acarians of animals and the part they play in the causation of the eruptive fevers and other diseases of Man. *Amer. J. trop. Med.* **22**, 67–132.

THE LINGUATULIDA (PENTASTOMIDA)

These peculiar parasites, no longer regarded as worms but as relatives of the Chelicerata (spiders), may be found in mammals and birds, but particularly in reptiles like snakes and lizards or crocodiles. Only once has one of these "tongue worms" been found in an amphibian. We owe the observation to Gedoelst who, in 1921, found one of them in the lungs of the Indian toad *Bufo melanostictus*. The parasite belonged to the genus *Raillietiella* and the author described it as *Raillietiella indica* without however furnishing an illustration. Our Fig. 239 shows the

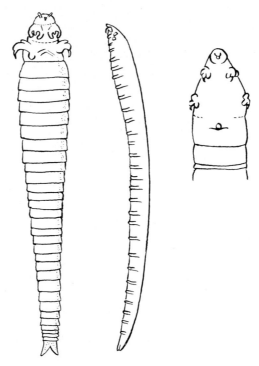

FIG. 239. *Raillietiella mabuiae* Heymons (left) and *Raillietiel'a boulengeri* Vaney and Sambon (middle and right). (After Kükenthal, 1926.)

very similar species *R. mabuiae* Heymons and *R. boulengeri* Vaney and Sambon, both of which occur in reptiles. The differences between the various *Raillietiella* species are insignificant.

Gedoelst reports a length of 3·6 mm for the *Raillietiella indica* and a width of at most 0·83 mm which makes it slightly smaller than the other known species of this genus. It is white, cylindrical, slightly flattened in front. The head is triangular, the oral aperture lies ventrally slightly behind the anterior tip of the head. There are two pairs of yellow tinted hooks, raised above the skin. In front of the first pair of hooks there are two pairs of lateral papilliform adnexa. Another pair of adnexa can be found on the second segment of the body. The body is segmented throughout as in all Linguatulida. The number of these, purely external, segments behind the second pair of hooks is twenty-five. The last segment is divided into two divergent lobes which enclose the anal aperture. The genital pore lies ventrally between the third and fourth segment. Externally, therefore, *R. indica* much resembles *R. boulengeri*. The presumptive existence of a secondary host is not mentioned.

REFERENCES

Gedoelst, L. (1921). Un Linguatulide, nouveau Parasite d'un Batracien. *Rec. Indian Mus.* **22**, 25–26.

Kükenthal, W. (1926). "Handbuch der Zoologie" Bd. III. De Gruyter, Berlin and Leipzig.

PREDACIOUS INSECT LARVAE

Only terrestial Amphibia are exposed to the ravages of insect larvae. Of these by far the best known is the "Toad Fly" *Bufolucilia bufonivora* Monicz (= *Lucilia bufonivora* Brumpt), a close relation of our "Blue-bottle" *Lucilia caesar*, and enjoying, like the latter, a world-wide distribution.

Bufolucilia bufonivora has developed the habit of laying its eggs in the nasal apertures mainly of toads. The larvae, after hatching, first feed on mucus; later they destroy the epithelial lining and may even perforate the bone surrounding the nasal capsule, penetrating thereby either into the orbit or the brain. The destruction wrought by these voracious larvae often produces the most pathetic picture (Fig. 240). Their power to damage and to destroy the host is enormous. Few toads ever survive an attack by bufonivorous larvae (Martini, 1952).

James and Maslin (1947) raised in the laboratory larvae extracted from ulcers of the toad *Bufo boreas boreas* Baird and Girard, and described the hatching flies as *Bufolucilia elongata* Shannon. The species is identical with *Bl. bufonivora*.

Hesse (1906–19), Fischer-Roth (1932), Stadler (1930) and Sandner (1955) have published detailed reports on these insects. Stadler raised twenty-four larvae found in a single toad. Hesse reports an attack on toads by *Lucilia caesar* L. (by him described as *L. splendida* Zett and Meigen). Gerber (1950) gave a report, well-illustrated by Herschel, on the damage done by these larvae.

Eberle (1937) gave a graphic account of an invasion by these redoubtable toad parasites. He discovered a ball of larvae in the mouth

Fig. 240. Common toad (*Bufo bufo* L.) parasitized by *Bufolucilia bufonivora* B. (Photo.: Fischer.)

of a common toad and observed their development. The larvae first burrowed in the direction of the right eye backwards towards the parotid gland, perforating the skin in one place. They next transformed the tongue into a slimy mass. There were about forty larvae in the oral cavity and another eight under the skin of the head. On the afternoon of the second day the skin was perforated between the eyes, both eyes were destroyed, the right completely dissolved. The skin was perforated in the gular region, the mandibular joint disarticulated; eventually the larvae migrated caudally as far as the region of the arms. The toad died, and shortly afterwards 117 flies of the species *Muscina pablorum* emerged. This species is not a particular parasite of toads. The sapro- and zoophagous larvae develop in any kind of organic detritus—even human cases of myiasis (infestation by fly larvae) have been described. We have to accept the fact that, occasionally, several *Lucilia* species may infest Amphibia. It is difficult to be certain in respect of larvae of *Calliphora silvatica* found by Schreitmueller and Lederer (1930). Equally the appearance of *Lucilia sylvarum* Meigen reported by Stadler (1930) has remained a single observation.

It is true to say that it is usually *Bufo bufo* which is attacked by these flies, but the common toad is by no means the only or exclusive victim. Smith (1951) reports on *Lucilia* eggs being found on the grass frog (*R. temporaria*) an observation supported by Stadler (1930). The same author also quotes Weigmanns, who found two larvae in a freshly caught *Hyla arborea*. Mertens (1921) saw infested specimens of *Bufo viridis* on the lower Danube. Even *Salamandra salamandra* may occasionally be attacked (Handlirsch, 1926).

The only factor which protects the toads and the frogs from even more devastating attacks by *Lucilia* species lies in the circumstance that the flies are diurnal and the anurans, particularly the toads, crepuscular in their habits. The flies, which hunt by smell, must therefore find the toads at a time when these are hidden in some well-concealed retreat. What instinct tells the flies that it would not be safe to linger near the mouth of the toad we do not know, but the eggs are often laid somewhere around the pelvic region (Smith, 1951). Another, even more amazing instinct directs the larvae after they have hatched, to the nasal cavity of the toad. They reach it either via the nostril or via the eye and the lacrimal canal. Obstruction of the nasal cavity suffocates the toad, which does not breathe through the mouth and dies a few days later. The complete development of the fly takes 2–3 weeks. Angel (1947) finds that the toads do not so much die of suffocation as of the destruction of the brain and the rest of the central nervous system. He also reports that, in order to suffocate the larvae, toads often seek refuge in the nearest pond. This would seem to be an efficient stratagem. Unfortunately it is only in the breeding season that toads live near ponds and they would have to submerge themselves as soon as they were infected with eggs, a combination of circumstances not likely to occur very often.

Das Gupta (1962) reported extensive feeding destruction in the orbital cavity of the Asian toad *Bufo melanosticus* by *Lucilia porphyrina* Walker.

Similarly Lindner and Mertens (1958) found *Batrachomyia* (Family Chloropidae) maggots parasitizing Australian frogs. One species, *Batrachomyia mertensi*, was described by Lindner as occurring on *Hyla c. caerulea*. Mertens found maggots in granulations of the tympanic and parietal region.

REFERENCES

Angel, F. (1947). "Vie et Moeurs des Amphibiens." Payot, Paris.
Das Gupta, B. (1962). On the myiasis of the Indian toad *Bufo melanostictus*. *Parasitology* **52**, 63–66.

Eberle, G. (1937). Befall und Tötung von Erdkröten (*Bufo vulgaris*) durch Fliegenbrut. *Natur-u. Volk* **67**, 250–254.

Fischer-Roth, H. (1932). Froschlurche im Sandfang. *Natur-u. Mus.* **62**, 362 365.

Gerber, R. (1950). Goldfliegen (*Lucilia*) als Schmarotzer der Erdkröten. *Zool. Garten* **17**, 47–52.

Handlirsch, A. (1926). Insecta. *In* "Handbuch der Zoologie" (Kükenthal, W., ed.), Vol. IV. De Gruyter, Berlin.

Hesse, E. (1906). *Lucilia* in *Bufo vulgaris* Laur. schmarotzend. *Biol. Zbl.* **26**, 633–640.

Hesse, E. (1908). *Lucilia* als Schmarotzer. *Biol. Zbl.* **28**, 753–758.

Hesse, E. (1919). *Lucilia* als Schmarotzer. *Biol. Zbl.* **39**, 401–406.

James, M. T. and Maslin, T. P. (1947). Notes on myiasis of the toad *Bufo boreas boreas*. *J. nat. Acad. Sci., Wash.* **37**, 366–368.

Lindner, E. (1958). *Batrachomyia mertensi*, ein neuer australischer Froschparasit (Chloropidae, Dipt.). *Senckenberg. biol.* **39**, 191–196.

Martini, G. (1952). "Lehrbuch der medizinischen Entomologie", 4th edn. Jena.

Mertens, R. (1921). Zoologische Streifzüge in Rumänien. *Bl. Aqu. Terr.* **32**, 247–252; 311–314; 323–327.

Mertens, R. (1950). Fliegenmaden als Schmarotzer der Kröten. *Wschr. Aqu. Terrk.* **44**, 218.

Mertens, R. (1958). Ergänzende Bemerkungen über *Batrachomyia*-Larven und ihre Wirte. *Senckenberg. biol.* **39**, 197–198.

Reichenbach-Klinke, H. (1950). Nasenparasiten bei Kröten. *Wschr. Aqu. Terrk.* **44**, 113–114.

Rostand, J. (1934). "Toads and Toad Life." Methuen, London.

Sandner, H. (1955). *Lucilia bufonivora* Moniez 1876 (Diptera) in Poland (in Polish). *Acta parasit. Polon.* **2**, 319–329.

Schreitmueller, W. and Lederer, G. (1930). "Krankheitserscheinungen an Fischen, Reptilien und Lurchen." Wenzel, Berlin.

Smith, M. (1951). "The British Amphibians and Reptiles." Collins, London.

Stadler, H. (1930). Ueber den Befall einer Erdkröte (*Bufo vulg.* Laur.) durch die Larven von *Lucilia sylvarum* Meig. Krankheitsgeschichte und Sektion. *Z. Parasitk.* **2**, 360–367.

G. Molluscan Larvae Encysting in Tadpoles

The larval stages of freshwater molluscs (*Anodonta, Unio, Lampsilis, Quadrula*, etc.) normally spend part of their life encysted in fish. Occasionally they may also invade tadpoles. Faussek (1901) was able to follow the complete development of *Anodonta cygnaea* L. in axolotls, other authors saw an analogous process taking place in *Necturus maculatus* Raf. The larval gills of this species were found occupied by cysts containing larvae of *Hemilastena ambigua* Arey (Howard, 1951). Findings like these must be regarded as rarities in amphibian pathology.

References

Arey, L. B. (1932). The nutrition of Glochidia during metamorphosis. A microscopical study of the sources and manner of utilization of nutritive substance. *J. Morph.* **53**, 201–219.

Faussek, V. (1901). Ueber den Parasitismus der *Anodonta* Larven. *Verh. Int. Zool. Congr. Berlin.* pp. 761–766.

Howard, A. D. (1951). A river mussel parasitic on a salamander. *Nat. Hist. Soc. Chicago Misc. Publ.* **77**, 1–6.

H. Diseases due to Fungi and Parasitic Algae

The field of fungal infection in amphibians is as yet still largely un-explored, apart from a few observations which have been published in special journals. Only one fungus, occasionally seen in frogs and called *Basidiobolus ranarum* Eidam, has been investigated in detail. It belongs to the Entomophthoraceae, algal fungi of the genus *Phyco-mycetes* which are related to the genus *Empusa* which includes the well-known fly-mould *Empusa muscae* Fres. Schreitmueller and Lederer even reported the infection of anurans by *Empusa*.

The developmental stages of *Basidiobolus ranarum* can be observed if the intestinal contents of their hosts are examined. The zygotes are surrounded by a hard shell and peculiarly shaped "beak cells" (Fig. 241). The germinating threads are hyalin in structure and not divided

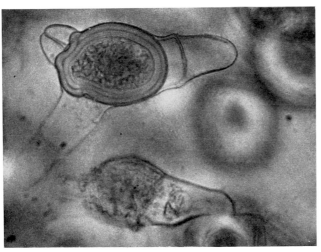

Fig. 241. The fungus *Basidiobolus ranarum* Eidam. Zygotes from the gut of *Rana temporaria.* × 1 000. (Photo.: Johannes.)

into separate chambers. They reach a width of approximately 10 μ; the diameter of the zygotes is 25–30 μ. It is as yet uncertain to what degree the frog is damaged by the fungus.

Reichenbach-Klinke (1956) saw a heavy accumulation of fungal spores in the mouth of a pleurodele newt (*Pleurodeles waltli*).

In the past *Basidiobolus* was thought to be merely an inhabitant of the large intestine of frogs, toads, lizards, geckos and chameleons, but an Indonesian worker, Lie Kan Joe, observed in 1956 a severe subcutaneous granulomatous infection in a child, caused by *B. ranarum*,

(a)

(b)

FIG. 242. (a and b) Two specimens of the common toad (*Bufo bufo*) with severe fungal infection of the skin and the subcutis. (Photos.: Elkan. Courtesy Zool. Soc. Lond.)

a condition which, since that time, is known as subcutaneous phycomycosis. Analogous observations were made by Harman (1963) working in Ibadan, Nigeria, where an identical fungus was grown from the faeces of local lizards and from subcutaneous lesions in several patients. Since then similar observations have been reported from Ghana, the Sudan, Uganda and the Cameroons. Both the clinical appearance and the histology of the *Basidiobolus* infection in humans are very similar to that presented by other fungal infections. Mycelial threads are seen surrounded by epithelioid cells or engulfed by foreign-body giant cells. Fibrous tissue develops but it does not succeed in preventing the slow spreading of the condition. Harman reports that the condition was amenable to treatment with potassium iodide, a cure being effected in about 3 weeks.

Elkan (1960) reported on a number of cases of severe fungal infection of common toads (*B. bufo.*) They occurred in freshly caught specimens as well as in others kept in captivity (Fig. 242a, b). The fungus which in most cases, attacked the skin first, produced thick pads of granulation tissue covering areas of deep ulceration. This granulation tissue showed a thick growth of a fungal mycelium, the exact nature of which could, in the absence of fruiting bodies, not be determined.

None of the affected toads survived the infection. If it had been discovered in its early stages it might have been possible to treat it by careful application of a weak solution of potassium permanganate.

Amphibian viscera may be attacked by fungi more often than is generally recognized. In the course of routine dissections of common toads a specimen was discovered which had died suddenly and without apparent cause. The kidneys looked pale and swollen. Sections showed extreme dilatation of the proximal uriniferous tubules (Figs. 243, 244) which were filled with a fluid giving a strong positive reaction on being stained by the periodic acid–Schiff method. On the renal surface and growing into the parenchyma grew the dense mycelium of a fungus. Here again the absence of fruiting bodies precluded exact identification. The skin of this toad seemed to be perfectly intact, yet one would assume that the renal infection was secondary to a primary external invasion. Here as on many other occasions we were impressed by the degree to which Amphibia can tolerate the destruction of vital organs before they succumb.

Just as in the case of acid-fast bacteria, fungi will rarely attack a healthy uninjured animal, but they will appear as soon as the animal is otherwise debilitated or injured. This refers particularly to the mould *Saprolegnia*, a ubiquitous inhabitant of fresh water and aquaria which can, as it does in fish, cause deep ulceration of skin, subcutis and muscle down to the bone. As soon as there is the slightest suspicion of an attack by this fungus an attempt should be made at saving the animal by treating it with a weak solution of potassium permanganate (1/1 000) or with a weak tincture of iodine.

Tiffney (1939) reviewed the moulds found on amphibians. The most commonly encountered species were *Saprolegnia parasitica* Coker on newts and frogs and *S. ferax* Gruith, on newts, both always occurring in connection with injuries. Infrequently there appeared *Achlya*

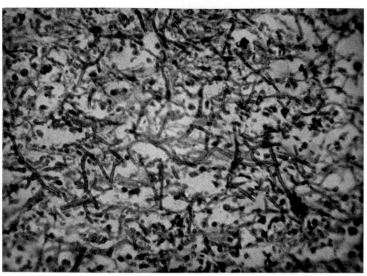

Fig. 243. Fungal mycelium from a dorsal subcutaneous tumour in *Bufo bufo*. (Photo.: Elkan.)

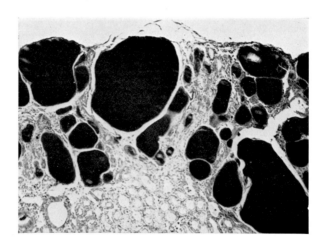

Fig. 244. *Bufo bufo.* Cystic degeneration of the kidney. The kidney was infected by fungal mycelium. PAS. (Photo.: Elkan. Courtesy Zool. Soc. Lond.)

flagellata Coker and *Dictyuchus monosporus* (?) Leitgeb, both in newts. Tadpoles, when injured, have also been found infected by moulds (Schnetzler, 1887).

Live and healthy amphibians obviously have an efficient defence against *Saprolegnia*. This even extends to their eggs, which remain free from moulds so long as they are alive and developing normally. Any non-viable eggs, however, are immediately attacked and they then represent a severe danger to the rest of the spawn. It goes without saying that they should be removed as soon as discovered. Details of the fight against *Saprolegnia* were published by Warthmueller, Wolterstorff and Herre (1932). Treatment of young amphibians with trypaflavine or methylene blue can be tried.

Authors have suspected the fungus *Ichthyosporidium hoferi* Plehn and Mulsow, a common parasite of the viscera of fish, to infect Amphibia as well. The reports, however are not, as yet, conclusive, The same must be said about the *Aspergillacae* which, common in fish, may very well attack Amphibia too.

We might finally mention a type of *blue algae, Oscillospora batrachorum* Collin (= *Arthromitus batrachorum* Collin) which has been found in the rectum of *Alytes obstetricians* and in tadpoles in Central France (Langeron, 1923). The algae appear only very rarely and do not seem to cause any damage. Our figure (Fig. 245) shows three stages in the development of the related type *Oscillospora media* Langeron which occurs in the appendix of the guinea-pig (*Cavia cobaya*).

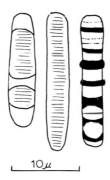

10μ

FIG. 245. Threads of the blue alga *Oscillospora media* Langeron from the caecum of a guinea-pig. (After Langeron.)

REFERENCES

Dhalival, S. S. and Griffiths, D. A. (1963). Fungal disease in Malayan toads: an acute lethal inflammatory reaction. *Nature, Lond.* **197**, 267–269.
Elebute Ea, and Okubadejo Oa (1962). Subcutaneous phycomycosis in a Nigerian. *West Afr. med. J.* **11**, 207–220.
Elkan, E. (1960). Some interesting pathological cases in amphibians. *Proc. zool. Soc. Lond.* **134**, 375–396.

Langeron, M. (1923). Les Oscillariees parasites du tube digestif de l'homme et des animaux. *Ann. Parasit. hum. comp.* **1**, 75–89.

Lie Kian Joe (1956). *Basidiobolus ranarum* as a cause of subcutaneous mycosis in Indonesia. *Arch. Derm.* **74**, 378–383.

Nowak, W. (1930). Untersuchungen an *Basidiobolus ranarum* Eidam *Arch. Protistenk.* **69**, 195–234.

Reichenbach-Klinke, H. (1956). Knochendegeneration beim Rippenmolch (*Pleurodeles waltli* Michahelles) in Zusammenhang mit intermuskulärer Melanophorenanreicherung. *Biol. Zbl.* 75, 407–416.

Schnetzler, J. B. (1887). Infection d'un Larve de Grenouille par *Saprolegnia ferax*. *Arch. Sci. Phys. Nat. Genève* **18**, 492.

Schreitmueller, W. and Lederer, G. (1930). "Krankheitserscheinungen an Fischen, Reptilien und Lurchen." Wenzel, Berlin.

Tiffney, W. N. (1939). The identity of certain species of the Saprolegniaceae parasitic in fish. *J. Elisha Mitchell Sci. Soc.* **55**, 134–151.

Wartmueller, W., Wolterstorff, W. and Herre, W. (1932). Erkrankungen an Eiern und Larven bei Molchen. *Bl. Aqu. Terrk.* **43**, 73–77.

CHAPTER 12

Tumours, Benign and Malignant

Parallel with the incidence of other diseases the incidence of tumours in amphibians increases as more attention is paid to the pathology of this class of animals. Compared with the number of infectious and parasitic diseases the appearance of tumours is not common among the Amphibia, but detailed accounts of some of the cases studied can be found in the journals specializing in this field. An early account by Schreitmueller and Lederer (1930) from the zoological gardens at Frankfurt am Main mentions dorsal tumours in various anurans and fibromata in urodeles. Since that time the number of tumours observed in amphibians has risen but it has never kept pace with that observed in fish. An extensive review of the literature available at that time was published by Schlumberger and Lucké in 1948 and 1949.

Just like the warm-blooded groups of animals, amphibians may suffer from benign tumours without secondary growths and from malignant tumours spreading by infiltration or by metastases. Benign tumours are far more commonly seen than malignant growths. They may originate in the skin as epitheliomata or papillomata; in the glands as adenomata; in the connective tissue as fibromata or lipomata; in the bone as chondromata; and in the viscera as hepatomata or nephromata. A case will, however, be described where a nephroblastoma, not malignant in itself, interfered with the life of a frog by the mere size to which it grew. The malignant tumours (carcinoma, sarcoma) may arise anywhere and they include the pigmented dermal tumours described as melanomata, erythrophoromata, guanophoromata and xanthophoromata according to the type of pigment-bearing cells playing a part in the malignant growth.

Squamous-cell Carcinoma in *Rana temporaria*

True epitheliomata are rarely seen in amphibians. Schlumberger and Lucké (*loc. cit.*) recorded twenty-two cases of malignant tumours in anurans, twenty-one of which were from the genus *Rana*. None of these tumours was classified as an epithelioma but in the same review eleven epitheliomata were recorded from fish, the commonest being the tumour of the lips of the dwarf catfish *Ameiurus nebulosus*. In earlier days, when frogs and newts were mainly kept as pets by amateurs

11

the paucity of reports on their diseases may have been due to lack of interest and lack of training on the part of the observers. Nowadays, large numbers of fish and particularly of amphibians are kept under close observation in laboratories. If epitheliomata occurred frequently they certainly would have been reported. The reason for the absence of such reports seems to lie in the fact that amphibian epitheliomata are—like some of their human counterparts—old age tumours, and that few animals, either in or outside the laboratory, live to the age at which such tumours might develop. It is from this point of view that the case here reported may be of interest.

The specimen, a female *Rana temporaria*, had been caught, fully grown, in S.E. England, and was kept, well-fed and cared for, in a terrarium for 4 years. Assuming that, at the time of its capture, it was at least 2 years old, it must have been of very "advanced" age when eventually it was found to be diseased. The course of the illness was observed for another 6 months. During this time a swelling appeared below the right eye, developing gradually into a tumour of 8 mm diameter. The tumour gradually displaced the eye upwards, but so long as only one eye was affected the frog was still able to feed. Eventually, however, the frog seemed to be blind on both sides, the left eye deteriorating much more rapidly than the right. The animal was still in a good nutritional state but since it was now quite unable to catch any prey the owner killed it with chloroform.

0·5mm

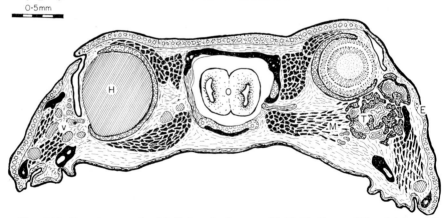

FIG. 246. *Rana temporaria*. Adult female, 5 years old. Epithelioma of the right maxillary region, invading the ocular muscles. Retroretinal haemorrhage in the left eye. *E*, Epidermis; *H*, haematoma in left eyeball; *T*, tumour; *V*, dilated cephalic veins; *M*, ocular muscle invaded by tumour. (Del. Elkan. Courtesy *Cancer Res.*)

Our illustration (Fig. 246) shows the picture presented in transverse section through the head. On the right a mass, well-visible to the naked

eye, occupied the maxillary region between the pterygoid bone and the
eyeball, displacing the latter upwards and protruding in the region of the

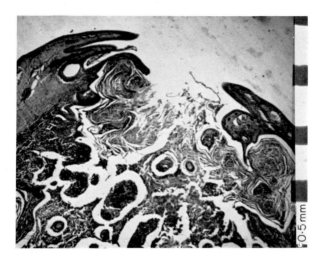

FIG. 247. *Rana temporaria*. Adult ♀. Epithelioma eroding epithelial surface. (H. and
E.) (Photo.: Elkan. Courtesy *Cancer Res.*)

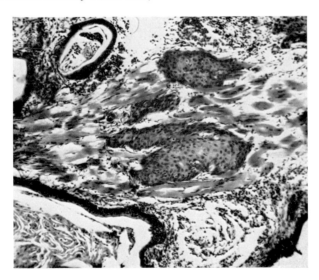

FIG. 248. *Rana temporaria*. Adult ♀. Epithelioma infiltrating the ocular muscles.
× 50. (H and E.) (Photo.: Elkan. Courtesy *Cancer Res.*)

lower eyelid. At the centre of this bulge the epidermis is seen eroded,
the tumour forming the base and the edge of the ulcer (Fig. 247).

The deeper part of the tumour can be seen to invade the ocular muscles (Fig. 248) and the Harderian gland, while a dorsal extension invades the right cornea from the periphery (Fig. 249). The laminae

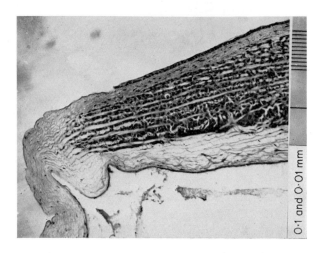

FIG. 249. *Rana temporaria*. Adult ♀. Epithelioma infiltrating the cornea.

of the cornea had a directional influence on the growth of the tumour and forced it to split up into sheets of 1–2 cell thickness. The bulk of the tumour presents the picture of a typical squamous-cell carcinoma with varying degrees of differentiation. In some sections typical epithelial cells with cell bridges could be seen while in others ab-scence of cell boundaries and nuclear polymorphism predomin-ated. Mitotic figures were rare. The stroma, consisting of badly differentiated fibroblasts, was poorly vascularized.

As to the left side of the head, two features demand our attention. The first is that of a massive retroretinal haemorrhage which detached the retina along the whole caudal half of the bulbus. Every vein in the left maxillary region was found dilated and filled with blood to capacity. No cause for the subretinal haemorrhage, which obviously caused the blindness on that side, could be found. The second interesting feature on the left is seen in the fact that, as on the right, malignant epithelial cells invaded the corneal periphery. They were not in continuity with the main tumour and probably presented a metastasis. No secondary growths were seen elsewhere.

A tumour of this type behaving very much like a rodent ulcer, has not previously been described for Amphibia and it is particularly interesting to see that it occurred in a frog well advanced in years.

More observations of this kind would be of value in the comparative study of malignant tumours.

Adenomata

Skin lesions resembling adenomata have been described by Eberth (1868), Pawlowsky (1912), Pentimalli (1914), Secher (1917/19) and Pirlot and Welsch (1934), all occurring in *Rana*. Smallwood (1905), Duany (1929), Downs (1932) and Lucké (*loc. cit.*) reported on adeno-carcinomata of the skin and the kidney in the American leopard frog (*Rana pipiens* Gmel.). This frog has proved to be a most interesting object of observation in that about 2% of the frogs caught were affected by a renal adenocarcinoma transmissible by implantation. The fact that new tumours do not arise at the site of the implant but always in the kidney has lent weight to the view that at least some of the malignant tumours are due to virus infections (Oberling, 1952; Dukes, 1961) (Fig. 250).

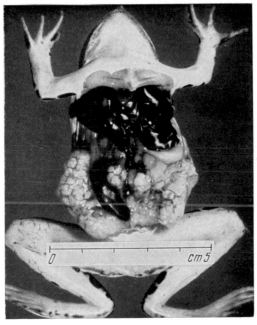

FIG. 250. *Rana pipiens* Gmel. Adenocarcinoma of both kidneys with secondary deposits in the liver. (After Schlumberger.)

A similar tumour was described by Elkan (1960). It occurred in an adult specimen of *Xenopus laevis*, arising from the left kidney and growing to such a size that it displaced all the intraperitoneal viscera

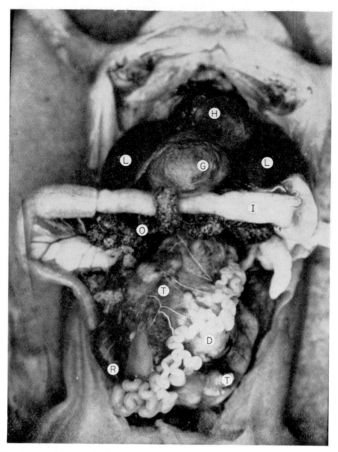

FIG. 251. (a) *Xenopus laevis*. Renal adenocarcinoma. The retroperitoneal tumour has displaced the right oviduct, the rectum and the intestine. The gall bladder is abnormally distended. *D*, Oviduct; *G*, gall bladder; *H*, heart; *I*, small intestine; *L*, liver; *O*, ovary; *R*, rectum; *T*, tumour.

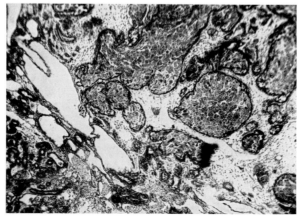

(b) *Xenopus laevis* D. Adult female. Renal carcinoma. Invasion of renal tubules. × 30.

forwards (Fig. 251a). It did not, however, produce any secondary deposits although the microscopical picture was that of a typical adenocarcinoma (Fig. 251b).

Murray (1908) reported on a widespread affection in a newt (*Trit. cristatus*) whose skin was, from the chin to the tail, full of adenomatous tumours emanating from the skin glands. Champy and Champy (1935)

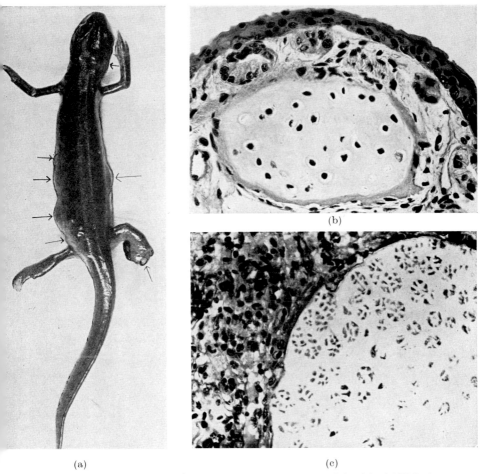

(a) (b) (c)

Fig. 252. *Triturus vulgaris* L. ♀ with multiple chondromata of the skin. (a) Naked eye appearance. (b and c) Microscopic sections. (After Broz.)

report on dermal carcinoma in *Triturus alpestris* and Vaillant and Pettit (1902) on a fibroma of 2 cm length in the forefoot of a giant salamander (*Megalobatrachus maximus* Schl.). Further accounts of tumours of the extremities can be found in Gheorghiu (1830), Schwarz

(1923) and Lucké and Schlumberger (1949) who found a myxosarcoma in a specimen of *Rana clamitans*. Broz (1947) gives a detailed description of a chondroma arising multiple in the subcutis of head, trunk and legs of a specimen of *Triturus vulgaris*. No secondaries were found and the condition was regarded as benign (Fig. 252).

The largest and most spectacular adenoma in an amphibian which we have ever seen occurred in a specimen of *X. laevis* D. which had been in captivity for about 2 years. In a routine examination it was found to have an abdominal tumour. The toad was kept in a separate tank until it died 2 months later. The pictures presented at the post-mortem examination are shown in Fig. 253a–c. The right lobe of the

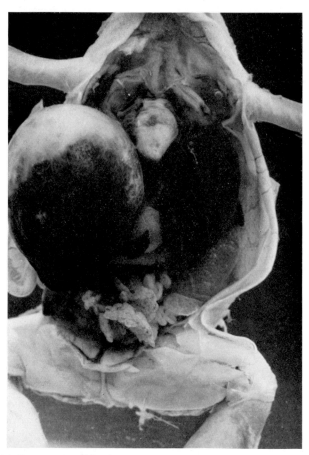

FIG. 253. (a) *Xenopus laevis* D. Adult female. Adenoma of liver. Post-mortem appearance. (Photo.: Elkan.)

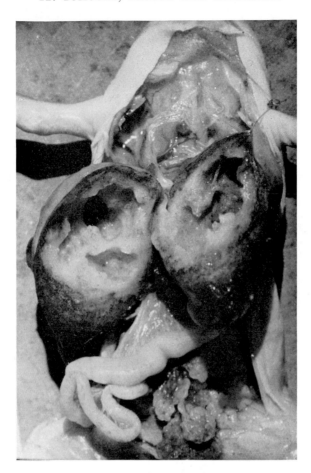

FIG. 253. (b) *Xenopus luevis* D. Adult female showing adenoma of liver. Right lobe of liver sectioned revealing large cavity filled with necrotic debris.

liver was enlarged to at least twice its natural size. A cut through the tumour revealed a large necrotic cavity containing debris and fluid which escaped under some pressure. The suspicion that this condition represented an abscess caused by bacterial infection was not borne out by histological examination, which showed that the normal liver tissue was entirely replaced by the tubules and the interstitial network of a badly differentiated adenoma (Fig. 253c). One could not hope, in a case as advanced as this one, to determine the origin of the tumour. The gall bladder itself being normal, it must be assumed that the tumour arose in one of the intrahepatic bile passages. A search for parasites which might have initiated such a growth remained negative.

11*

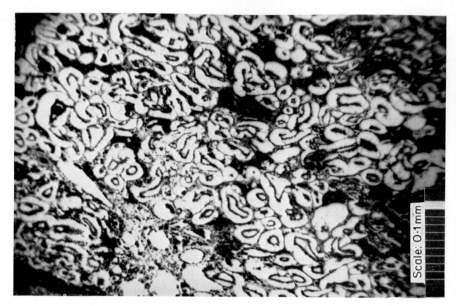

Fig. 253. (c) *Xenopus laevis* D. Adenoma of the liver. Section through part of the tumour showing glandular structure and absence of normal hepatic tissue. Alcian blue-chloranthin F. (Photo.: Elkan.)

Tumours of the Visceral Organs

Tumours of the visceral organs of amphibians are, with the exception of Lucké's tumour, very rare. Pick and Poll (1903) described a cystic adenocarcinoma in the testis of a giant salamander, Plehn (1906) an ovarian carcinoma in *Rana esculenta*. A pulmonary carcinoma in *Bufo calamita* was described by Elkan (1960) (Fig. 254), renal tumours by Carl (1913) and Schlumberger (1958) (Fig. 250), hepatomata by Willis (1948). A neurosarcoma seen in *Rana catesbeiana* and described by Lucké and Schlumberger in 1949 is of particular interest. The latest review of the bibliography on amphibian tumours may be found in Willis's (1960) standard work on the pathology of tumours.

A routine post-mortem dissection on common toads (*B. bufo*) which died in captivity revealed an unusual tumour of the urinary bladder. The bladder of the frog is normally a bilobed organ. In this case the division into two lobes was emphasized by the fact that the right lobe was completely filled by a solid white tumour, the left normal. No other abnormalities and no secondary deposits were seen. The tumour, on sectioning, was found to be a lipoma (Fig. 255) issuing from the bladder wall. The bladder contained no parasites. It has been observed in another case (p. 332) that tumours obstructing the bladder kill

the frogs without, as in this case, apparently doing any traceable
damage to the kidney. Considering the anatomical relations of the

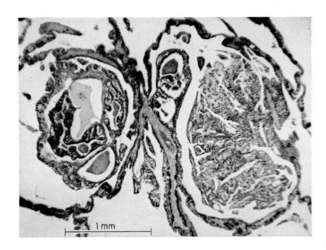

FIG. 254. *Bufo calamita*. Pulmonary carcinoma. (Photo.: Elkan.)

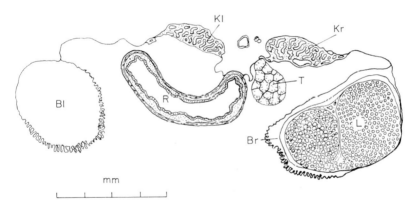

FIG. 255. *Bufo bufo*. Lipoma filling the right diverticulum of the urinary bladder.
Bl, Left diverticulum of the bladder; *Br*, right diverticulum of the bladder with tumour;
Kr, right kidney; *Kl*, left kidney; *L*, lipoma; *R*, rectum; *T*, testis. (Del. Elkan.)

organs concerned, obstruction to the bladder should not indeed impede
the flow of urine, and microscopy of the kidney in these cases reveals
a normal picture. In the absence of any other pathological lesion the
cause of death in these cases remains conjectural.

Nephroblastoma

Embryonic blastomata have so far not been described for Amphibia.

The following observation may therefore be of interest. Nephro-blastomata are, according to Willis (*loc. cit.*), commonly found in the

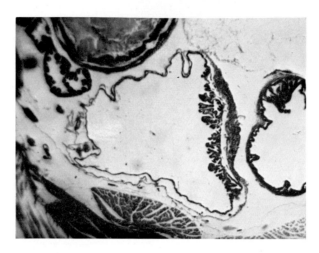

FIG. 256. *Xenopus laevis*. Urinary bladder, normal, transverse. × 15. (H. and E.) (Photo.: Elkan. Courtesy Zool. Soc. Lond.)

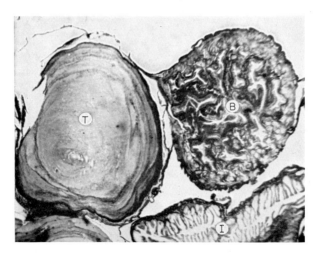

FIG. 257. *Xenopus laevis*. Pelvic tumour impinging upon the urinary bladder. *B*, Urinary bladder, grossly hypertrophic; *I*, intestinal loop; *T*, tumour impinging upon the bladder. (Stained after van Gieson.) (Photo.: Elkan. Courtesy Zool. Soc. Lond.)

pig, the rabbit and the domestic fowl, less commonly in hares, rats and mice. Their classification into renal teratomata and nephroblastomata depends on the type and the degree of differentiation seen. It cannot

be regarded as certain that these tumours are really as rare in poikilothermic animals as their rarity in the literature may suggest. These
animals are usually kept in heated cages. They are nocturnal in their
habits and hide, particularly when they are ill. When their death is
discovered, advanced decomposition often makes further investigation
impossible and much interesting material is lost in this way. Circumstances are a little more promising where animals are kept in laboratories where less attention is paid to duplicate natural surroundings
and more to the state of health of the animals. Even in the best conditions, however, tumours of the visceral organs are rarely seen. Twenty-
five years of observing large stocks of *Xenopus*, for example, have
yielded only two cases of renal carcinoma and the single case of nephroblastoma here described.

It occurred in a fully grown female of 120 g weight which had been
kept in a steel tank, together with fifty-nine other female *Xenopus
laevis* for over a year. It had, during that time, like the other toads,
been used for pregnancy tests on several occasions and had given
correct results. It did not, in the end, attract attention because it
looked ill or because it showed any difference in behaviour, but because
a large firm tumour could be felt through the abdominal wall when the
animal was handled. It should be emphasized that this toad was neither
disfigured by hydrops, a very common symptom in diseased anurans,
nor discoloured. It was however considered that, whatever the nature
of the tumour, the toad could not be treated and would not recover
spontaneously. It was therefore killed with urethane.

The naked-eye appearance of the viscera (Fig. 258) varied little from
that seen in cases of renal carcinoma (Fig. 251) with the exception
that the tumour in this case was very much larger than those previously
seen. Its retroperitoneal origin was shown by the fact that the vena
cava inferior, the large intestine and the right oviduct were displaced
ventrally. No trace of the right kidney could be found even with a
hand lens. The left kidney was found compressed between the tumour
and the left dorso-lumbar muscles. It showed no histological abnormality. Both the liver and the spleen were found to be considerably
congested and enlarged to twice their normal size. The ovaries were
atrophic and reduced to less than half their normal size, but the fat-
bodies, surprisingly, were found of normal volume. This is quite at
variance with the picture usually found in diseased anurans where, if
the ovaries atrophy, the fat-bodies do so as well.

No metastases of the tumour were found anywhere and invasion of
veins could not be demonstrated. The tumour had grown entirely by
expansion, displacing but not invading neighbouring structures.

The neoplastic mass was firm, white, with an irregularly bulging surface of the cauliflower type. Cross section showed a few small darkly stained patches but no signs of softening or degeneration. The

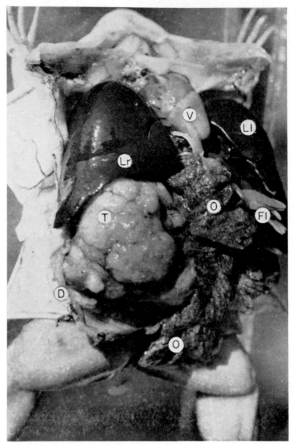

FIG. 258. *Xenopus laevis*. Adult female, 110 g from stock. In captivity for ±1 year. Nephroblastoma, 3×3×3 cm displacing inferior vena cava and right oviduct forward, large intestine and ovary to the left. Fat bodies normal. The animal showed no signs of distress. The tumour could be palpated through the abdominal wall. *D*, Oviduct; *Fl*, left fat-body; *Lr*, right lobe of liver; *Ll*, left lobe of liver; *O*, ovary; *S*, spleen; *T*, tumour; *V*, ventricle. (Photo.: Elkan.)

whole tumour was contained in a thin capsule which, in the right lumbo-dorsal region, contained parts of the compressed and thinned-out right kidney (Fig. 259). Histologically, a mixture of undifferentiated and well-differentiated cells, both probably derived from the renal blastema, could be seen. The stroma showed a loose network of fibroblasts embedded in abundant intercellular substance which stained well with PAS, alcian blue and mucicarmine (Fig. 260). Clear spaces

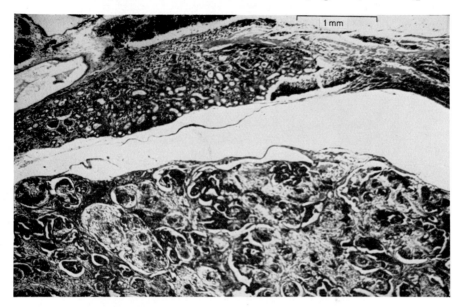

FIG. 259. *Xenopus laevis*. Nephroblastoma at low magnification. Compressed renal tissue forms part of the capsule surrounding the tumour. (Photo.: Elkan.)

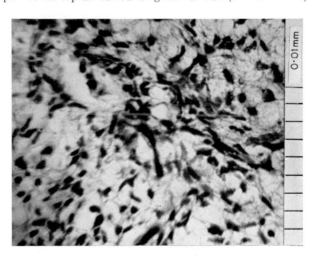

FIG. 260. *Xenopus laevis* D. Nephroblastoma. Undifferentiated stroma and ground substance. (Photo.: Elkan.)

within the stroma contained phagocytes full of fatty droplets. No areas of obvious necrobiosis were seen in spite of the scanty blood

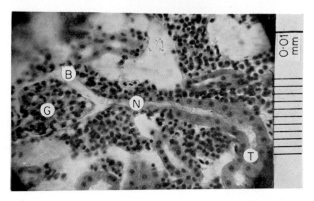

FIG. 261. Normal nephron of 2-week-old tadpole. *B*, Bowman's capsule; *G*, glomerulus; *N*, ciliated neck; *T*, proximal convoluted tubule. (Photo.: Elkan.)

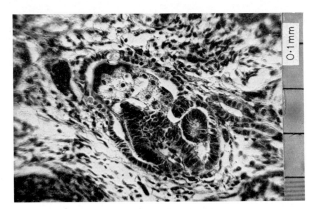

FIG. 262. *Xenopus laevis*. Nephroblastoma. Abortive attempt at glomerulus formation. Bowman's capsule filled with large cells with clear cytoplasm and lined with cuboidal epithelium. (Photo.: Elkan.)

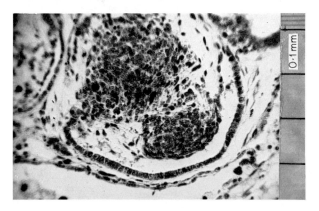

FIG. 263. *Xenopus laevis*. Nephroblastoma. Abortive attempt at glomerulus formation. Undifferentiated blastema instead of capillaries. Bowman's capsule partly formed and lined with cuboidal epithelium. (Photo.: Elkan.)

supply of the tumour. All its parts stained well and seemed of good viability even at the centre of the growth.

In the parenchyma every degree from undifferentiated to highly organized epithelium could be seen. The normal epithelial components of an aglossan nephron would be (Fig. 261):

Low endothelium, lining Bowman's capsule;
Ciliated, cuboidal epithelium lining the neck of the nephron;
High columnar epithelium lining the convoluted tubules;
Low columnar epithelium and flask cells lining the collecting ducts.

Fig. 264. *Xenopus laevis*. Nephroblastoma. "Palisade" epithelium attempting to form a Bowman's capsule.

Of all these cell types only the low cuboidal, non-ciliated epithelium appears in the sections (Fig. 262, 263). Instead of the other types two or perhaps three new kinds of cells appear which are not found in the normal aglossan mesonephros:

Undifferentiated renal blastema occurring either in loose concentric rings or in dense conglomerations in the place of glomerular capillary loops (Fig. 263):

(1) Large clear cells with a small nucleus and well defined cell walls;
(2) These cells are always seen to fill some kind of cavity either wholly or partly. These cavities may be abortive Bowman's capsules (Figs. 262–264);
(3) High columnar epithelium of the "palisade" type. The nuclei are long and thin and lie so closely together that no cytoplasm can be seen between them (Fig. 264). These palisade cells are seen either forming the wall of a tubule or they are seen protruding in papillary fashion into smaller and larger cystic spaces (Figs. 262, 263);
(4) Among these palisade cells there appear occasionally slightly larger oval cells whose nuclei do not fill the whole cell, leaving a clear ring of cytoplasm between nucleus and cell wall.

The numerous cystic cavities which can be seen in every field are lined with many different types of epithelial cells. Their nuclei vary much in size. The palisade arrangement, although prevalent, is not always present (Fig. 263). The two types of cells most typical for the aglossan kidney, the ciliated columnar and the flask cell were not seen in the tumour.

The nuclei stained more heavily than normal. Mitotic figures were not seen. From this fact and from the absence of metastases or even of local infiltration it was concluded that this embryoma had been growing very slowly to its present size, was essentially non-malignant, and pathogenic only in so far as it caused pressure atrophy of the right kidney and congestion of the spleen and the liver. The general histological picture is that of ad infinitum repeated but unsuccessful attempts at producing a kidney (Figs. 262–264). The normal mesonephros develops between the fifth and the fifty-eighth day (Nieuwkoop and Faber, 1956). The beginnings of this nephroblastoma may therefore go very far back in the development of this particular toad.

Pigmented Tumours

Pigmented tumours, in particular the *Melanomata*, are of great interest, partly because of their great malignancy, partly because of their genetic peculiarities. They are more common in fish where they have been widely studied, but occasional cases have also been seen in amphibians. One of the first cases was reported by Krontowsky (1916) who found a "malignant chromatophoroma" in a specimen of *Siredon mexicanum*. Further melanomata in axolotls were studied by Sheremetieva-Brunst in 1953, among them a melanotic epithelioma from the chin of a black axolotl. In fourteen out of twenty-one attempts this tumour could successfully be transplanted to white specimens.

The case of an atypical facial papilloma, probably a melanoma, recently seen in a specimen of *Xenopus laevis*, may here be quoted because of its peculiar histological features.

It occurred in an adult female of 110 g kept in stock for pregnancy tests together with about sixty others, none of which showed any signs of disease. The toad attracted attention, not because it showed any obvious tumour or signs of disease but because it became gradually paler, refused food and had, apparently, difficulties in breathing. Close inspection revealed a pink-yellow discoloration of the right nostril, the lining of which seemed to be thrown into folds obstructing the airway (Fig. 265). The toad was isolated for observation. It would not feed,

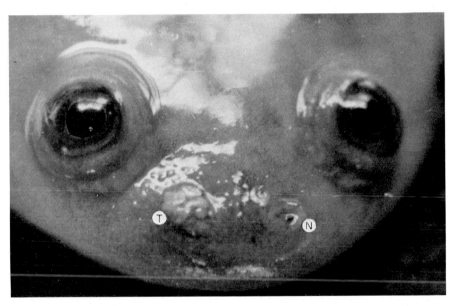

Fig. 265. *Xenopus laevis*. Atypical facial papilloma (melano-carcinoma?) of the right nostril. *N*, Normal nostril; *T*, tumour obstructing right nostril. (Photo.: Elkan. Courtesy *Cancer Res.*)

became gradually paler and lost weight. After 4 weeks it died without having developed any other obvious symptoms. Dissection revealed no abnormality of the viscera apart from complete atrophy of ovaries and fat-bodies, always a sign of serious illness in a female toad. Serial sections were made through the affected rostral part of the skull.

At low magnification these revealed the presence of a papillomatous growth at the edge of the nostril. Papillomata being among the commonest of tumours little attention might have been paid to this finding but for the unusual relation of the tumour to the overlying epidermis.

In a typical papilloma, arising from the dermis or the subcutis, the epidermis, otherwise unaffected, is thrown into folds, covering the papillae, and may show a greater or lesser degree of keratinization at the surface. In this case the epidermis still covered the main polypous mass, but instead of presenting a homogenous layer of stratified epithelium, it was eroded from below by many oval or circular pockets of varying depth. The pockets were sharply defined (Fig. 266) and were,

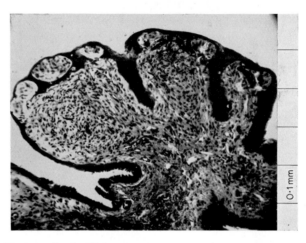

Fig. 266. *Xenopus laevis*. Melano-carcinoma of nostril. Compare with Fig. 268. (Photo.: Elkan.)

in many instances, seen to approach the surface so closely that only one layer of cells remained of the original epithelial covering, 5–7 cells thick. At the extremity of the polypus the epithelium was completely eroded, but this area of ulceration was small.

The dermal glandular coat and the layer of dermal connective tissue, which is very tough in *Xenopus*, was completely destroyed in the affected area and replaced by cells of three types: (1) fibroblasts with elongated nuclei; (2) capillary loops, either single or in large agglomerations; (3) cells with large, oval, badly staining nuclei.

The undifferentiated fibroblasts which, in other circumstances, one might have regarded as sarcomatous, made up the main mass of the tumour, particularly in the deeper parts. There was, however, no evidence of invasion and destruction of neighbouring organs apart from that of the dermis.

The capillary loops were most numerous near or at the surface where, in many places, they were only covered by one or two layers of cells. Their presence at the surface probably caused the pink discoloration of the nostril observed intra vitam (Fig. 267).

It was difficult to determine the derivation of the large cells which filled the epithelial pockets. The epithelium itself looked as if it had been yielding to pressure rather than to disintegration. On the other hand, round melanophores, typical of the facial epidermis, could be seen lying free within the pockets. Where the epidermis had been

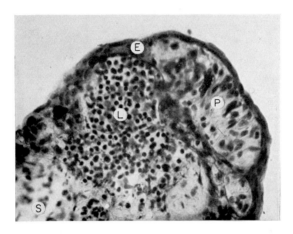

Fig. 267. *Xenopus laevis*. Atypical papilloma. Disintegration of the epidermis in the form of pockets. The one on the left is filled with capillary loops; the one on the right is filled with cells having large, oval nuclei. *E*, Epidermis; *L*, capillary loops at the surface of the papilloma; *P*, epidermal pocket; *S*, stroma of papilloma. (Photo.: Elkan.)

destroyed, remnants of dermal glands remained. The glands withstood the dissolving activity of the tumour longer than the rest of the epidermis. It remains to explain why this dissolving action did not take place on a broad front but in the form of pockets. Equally the part played by the capillary loops is not clear, since their distribution was uneven, and while they filled some of the pockets they were entirely absent from others.

It is no less difficult to understand why this condition which, after all, affected only one nostril and its immediate neighbourhood, caused the death of the animal. Breathing must still have been possible by way of the other nostril and no damage to visceral organs could be demonstrated. Considering that the resistance of amphibians against diseases of all kinds is surprisingly great, it must be assumed that a potent toxic agent caused the epithelial disintegration and at the same time interfered with the general metabolism of the toad.

There finally remains the question how this tumour should be classified. Its closest counterpart in human dermatology can be found in Dawson's (1925) classical treatise on the melanomata. Under the heading "Melano-Carcinoma" Dawson describes the development of a tumour very similar in appearance to the one observed in *Xenopus*. His drawings (Fig. 268) show how cells in the basal layer of the epi-

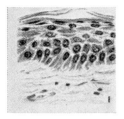
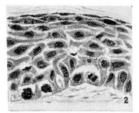
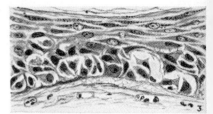
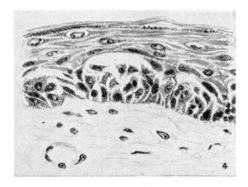
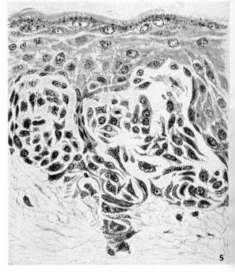

FIG. 268. Stages in the formation of melano-carcinoma in *Homo*. Formation of "cell-nests" which break through the basal membrane into the dermis. (From Dawson, 1925.)

dermis lose their cell bridges, become detached from each other and form "cell-nests" which are, at first, without contact with the dermis. Later on, this barrier is broken down, and the cells invade the dermis through an opposing layer of lymphocytic infiltration. The analogy of the two tumours is, however, not complete. In *Homo* the epithelial cells starting the tumour were heavily pigmented since they started from a pigmented naevus, and their nuclei were found to be hyper-chromatic. Their counterparts in *Xenopus* were not excessively pig-mented and showed no increased affinity to basic dyes. The pronounced vascularity of the *Xenopus* tumour was not seen in *Homo*, while both species showed a pronounced cellular polymorphism of the malignant tissue. Considering the great evolutionary distance between the two species, complete parallelism in the phenomenology of the two tumours is not to be expected, but enough similarity remains to bring this tumour into the group of dermal melanoma or melanocarcinoma, a condition frequently seen in fish, sometimes in reptiles but rarely in amphibians. In *Xenopus* spontaneous dermal tumours are exceedingly rare and, considering the location of this growth, it seems possible that it was initiated by trauma. All frogs are impetuous in their movements and they frequently injure their heads in collision with their cages when trying to escape.

Other pigmented tumours than melanomata have been seen in amphibians. Stolk (1959) reports on erythrophoromata (red), guano-phoromata (brown) and xanthophoromata (yellow) caused by cells filled with other pigments than black.

Goitre

Disturbances in the growth, development and function of the thyroid gland are occasionally seen in amphibians but not nearly as frequently as in fish. The development of a goitre is often attributed to a lack of iodine in the local water supply, but other causes may play a part. Dodd and Callan (1955) reported on a batch of *Triturus helveticus* found in a small pond in Scotland. The thyroid gland in these newts was 6–8 times enlarged and microscopically highly hyperplastic. The authors were rightly reluctant to put the blame on an iodine deficiency, seeing that the pond was only 2 miles distant from the sea. They suspected as cause the "*Brassica* factor", a substance contained in cabbage and root crops and transmitted to the pond water via the excreta of rabbits feeding in the adjoining fields. The *Brassica* factor is known to be goitrogenous (Fig. 269). The newts in this pond failed to metamorphose.

The fate of amphibian tadpoles whose thyroids, for one reason or another, fail to develop normally, is always the same. They grow to a size of two or three times the normal, fail to metamorphose and die. The first observation of that kind came from Yung (1905) who caught giant tadpoles of *Rana esculenta* near Geneva. Hahn (1912) working in the laboratory of Hertwig examined some *R. esculenta* tadpoles of 116–120 mm length against a normal length of 35 mm. Smith (1951) also mentions an *esculenta* tadpole, caught in Surrey which lived for 11 months and grew to a length of 122 mm. Finally Elkan and Finnis (1959, unpubl.) examined a batch of 176 giant tadpoles, probably of *Rana temporaria*, found in a pond near Dartford, Kent. The chart (Fig. 270) shows the life span of 100 of these tadpoles and the rate at

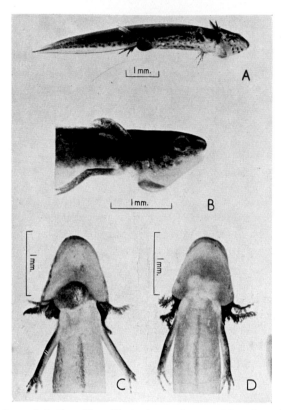

Fig. 269. *Triturus helveticus* Raz. Neotenic specimens with goitre. A, Male; length 6·7 cm. B, Female; length 7·5 cm. C as B, ventral view. D, Female with small goitre; length 7·0 cm. (After Dodd and Callan.)

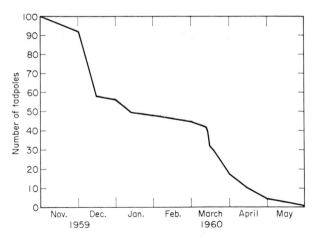

Fig. 270. Record of deaths of 100 giant tadpoles of *Rana temporaria*.

which they died. The length of the preserved specimens varied between
65 and 122 mm against a normal of $\pm$ 42 mm. All the tadpoles caught
looked bloated and unhealthy and their swimming movements were
clumsy. Very probably the pond contained an additional number to

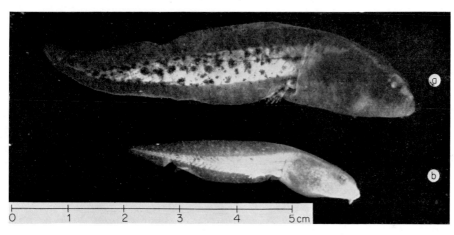

FIG. 271. (a) *Rana temporaria*. Giant tadpole from Dartford, Kent. Born Spring 1959.
Lived for 12 months without metamorphosing. (b) *Rana temporaria*. Normal tadpole
(1960 vintage), 8 weeks old. (Photo.: Elkan.)

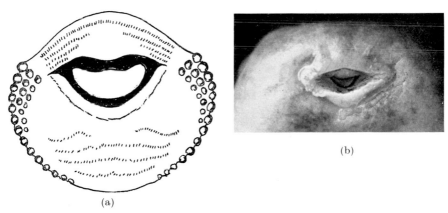

FIG. 272. (a) *Rana temporaria*. Tadpole. Mouth. × 20. (After Boulenger.) (b) *Rana
temporaria*. Giant tadpole, 17 months old. Mouth. (Photo.: Elkan.)

those that were caught. Attempts were made to keep them under
varying conditions in outdoor and indoor aquaria and to offer them
the kinds of food usually accepted by tadpoles. The older they became
the less interested were they in feeding. Treatment with the most

powerful thyroid preparations available like 3,5,3′ tri-iodo-L-thyronin and 3,5,3′ tri-iodo-thyro-acetic acid was without any effect. Treated and untreated tadpoles died at the same rate while their legs were only a few millimetres long. Their arms stopped developing under the operculum and never broke through. Not one specimen metamorphosed (Fig. 271).

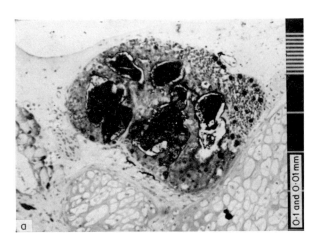

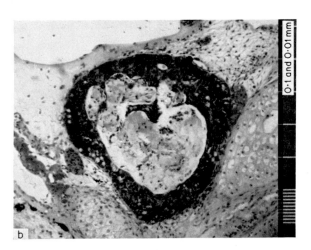

FIG. 273. (a) *Rana temporaria*. Giant tadpole. Thymus with cysts. PAS. (b) *Rana temporaria*. Giant tadpole. Thymus. Cystic degeneration of medulla. The contents stain faintly with eosin. (H. and E.) (Photo.: Elkan.)

The decision to regard these tadpoles as *temporaria* could only be based on the fact that no other anuran species had ever been seen in the area. The configuration of the mouth, usually a good guide for the determination of tadpoles, could not be used because the mouth was deformed in every specimen (Fig. 272a, b).

As might expected, most extreme histological abnormalities were found in the endocrine glands, i.e. in the thyroid, the thymus and the pituitary, but they were not all of the same kind. While the thyroid, in all the specimens examined, was replaced by large, thin-walled cysts containing no colloid, the thymus in most cases showed one or two cystic spaces, filled with a strongly PAS-positive fluid, at the centre, but a normal cortex (Fig. 273). The pituitary, on the other hand, was always found considerably enlarged and only in a few cases partially replaced by large cysts (Fig. 274). Other, minor irregularities

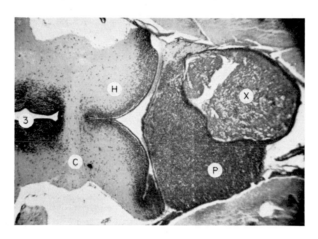

FIG. 274. *Rana temporaria.* Giant tadpole. Frontal section through mesencephalon. Pituitary cyst. PAS-haematoxylin-tartrazine. 3, Third ventricle; *C*, chiasma opticum; *H*, hypothalamus; *P*, pituitary, pars glandularis; *X*, pituitary cyst, filled with PAS-positive material. (Photo.: Elkan.)

were found in the skin, the distribution of lymphatic plaques and the structure of the cartilage. They were too numerous to attribute them all to one cause like the *Brassica* factor, the more so as, in this case, pollution of the pond by rabbits could not be proved. It seems far more likely that the event was caused by a complex genetic deficiency, perhaps by the production of immature or over-mature eggs. Thyroid aplasia obviously prevented collaboration between thyroid and pituitary glands and made metamorphosis impossible, but even when the missing thyroxin was replaced artificially the animals did not react. It remains to be seen whether the pond where they were found will produce similar generations of tadpoles in the future.

Pseudotumours

Pseudotumours may be caused by encysting parasites which may produce cyst walls of their own and induce the laying down of a second cyst wall by the host. Even after the invading organism has died, such a cyst may transform itself into a fibroma and endanger the life of the host. Elkan (1960) reported a case in question where a tumour of this kind obstructed the pelvic outlet, killing the frog. The parasite itself had completely disappeared from the tumour (Fig. 257). In other cases where well-preserved parasites are still found in the tumours, it may

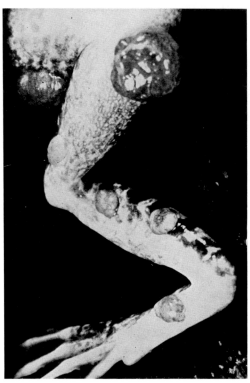

Fig. 275. *Rana temporaria* L. Adenomata of the leg caused by *Filaria rubella* Rud. (After Pflugfelder and Eilers.)

be difficult to decide whether they caused the growth and were immured in it or whether they immigrated into the tumour after it had grown. Doubtful cases of this kind are, for example, the adenomata reported by Pflugfelder and Eilers (1959) which contained nematodes (Fig. 275).

The authors treated the diseased animals with benzpyren but saw no malignant degeneration, even after a year's treatment. Meningeal tumours with trematode infection have been described by Lautenschlager (1959).

There remain non-parasitic pseudotumours due to local hypertrophy during the healing of injuries or in the course of regeneration and granulomata like the one pictured by Elkan (1960), which are entirely composed of small round cells, and where no causative organism can be demonstrated, belong into this group. They are not infrequently seen on the inner (lymphatic) surface of the skin of *Xenopus laevis*, where they usually occur in small groups, each tumour having a diameter of 1–3 mm (Fig. 276).

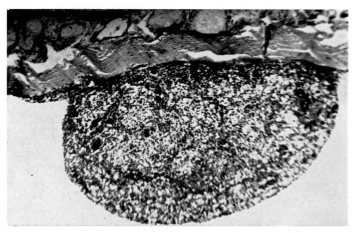

Fig. 276. *Xenopus laevis* D. Granuloma from the dorsal lymph sac. × 33. (Photo.: Elkan. Courtesy Zool. Soc. Lond.)

Means of Observing Tumours

The Amphibia are particularly suitable objects for the study of malignant tumours because they permit direct observation of the effect of external factors on the implanted tissue. Lucké and Schlumberger (1950) reported on most interesting transplantations of renal adenocarcinoma tissue into the anterior ocular chamber of *Rana pipiens* and the reaction of these transplants to X–rays. The experiment revealed the presence of three kinds of cells in the transplant: (1) cells which, after irradiation, showed shrinking and granulation of the neoplastic tissue; (2) cells which simply showed no further sign of growth; and (3) cells which showed no effect of the irradiation at all.

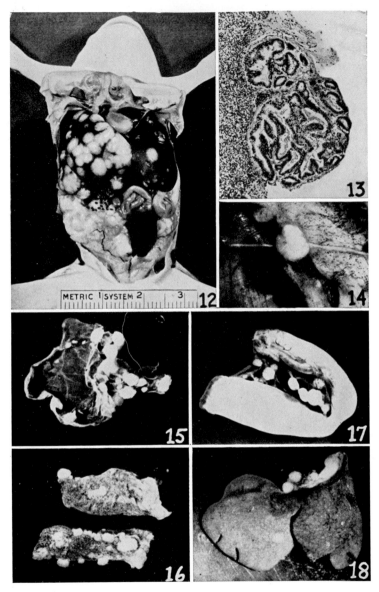

Fig. 277. *Rana pipiens* Gmel. with numerous tumours whose growth was accelerated by a raised temperature.

Left middle: Metastases in the urinary bladder.

Below: Metastases in both lungs.

Right, from top to bottom: Metastases in the spleen, the lumbar nerves, the mesentery and the liver. (After Lucké and Schlumberger. By kind permission of *J. exp. Med.*)

The same authors also reported on the effect of raised temperatures on the renal carcinoma of *Rana pipiens* (1949) and found that with rising temperatures the formation of metastases increased. The frogs, all of which suffered from renal carcinoma, were kept at 28°C for 50 days. Fifty-four per cent of them developed secondaries, whereas 6% only were observed in frogs kept at 7–18°C. The better-nourished the specimens the quicker did the formation of metastases proceed. Fig. 277 shows a frog with primary renal carcinoma and secondaries in liver, spleen, lungs, lumbar nerves, urinary bladder and mesentery. These findings open up a large field of further studies in the behaviour of malignant tumours in amphibians, perhaps also in the higher vertebrates.

REFERENCES

Angel, F. (1937). Sur deux têtards géants de *Rana esculenta* L. *Bull. Mus. Hist. nat.* 2nd series. **9**, 54–55.

Balls, M. (1962). Spontaneous neoplasms in amphibia. A review and description of six new cases. *Cancer Res.* **22**, 442–454.

Broz, O. (1947). Mnohočetne "chondromy" v kuzi *Triton taeniatus*. Multiple Chondromata in the skin of *Triton taeniatus*. *Vestn. česhl. zool. spol.* **11**, 89–91.

Carl, W. (1913). Ein Hypernephrom beim Frosch. *Zbl. allg. Path.* **24**, 436–438.

Champy, C. and Champy, Mlle. (1935). Sur un épithélioma transmissible chez le Triton. *Bull. Ass. franç. Cancer* **24**, 206–220.

Dawson, J. W. (1925). "The Melanomata." Oliver and Boyd, Edinburgh.

Dodd, J. M. and Callan, H. G. (1955). Neoteny with goiter in *Triturus helveticus*. *Quart. J. micr. Sci.* **96**, 121–128.

Downs, A. W. (1932). An epithelial tumour of the intestine of the frog. *Nature, Lond.* **130**, 787.

Duany, J. (1932). Un epithelioma glandular en una *rana*. *Arch. Soc. Estud. clin. Habana* **29**, 186–189.

Dukes, C. E. (1961). Clues to the causes of cancer of the kidney. *Lancet* 1157–1160.

Eberth, C. J. (1868). Multiple Adenome der Froschhaut. *Virchow's Arch.* **44**, 12–22.

Elkan, E. (1960). Some interesting pathological cases in amphibians. *Proc. zool. Soc. Lond.* 375–396.

Elkan, E. (1963). Three different types of tumors in Salientia. *Cancer Res.* **23**, 1641–1645.

Gheorghiu, J. (1860). Contribution á l'étude du cancer de la grenouille. *C.R. Soc. Biol., Paris* **103**, 280–281.

Gresham, G. A. and Jenkins, A. R. (1962). "An Introduction to Comparative Pathology." Academic Press, London.

Hahn, A. (1912). Einige Beobachtungen an Riesenlarven von *Rana esculenta*. *Arch. mikr. Anat.* **80**, 1–35.

Kent Messenger (1959). Giant tadpoles in school pond are causing a stir. 23 October.

Krontowsky, A. (1916). Comparative and experimental pathology of tumours. (in Russian). Kiev. Quoted in Schlumberger and Lucké, 1948.

Lautenschlager, E. W. (1959). Meningeal tumors of the newt associated with trematode infection of the brain. *Proc. hel. Soc. Wash.* **26**, 11–14.

Lucké, B. (1938). Carcinoma in the leopard frog: Its probable causation by a virus. *J. exp. Med.* **68**, 457–468.

Lucké, B. (1949). Neoplasia in cold-blooded vertebrates. *Physiol. Rev.* **29**, 91–126.

Lucké, B. (1950). Effects of Roentgen rays on Cancer. I. Direct microscopic observations on living intraocular transplants of frog carcinoma. *J. Nat. Cancer Inst.* **11**, 511–543.

Lucké, B. and Schlumberger, H. G. (1949). Induction of metastasis of frog carcinoma by increase of environmental temperature. *J. exp. Med.* **89**, 269–278.

Murray, J. A. (1908). The zoological distribution of cancer. *Sci. Rep. int. Cancer Res. Fund* **3**, 41–60.

Nieuwkoop, P. D. and Faber, J. (1956). "Normal Tables of *Xenopus laevis* (Daudin)." N. Holland Publ. Co., Amsterdam.

Oberling, C. (1952). "The Riddle of Cancer." London.

Pawlowsky, E. N. (1912). Zur Casuistik der Tumoren beim Frosch. *Zbl. allg. Path. Anat.* **23**, 94.

Pentimalli, F. (1914). Ueber die Geschwülste bei Amphibian. *Z. Krebsforsch.* **14**, 623–632.

Pick, L. and Poll, H. (1903). Ueber einige bemerkenswerthe Tumorbildungen aus der Thierpathologie, insbesondere über gutartige und krebsige Neubildungen bei Kaltblütern. *Berl. klin. Wschr.* **40**, 518, 572.

Pirlot, J. M. and Welsch, M. (1934). Étude anatomique et expérimentale de quelques tumeurs chez la grenouille rousse (*Rana fusca*). *Arch. int. Med. exp.* **9**, 341–365.

Pflugfelder, O. and Eilers, W. (1959). Auslösung von Adenomen in der Epidermis von *Rana temporaria* durch "*Filaria*" *rubella* Rudolphi. *Z. Parasitenk.* **19**, 101–110.

Plehn, M. (1906). Ueber Geschwülste bei Kaltblütern. *Z. Krebsforsch.* **4**, 525–564.

Schlumberger, H. G. (1953). Comparative pathology of oral neoplasms. *Oral Surg.* **6**, 1078–1094.

Schlumberger, H. G. (1958).Krankheiten der Fische, Amphibien und Reptilien. *In* "Pathologie der Laboratoriumstiere" (Cohrs, Jaffé and Meesen, eds.), Vol. II. Springer, Berlin-Göttingen-Heidelberg.

Schlumberger, H. G. and Lucké, B. (1948). Tumours of fishes, amphibians and reptiles. *Cancer Res.* **8**, 857–754.

Schreitmueller, W. and Lederer, G. (1930). "Krankheitserscheinungen an Fischen, Reptilien und Lurchen." Berlin.

Schwarz, E. (1923). Ueber zwei Geschwülste bei Kaltblütern. *Z. Krebsforsch.* **20**, 353–357.

Secher, K. (1917/19). Casuistische Beiträge zur Kenntnis der Geschwülste bei Tieren. *Z. Krebsforsch.* **16**, 297–313.

Sheremetieva-Brunst, E. A. (1953). An epithelioma in the axolotl. *Proc. Amer. Cancer Res.* I. 1. Abst. 51.

Sheremetieva-Brunst, E. A. (1954). Further investigation of epithelioma in axolotl. *Proc. Amer. Canc. Res.* I. 2. Abst. 44.

Smallwood, W. M. (1905). Adrenal tumours in the kidney of the frog. *Anat. Anz.* **26**, 652–658.

Smith, M. (1951). "The British Amphibians and Reptiles." Collins, London.

Stolk, A. (1957). Tumours in amphibians. IIa and b. *Proc. Koninkl. Ned. Akad. Wetensch.* Ser. C. **60**, No. 4, 537–556. (Reviews the literature on tumours in cold-blooded animals up to 1957.)

Stolk, A. (1958). Tumours of amphibians. IVa and b. Development of the multiple fibroma of the adepidermal reticular network in the skin of the newt *Triturus taeniatus*. *Proc. Koninkl. Ned. Akad. Wetensch.* C. **61**, 610–630.

Stolk, A. (1959). Tumours of amphibians. VII. Erythrophoroma in *Dendrobates typogvaphicus*. *Proc. Koninkl. Med. Akad. Wetensch.* C. **62**, 381–389.

Stolk, A. (1959). Tumours in amphibians. VIII. Guanophoroma in the frog *Hyla arborea meridionalis*. *Proc. Koninkl. Med. Akad. Wetensch.* C. **62**, 390–395.

Stolk, A. (1959). Tumours in amphibians. IX. Xanthophoroma in the frog *Hyla arborea*. *Proc. Koninkl. Med. Akad. Wetensch.* C. **62**, 568–575.

Vaillant, L. and Pettit, A. (1902). Fibrome observé sur un *Megalobatrachus maximus* Schlegel à la ménagerie du Muséum. *Bull. Mus. Hist. nat., Paris* **8**, 301–304.

Willis, R. A. (1948). "Pathology of Tumours." Butterworth, London. (Reviews the literature on tumours in cold-blooded animals up to 1948.) 3rd edn., 1960.

Yung, E. (1905). On a collection of giant larvae of *Rana esculenta* from the neighbourhood of Geneva. *Arch. Sci. phys. nat.* **20**, 595–597.

CHAPTER 13

Damage through Various Environmental Factors

If in their natural surroundings animals find that their habitat changes to their disadvantage they disperse if there is time, they die individually or *en masse*. Single diseased specimens are rarely seen, since they become early victims of predators or of members of their own species. The deleterious factors which may overtake captive animals are quite different from those that may affect them at liberty. The animals may not die at once but they may linger on for weeks, watched agonizingly by the owner who is at a loss to determine which of the various possibilities is killing his stock. The number of such causes is great; we have to confine ourselves to the most common ones. Lack of illumination in animals which are, for the most part nocturnal and extremely light-shy might not be thought worth considering. Yet, quite apart from the fact that some frogs are very definitely diurnal, a terrarium never exposed to sunlight is an unhealthy place, even for a salamander which spends all the daylight hours under a piece of bark. Lack of u.v. light is particularly dangerous while the animal still grows and needs a sufficient amount of vitamin D. Open (1950) investigated the development of hatchlings of *Triturus alpestris* and found that they could live on their own vitamin D supplies only as long as they were still nourished by yolk. It did not matter, during that period, whether they were kept in a lighted or in a darkened tank. But this maternal supply is used up by the time the larvae begin to swim. From that moment on only those receiving their normal vitamin ration will do well, particularly those feeding on algae or bacteria which will not grow without sufficient illumination.

Unsuitable temperatures can and often do kill large numbers of aquatic amphibians in a short time. Few of them, even among those coming from tropical countries, can safely be exposed to more than 28°C and their greatest danger lies in the fact that aquaria are now universally controlled by thermostats which are notoriously unreliable. Whoever keeps amphibians may safely apply the rule: when in doubt err on the cold side. Many Amphibia survive at temperatures close to freezing; few tolerate anything above 28°C. They breathe for a large part through their skin which, to fulfil this function, must be moist. Tolerance to drying may be different among the various species but even a tree-frog may be killed by overheating. Before arranging a cage for any imported amphibian, its natural ecology should be studied. Animals from different environments should not be forced to share the same cage.

The deleterious effect of irradiation has already been mentioned in the chapter dealing with tumours. While we may discount the effect of short-wave rays in their natural habitat we must remember that, in the laboratory, they may give rise to a multitude of genetic abnormalities.

In establishments where aquatic Amphibia are kept in such large numbers that their husbandry becomes almost a matter of pure routine "industrial" accidents may happen. Of these thermostat failure is perhaps the most common, and the most painful disasters happen not when the thermostat fails to "make" but when it fails to "break" and the water becomes overheated. Regular inspection of any temperature controlling devices installed in the water circuit supplying such installation is imperative.

Chemical substances may have beneficial, toxic or even lethal effects according to their nature and concentration. In a laboratory where about 3 000 specimens of *Xenopus laevis* are kept under rather crowded conditions, the raising of the sodium chloride level to about 0·4% has reduced the morbidity rate of the toads by about one half. This precautionary method is so simple that it cannot be sufficiently strongly recommended. Even when breeding *Xenopus*, it will be found that the mortality of the tadpoles can be reduced by the addition of some NaCl to their water.

As to toxic substances it is above all the dilemma of the insecticides which has lately attracted the attention of herpetologists (Voitlaender, 1955). It was fortunately found that Amphibia, in particular frogs, are not as easily poisoned by these substances as fish. A substance marketed as E 605 forte was tolerated in concentrations between 1 : 15 000 –1: 20 000; the same substance in powder form at 1 : 500–1 : 1000; another proprietary substance marketed as "Hortex–fluid" at 1 : 10 000–1 : 16 000. Fish would not tolerate any of these concentrations.

Other potential sources of disaster are water taps which, because they were difficult to manipulate, were overhauled and lubricated with thin oil containing a detergent. The first time such taps are turned on all the animals in the tank supplied will be killed. Only heavy, entirely insoluble lubricants like Vaseline-graphite mixtures should be used in aquarium circuits.

Contact insecticides and their influence on toad tadpoles were extensively investigated by Luedemann and Neumann (1960). Even small doses of "Endrin", "Thiodan", DDT, "Toxaphen", "Dieldrin" and "Aldrin" proved to be extremely toxic.

It should not surprise us that, as with fish, the acidity or alkalinity of the water has been found to be of great importance to amphibians, particularly to their larvae. Witschi (1936) reports that *Rana clamitans* and *Rana pipiens* tadpoles die within a few hours if the pH is lowered below 2·9 or raised above 10·6, while larvae of *Ambystoma maculatum* tolerate levels between 3·1 and 9·7. Bandt and Freytag (1950), working on *Siredon mexicanum*, found that the larvae died on the acid side between pH 3·5–4 and on the alkaline side between 11–12; young larvae even at 10·5. Symptoms due to pH damage appear gradually: excessive production of mucus; irritation leading to ulceration of the rostral region; spastic movements; hyperaemia of tail or webs of feet culminating in haemorrhages; discoloration of gills up to gill destruction and corneal turbidity may be observed. The authors emphasize that animals may also be seriously damaged by oversaturation of their water with oxygen which, in excess, has an irritant action on the skin and particularly on the gills of larvae. Savage (1961) mentions that this may even happen in natural ponds when these are overgrown with water weeds and then exposed to heavy evaporation and strong sunshine. It goes without saying that lack of oxygen has an equally deleterious effect. Ruebsamen (1950) studied the deceleration effect of anoxia on the development of *Triturus* eggs which, in some cases went so far as to produce malformations.

It is difficult to assess which, if any, of the factors mentioned, account for the disturbances in skin-casting frequently seen in reptiles and amphibians. The skin, instead of being cleanly shed in one piece, may adhere in parts and may be shed incompletely. Salamanders may, during moulting, produce a watery or even purulent secretion. Any symptom of this nature should be taken as a sign of faulty husbandry in some respect or other. It will usually not be difficult to remedy the mistake. Wolterstorff (1939) reports on such cases in salamanders which cast their black skin frayed in pieces, leaving patches of raw skin behind. How dangerous it may be to keep various species in the same small cage could be seen in some tree-frogs which, together with *Rana arvalis* and *Rana dalmatica*, were made to share their quarters with some toads. Their skin became inflamed where the two species had been in contact. Shortage of vitamin B_2 has been blamed for skin-casting troubles in amphibians just as vitamin E shortage has been blamed for sterility, but it is usually difficult to substantiate these claims and unwise to put all the blame on one factor. Amphibians have a great power of resistance and it may take a combination of deficiencies before they fall ill.

REFERENCES

Bandt, H. J. and Freytag, G. (1950). Die tödlichen p_H-Werte für den Axolotl (*Siredon mexicanum*). *Mitt. Mus. Naturk. Magdeb.* **2**, 129–132.
Lüdemann, D. and Neumann, H. (1960). Versuche über die akute toxische Wirking neuzeitlicher Kontaktinsektizide auf Süsswassertiere. II. *Z. angew. Zool.* **47**, 303–321.
Open, H. (1950). Über die Frühentwicklung von *Triton alpestris* bei Dunkelheit. *Roux' Arch.* **144**, 322–328.
Rübsamen, H. (1950). Die Wirkung des experimentellen Sauerstoffmangels auf die Entwicklung von Tritonkeimen nach beendeter Gastrulation. *Roux' Arch.* **144**, 301–321.
Savage, M. (1961). "The Ecology and Life History of the Common Frog." Pitman, London.
Voitländer, U. (1955). Über die Wirkung von Kontaktinsektiziden insbesondere E 605 und Hexachlorcyclohexan auf Fische und Frösche. Diss. Univ. München.
Witschi, E. (1936). Aufzucht und Heilung der gebräuchlichsten Laboratoriumstiere (Amphibien und Reptilien). *In* "Abderhalden: Handbuch der biologischen Arbeitsmethoden", Abt. IX, 7, 4, 611–651.
Wolterstorff, W. (1939). Eigenartige Hauterkrankungen bei *Euproctus montanus* Savi, dem korsischen Bergmiolch. *Wschr. Aqu. Terrk.* **36**, 89–90.

CHAPTER 14

Syndromes from Various Causes

A. OVARIAN CYSTS

A distinction is made in the amphibians between ovulation, when eggs are liberated from the ovaries, and oviposition, when eggs are laid by way of the oviduct and the cloaca. During the interval between these two events and while the egg travels through the long and tortuous oviduct, it matures and receives its protective jelly envelopes. Anything interfering with this chain of events may be of serious consequence to the female, to the eggs or to both.

If at the time of oviposition the female finds herself in an unsuitable

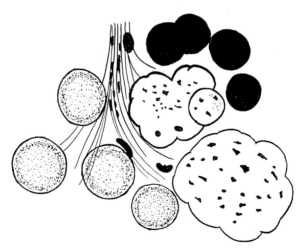

FIG. 278. *Rana esculenta* L. Ovary with normal and degenerating melanotic eggs. (Orig.)

environment, she may retain the eggs in the ovisac. The eggs may then stick to one another and coagulate into a hard lump recognizable even by external palpation. Toxic products derived from the degenerating mass of eggs may seriously interfere with the metabolism of the female already burdened by the presence in her abdomen of a large hard mass displacing viscera and interfering with blood circulation. Plehn (1906) even mentions a rare case where egg retention caused the development of ovarian carcinoma in a specimen of *Rana esculenta.*

Cystic degeneration of the ovary, need, however, not necessarily be neoplastic. It may also be caused by parasites. One of us (R.–K.) investigating the ovary of a female *R. esculenta,* found it full of free melanin mixed with rounded and oval objects which might well have been necrotic remains of the parasitic fungus *Ichthyosporidium hoferi* Plehn and Mulsow (Fig. 278). Our illustration shows the various objects seen in this ovary.

B. "MOLCHPEST"

The name of this internationally infamous disease is derived from the Greek *molgos*: a skin or hide; *Molch* being the German for "newt". It well-deserves the suffix of "pest" since it is at the same time one of the most dreaded and least-explained epidemics that may appear in our collections of urodeles. The affected animals show a variety of symptoms, none of which need always be present, and the result is invariably fatal. Newts become sluggish and refuse food. They lose their sense of equilibrium and begin to show external signs of the disease. The skin, no longer glossy, becomes red and inflamed, and is soon covered with dermal abscesses which erupt and spread all over the animal. They start as small whitish spots of 1 mm diameter, growing soon to 2 mm and more. The body, particularly the abdominal region, becomes oedematous. If, as commonly seen at this stage, a super-infection with a fungus takes place, the disease takes a lightning course and the affected animals die within a few hours. Authors repeatedly report noticing at this stage a peculiar smell, resembling that of parsley, which emanates from the diseased animals and transmits itself to the water (Huebener, 1952; Wolterstorff, 1923). This smell is taken to be the most significant symptom of the disease.

Engelstadt and Wolterstorff (1923) mention that molchpest is frequently heralded by incomplete skin shedding; nor would the newts eat the cast-off skin as they usually do. Although the animals refused all food they increased in girth. They became oedematous and tried to leave the water. They were short of breath and soon the typical smell of the disease could be noticed.

The skin changed more and more, became covered with grey pustules and super-infected with a fungus. In the final stages a mucous fluid was excreted from the mouth.

The cause of this most unpleasant disease is as yet unknown and the repeated search for an organism that could be held responsible has so

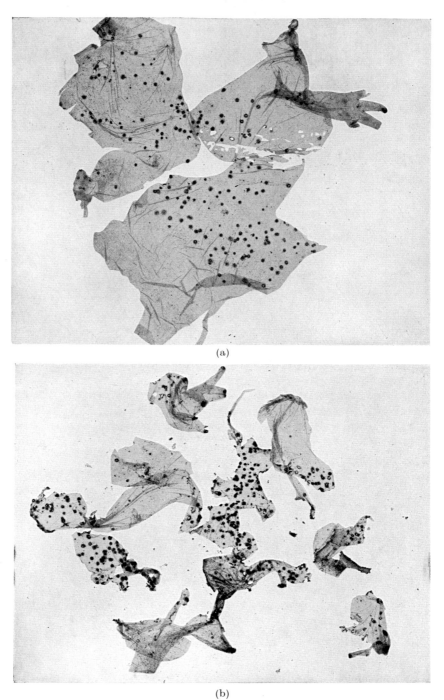

(a)

(b)

Fig. 279. Skin shreds from a newt suffering from "Molchpest". (Photo.: Geyer.)

far been in vain. The multitude of symptoms may indicate a multiplicity of causes, perhaps of metabolic disturbances enhanced by unfavourable factors in the immediate environment of the animals. Further investigations of the disease are urgently required. While its cause is unknown it is no wonder that therapeutic attempts have been without success. Chinosol has been recommended for the immediate disinfection of the animals and their cages, and all the many factors controlling their lives should be carefully checked. Our Fig. 279 shows pieces of skin from a newt suffering from molchpest.

C. Diseases of the Digestive Organs

Digestive disturbances in captive amphibians are often due either to faulty or to over feeding. Starvation is only likely to occur where

Fig. 280. *Xenopus laevis.* Rectal prolapse. × 0·5.

animals are already ill and refuse to feed. Diet should be as close to the natural choice of the animal as feasible and it must not be forgotten that species normally feeding on insects require some "roughage" to avoid constipation. A varied diet seems preferable to a monotonous one

12*

but some Amphibia seem to have such a preference for one item that they refuse to accept anything else. One of the commonest intestinal complaints we see in amphibians is that of rectal prolapse. It seems doubtful if this complaint can be solely ascribed to a faulty diet as suggested by Schreitmueller and Lederer (1930), because it has been seen to occur in one of many animals (frogs), all fed on the same diet (minced meat and liver) for many months. Nor did the condition recur, although the same diet was continued after the prolapse had reduced itself. It seems possible that the cause may lie in one particularly large and indigestible piece of excreta rather than in the general diet given. It seems to be a wasted effort to try and treat the condition as suggested by placing the animals into cold water. The procedure only makes them generally sluggish but has no immediate effect on the prolapse. It seems a better plan to isolate the animal and to stop feeding it until the prolapse has subsided. This will in most cases be the case within a week (Fig. 280).

Cases of enteritis and peritonitis are undoubtedly common in amphibians, but since it is impossible to diagnose them *in vitam* they are only seen at the post-mortem examinations. This also applies to diseases, degenerations and tumours of the liver. The latter have been described by Willis (1948).

D. Bone Damage

It is difficult to prove but very likely that faulty diets act by producing vitamin shortages in the affected animals. Shortage of vitamin E has been blamed for abnormal development of the reproductive organs; shortage of vitamin D, according to Bruce and Parkes (1950), produces deformities of the skeleton. These authors fed *Xenopus* toads on horse liver and observed a host of skeletal deformities. When the horse liver was replaced by beef or rabbit liver and when cod liver oil and calcium were added to the diet the symptoms did not appear. Wolterstorff and Freytag (1942) described spine deformities. Schlumberger and Burk (1933) reported on deformities seen in toads which received no live food for two years.

A peculiar type of degeneration of the tail and the legs occurs in newts. We have seen it start with a degeneration of the skin followed by that of the underlying structures to the effect that the toes first lost their skin and that finally the whole foot was lost. The cause of this alarming disease is not known. It may be connected with a deficiency in some indispensible part of the animal's diet. Fig. 281 shows the deplorable state of affairs in a newt affected with this disease. In the same way as the legs the tail may be affected. The condition does not seem to be due to parasites or other external causes.

E. PARALYSIS

Paralysis of the extremities, particularly of the legs, is not uncommonly seen in frogs. It remains intractable and mysterious because the animals usually seem perfectly healthy and well-nourished. Yet they become single victims of a condition which does not seem to affect the other frogs kept in the same conditions. Apart from the legs paralysis is seen in the tongue and newts may suffer from spastic contractions of the arms or of the whole body. Attempts to arrive at an explanation of these symptoms have included excessive feeding with meat (Schreitmueller and Lederer, 1930) and the presence of parasites or tumours. Among the former the ciliates *Tetrahymena* and the trematode *Tylodelphis*, both of which may occur in the cerebrospinal fluid, must be considered. Tumours may affect nerve tracts (Lucké and Schlumberger, 1949) and microsporidiosis may affect the whole skeletal muscular system to such an extent that the abdominal muscles are reduced to a thin transparent sheet and the thigh muscles in a frog wasted to such a degree that the animal can no longer jump but only crawls with difficulty. Cases of this kind represent interesting material for study but hold out no hope in respect of therapeutic efforts.

F. BLINDNESS

As reported in the relevant chapter on fish (p. 82), blindness may be the consequence of the presence of a trematode larva in the eye, particularly in the anterior chamber. Turbidity of the cornea may occur in the course of metabolic disturbances and may be reversible if corrected early. It may also be due to vascular disease or to the pollution of the water with irritant substances. An attempt should be made to ascertain whether blindness is due to a disease of the eyelids (blepharitis; conjunctivitis) or to the eye itself. In small amphibians this may by no means be easy. Conjunctivitis may sometimes successfully be treated with silver-proteinate preparations.

G. HYDROPS

The excessive accumulation of fluid in one, several or all the subcutaneous lymph sacs occurs in wild frogs and, much more frequently, in captive animals. Keeping in mind that all the lymph sacs communicate and that they all drain into the venous system via the posterior

Fig. 281. Degeneration of limbs in *Pleurodeles waltli* Mich. Spec. Kleinschmidt. (Photo.: Reichenbach-Klinke.)

lymph hearts; considering also that the frog does not drink but satisfies his fluid requirements by absorption through the skin, one would assume that every case of hydrops must be due to some form of damage to the posterior lymph hearts, but this is not so. Cases have been seen (Elkan, 1957) where the posterior lymph hearts were blocked, but no hydrops developed. The lymph hearts apparently offer only one of alternative ways of draining the subcutaneous sacs. In most cases hydrops is seen in frogs which have been used for experiments involving injections into the subcutaneous lymphatic spaces. It is remarkable to observe that, although such injections are given by the thousand with unsterilized instruments, cases of infection and subsequent thrombosis of the posterior lymph hearts are rare. Where they occur they are unfortunately irreversible. John (1936) describes cases of ascites in axolotls and claims cures by aspiration of the fluid, medication with cod liver oil and, in the earliest stages, baths in potassium permanganate solution. Attempts at treating hydrops with antibiotics combined with repeated aspiration have always failed.

Hydrops, i.e. an excessive accumulation of fluid in the subcutaneous lymphatic spaces, is also commonly seen in young tadpoles bred by way of artificially induced oviposition. It is well known that frogs, in particular *Xenopus*, can, with the aid of gonadotrophic extracts, be induced to spawn at any time of the year, but it is very difficult, if not impossible, to arrange the necessary injections so that the normal rate of egg-laying is induced. The females behave as if they worked to an "all or nothing" rule, and the eggs, instead of maturing and receiving their proper jelly enveloped in the oviduct, are laid in an immature condition. Immaturity is as fatal to the egg as over-ripeness and although tadpoles may develop from such eggs they often show deformities, hydrops being one of the commonest seen (Fig. 282a, b).

H. HYPERTROPHY OF THE LIME SACS

The segmental endolymphatic lime deposits which normally occur in frogs on both sides of the spinal column have frequently attracted the attention of observers, and the part they play in the frog's physiology has never been understood. Kuhl (1920) reports cases of pathological hypertrophy of these organs. Both he and Schlumberger and Burk (1933) are inclined to explain the excessive accumulation of calcium salts with a disturbance of the vitamin balance of the animals. Excessive calcium deposition and even osteoporosis could be experimentally produced by injection of 30 000 U of vitamin D.

(a)   (b)

FIG. 282. *Xenopus laevis*. Hydrops in artificially bred froglets.

I. VESICAL CALCULUS

An interesting observation, unique so far in the annals of amphibian pathology, has recently come from New Zealand (Richardson and Truscoe, 1963). The authors, in the course of class dissection of native frogs, found three specimens of *Hyla aurea* afflicted by a calculus of the urinary bladder so large that it filled the organ completely and indeed made a cast of the bladder. Even so there is no indication that the frogs died of this condition or that they even suffered from the inability to empty the bladder. They were, apparently, all caught in the same district of Rotorua—though this fact could not be ascertained with absolute certainty—and killed for teaching purposes. The calculi, described as consisting of a soft, friable core with a denser brown shell, were analysed as a type of calcium phosphate designed as calcium hydroxylapatite. Apart from water and protein they contained 40·58% of calcium and 18·86% of phosphorus. No signs of any concomitant pathology were found in any of the other organic systems of these three frogs. The cause of the appearance of this interesting series of cases of urinary calculus in frogs awaits further investigation.

REFERENCES

Bodenstein, D. (1930). Einige Krankheiten der Tritonen und Axolotl. *Bl. Aqu. Terrk.* **41**, 325–327.

Bruce, H. M. and Parkes, A. S. (1950). Rickets and osteoporosis in *Xenopus laevis*. *J. Endocrin.* **7**, 64–81.

Elkan, E. (1957). Observations on the lymphatic system of the South African claw footed toad (*Xenopus laevis* Daudin). *Brit. J. Herpet.* **2**, 37–53.

Engelstadt, G. and Wolterstorff, W. (1923). Ein schwerer Fall von Molchpest. *Bl. Aqu. Terrk.* **34**, 117–119.

Freytag, G. E. (1954). Molche mit Wirbelsäulenverkrümmungen. *Aqu. Terr.* **1**, 184–185.

Freytag, G. E. and Huebener, H. E. (1958). Drei Anomalien in einer Bergmolchzucht. *Aqu. Terr. Z.* **11**, 82–83.

Huebener, H. E. (1952). Molchpest beim japanischen Feuerbauchmolch *Cynops pyrrhogaster* Boie und eine andere tödliche Krankheit. *Aqu. Terr. Z.* **5**, 219–220.

John, H. (1936). Heilung von Wassersucht beim Axolotl (*Ambystoma mexicanum*). *Bl. Aqu. Terrk.* **47**, 207–209.

Kuhl, W. (1920). Über einen Fall abnorm vergrösserter Kalksäckchen bei Rana temporaria. *Seckenberg. biol.* **3**, 66–72.

Lucké, W. and Schlumberger, H. G. (1949). Induction of metastasis of frog carcinoma by increase of environmental temperature. *J. exp. Med.* **89**, 269–278.

Plehn, M. (1906). Ueber Geschwülste bei Kaltblüten, *Z. Krebsforsch.* **4**, 525–564.

Reichenbach-Klinke, H. (1956). Knochendegeneration bei einem Rippenmolch (*Pleurodeles waltli* Michahelles) im Zusammenhang mit intermuskulärer Melanophorenanreicherung. *Biol. Zbl.* **75**, 407–416.

Richardson, L. R. and Truscoe, R. (1963). Vesical calculus in the frog *Hyla aurea. Trans. roy. Soc. N.Z. Zool.* **3**, No. 1, 1–3.

Schlumberger, H. G. and Burk, D. H. (1933). Comparative study of the reaction to injury. II. Hypervitaminosis D in the frog with special reference to the lime sacs. *A.M.A. Arch. Path.* **56**, 103–124.

Schreitmueller, W. and Lederer, G. (1930). "Krankheitserscheinungen an Fischen, Reptilien und Lurchen." Berlin.

Schwabacher, H. and Elkan, E. (1952a). Breeding of *Xenopus laevis* in captivity. *S. Afr. J. med. Sci.* (1953) **18**, 13–18.

Schwabacher, H. and Elkan, E. (1952b). Countermeasures for difficulties observed during the breeding of *Xenopus laevis* in captivity. *Brit. J. Herpet.* **1**, 132–133.

Willis, R. A. (1960). "Pathology of Tumours", 3rd edn. Butterworth, London.

Wolterstorff, W. (1939). Eigenartige Hauterkrankungen bei *Euproctus montanus* Savi, dem korsischen Bergmolch. *Wschr. Aqu. Terrk.* **36**, 89–90.

Wolterstorff, W. and Freytag, G. E. (1942). Rückgratsverkrümmung beim Kammolch (*Triturus cristatus* Laur.) *Zool. Anz.* **138**, 90.

Chapter 15

Surgical Conditions, Wound Healing and Regeneration

A. Surgical Conditions

In large populations of newts or frogs specimens deprived of one or several toes or of whole hands or feet are frequently seen. In animals of such great fertility perfection is not always achieved and even perfect larvae may lose limbs or parts of limbs early in their lives during fights with members of their own or other species. The handicap they suffer from such losses must be less than one would expect since we find that toads with only one eye or only one foot nevertheless grow up to maturity. They may even survive greater handicaps than the loss of limbs. In a population of *Xenopus*, bred in the laboratory, several specimens were observed which developed tumours in the sternal region. These tumours grew to a considerable size (Fig. 283) without, however,

Fig. 283. *Xenopus laevis*. Cardiac hernia.

lessening the animal's growth and general vitality. It was only by dissection that it could be shown that the tumours were caused by cardiac hernia. The toads had a deficient sternum and the heart, deprived of its ventral support, came to lie outside the thorax, directly under the skin. Gross herniation was also seen in the case of a common newt (*Trit. vulgaris*) which was found to have a tumour at the border of the thoracic and the abdominal region. In this case transverse sections showed that the whole body wall of the animal had ruptured and that the suspected "tumour" was in fact part of the stomach which had herniated through the rupture. The stomach itself was filled with plant debris, material quite alien to the normal food of newts. This botanical material had apparently fermented and distended the body wall to such an extent that it ruptured. It remains unexplained why the newt fed on this unsuitable material, nor is it suggested that it would have been able to survive this accident for a very long time (Elkan, 1960).

B. HEALING OF WOUNDS AND REGENERATION

Many observations on wound healing and regeneration in amphibians have been published. Small skin defects usually heal quickly with production of thickened epithelium in the region of the scar.

Wurmbach (1927) and Schlumberger and Burk (1953) investigated the healing of fractures. A blastema is produced by the external layers of the periosteal connective tissue and this produces cartilaginous callus. The callus calcifies slowly, particularly perivascularly. Pritchard and Ruzicka (1950) studied the histological detail of this process and compared it with the healing of fractures in reptiles and mammals.

Amphibia are capable of regenerating tails and extremities. The process has been reviewed by Manner (1953).

REFERENCES

Elkan, E. (1960). Some interesting pathological cases in amphibians. *Proc. zool. Soc. Lond.* **134**, 375–396.

Manner, M. W. (1953). The origin of the blastema and of new tissues in regenerating forelimbs of adult *Triturus viridescens*. *J. exp. Zool.* **122**, 229–257.

Pritchard, J. J. and Ruzicka, A. J. (1950). Comparison of fracture repair in the frog, lizard and rat. *J. Anat., Lond.* **84**, 236–261.

Schlumberger, H. G. and Burk, D. H. (1953). Comparative study of the reaction to injury. II. Hypervitaminosis D in the frog with special reference to the lime sacs. *A.M.A. Arch. Path.* **56**, 103–124.

Wurmbach, H. (1927). Histologische Untersuchungen über die Heilung von Knochenbrüchen bei Amphibien. *Z. Zool.* **129**, 253–258.

CHAPTER 16

Abnormalities

A. DUPLICATION

Duplication or multiplication of various parts of the amphibian body are not very rare. They cannot, strictly, be regarded as diseases since they are due to genetic disturbances. Duplication of various kinds has been seen in urodeles either in the form of two individuals with one head, of one individual with two heads, or of supernumerary legs or arms. Embryologists and teratologists have made use of the fact that such monstrosities can be produced artificially and the literature on the subject is extensive. Leeke (1912) reports on a specimen of *Pelobates fuscus* with six and on another with three legs. Similar specimens have been pictured by Hellmich (1929) (Fig. 284). Wolterstorff and Freytag (1942) reported on a hybrid tadpole of *Triturus vulgaris* × *Triturus helveticus* which was doubleheaded. A series of twins, duplications of arms and legs (anadidymus and katadidymus) in frogs, toads, salamanders and axolotls has been collected by Schlumberger and Schwind (1942). Perhaps the most extensive studies of the subject have been made by the French biologist Rostand (1955) who reported his findings in a monograph on the genetics of frogs and toads. The book is indispensable for anybody interested in the subject which, however, lies outside of what we commonly mean by "diseases".

B. DISTURBANCES DURING METAMORPHOSIS

The transition in amphibians from the aquatic to the terrestrial state, which has been so extensively studied, still presents unsolved problems, one of the most obvious of which is the question why frogs which have well-developed lungs early in the tadpole stage and which can hibernate submerged, breathing through their skins, should so easily drown during the transition period from water to land (Savage, 1961). This occurs commonly if the tadpoles are kept in unsuitable containers from which they cannot escape, but it also surprisingly happens in ponds where the metamorphosis mortality, combined with other causes, reduces the tadpole survival rate to about 1% (*ibid.*).

The fact that the tadpoles cannot feed during the period of change can hardly be the cause of their mortality, since amphibians can starve

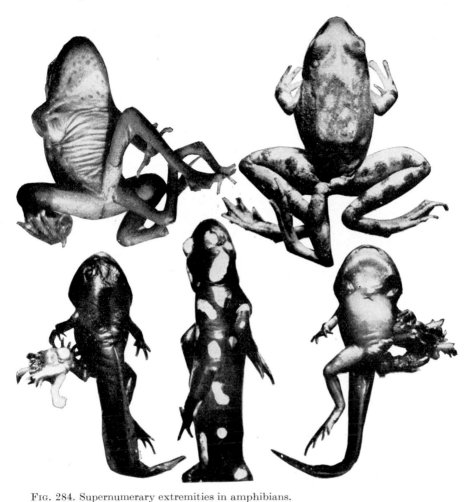

FIG. 284. Supernumerary extremities in amphibians.
Above left: *Rana graeca* Blg. with four legs.
Above right: *Rana esculenta* L. with three legs.
Below, middle: *Salamandra salamandra* L. with five legs.
Below, both sides: Larva of *Alytes obstetricans* Laur. with abnormal regeneration of left posterior leg. (After W. Hellmich, 1929.)

much longer without ill-effects than it takes them to metamorphose. Nor are they, at this time of their lives, more exposed to their external and internal enemies than at others. From accounts received it would appear that at the edge of pools in Venezuela the larger specimens of

Gastrotheca can be seen waiting for their younger generations to emerge from the water to be swallowed by their elders. Such cannibalism also occurs in the common frog (Lees, 1960) but the main cause for the high metamorphosis mortality in batrachians remains unknown.

Delayed or entirely frustrated metamorphosis is not rare in amphibians. It has frequently been the subject of investigation by experimental zoologists and comparative physiologists. Metamorphosis is regulated by hormones issuing from the thyroid, the pituitary and, perhaps, the thymus, and the whole complicated process depends on the normal interaction of these glands. The thyroid gland is probably the most important contributor at this stage. If it is deficient, the larva grows into a giant tadpole but no metamorphosis takes place. If excessive doses of thyroxin or similar substances are given, growth is inhibited and the tadpoles metamorphose prematurely (Fig. 285). The

FIG. 285. *Xenopus laevis* D. Metamorphosis of tadpoles accelerated with thyroxin. Left: Result of 3 weeks treatment with thyroxin. Right: Untreated control. (After Wilhelmi.)

literature on this subject is far too extensive to be quoted here. A review up to 1930 can be found in Noble's classic "The Biology of the Amphibia". For the more recent papers, textbooks on comparative physiology should be consulted. This also applies to the phenomena summarized under the name of neoteny, a developmental deviation which cannot strictly be called a disease because not only can neotenic larvae, i.e. larvae which never metamorphose but become mature and reproductive while still in the larval state, be perfectly healthy—the neotenic state may be their normal and final state of development.

C. Sex Reversal

It has been known for some time that apart from definite males and females, some Anura produce individuals whose sexual glands remain indeterminate for the early part of their lives. Later on, these specimens usually develop into males, but ova may often be found in their testicles. Indeterminate sexuality is particularly prevalent in the genus *Bufo* where next to the testis we find quite normally Bidder's organ, which consists mainly of ovarian tissue but may also contain mature spermatozoa. It does not become functional in the normal toad but may act as an ovary if the testicles are removed.

Sex reversal has been seen in anurans even without surgical interference. Female specimens of *Rana temporaria* with intermediate reproductive glands can develop into males. In tadpoles of *Rana sylvatica* it has been possible to induce this reversal experimentally by raising the environmental temperature from 16–20°C to 32°C.

If in male specimens of *Bufo bufo* Bidder's organ takes the lead and begins to function as an ovary, the toads become hermaphrodites although they preserve the original shape of males (Fuhrmann and Ponse, 1924). Males of *Triturus alpestris*, subjected to a deficient diet, changed into females. A hybrid of *Triturus cristatus* and *Salamandra salamandra* is reported to have had ovarian tissue within the testes. Here again details will have to be found in the very extensive literature on the subject.

D. Albinism and Melanism

Albinism and melanism are uncommon in amphibians. The occasional appearance of a white frog always arouses great interest and the hope that a pair may be found to be handed over to the experimental geneticists. So far, nobody has bred a line of white frogs. The axolotls are the only amphibians commonly displaying albinism. They may be partly or completely albinotic. Very rarely albinotic specimens of *Salamandra* and of *Necturus* have been seen (Hutt, 1945). *Proteus anguineus*, probably in consequence of its life in complete darkness, is naturally albinotic, but it may regain its pigmentation when exposed to light.

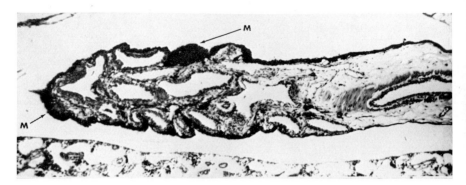

FIG. 286. *Rana clamitans*. Longitudinal section through right lung. Note the dense agglomeration of melanophores in the pleuro-peritoneum. *M*, Melanin depots. The picture is that of a normal lung at the tadpole stage. × 70. (Photo.: Elkan.)

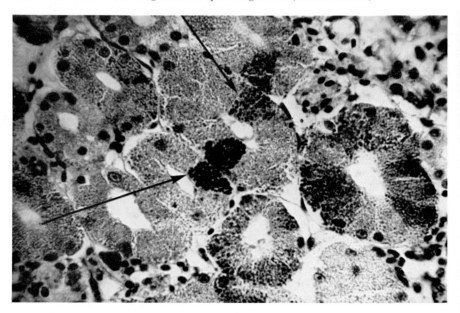

FIG. 287. *Bufo bufo*. Section through part of the kidney. The toad suffered from severe tuberculosis of the liver. Through the destruction of pigmented liver tissue melanin has been liberated and transported to the kidney, and has been reabsorbed by the epithelial cells of the uriniferous tubules. The degree, however, in which these cells take part in this re-absorption is very unequal. Some cells (arrowed) are seen filled with melanin while others, immediately adjacent, are entirely free from pigment. The cause of the different behaviour of cells which should be physiologically equal is not known. (Photo.: Elkan.)

Albinotic Anura are very rare. Three specimens were described by Eales (1933). He succeeded in raising completely white *temporaria* tadpoles, found in Somerset. He also found a *temporaria* female with a yellow skin and red eyes in Wiltshire which laid unpigmented eggs that could not be fertilized.

Smallcombe (1949) reported on partially albinotic *temporaria* tadpoles (white with black eyes) which, in special conditions, could be raised into adult albinos.

We owe an interesting account to Herkner (1959) who reports on the development of some pure white *Hyla arborea* tadpoles. These tadpoles started to metamorphose but were unable to leave the water and died. The low vitality of albinotic amphibians explains their rarity. Both Eales and Herkner state that the factor causing albinism is recessive and becomes apparent only when present in both parents.

The albinos described by Fischer-Sigwart (1897) were partial albinos of *R. temporaria*. Some unpigmented eggs developed into white tadpoles with black eyes. Gradually the frogs darkened and assumed their normal pigmented colour. The specimen described by Williams (1959) also was *R. temporaria*. This was a totally albinotic male with red eyes.

Rare varieties are represented by albinotic specimens of *Triturus vulgaris* L. and individuals of *T. cristatus* Laur. with a yellow tinge. Complete melanosis has been seen in *Salamandra salamandra* L. and *Triturus cristatus* Laur.

In an examination of sections made of any amphibian material it must always be remembered that in these animals large quantities of melanin are stored in almost any part of the body. The meninges, the blood vessels, the liver, the ovaries, the lungs, in short almost any organ may either be lined, covered or permeated by dense coats of melano phores. We have no knowledge of the physiological significance of the storage of such large quantities of melanin in animals which, in most cases, have a melanin-coloured skin anyway. But these chromatophores are normal and must not be regarded as indicating the presence of melanotic tumours (Fig. 286). It is different if melanin deposits appear in the renal epithelium. These cells re-absorb pigment which has been mobilized elsewhere, and renal melanin absorption is particularly noticeable in cases of liver tuberculosis where large parts of the liver have been destroyed and the blood circulation has been flooded with the mobilized pigment (Fig. 287).

REFERENCES

Buddenbrock, W. (1950). "Vergleichende Physiologie", Vol. IV. Hormone. Basle.
Eales, N. B. (1933). Albinism in the common frog. *Nature, Lond.* **132**, 278–279.
Fischer-Sigwart, H. (1879–98). Biologische Beobachtungen an unseren Amphi-
bien. *Vierteljahrsschrift d. naturf. Ges., Zürich* **42**, 238–316; **43**, 279–316.

Fuhrmann, O. (1914). L'hermaphroditisme chez *Bufo vulgaris*. *Rev. suisse Zool.* **21**, 331–345.

Hellmich, W. (1929). Mehrfachbildungen von Extremitäten bei Amphibien. (Naturfunde). *Roux' Arch.* **115**, 409–414.

Hellmich, W. (1929). Untersuchungen über Herkunft und Determination des regenerativen Materials bei Amphibien. *Roux' Arch.* **121**, 135–203.

Herkner, H. (1959). Albinismus bei Laubfroschkaulquappen. *Aqu. Terr. Z.* **12**, 126–127.

Hutt, F. B. (1945). Complete albinism in the mud puppy, *Necturus. J. Hered.* **36**, 145–147.

Leeke, P. (1912). Regeneration und Selbstverstümmelung. *Wschr. Aqu. Terrk.* **9**, 447–450, 463–464.

Lees, E. (1960). The Bionomics and Life Cycle of *Gorgodera vitelliloba*. Thesis. Bradford.

Meisenheimer, J. (1931). "Geschlecht und Geschlechter im Tierreiche", 2 vols. G. Fischer, Jena.

Noble, K. (1931). "The Biology of the Amphibia." McGraw-Hill. Dover Publ. 1954.

Ponse, K. (1924). L'Organe de Bidder et le déterminisme des caractères sexuels secondaires du Crapaud (*Bufo vulgaris*). *Rev. suisse Zool.* **31**, 177–336.

Rostand, J. (1955). "Les Crapauds, les Grenouilles et quelques grands problèmes biologiques," 5th edn. Gallimard, Paris.

Savage, M. (1961). "The Ecology and Life History of the Common Frog." Pitman.

Schmelcher, D. and Hellmich, W. (1951). Ueber eine merkwürdige Larve eines Feuersalamanders. *Aqu. Terr. Z.* **4**, 300–302.

Schlumberger, H. G. (1958). Krankheiten der Fische, Amphibien und Reptilien. *In* "Pathologie der Laboratoriumstiere" (Cohrs, Jaffé and Meesen, eds.), Vol. II. Springer, Berlin.

Schwind, J. L. (1942). Spontaneous twinning in the amphibia. *Amer. J. Anat.* **71**, 117–151.

Smallcombe, W. A. (19149). Albinism in *Rana temporaria. J. Genet.* **49**, 286–290.

Smith, M. (1951). "The British Amphibians and Reptiles." Collins, London.

Wilhelmi, G. (1957). Zur Frage einer thyreostatischen Wirkung von Antipyretica (Metamorphoseversuche an Froschlarven). *Arch. int. Pharmacodyn. Therap.* **112**, 155–173.

Williams, G. E. (1959). Ein Albino-Frosch im Horniman Museum, London. *Aqu. Terr. Z.* **12**, 149.

Witschi, E. (1952). Overripeness of the egg as a cause of twinning and teratogenesis; A review. *Cancer Res.* **12**, 763–785.

Wolterstorff, W. and Freytag, G. E. (1942). Ueber eine zweiköpfige Bastardlarve. *Wschr. Aqu. Terrk.* **38**, 217–218.

Wurmbach, H. (1951). Untersuchungen über die Rolle des Wassers beim Wachstum und der Metamorphose der Amphibienlarven. *Verh. dtsch. zool. Ges. Marburg*, 1950. *Zool. Anz.* Suppl. **14**, 59–91.

CHAPTER 17

Table of Main Symptoms and Causes of Diseases

Region	Symptom	Cause
Skin	Haemorrhages, inflammations	Infection; injury; avitaminosis; "Red Leg"; secretion of other amphibians
	Gray patches	*Oodinium*; *Trichodina*; fungi
	Pustules; tubercles	*Dermocystidium*; *Dermosporidium*; *Dermomycoides*; *Cercariae*; mites; "Molchpest"
	Secreting ulcers	"Red Leg"; "Molchpest"; *Pseudomonas* infection; acid-fast bacilli; disturbed skin-shedding; avitaminosis
	Disturbed skin-shedding	Metabolic disturbance; avitaminosis; delayed metamorphosis; fungus infection
	Albinism; melanism	Hereditary
Digestive organs	Intestinal inflammation	Infection by bacteria: *Pseudomonas*; tuberculosis Infection by Protozoa: *Eimeria*; Flagellates Helminthiasis: cestodes, nematodes, trematodes Acanthocephala; intestinal obstruction; feeding faults
	Liver abscess Liver, fatty Liver, congestion Liver, degeneration Liver, enlargement	Tuberculosis; feeding faults; abdominal tumours; septicaemia; avitaminosis
	Hydrops; peritonitis; ascites	Infections; destruction of lymph hearts; congenital fault; visceral tumours; infections (*Pseudomonas*); helminthiasis; intestinal obstruction; tuberculosis

Region	Symptom	Cause
	General symptoms: Apathy; refusal to feed	Septicaemia; trypanosomiasis; haemo- sporodiosis; microsporodiosis; micro- filaria; tuberculosis; faults in environ- mental temperature; overcrowding; faults in illumination
Lungs	Breathing difficulties	Tuberculosis; nematodes; trematodes; carcinoma; nematomorphae
Gills	Cysts, inflammation Loss of gills Furry gills	Myxosporodiosis; encysted larvae of molluscs; attacks by other amphi- bians; *Oodinium*; *Trichodina*
Urogenital organs	Kidney, tumours of, Kidney, enlarged	Tuberculosis; carcinoma; blastoma; nematodes; obstruction of uriniferous tubules; fungal infection
	Urinary bladder in- fection	*Polystoma*; pelvic tumours
	Ovary and fat-body atrophy	Any serious infection or tumour; tuber- culosis; metabolic disturbances
	Retention of ova	Unsuitable environment
Muscular system	Excessive starvation	Microsporidiosis; *Glugea*, *Plistophora*; metacercariae; feeding faults; over- crowding
Nervous system	Paralysis	*Tylodelphis rhachiaea*; avitaminosis *Tetrahymena*; infection; septicaemia; tuberculosis
Nervous receptors	Lateral line system Blindness	Cercarial infestation Trematodes; carcinoma; avitaminosis
Skeletal system	Rickets; osteoporosis	Avitaminosis; feeding faults; congenital faults; overcrowding
Endocrine glands	Gigantism; dwarfism; delayed metamor- phosis; sex reversal; sterility	Congenital faults; pituitary and thyroid aplasia and cystic degeneration; hormonal imbalance

CHAPTER 18

Therapy

A. TABLE OF CHEMICAL MEANS OF TREATMENT

Diagnosis	Drug	Application
Dermal parasites	Atebrin	Bath 1 : 100
	Quinine	Bath 1 : 100
	Iodine 10% alcoholic	Apply with brush
	Pot. permanganate	Bath 1 : 1 000
	Salt (NaCl)	Keep animals permanently in 0·4% solution
	Copper sulphate	Stock solution: 1 g : 1 000 for treatment: 2cm³ of stock sol. 1 : 1 000
	Methylene blue	Stock solution: 1 : 1 000 treatment: 3 : 10 000
	Rivanol	Bath, 1 : 100
	Trypaflavin	Bath, 1 : 100
Bacterial infections	Aureomycin	Add small doses to food according to size of animal
Removing chlorine	Sod. thiosulphate	1 : 10
Skin defects, Ulcers	Formaldehyde Stock sol. 40%	20–50 cm³ : 100 cm³ of water for external application
Conjunctivitis	Silver proteinate sol. 1%	Eyedrops

There is no doubt that this table could be enlarged and extended to include almost every drug used in human pathology. But the science of treating amphibians is still young, diagnosis is usually difficult and we are dealing with extremely sensitive patients. All drugs should therefore be used tentatively and in small doses. Nowhere is prevention

of trouble more important than in the lower vertebrates. In addition to
drugs vitamin medication is often of great value.

B. TREATMENT BY PHYSICAL MEANS

Physical therapeutic means at our disposal are:
(1) Raising or lowering of temperature;
(2) Increasing or decreasing illumination;
(3) Changing the quality of light (u.v. filtering, etc.);
(4) Changing degree of humidity in terraria;
(5) Changing the pH and lime content of water;
(6) Improving oxygenation of aquaria or terraria.

The right line of approach depends on the circumstances of each
case. Where the effect of the means to be employed cannot with certainty be foreseen these should first be tried out, in small steps, on
one or two animals before the whole stock is subjected to treatment
which may not have the desired consequences. In the construction of
animal houses for terrestrial amphibians it should be remembered that
frogs and salamanders appreciate a constant supply of fresh air even
though they lie hidden under stones or bark for most of the time.

The same might be said about direct sunlight. Nothing is more likely
to keep a cage for amphibians healthy than a few hours of daily sunlight
even when the animals are nocturnal. To replace sunlight by artificial
means is expensive and not always successful. Sources of u.v. light
should be used with the greatest care, particularly if the animal is
not submerged. In the water u.v. rays are soon absorbed and are unlikely to be dangerous.

Of all the deleterious factors we must consider that of overcrowding
as perhaps the most serious. After leaving the tadpole stage behind
amphibians are not gregarious. Even at the breeding season they only
congregate for a few days, leading solitary lives for the rest of the year.
They do not appreciate the presence either of a member of their own
or of another species in their cage. Having to fight for their food does
not sharpen their appetite but often depresses it. The only exception
to this rule is found in *Xenopus*, which does well under the most adverse conditions. It is therefore a far more suitable laboratory animal
than any species of *Rana* or *Bufo*.

It should finally be emphasized that frequent inspection of amphibians
during the months when they are not hibernating is of the greatest
importance. Only the watchful owner will discover a disease in the early
stages and prevent it from spreading by isolating the "patient" and
applying treatment where possible. During hibernation amphibians

should not be disturbed, but in the summer they should be inspected daily and should be handled with disinfected rubber gloves to prevent the transmission of any infection. The larger the number of animals kept the stricter should be the supervision. Nobody who has ever seen a whole collection of frogs die of "Red Leg" within a few days will be in doubt about the value of this warning.

Part III

Reptilia

Chapter 19

Technique of Investigation

A. Symptoms of Disease. Ages of Reptiles

Like other animals reptiles have to be closely watched if their state of health is to be accurately assessed. Concealment, away from the other inhabitants of the cage, abnormal sluggishness or restlessness may be indications of a bad state of health. Attention should also be paid to difficulties and irregularities in skin shedding and to a loss of the brilliance of the natural colours. Simple measures may sometimes be sufficient to restore the environmental conditions under which the animals have to live to their optimum. The food may be changed or supplemented, the soil improved, the humidity adjusted, sources of light and heat revised. Detailed suggestions concerning these factors will be made in Chapter 26.

One of the most important items in an attempt to diagnose the disease of any animal is a knowledge of its age since advanced age may in itself be responsible for symptoms which, for obvious reasons, cannot be cured. The maximal age attainable by a reptile varies considerably according to the species. Small types like chameleons and lizards are short-lived. Hesse and Doflein (1935) give the following figures:

Species	Years
Scincus officinalis L.	$9\frac{1}{2}$
Uromastix acanthinurus Bell	$9\frac{1}{2}$
Anguis fragilis L.	33

Krefft (1949) gives the following figures for tortoises:

Amyda ferox Schn.	25
Kinosternon subrubrum Lac.	38
Clemmys guttata Tr.	42
Macrochelys temmincki Tr.	42
Terrapene carolina L.	over 100

A Mauritian giant tortoise is said to have lived for 150 years, but the figure of 300 years claimed by Hesse for *Testudo gigantea daudini* D. and B. is of doubtful validity.

The life span of *Testudo graeca* L., one of the reptiles most commonly found in captivity, would interest us particularly. Flower (1944) kept a specimen for 39 years. This tortoise continued to grow to the very end of its life, reached a length of 36·5 cm and a weight of 4 kg. Authors even report on specimens of 54 years of age.

The life span of crocodiles can only be determined in specimens kept in zoological gardens and the figures so obtained are certainly not maximal ones. The greatest, well-authenticated age of a crocodile is 40 years. Brehm ("Tierleben") reports that Nile crocodiles reach the age of "several human generations", also that the natives estimate the age of a crocodile of 5–6 m at about 100 years. None of these estimates are reliable.

Of much greater interest is a report by Dawbin (1962) on the age of the tuatara (*Sphenodon punctatus* Gray). These large lizards grow very slowly and reach sexual maturity only after about 20 years. The author estimates the life span of this species as of 100 years or more.

B.   ANAESTHESIA, KILLING OF SPECIMENS, DISSECTION

The removal of external parasites, the painting of ulcerations or other minor items of treatment can, in small animals, be carried out without anaesthesia. It is advisable to envelop the animal with a cloth, leaving only the field of operation exposed. Tails of lizards have to be treated with great respect. Even if a new stump grows after a tail has been cast off, the animal will never be a show specimen again. Larger reptiles can inflict painful and even dangerous bites. Such specimens can only be treated under carefully administered general anaesthesia. The rules governing this procedure are the same as elsewhere, only the dosage must be appropriately reduced. Ether, which is most generally available, can be used on cotton wool in a closed glass jar, but if the animal is not to be killed it must be removed from the jar the very moment it becomes unconscious. "Nembutal" (pentobarbitone sodium, Abbott) can be given by intramuscular or intraperitoneal injection. The dose has to be adjusted according to the weight of the "patient". Urethane, popular in 2–4% solutions for the anaesthesia of aquatic animals, has a depressing effect on the bone-marrow and is now often superseded by M.S. 222 Sandoz, introduced for the anaesthesia of amphibians and fish. It has, apparently, not yet been used on reptilians but these too might lend themselves to the method, used on fish, of

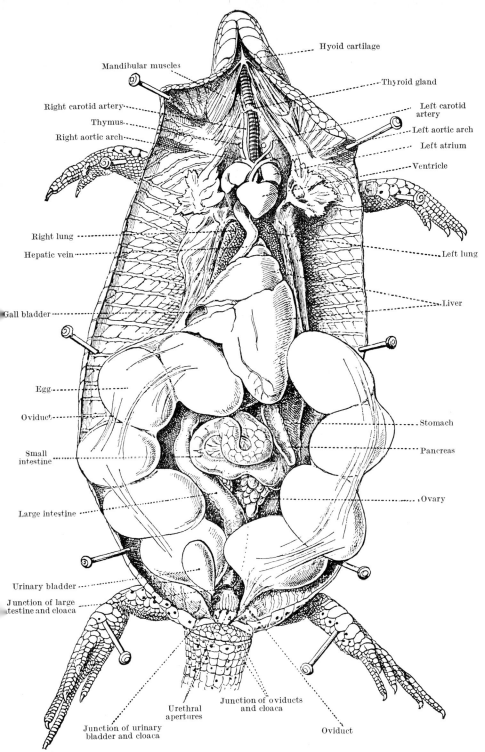

Hyoid cartilage

Mandibular muscles

Thyroid gland

Right carotid artery

Left carotid artery

Thymus

Left aortic arch

Right aortic arch

Left atrium

Ventricle

Right lung

Left lung

Hepatic vein

Liver

Gall bladder

Egg

Stomach

Oviduct

Pancreas

Small intestine

Large intestine

Ovary

Urinary bladder

Junction of large intestine and cloaca

Junction of oviducts and cloaca

Urethral apertures

Oviduct

Junction of urinary bladder and cloaca

FIG. 288. Dissection of a female wall lizard (*Lacerta muralis* L.). (From Kükenthal-Matthes.)

placing a wad of cotton wool, soaked in the solution, into their mouths.

All these chemicals, including chloroform, can in higher doses be used to kill animals too ill to be treated. In addition, the preparations Euthanal (3 cm^3 to be injected into the thorax of a medium-sized tortoise) and Nicotin (a small sponge, soaked in the solution, is placed into the animal's mouth) can be used. In particular cases where no drugs are available it may be necessary to decapitate in the region immediately behind the head.

The dissection of all reptilians with the exception of turtles and tortoises can begin with the opening of the visceral cavity from the anus to the thorax. The opening of the peritoneal cavity is particularly important when animals cannot be examined on the spot but have to be fixed and preserved to be sent away to a laboratory. To maintain the integrity of the animal fixation by injection is, of course, preferable, but even a syringe may not always be available. The later dissection of formaldehyde-hardened specimens is much more time-consuming than that of fresh material, but such dissections are made much easier if the specimen has been pinned down fully stretched during fixation.

The skin of reptilians adheres to the superficial fascia and cannot be stripped off without careful use of a very sharp scalpel. On the head, in particular, it is so strongly attached to the bone that a separation is often impossible.

Tortoises can only be dissected after the bridges between the dorsal and ventral shields have been cut either with a wire saw or very strong scissors. Even when this has been done the ventral shield can only be removed after it has been carefully dissected off the underlying muscles.

Bacteriological examination of body fluids is of value in freshly killed specimens only. Blood smears, smears from any other organ and samples of peritoneal fluid should be taken as a first step in the dissection and before any secondary contamination has taken place.

C. Detailed Examination of Organic Systems

The examination of the various organic systems begins with that of the skin. The axillary and the inguinal folds should be inspected; they are frequently the seat of ticks. Swabs can be taken from ulcers; fresh or stained preparations from exudations may be examined with the aid of the microscope. Cysts or tumours of doubtful nature are either removed *in toto* or fixed together with the surrounding skin so that, in the final section, the relation of the tumour and the skin is maintained.

In the laboratory fixation fluids are chosen according to the staining methods to be employed. Outside the laboratory only alcohol (70%) or formaldehyde (10%) are likely to be available. In either case the specimen should be fixed in at least 10 times its volume of fixing fluid. Further details may be found in textbooks on histological technique.

Muscular and connective tissue are carefully teased in a drop of saline on the microscopic slide and inspected under a cover glass. The digestive tract attracts our attention more than any other organic system since it is most frequently the seat of symbionts and parasites likely to cause disease and death. The oral cavity too should be inspected for parasites, inflammation and ulcers. The intestinal canal should be split along its whole length. In the case of small animals this should be done under saline so that any escaping parasite is not lost but immediately noticed.

Unless it is desired to examine fresh preparations of the bile or the mucous surface of the gall bladder the latter is dissected out together with a portion of the surrounding liver. Both liver and gall bladder are frequently the seat of parasites which can only be detected microscopically.

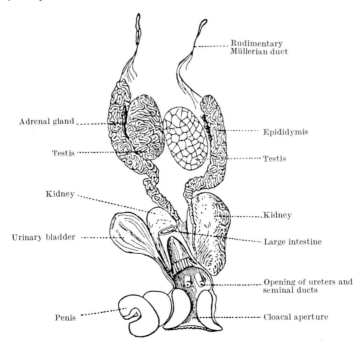

FIG. 289. Urogenital organs of a male wall lizard (*Lacerta muralis* L.). (From Kükenthal Matthes.)

Kidney, ureter, urinary bladder and the gonads should either be examined fresh or in sections. The lungs too are frequently invaded by parasites and bacteria.

Blood smears serve for the detection of parasites and for counts of normal and abnormal cells. Schulz and Krueger (1925) have published the following figures as representing the normal for a few reptilian species:

Species	Erythrocytes	Leucocytes
Emys orbicularis L.	500 000	8 000
Testudo graeca L.	629 000	13 200
Tarentola mauretanica L.	690 000	30 000
Lacerta viridis L.	840 000	
Natrix natrix L.	850 000	8 400
Lacerta agilis L.	0·95–1·29 million	10 500–19 000
Lacerta muralis L.	1–1·6 million	2 000–8 000
Anguis fragilis L.	1·5 million	7 000

On the whole the number of erythrocytes in reptiles varies between 500 000 and 1·5 million mm³; it therefore surpasses that of the Amphibia but does not reach the level of the Mammalia. Figure 290 gives some information on the size of the red blood corpuscles.

Wintrobe (1933) gives the following erythrocyte figures from some reptiles:

Alligator mississippiensis	670 000
Cistudo carolina (Tortoise)	740 000
Freshwater terrapin	740 000
Heterodon contortrix (Snake)	500 000
Heterodon contortrix (Snake)	630 000
Eutaria sirtalis (Garter snake)	1 390 000
Garter snake	710 000
Natrix sipedon (Water snake)	770 000

to which Ryerson (1949) added:

Coleonyx variegatus (Gecko)	491 000
Heloderma suspectum (Gila monster)	646 000
Phrynosoma solare (Horned toad)	745 000
Sceloporus magister (Lizard)	1 224 000
Pituophis sayi (Snake)	1 095 000

Finally Pienaar (1962) gives the following detailed figures for the S. African lizard *Cordylus vittifer*:

Total red count: 790 000–650 000 mm³   Average 830 000/mm³
Haemoglobin: 8·0–8·75 g per 100 cc
Length of erythrocytes: 12–18 μ; average 16·5 μ
Width of erythrocytes: 7–10 μ; average 8·5 μ

Parasitic infections as well as seasonal and dietary changes produce severe fluctuations of these figures.

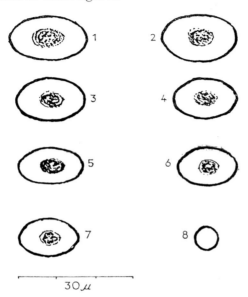

30 μ

FIG. 290. Comparison of reptilian and human red blood corpuscles. 1. *Testudo graeca* L. 2. *Emys orbicularis* L. 3. *Natrix natrix* L. 4. *Natrix flavescens* Werner. 5. *Anguis fragilis* L. 6. *Tarentola mauretanica* L. 7. *Lacerta agilis* L. 8. *Homo sapiens* L. (1, 4–7, after Schulz and von Krüger. 2 and 3, after Jung.)

Bernstein (1938) found in *Testudo geometrica* (Tortoise) 642 000 mm³ and the following four species were examined by Alder and Huber in 1923:

	Erythrocytes
Lacerta agilis	945 000
Anguis fragilis (Slow-worm)	1 615 000
Tarentola mauretanica (Gecko)	692 000
Emys orbicularis (Terrapin)	503 000

To these Pienaar (1962) added:

Agama atra (Lizard)	1 250 000
Chamaeleo dilepis	1 180 000
Cordylus giganteus (Lizard)	650 000

The latest data about other blood constituents of *Cordylus* come from Pienaar (1962):

Leucocytes: Normal variation between 20 000 and 27 000
Thrombocytes: Normal variation from 10 000 to 19 000

Differential normal blood counts of the lizard *Cordylus vittifer* (Pienaar, 1962):

Type of leucocyte	Young ♂♂	Adult ♂♂	Adult ♀♀
Type I eosinophils with spindle-shaped or crystalloid granules	8·64	15·4	13·6
Type II eosinophils with coarse, spheroid granules	0·12	0·18	0·07
Basophil granular lymphocytes (mast myelocytes)	1·00	0·97	0·9
Eosinophil (Type I) myelocytes and metamyelocytes	0·21	1·0	0·33
Basophil (mast) leucocytes	6·38	6·31	6·0
Giant vacuolated "athrocytic" azurophil leucocytes	2·08	0·91	0·8
Typical azurophil granulocytes	1·18	0·54	0·4
Lymphocytoid and plasmacytoid azurophils	3·32	6·8	3·7
Monocytoid azurophils and para-monocytes	0·73	1·35	0·73
Mononuclear neutrophil granulocytes	1·26	2·22	6·2
Large lymphocytes	4·38	4·85	4·57
Medium-sized lymphocytes	20·12	16·83	18·4
Small lymphocytes	48·52	40·01	42·6
Lymphocyte-erythroblast transitions	0·68	0·98	0·44
"Stem-cell" types	1·28	1·65	1·26
Thrombocytes per 100 leucocytes	43·0	48·0	59·0
Erythroblasts and basophilic normoblasts per 100 leucocytes	4·0	6·0	4·0
Polychromasic normoblasts and pro-erythrocytes per 100 leucocytes	90·0	103·0	53·0
"Megalocytes"—per 100 leucocytes	2·0	4·0	4·0
Mitosing erythrocytes per 500 leucocytes	0–1·0	0–1·0	0–1·0
Binucleate or amitosing erythrocytes per 500 leucocytes	1·0	1–2	1–3
Erythroplastids—per 500 leucocytes	1·0	1·0	1·0

In conformity with repeated observations made by other authors on other vertebrates Pienaar found that it is the eosinophil granulocytes which react most markedly to any abnormal condition. In helminth infections a rise of up to 27% occurred. Eosinophilia was similarly marked in haemoprotozoal infections. In the disease of the Harderian gland of terrapins we can see how large abscesses may even be formed exclusively by eosinophile leucocytes in complete absence of the neutrophile granulocytes usually active in abscess formation. Going by results the neutrophile leucocytes seem to effect a better defence since they produce liquid pus and allow the abscess to break through to the surface and to evacuate itself. The eosinophile leucocytes, however numerous they may be in these glandular abscesses, are unable to do this even if they may sterilize the seat of the original infection. They can therefore never be instrumental to effect a complete cure (p. 518 f.).

Tables of differential blood counts of 23 further S. African reptiles may be found in Pienaar (loc. cit.).

REFERENCES

Cater, D. B. (1953). "Basic Pathology and Morbid Histology." Wright, Bristol.

Dawbin, W. H. (1962). The Tuatara in its natural habitat. *Endeavour* **21**, 16-24.

Flower, S. S. (1944). Persistent growth in the tortoise *Testudo graeca* for thirty-nine years, with other notes concerning that species. *Proc. zool. Soc. Lond.* **114**, 451–455.

Graham-Jones, O. (1961). Notes on the common tortoise. *Vet. Rec.* **73**, 313–323.

Guyer, M. F. (1953). "Animal Micrology." University of Chicago Press.

Hesse, R. and Doflein, F. (1935). "Tierbau und Tierleben", 2nd edn., Fischer, Jena.

Humason, G. L. (1962). "Animal Tissue Techniques." W. H. Freeman, San Francisco.

Jung, T. (1955). Zur Kenntniss der Ernährungsbiologie der in dem Raum zwischen Harz und Heide vorkommenden Hirudineen. *Zool. Jahrb. Phys.* **66**, 79–129.

Klingelhoeffer, W. (1959). "Terrarienkunde." A. Kernen, Stuttgart.

Korschelt, E. (1924). "Lebensdauer, Altern und Tod", 3rd edn., Fischer, Jena.

Krefft, G. (1949). "Die Schildkröten." Wenzel, Braunschweig.

Pienaar, U. de v. (1962). "Haematology of some South African Reptiles." Witwatersrand University Press, Johannesburg, S. Africa.

Romeis, G. (1948). "Mikroskopische Technik." 15th edn., Leibniz, Munich.

Ryerson, D. L. (1949). A preliminary survey of reptilian blood. *J. Ent. Zool.* **41**, 49.

Sandoz A.G. (1961). MS-222. The preferred anaesthetic. *Information Bulletin.*

Schulz, P. N. and v. Krueger, (1925). Das Blut der Wirbeltiere. *In* "Handbuch der vergleichenden Physiologie" (Winterstein, H., ed.), Vol. I. I. Fischer, Jena.

Smith, H. M. (1957). A record of longevity for the greater five-lined skink. *Herpet.* **13**, 24.

United States Navy (1960). "Manual of Histologic and Special Staining Techniques." The Blakiston Division, McGraw-Hill Book Co.

Wintrobe, M. M. (1933). Variations in size and haemoglobin concentration in the blood of various vertebrates. *Fol. haematol. Lpz.* **51**, 32.

CHAPTER 20

Infectious Diseases

A. BACTERIAL INFECTIONS

Bacterial epizootics are not of unusual occurrence in reptiles. They mainly appear in animals already weakened by other causes and the observations available have mostly been made on caged specimens. The causative bacteria can be divided into two groups according to whether they are themselves the cause of the disease or whether they are merely found on or in the reptile which acts as a carrier. The *Salmonella* group of bacteria often comes into this second category.

Bergey's "Manual of Determinative Bacteriology" (1957) lists the following bacteria as occurring commonly in reptiles:

Pseudomonadales
Enterobacteria
Mycobacteria
Bartonella
Spirochaetales

Pseudomonas reptilivorus was described by Caldwell and Ryerson (1940) from the Mexican beaded lizard *Heloderma suspectum* Cope, from chuckawalla lizards (*Sauromalus ater*) and from the horned toad *Phrynosoma solare* Gray. The strains were described as being equally pathogenic for reptiles, guinea-pigs and rabbits. On autopsy, the animals showed haemorrhagic areas in the stomach, lungs and at the injection site, whilst the liver had assumed a greyish colour. Pseudomonads were recovered by cultivation from heart blood and from peritoneal fluid. They gave rise to marked haemolysis on rabbit blood agar. The authors assumed that an analogous disease occurred among free-living animals.

Pseudomonas fluorescens and *Ps. fl. liquefaciens* are commonly seen in reptiles. The latter was described by Burtscher (1931) as being the causative agent of an ulcerative inflammation of the oral cavity in snakes going by the name of "Mouth Rot". The organism was isolated from fourteen species of snakes including both venomous and non-venomous species. Reinhardt (1927) recorded the same disease as occurring among snakes and lizards kept in zoological gardens. It starts with oedema and inflammation of the oral mucous membrane which swell so much that the animals can no longer close the mouth and are unable to feed (Fig. 291).

Graham Jones (1961) suggests that various fungi supervene and take

(a)

(b)

Fig. 291. Oral scurvy of reptiles. (a) A skink, *Mabuya striata* Peters. Healthy specimen. (Photo.: Stemmler-Gyger.) (b) The same, suffering from oral scurvy. (Photo.: O. Stemmler-Gyger.)

(c)

Fig. 291. (c) A day gecko, *Phelsuma madagascariensis kochi* Mertens which died of oral scurvy. (Orig.)

part in the development of the condition. The idea that ulcerative stomatitis may be caused by more than one agent seems to derive support from occasional successes with vitamin treatment. (O. Stemmler, Basle, personal communication.)

Pseudomonas jaegeri, *Ps. smaragdina*, *Ps. viscosa* and *Ps. puris* were isolated by Patrick and Werkman (1930) from a condition in snakes resembling typhoid. A detailed account of the bacteriology and pathology of these species is not yet available.

The same applies to another bacillus, *Pasteurella haemolytica* Newson and Cross, also found in cases of ulcerative stomatitis in reptile collections.

One of the commonest bacteria, always threatening reptile collections, is *Aeromonas hydrophila* (formerly *Proteus hydrophilus*) Sanarelli. This is the bacillus which causes the dreaded disease of "Red Leg" in frogs. Camin (1948) found these bacilli in the heart and in other viscera of snakes. Brison, Tysset and Vacher (1959) found *Testudo graeca* resistant to *Aeromonas* while the aquatic species *Emys orbicularis* was very susceptible.

Equally susceptible is the common grass snake *Natrix natrix* L. as confirmed by the work of Brisou, Tysset and Vacher (quoted by de Rautlin de la Roy, 1960). The authors isolated the bacterium from pus present in the peritoneal cavity as well as from heart blood of grass snakes. *Proteus vulgaris* was isolated from the same material.

Aeromonas can be transmitted by the mite *Ophionyssus serpentinum* Hirst. While the disease could not be directly transmitted from snake to snake, transmission via the mite succeeded in every experiment. Hirst reported mites to be infectious from 48 hours onwards after ingestion of pathogenic bacteria.

The family Enterobacteriaceae (Order Eubacteriales) contains a parasite *Serratia anolium* isolated from the lizard *Anolis equestris* Merr. Clausen and Duran-Reynals (1937) isolated this bacillus from a kind of tumour first from Cuban lizards, later from Mexican iguanids (*Basiliscus vittatus*). They showed the organism to be haemolytic and pathogenic to a wide variety of poikilothermic animals, among them *Anolis equestris, A. carolinensis, Tarentola mauretanica, Hemidactylus brookii, Thamnophis butleri, Storeria dekayi* and *Sternothaerus odoratus*. They considered the disease as contagious but not necessarily fatal.

The position of "pneumococci", found by Graham-Jones in the lungs of tortoises seems to be systematically uncertain. The bacillus may have been of the genus *Peptostreptococcus*.

Equal uncertainty prevails regarding the description of a *Bacterium sauromali*, Conti and Crowley 1939, found in a specimen of *Sauromalus varius* Dickerson, the "Chuckawalla" of California. The bacillus again caused a kind of tumour in the lizards. The tumours were enclosed in a fibrous capsule and connected with the surrounding tissue by a fibro-vascular neck. The capsule, heavily infiltrated by monocytes, also contained desquamated cells embedded in layers of an amyloid, substance. The tumours were found in the buccal cavity, at the base of the tongue, in the inferior cervical region and in the leg. The bacillus is described as Gram negative, chromogenous, motile but not sporogenous. Full details of the histopathological findings, together with excellent photographs of the condition, are given in the original paper.

The occurrence of the genus *Salmonella* in reptiles is of the greatest importance. Jaksztien and Petzold (1959) reported on *Salmonella* infections of snakes. They were able to identify the serotypes "Arizona", "Charrau", and "Oranienburg" in *Agkistrodon piscivorus* Lacépède, the Water Mocassin snake. One of the snakes dissected was found afflicted with peritonitis, gastric and intestinal inflammation, liver oedema and renal degeneration. Snakes in the early stages of the disease could be cured by intraoral infusion of an aqueous solution of Chloronitrin in doses of 25 cc.

Boycott, Taylor and Douglas (1953) published an extensive report on the occurrence of *Salmonella* in tortoises. Infected specimens seem to be able to carry the most varied serotypes without falling ill themselves. Seventeen such serotypes have so far been recognized, among them "Coruvallis" and "Canastel". Some of these serotypes were found to play a part in human pathology as well. An outbreak of *Salmonella* dysentery in a group of children was thought to have been caused by infected tortoises. Considering the great number of tortoises imported as pets every year the danger does not seem negligible. (See also Buxton (1957) and Kiesewetter *et al.* (1960).)

The occurrence of tuberculosis in reptiles was reviewed by Griffith in 1930. Bergey's manual only mentions *Mycobacterium thamnopheos* Aronson from snakes. *M. tropidonotus* has been reported from *Boa constrictor*, *Coluber catenifer* and *Python molurus*. The names of *M. testudinis* Friedman and Piorkowski and *M. friedmanni* Holland (= *M. cheloni* Bergey *et al.*) are no longer considered valid. The many cases of cold-water tuberculosis seen in reptiles are, on the other hand, doubtlessly not all due to *M. thamnopheos*. Griffith (loc. cit.) separates types pathogenic for turtles (Friedmann's turtle strain), a snake strain and several crocodile strains, among them one for the cayman. The clinical picture is that of typical tuberculosis with pulmonary tubercles (tortoises, turtles) and analogous lesions in skin, liver and spleen (snakes and crocodiles).

Spirochaeta have on several occasions been found both in snakes and in lizards but it is very doubtful whether they should be regarded as pathogenic for these hosts. It is equally uncertain whether the spirochaetes found belong to the genus *Spirochaeta* or *Treponema*. Both names have been used: *Treponema* for lizards; *Spirochaeta* for snakes (Breed, Murray and Hitchens, 1957). Dobell found spirochaetes in Indian grass snakes and described them as *Spirochaeta tropidonoti*. Scharrer (1935) found similar types in specimens of *Natrix natrix* L.

REFERENCES

Aronson, J. D. (1929). Spontaneous tuberculosis in snakes. *Arch. Path.* **8**, 159.
Boycott, R. S., Taylor, J. and Douglas, S. H. (1953). *Salmonella* in tortoises. *J. Path. Bact.* **65**, 401–411.
Breed, R. S., Murray, E. G. D. and Hitchens, A. F. (1927). *In* Bergey's "Manual of Determinative Bacteriology", 7th edn. Baltimore.
Brison, I., Tysset, C. and Vacher, F. B. (1959). Recherches sur les Pseudomonaceae. *Ann. Inst. Pasteur* **96**, 633.
Burtscher, J. (1931). Ueber die Mundfäule des Schlangen. *Zool. Garten* **4**, 235–244.
Buxton, A. (1957). "Salmonellosis in Animals." Farnham Royal, Bucks.
Caldwell, N. E. and Ryerson, D. L. (1940). A new species of the genus *Pseudomonas* pathogenic for certain reptiles. *J. Bact.* **39**, 323–336.
Camin, J. (1948). Mite transmission of a haemorrhagic septicaemia in snakes. *J. Parasit.* **34**, 345–354.
Clausen, H. J. and Durand-Reynals, F. (1937). Studies on the experimental infection of some reptiles, amphibia and fish with *Serratia anolium*. *Amer. J. Path.* **13**, 441–451.
Conti, L. F. and Crowley, J. H. (1939). A new bacterial species, isolated from the Chuckawalla (*Sauromalus varius*). *J. Bact.* **33**, 647–653.
Dobell, C. (1910). On some parasitic protozoa from Ceylon. *Spolia zeylanica* **3**, 78.
Graham-Jones, O. (1961). Notes on the common tortoise. *Vet. Rec.* **73**, 313–321.

Griffith, A. S. (1930). Tuberculosis in cold-blooded animals. *In* "A System of Bacteriology in relation to Medicine." Vol. *v*, 326–332.

Hunt, T. J. (1957). Notes on diseases and mortality in Testudines. *Herpetologica* **13**, 19–23.

Jaksztien, K. P. and Petzold, H. G. (1959). Durch *Salmonella* Infektion bedingte Schwierigkeiten bei der Aufzucht von Schlangen und ihre Behandlung. *Bl. Aqu. Terrk.* **6**, 79–80.

Kiesewetter, J., Rudat, K. D. and Seidel, G. (1960). Salmonellen und Reptilien. *Zbl. Bak.* I. Orig. **180**, 503–509.

Patrick, R. and Werkman, C. H. (1930). Notes on the bacterial flora of the snake. *Proc. Iowa Acad. Sci.* **37**, 330.

Rautlin de la Roy, Y. (1960). Révision taxonomique et intérêt en pathologie des bactéries gram-négatifs à pigments jaunes. Thesis for the degree of M.D. Univ. Toulouse, France, p. 89.

Reinhard, W. (1927). Ueber die Mundfäule der Schlangen. *Bl. Aqu. Terrk.* 318–321.

Scharrer, B. (1935). Ueber *Spirochaeta* (*Treponema*) *minutum* Dobell bei Amphibien. *Zool. Anz.* **111**, 1–7.

Willis, R. A. (1932). A bacillary disease of the blue-tongued lizard (*Tiliqua scincoides*). *Med. J. Austr.* **19**, 144–157.

B. PROTOZOAL DISEASES

Flagellata

Flagellates (unicellular organisms, equipped with a whip or flagellum) may be found in the blood or in the fluid contents of the gut of reptiles. Among the blood parasites trypanosomes are most frequently encountered. They are comparatively large and similar to those seen in birds.

In terrestrial reptiles the trypanosomes are commonly transmitted by insects (Diptera), probably also by mites (Acarina). In aquatic forms the transmission takes place through the sucking activities of leeches (Hirudinea). The degree to which trypanosomiasis damages the health of an infected reptile depends probably on the severity of the infection.

Trypanosoma grayi Novy, which occurs in the blood of African crocodiles, has been extensively studied (Fig. 292 g–n). The developmental cycle of this parasite is well known because it relies, as intermittent host on the tsetse fly (*Glossina palpalis*) which transmits sleeping sickness in man. The length of *T. grayi*—including flagella— may reach 91 μ. The body shows longitudinal stripes. Reproduction has so far only been observed to take place in the transmitting flies. According to Hoare (1931) it takes place in the mid-gut of the insect. In the end-gut young trypanosoma of 12–20 μ can be found. These are excreted with the faeces of the fly. It is assumed that flies are either accidentally squashed in the mouth of the crocodile or that they defaecate there.

Trypanosoma varani Wenyon has been found in various species of *Varanus*. It is transmitted by the fly *Glossina tachinoides* Westwood. The Indian gecko *Hemidactylus frenatus* Schlegel suffers from *Trypanosoma phlebotomi* Mackie transmitted by *Phlebotomus babu* var. *shorti* Adler and Theodor (Short and Swaminath, 1931). The authors, studying the reproductive phase of this parasite in the gut of the *Phlebotomus* fly reported the appearance of spherical cysts containing trypanosomes without flagella similar to *Leishmania* types. These divide and change into the "crithidial" form.

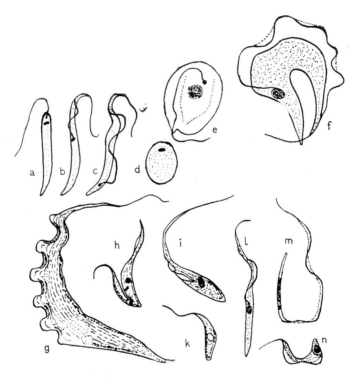

Fig. 292. Trypanosomes from reptiles. a, *Leptomonas*; b, *Crithidia*; c, *Trypanosoma*; d, Leishmania type. (From Reichenow, 1953.) e, *Trypanosoma platydactyli* Carr. × 1 600; f, *Trypanosoma martini* Bouet. × 1 000. (From Hoare.) g–n, *Trypanosoma grayi* Novy; g, From the blood of a crocodile; h–n, from the intestine of *Glossina palpalis* Rob.-Desv.; l–n, *Crithidia*. (After Hoare from Doflein-Reichenow, 1953.)

Further species of *Trypanosoma* have been described from the African gecko *Tarentola mauretanica* L., from *Chamaeleo vulgaris* L. from the Sudan, and from the Central African skink *Mabuya raddoni* Gray. The skinks *Mabuya maculilabris* Gray and *Mabuya striata* Peters harbour *Trypanosoma martini* Bouet; other types are *T. platydactyli* Catouillard, *T. chamaeleonis* Wenyon and *T. boueti* Martin.

Trypanosomes have also been found in the blood of various snakes. Reichenow (1953) mentions:

Trypanosoma erythrolampri Wenyon from *Erythrolamprus aesculapii* L. one of the South American "false coral snakes";

Trypanosoma najae Wenyon from *Naja nigricollis* Reinh., the black-necked cobra from the Sudan;

Trypanosoma clozeli Bouet from *Tropidonotus ferox*, a grass snake;

Trypanosoma primeti Mathis and Léger from *Natrix piscator* Schn., a S.E. Asian adder;

Trypanosoma brazili Brumpt from *Helicops modestus* Gthr., a Brazilian aquatic snake. (Intermediate hosts: the leeches *Placobdella brasiliensis* and *Placobdella catenigera*.)

The same author lists the following species of *Trypanosoma* as occurring in tortoises:

Trypanosoma vittatus Robertson from *Lissemys punctata granosa* (Schoepff) from Ceylon. The parasite is up to 70 μ long and is transmitted by a species of *Glossiphonia;*

Trypanosoma damoniae Laveran and Mesnil from *Chinemys reevesii* Gray;

Trypanosoma pontyi Bouet from *Pelusios subniger* Lac;

Trypanosoma chelodina Johnson from *Chelodinia longicollis* Shaw.

The more primitive types of the trypanosomids are also commonly seen in reptiles, particularly the genus *Leptomonas* which lacks the undulating membrane typical of the higher forms. Quoting from the literature, particularly from Reichenow (1953) we find:

Leptomonas chamaeleonis Wenyon in the gut of Chamaeleontidae;

Leptomonas sp. in the gut and the blood of *Anolis* and *Chalcides ocellatus* Forsk.;

Leptomonas sp. in *Agama stellio* L. (in the blood only) (Hindle, 1930);

Leptomonas sp. in the gut of *Cnemidophorus lemniscatus*.

The type *Leishmania* which is spherical and lacks a flagella has been found in the blood of several lizards. Reichenow (1953) lists:

Leishmania tarentolae Wenyon from *Tarentola mauretanica* L.;

Leishmania hemidactyli Mackie *et al.* from the Indian *Hemidactylus gleadovii* Murray;

Leishmania ceramodactyli Adler and Theodor from the oriental *Ceramodactylus doriae;*

Leishmania agamae;

Leishmania adleri Heisch from *Latastia longicauda revoili* Vaillant (Heisch, 1958).

Heisch gave a detailed description of this species. Apart from typical *Leishmania* types he found many of the more primitive *Leptomonas* stages. The *Leishmania* parasites are transmitted by *Phlebotomus* flies.

The Bodonidae occur in their majority free-living in slightly saprobic waters. Some species appear occasionally or permanently as parasitic

Fig. 293. *Bodonidae* from reptiles. Above: *Proteromonas lacertae-viridis* Grassi. (After Belar from Reichenow, 1953.) Left, resting form, right, reproductive stages. × 1 600. Below: a and b, *Chilomastix wenyoni* Janakidevi. c, *Chilomastix caulleryi* Alexeieff. × 1 000.

forms, both in the blood and in the intestine. *Proteromonas lacertae viridis* Grassi, which belongs to this group, is frequently found in the gut of lizards. It is a slender, pear-shaped protozoon with two flagella of 10–30 μ length (Fig. 293). It reproduces by longitudinal or multiple division within so-called pseudocysts. Chatton described a similar type from *Tarentola mauretanica* as var. *tarentolae*.

Proteromonas uromastixi from *Uromastix hardwicki* Gray was described by Janakidevi (1961).

The genus *Chilomastix* is distinguished by having three anterior and one posterior flagella. Reichenow (1953) saw a small type, not described in detail, in lizards and Janakidevi described a closely allied type *Retortomonas cheloni* in tortoises (1962) (Fig. 293).

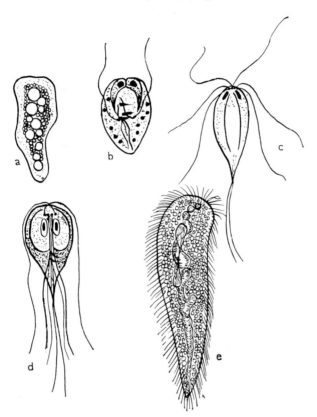

FIG. 294. a, *Vahlkampfia ranarum* Epstein and Ilowaisky. × 666. (From Reichenow.) b, *Trepomonas agilis* Duj. × 1 333. (After Bishop from Reichenow, 1953.) c, *Hexamita intestinalis* Duj. × 2 000. (From Reichenow, 1953.) d, *Lamblia microti* Kofoid and Christiansen. (From Reichenow, 1953.) e, *Protoopalina intestinalis* Stein. (After Metcalf from Reichenow, 1953.) (Note the long, excretory organelle.)

The genus *Vahlkampfia*, which has no flagella and has the shape of an oblong amoeba, is very occasionally seen in the reptilian intestine. Reichenow mentions *Vahlkampfia dobelli* Hartmann from *Lacerta muralis* L. and *Vahlkampfia reynoldsi* McFall from *Sceloporus undulatus* Latr. (see Wood, 1953).

Hexamita, a flagellate with eight flagella, usually found in fish and amphibians, can occasionally invade the intestine of chelonians. Alexeieff assigned these forms to a new species *Octomastix parvus*, which is not generally accepted as valid. Among other authors Lavier (1942) described *Hexamita* from chelonians (Fig. 294). Occasionally the parasite invades the circulatory system. Possibly identical with the free-living form is the related *Trepomonas agilis* Duj., equally equipped with eight flagella (Das Gupta, 1935) (Fig. 294).

Lamblia varani Lavier is a rare intestinal parasite from *Varanus niloticus* L. It is distinguished by a well-defined dorsal and ventral side, equipped with four pairs of flagella, and forms spherical cysts.

The genus *Trichomonas* too occurs parasitic in reptiles. *Monocercomonas colubrorum* Hammerschmidt is a commonly seen protozoon inhabiting the gut of lizards and snakes (Fig. 296a). Grassé (1926) considers this parasite, which has three posterior flagella, as identical with several other flagellates, described as *Trichomastix lacertae* Blochmann; *T. viperae* Léger; *T. serpentis* Dobell; *T. mabuiae* Dobell; and *T. saurii* Da Fonseca. The genus has, on occasion, been found to invade the blood stream of reptilians.

Das Gupta (1930) described a similar type of *Trichomonas*, found in the intestine of a chameleon, as *"Eutrichomastix"*. The exact species was not determined (Fig. 296c).

Monocercomonoides varies from *Monocercomonas* by the fact that the flagella issue in pairs from two basal bodies. The axillary rod is slender. *M. lacertae* Tanabe occurs in the rectum of the lizard *Eremias arguta* Pallas (Reichenow, 1953). *M. filamentum* Janakidevi (1961) was found in chelonians. Honigberg (1935) reported an investigation of the related genus *Hexamastix* and found the species *H. kirby* and *H. crassus* in *Sauromalus obesus* Baird and *Eumeces gilberti* van Denburgh (Fig. 295c, d).

In 1961 Janakidevi found two further species, *Hexamastix lacertae*, an intestinal parasite of *Uromastix hardwicki* Gray, and *Hexamastix dobelli* which occurs in *Testudo elegans* Schoepff (Fig. 295e). Both authors demonstrate in their illustrations the great variability of these species.

Occasionally the related genus *Tritrichomonas* may be met with. *T. lacertae* Prowazek inhabits the cloaca of several lizards (Fig. 296d), *T. boae* Reichenow was found in *Constrictor constrictor* L. The latter species has three anterior and one posterior flagella; the posterior one forms the edge of an undulating membrane which connects it with the body of the flagellate. In *Tritrichomonas lacertae* we find three anterior

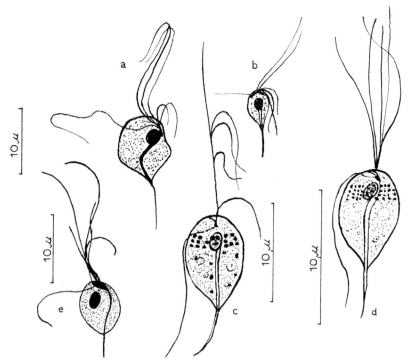

FIG. 295. Trichomonadina from reptiles. a and b, *Hexamastix lacertae* Janakidevi;
c, *Hexamastix kirby* Honigberg; d, *Hexamastix crassus* Honigberg; e, *Hexamastix dobelli*
Janakidevi. (a, b, and c, after Janakidevi; c and d, after Honigberg.)

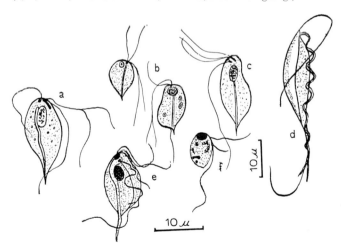

FIG. 296. a, *Monocercomonas colubrorum* Hammerschmidt. × 1 000. (After v. Prowazek
from Reichenow, 1953.) b, *Tritrichomonas alexeieffi* Grassé. c, "*Eutrichomastix*" (=
Monocercomonas) sp. from a chameleon. (From Das Gupta.) d, *Tritrichomonas lacertae*
Prowazek. (After Grassé.) e, *Tritrichomonas lissemyi* Janakidevi. f, *Alexeiefella cheloni*
Janakidevi.

flagella of equal length, whereas those of *T. boae* are of unequal length. Some similar types found in *Natrix natrix* L. and in *Python molurus* have not been described in detail. Grassé (1926) described *Tritrichomonas alexeieffi* from the rectum of the slow-worm (*Anguis fragilis* L.) and Janakidevi (1961) from that of *T. lissemyi* (Fig. 295e).

One group of trichomonads is described as *Trichocercomitus* (formerly *"Trimitus"*). Saxe and Schmidt found *T. parvus* in snakes and *T. trionyci* Knowles and Gupta in chelonians. Janakidevi determined a similar parasite, found in the Indian *Lissemys punctata granosa* Schoepff, as *Alexeiefella cheloni* (Fig. 296f).

Some Reptilia harbour representatives of the genus *Trichomonas* which is equipped with four anterior flagella. Alexeieff (1911) found *Trichomonas brumpti* in the chelonians *Nicoria* and *Testudo*, Parasi (quoted after Reichenow, 1953) discovered a trichomonad in *Crocodilus palustris* Lesson which he took to be *T. provazeki* A., an intestinal parasite of amphibians. Das Gupta (1936) found unknown species of *Trichomonas* in the Indian snake *Liopeltis calamaria* Gthr. and in the N. American snake *Natrix erythrogaster*.

The flagellate genus *Opalina*, so commonly seen in frogs, may occasionally also be encountered in saurians. Lavier (1927) reports on finding *Protoopalina nyanzae* Lavier in *Varanus niloticus* from Lake Victoria. Carini (1943) found *Zelleriella* spp. in Brazilian snakes but considered them as derived from frogs eaten by the snakes.

Rhizopoda

Amoebae seem to be more common parasites in reptiles than in amphibians. *Entamoeba invadens* Rodhain is known to cause losses among lizards and snakes (Geiman and Ratcliffe, 1936). The species proved harmless to mammals. Morphologically it closely resembles *Entamoeba histolytica* Schaudinn, which plays such an important part in human pathology. Like the latter species *E. invadens* produced the clinical picture of membranous enteritis. There are recent reports (Hill, 1953) from the London Zoo about the ravages caused by this rhizopod in lizards and snakes. The affected gut becomes inflamed and oedematous. The inflammation gives cause to peritoneal adhesions. The intestinal mucosa becomes ulcerated, the parasite invades the submucosa and reaches the liver by way of the portal vein. Massive infarction occurs in the liver and the affected animal dies. Figure 297 shows various stages in the development of the parasite in a case of ulcerative colitis.

Steck (1962), investigating the amoebic dysentery of snakes, found them suffering from haemorrhagic colitis with much cellular damage and subsequent necrosis caused, perhaps, by the effects of a toxic colonic flora. Amoebic invasion of the liver produced foci of thrombosis and necrobiosis.

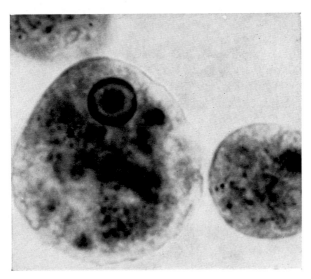

Fig. 297. *Entamoeba invadens* Rodhain from ulcerations in the colon of an aquatic snake *Natrix rhombifera* Hallowell. × 1 600. (After Ratcliffe from Schlumberger in Cohrs, Jaffé and Meesen, 1958.)

Reichenow (1953) mentions the following types of *Entamoeba* as occurring in reptilians:

Entamoeba varani Lavier from *Varanus niloticus* L. (perhaps identical with *E. invadens*?);

E. lacerticola Wood from various lizards (Wood, 1933);

E. terrapenae Sanders and Cleveland from *Pseudemys scripta elegans* Wieg.;

E. insolita Geiman and Wichterman from *Testudo elephantina* Harlan;

E. barreti Taliaferro and Holmes (cysts with eight nuclei as against four in *terrapenae* and *insolita*) from *Chelydra serpentina* L.;

E. flaviviridis Knowles and Das Gupta (similar to the last mentioned) from *Hemidactylus flaviviridis* Rüpp.;

E. spec. in *Lacerta* spp. and in *Agama stellio* L.;

E. testudinis Hartmann (size up to 70 μ; no cysts seen) from *Testudo graeca* L. and from other terrestrial tortoises;

E. serpentis Cunha and Fonseca (no cysts seen) from the snake *Drimobius bifossatus* Radday.

Sporozoa

Sporozoal infections are comparatively common in reptilians and are mostly due either to intestinal infection of the gut with *Eimeria* or to *Plasmodia* invading the blood.

Sub-class Telosporidia

In spite of assertions to the contrary the Order Gregarinida have not definitely been proved to be pathogenic for Reptilia. Schöppler (1917) who found Gregarinida in *Lacerta agilis* L. thought that they had gained access through mealworms used for feeding the lizards.

Order Coccidia
Sub-order Adeleidea

Karyolysus lacertae Danilewsky is a haemoparasite of lizards which requires an intermediate host. It is found in the endothelial lining of blood vessels of *Lacerta muralis* L. where it reproduces asexually. Sexual reproduction takes place in the mite *Neoliponyssus saurarum* Oudemans. The merozoite, having gained access to the blood of the lizard, surrounds itself with a membrane and divides into 8–30 macro-merozoites. They immigrate into new endothelial cells where, in turn, they again grow to schizonts. Eventually two types of schizonts of different sizes appear: macro- and micromerozoites (Fig. 298a). They invade the erythrocytes of the lizard and form a capsule. Further development can only take place in the next host, the mite. If *Neoliponyssus* sucks up infected blood the encapsulated sexual forms are freed and are now easily distinguished as broad macro- and slender microgametes. A pair of these adhere closely to one another, penetrate an intestinal mucosal cell, and surround themselves with a membrane. The macrogamete grows; the microgamete divides. One of the micro-gametes fertilizes the macrogamete which now grows into a large oocyst. The oocyst disintegrates into filariform sporokinetes which in their turn invade the eggs of the acarid. Here they change into spores which eventually divide into 20–30 sporozoites. If the lizard feeds on infected acarid nymphs the sporozoites or merozoites gain access to the intestinal canal and the circle is repeated. These merozoites are very motile and move across the intestinal epithelium until they gain access to a capillary vessel.

The deleterious effect of this infection rests mainly on the deformation or fragmentation, rarely in the complete destruction of the erythrocyte nucleus.

The number of *Karyolysus* species pathogenic for reptiles is probably large. Few, however, have been as thoroughly studied as *K. lacertae*.

Mixed infections are also likely to occur. Among other species of *Karyolysus* which develop in acarids we may mention *K. bicapsulatus*

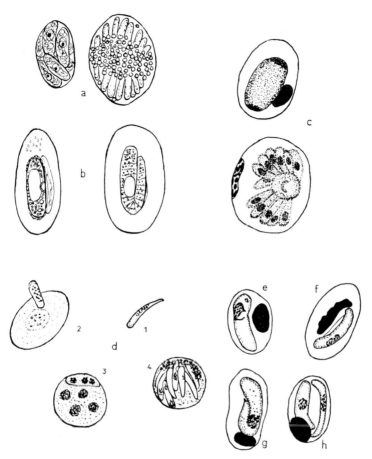

FIG. 298. Adeleidea from reptiles. a, *Karyolysus lacertae* Danilewsky. × 666. (From Reichenow, 1953.) b, *Karyolysus bicapsulatus* Franca. × 1 200. (From Reichenow, 1953.) c, *Hepatozoon pettiti* Thiroux. (From Hoare.) d, *Haemogregarina stepanovi* Danilewsky. 1, Infectious sporozoite; 2, schizont, penetrating the erythrocyte of a tortoise; 3, syncarion in the process of dividing, with three remaining microgametes; 4, eight sporozoites. (From Reichenow, 1953.) e, *Haemogregarina musotae* Hoare. f, *Haemogregarina enswerae* Hoare. g, *Haemogregarina sternothaeri* Hoare. h, *Haemogregarina crotaphopeltis* Hoare. (e–h, After Hoare.)

Franca (Fig. 298b) from *Lacerta muralis* L. and *K. zuluetai* Reichenow from the same host. The species *K. lacazei* Labbé from *Lacerta viridis* Laur., *Lacerta ocellata* Daud. and *Psammodromus algirus* L. develop not in the ovary but in the peritoneal cavity of the mite.

It is difficult to distinguish the various species of *Karyolysus* from one another. The capsules containing the gametocytes of *K. bicapsulatus* and *K. zuluetai* for example are recognized by a polar reinforcement which has been likened to a skull-cap. *K. lacazei* is distinguished as having large gametocytes which assume a curved shape in the erythrocytes (Fig. 298b).

The genus *Hepatozoon* is closely related to *Karyolysus*. It differs in the fact that the oocyst does not produce sporokinetes but numerous spores containing sporozoites (Fig. 298c). Like *Karyolysus*, *Hepatozoon* invades the erythrocytes and a change of host takes place between reptile and arthropod. Hoare (1933) found various stages of schizogony and sexual types in erythrocytes of *Crocodilus niloticus* Laur. the parasite being *Hepatozoon pettiti* Thiroux. Sporogony stages were also found in the peritoneal cavity of the tsetse fly *Glossina palpalis* Rob.-Desv. Actual stages of copulation could not be observed but the author succeeded in transmitting the disease experimentally from the fly to the crocodile.

The intestinal submucosa, the lung and the liver of *Gecko verticillatus* has been found infected with *Hepatozoon mesnili*. Oocysts and sporozoites were found in *Culex fatigans* Wied. Another invader of erythrocytes, *Hepatozoon mauretanicum*, was found in chelonians (*Testudo graeca* L.). *Hepatozoon mauretanicum* Sergent is thought to be transmitted by the acarid *Hyalomma aegyptium* (*syriacum*), a mite which is frequently found attached to tortoises imported as pets (Arthur, 1963). In the case of *Hepatozoon triatomae* Osimani which parasitizes the lizard *Tupinambis teguixin* L. infectious spores have been found in the peritoneal cavity of the bug *Triatoma rubrovaria* Pinto.

The genus *Haemogregarina*, the oocyst of which produces 8 sporozoites without producing spores first, has been found in snakes and tortoises. Leeches function as intermediate hosts. While they are sucking blood from the reptiles young sporozoites gain access to the circulatory system and invade erythrocytes (Fig. 298e). Gametes may be found in the red blood corpuscles of the leech (Fig. 298e–g). Conjugation of the macrogamete with one of the four available microgametes takes place in the intestinal epithelium; finally eight sporozoites develop from a synkarion and these gain access to the proboscis of the leech. *Haemogregarina stepanovi* Danilewsky from *Emys orbicularis* L. is transmitted by *Haementeria costata* (Müller). The lungs of the Indian tortoise *Geomyda trijuga* (Schweigg) are occasionally invaded by *Haemogregarina castellani* Wiley, the leech *Ozobranchus shipleyi* serving as intermediate host.

Hoare (1932) made extensive investigations of haemogregarines in snakes and tortoises of East Africa and established the following species:

Haemogregarina rubirizi Hoare, from *Mehelya capensis savergnani*;

H. musotae Hoare, from *Boaedon lineatus* Dum. and Bib. (Fig. 298e);

H. crotaphopeltis Hoare, from *Crotaphopeltis hotamboeia* Laur. (Fig. 298h);

H. enswerae Hoare, from *Naja melanoleuca* Schl. (Fig. 298f);

H. sternothaeri Hoare, from the tortoise *Pelusios sinuatus* Smith (Fig. 298g).

Figs. 298e–h, which are taken from C. A. Hoare's papers, reproduce some of the developmental stages of this parasite.

Sub-order Eimeriidea

Many members of this group are reptilian parasites. They are commonly found in the gut or the gall bladder, more rarely in the liver or the blood. There are usually no intermediate hosts, only *Schellackia* passes a part of its development in acarids. Systematically the group is distinguished by the fact that macro- and microgametes develop separately. Genera are distinguished by the number of the final sporozoites into *Eimeria*, *Globidium*, *Isospora*, *Cyclospora*, *Caryospora*, *Tyzzeria*, *Wenyonella* and *Schellackia*. While *Eimeria* develops four spores, each with two sporozoites, *Isospora* develops two spores with four sporozoites each; *Cyclospora* two spores, each with two sporozoites; *Caryospora* one spore containing eight sporozoites; and *Wenyonella* four spores with four sporozoites each. *Globidium* differs from *Eimeria* by causing the host cell to hypertrophy and by producing double-walled oocysts. *Tyzzeria* and *Caryospora* are similar in their morphology. For details the special literature, particularly Reichenow (1953), should be consulted.

Eimeriidea commonly found in reptiles are:

Eimeria railleti Léger in the intestine of the slow-worm (Lavier, 1938);

Eimeria geckonis Tanabe in the intestine of *Emys orbicularis* L.;

Eimeria mitraria Laveran and Mesnil in the intestine of the Asiatic turtle *Chinemys reevesii* Gray;

Eimeria tropidonoti Guyénot, Naville and Ponse from the intestine of *Natrix natrix* L. (Fig. 299a);

Eimeria legeri Simond from the gall bladder of the Indian *Lissemys punctata granosa* Schoepff.;

Eimeria agamae Laveran and Pettit in the bile of *Agama agama* L.;

Eimeria scinci Phisalix in the bile of *Scincus officinalis* L.;

Eimeria flaviviridis Setna and Bana in the bile of *Hemidactylus flaviviridis* Rüpp. (Fig. 299b);

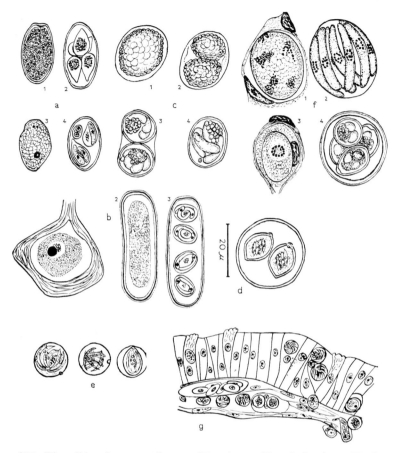

FIG. 299. Eimeriidea from reptiles. a, *Eimeria tropidonoti* Guyénot, Naville and Ponse. × 725. 1, oocyst; 2, sporoblasts; 3, macrogamete; 4, oocyst with spores. (After Guy. Nav. and Ponse.) b, *Eimeria flaviviridis* Setna and Bana. c, *Isospora dirumpens* Hoare. 1, oocyst; 2, oocyst with sporoblasts; 3, sporocysts; 4, mature sporocyst. (From Hoare.) d, *Isospora xantusiae* Amrein; e, *Caryospora simplex* Léger. × 600. (From Reichenow, 1953.) f, *Wenyonella africana* Hoare. 1, Schizone; 2, merozoites; 3, macrogametocyst; 4, oocyst with spores. × 1 200. (After Hoare.) g, *Schellackia bolivari* Reichenow. (From Reichenow, 1953.)

Eimeria cystis-felleae Debaisieux in the bile of *Natrix natrix* L.;
Eimeria zaenuis Phisalix in *Coluber constrictor* L. (Roudabush);
Eimeria amydae Roudabush in *Amyda spinifer* Le Sueur;
Eimeria clericksoni Roudabush in *Amyda spinifer* Le Sueur;
Eimeria hermoganti Simond in the spleen of *Gavialis gangeticus* Gmel.;

Globidium navillei Harant and Cazal. Subepithelial in the gut of
Natrix natrix L. and in *Natrix maura* L. (Harant and Cazal, 1954);
Isospora dirumpens Hoare in *Bitis arietans* (Fig. 299c);
Isospora fragilis Léger in the intestine of *Vipera aspis* L.;
Isospora knowlesi Ray and Das Gupta in *Hemidactylus flaviviridis*
  Rüpp.;
Isospora mesnili Sergent in the gut of *Chamaeleo vulgaris* L.;
Isospora natricis Yakimoff and Gousseff in the gut of *Natrix natrix* L.;
Isospora phisalix Yakimoff and Gouseff in the gut of *Elaphe quatuor-
  lineata* Lac.;
Isospora xantusiae Amrein in the intestinal epithelium of *Xantusia
  vigilis* Baird and *Xantusia henshawi* Stejneger (Fig. 299d);
Cyclospora viperae Phisalix intestinal in French vipers and adders;
Cyclospora sp. in *Hemidactylus frenatus* Dum. and Bibr.;
Caryospora brasiliensis Carini in *Cobra* species;
Caryospora jararacae in *Bothrops jararaca* Wied.;
Caryospora legeri Hoare in *Psammophis sibilans* L.;
Caryospora simplex Léger intestinal in *Vipera aspis* L. (Fig. 299e);
Tyzzeria natrix Matubayasi in the Japanese *Natrix tigrina*;
Wenyonella africana Hoare, intestinal in the African snake *Boaedon
  lineatus* Dum. and Bibr. (Hoare, 1933) (Fig. 299f).

The genus *Dorisiella* resembles *Isospora* in producing two sporocysts,
but while those of *Isospora* contain four sporozoites, those of *Dorisiella*
contain eight. Yakimoff and Gouseff (1953) found, however, a type of
Dorisiella hoari in an Italian species of *Elaps*, with four or six sporozoites.
The systematic position of the genus therefore remains doubtful.

Fig. 299g shows the invasion of the intestinal mucosa of *Psammodromus hispanicus* Fitzinger and the presence of several stages of the
eimerid *Schellackia bolivari* Reichenow. The parasite develops in the
mid-gut of lizards. The sporozoites invade lymphocytes or erythrocytes
and are eventually sucked up by the acarid *Neoliponyssus saurarum*
Oudemans, which merely acts as a transmitting vehicle for the parasite.
Lizards may also harbour a closely related eimerid, *Wenyonella minuta*
Franca.

Sub-order Haemosporidia

Analogous to the well-known malaria parasite of man there are blood
parasites in other mammalians, birds and reptiles. Most of the intermediate transmitting hosts are arthropods.

Haemoproteus tarentolae Riding occurs in the erythrocytes of geckos;
H. metchnikovi Simond in the tortoise *Chitra indica* Gray. Similar types
are listed by Reichenow (1953):

Haemoproteus simondi (Castellani and Viley from *Hemidactylus* spp.) (Fig. 300);

H. grahami Shortt from *Agama nupta* de Filippi;

H. gonzalesi Iturbe from *Anolis biporcatus* Gray;

H. mesnili Bouet from African snakes (Fig. 300).

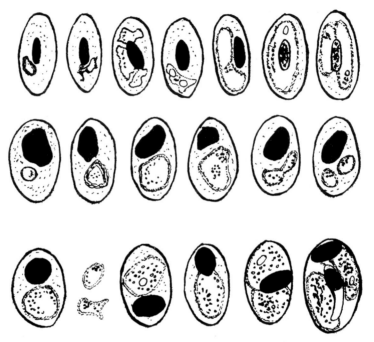

Fig. 300. Above: *Haemoproteus mesnili* Bouet. Approx. × 1 000. (After Macfie from Reichenow, 1953.) Middle and below: *Haemoproteus simondi* Castellani and Wiley. Approx. × 1 000. (From Dobell and Mühlens in Reichenow, 1953.)

Plasmodium (Family Plasmodiidae *Mesnil*) has so far only been seen in lizards. *Plasmodium minasense* Carini and Rudolph (Fig. 301, 1–6) from *Mabuia agilis* Radday, and *Goniocephalus borneensis* Schlegel (Laird, 1960) may serve as examples. *Plasmodium vastator* Laird has been seen in the flying lizard *Draco volans* Gray. The intermediate hosts of these parasites are as yet unknown.

Reichenow (1953) and Laird (1960) mention the further species of *Plasmodium* as occurring in reptilians:

Plasmodium agamae Wenyon in *Agama agama* L.;

P. diploglossi Arago and Neiva in *Diploglossus fasciatus* (Gray);

P. cnemidophori Carini in *Cnemidophorus lemniscatus* D.;

P. mabuiae Wenyon in *Mabuia quinquetaeniata* Sternfield;

P. maculilabre Schwetz in *Mabuia maculilabris* Gray;

P. pitmani Hoare in the same host and in *Mabuia striata* Peters;

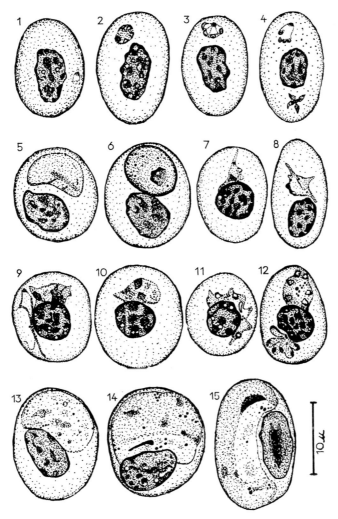

FIG. 301. 1–6. *Plasmodium minasense* Carini and Rudolph. × 1 900. (From Laird, 1960.) 7–15. *Plasmodium vastator* Laird. × 1 900. (From Laird, 1960.)

P. lacertiliae Thompson and Hart in *Leiolepisma fuscum* (D. & B.);

P. terrealbae Scorze and Dagert Boyer in *Anolis*;

P. pifanoi Scorze and Dagert Boyer in *Ameiva ameiva ameiva* L.;

P. lygosomae Laird in *Lygosoma moco* Gray;

P. tropiduri Aragao and Neiva in the Brazilian *Tropidurus torquatus*;

P. mexicanum Thompson and Huff in *Sceloporus ferrariperezi*;

P. rhadimurum Thompson and Huff, in *Iguana iguana* L. (Mexico);

P. floridense Thompson and Huff in *Sceloporus undulatus* Latr. (Florida).

Piroplasmida *Patton*

A brief mention should here be made of the *Piroplasmida*. The

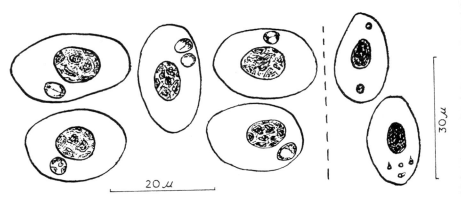

FIG. 302. Left: *Aegyptianella emydis*, a parasite of erythrocytes. (From Brumpt and Lavier.) Right: Another parasite of erythrocytes, *Nuttalia guglielmi* Carpano.

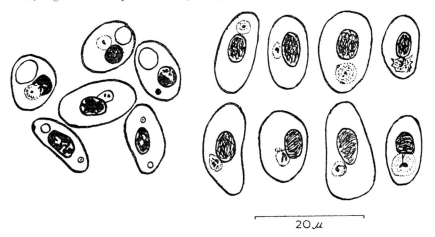

FIG. 303. Left: *Pirhemocyton tarentolae* Chatton and Blanc from *Tarentola mauretanica* L. (From Chatton and Blanc.) Right: *Pirhemocyton lacertae* Chatton and Blanc from *Lacerta viridis* L. (After Brumpt and Lavier.)

systematic position of the whole order or group is as yet uncertain. Carpano (1939) described *Nuttalia guglielmi*, a blood parasite of this group from the tortoise *Testudo marginata* (Fig. 302, right). *Sauroplasma thomasi* du Toit is reported as producing similar annular inclusions in the erythrocytes of the S. African *Cordylus giganteus* Smith. Brumpt and Lavier (1935) succeeded in experimental infections of *Lacerta viridis* L. with *Babesia pirhemocyton* Chatton and Blanc. They established *Pirhemocyton tarentolae* Chatton and Blanc from the gecko *Tarentola mauretanica* L. and the allied species *P. lacertae* Brumpt and Lavier (Fig. 303, right).

The same authors found piroplasmids in erythrocytes of *Clemmys caspica leprosa* Lov. and Williams. They called the parasite *Tunetella emydis* (Fig. 302, left). Carpano (1939) suggests the name of *Aegyptianella* for this genus, in which case the specific name should be changed to *Aegyptianella emydis*.

Sub-class Cnidosporidia

Few members of this sub-class, mostly Myxo- and Microsporidia, have been found in reptilians, among them the genera *Myxidium* and *Glugea*. Kudo (1919) found *Myxidium danilewskyi* Laveran in renal tubules of *Emys orbicularis* L., *Myxidium mackiei* Bosanquet in *Trionyx gangeticus* Cuv. and *Myxidium americanum* Kudo in *Trionyx spiniferus* Le Sueur.

The microsporidian *Glugea danilewskyi* Pfr. (Fig. 304) is described

FIG. 304. *Glugea danilewskyi* Guyénot and Naville (probably a *Plistophora*). Left: Sporoblast with maturing spores. × 2 350. Right: Mature spores. × 4 700. (From Guyénot and Naville.)

from frogs, *Emys orbicularis* L. and from *Natrix natrix* (Danilewsky, 1891). Guyénot and Naville reported on the appearance of *Glugea ghigii* in snakes. *Glugea* has also occasionally been seen in trematodes infesting reptilians where they may serve as intermediate or transmitting hosts.

Sub-class Sarcosporidia

Sarcosporidia, well known from the muscle-fibres of mammals and birds, appear occasionally in reptiles in the form of small grey tubes

14

containing spores. *Sarcocystis platydactyli* Bertram has been found in *Platydactylus mauretanicus*, *Sarcocystis gongyli* Trinci in *Chalcides ocellatus* Fors., *Sarcocystis lacertae* in *Lacerta muralis* L. and *Sarcocystis pythonis* Tiegs in *Python spilotes* (Tiegs, 1931).

Ciliata

The ciliates do not play a large part among the intestinal parasites of reptiles. Johnston and Amrein (1952) have drawn our attention to the genus *Nyctotherus*, a bean- or heart-shaped ciliate, uniformly covered with ciliary rows. It has a long, curved cytostom (Fig. 305). The species that may be encountered are in particular:

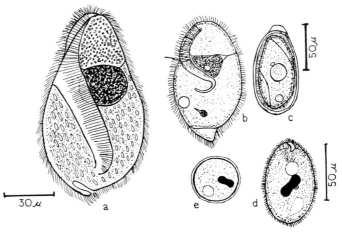

Fig. 305. Ciliates from reptiles. a, *Nyctotherus hardwickii* Ianakidevi; b, *Nyctotherus teleaceus* Geiman and Wichterman; c = b, encysted; d, *Balantidium testudinis* Chagas. e = d, encysted. (After Janakidevi. b–e, after Geiman and Wichterman.)

Nyctotherus haranti Grassé in *Tarentola mauretanica* L.;

N. beltrani Hegner in *Ctenosaurus acanthurus* Shaw;

N. kyphodes Geiman and Wichtermann from the tortoises *Testudo elephantopus hoodensis* van Denburgh and *Testudo vicina* Spix;

N. teleacus Geiman and Wichterman from the same host (Fig. 305b);

N. woodi Amrein from the Californian reptiles *Xanthusia vigilis* Baird, *Xanthusia henshawi* Stejneger, *Dipsosaurus dorsalis* B. and G. and *Sauromalus obesus*;

N. sokoloffi Schouten from *Amphisbaena albocingulata* Boettger;

N. trachysauri Johnston from *Trachysaurus rugosus* Gray;

N. hardwickii Janakidevi from *Uromastix hardwickii* Gray (Fig. 305c).

These ciliates usually populate the large intestine. They are not known to have any definite pathogenic effect and may be simple symbionts.

The same may be said of the closely related genus *Balantidium* which Geiman and Wichtermann (1937) found in the Galapagos tortoise *Testudo elephantopus hoodensis* van Denburgh (Fig. 305d). The authors described the species as *Balantidium testudinis* Chagas. Both this and the closely related species *Nyctotherus teleaceus* as well as *N. kyphodes* and *N. woodi* Amrein have a tendency to form cysts (Fig. 305c and e).

REFERENCES

Alexeieff, A. (1911). Notes sur les Flagellées. *Arch. Zool. exp.* gen. ser. 5, **6**, 491–527.

Amrein, Y. U. (1952a). A new species of *Isopora*, *I. xantusiae* from S. Calif. lizards. *J. Parasit.* **38**, 147–150.

Amrein, Y. U. (1952b). A new species of *Nyctotherus*, *N. woodi* from S. Calif. lizards. *J. Parasit.* **38**, 266–270.

Arthur, D. R. (1963). "British Ticks." Butterworths, London.

Brumpt, E. and Lavier, G. (1935). Sur un Hématozoaire nouveau du Lézard vert, *Pirhemocyton lacertae* n. sp. *Ann. Parasit. hum. comp.* **13**, 537–543.

Brumpt, E. and Lavier, G. (1935b). Sur un Piroplasmide nouveau, parasite de Tortue *Tunetella emydis* n. g. n. sp. *Ann. Parasit. hum. comp.* **13**, 544–550.

Carini, A. (1943). Novas observacones en batraquios e ofidios, de zelleriellas hiperparasitadas por entamebas. *Arqu. Biol. S. Paulo* **27**, No. 255, 64–68.

Carpano, M. (1939). Sui piroplasmidi dei cheloni e sua una nuova specie rinvenuta nelle tartarhuge *Nuttallia guglielmi*. *Riv. parasit.* **3**, 267–276.

Danilewsky, B. (1891). Ueber die Myoparasiten der Amphibien und Reptilien. *Zbl. Bakt.* **9**, 9–10.

Das Gupta, B. M. (1935). The occurrence of a *Trepomonas* sp. in the caecum of turtles. *J. Parasit.* **21**, 125–126.

Das Gupta, B. M. (1936). *Trichomonas* from the gut contents of a coral snake. *Parasitology* **28**, 202–205.

Das Gupta, B. M. (1936). Observations on the flagellates of the genera *Trichomonas* and *Eutrichomastix*. *Parasitology* **28**, 195–201.

Geiman, Q. M. and Ratcliffe, H. L. (1936). Morphology and life cycle of an amoeba producing amoebiasis in reptiles. *Parasitology* **28**, 208–228.

Geiman, Q. M. and Wichterman, R. (1937). Intestinal protozoa from Galapagos tortoises with description of three new species. *J. Parasit.* **23**, 331–347.

Grassé, P. (1926). Contribution à l'étude des flagellées parasites. *Arch. Zool. exp.* **65**, 345–602.

Guyénot, E. and Naville, A. (1922). Recherches sur le parasitisme et l'évolution d'une microsporidie, *Glugea danilewskyi* Pfr. (?) parasite de la couleuvre. *Rev. suisse Zool.* **30**, 1–62.

Guyénot, E. and Naville, A. (1924). *Glugea encyclometrae* n. sp. et *G. ghigii* n.sp. parasites de platodes et leur développement dans l'hôte vertébré *Tropidonotus natrix* L. *Rev. suisse Zool.* **31**, 75–115.

Harant, H. and Cazal, P. (1934). Remarques sur le genre *Globidium: Globidium navillei* n. sp. parasite de la couleuvre. *Ann. Parasit. hum. comp.* **12**, 162–169.

Hegner, R. (1940). *Nyctotherus beltrani* n. sp., a ciliate from an iguana. *J. Parasit.* **26**, 315–317.

Hegner, R. and Hewitt, R. (1940). A new genus and new species of amoeba from Mexican lizards. *J. Parasit.* **26**, 319–321.

Heisch, R. B. (1958). On *Leishmania adleri* sp. nov. from lacertid lizards (*Latastia* sp.) in Kenya. *Ann. trop. Med.* **52**, 68–72.

Hewitt, R. (1940). *Haemoproteus metchnikovi* Simond, 1901 from the yellow-bellied terrapin *Pseudemys elegans*. *Ann. trop. Med.* **52**, 273–278.

Hill, W. C. O. (1953). An epizootic due to *Entamoeba invadens* at the Garden of the Zoological Society. *Proc. zool. Soc. Lond.* **123**, 731–737.

Hindle, E. (1930). Attempts to infect hamsters with various flagellates. *Trans. roy. Soc. trop. Med.* **24**, 97–104.

Hoare, C. A. (1931). Studies on *Trypanosoma grayi*. III. Life cycle in the tsetse fly and in the crocodile. *Parasitology* **23**, 449–484.

Hoare, C. A. (1932). On protozoal blood parasites, collected in Uganda, with an account of the life cycle of the crocodile haemogregarine. *Parasitology* **24**, 210–224.

Hoare, C. A. (1933). Studies on some ophidian and avian coccidia from Uganda with a revision of the classification of the *Eimeridae*. *Parasitology* **25**, 359–388.

Honigberg, B. M. (1955). Structure and morphogenesis of two new species of *Hexamastix* from Liberia. *J. Parasit.* **41**, 1–17.

Ippen, R. (1959). Die Amoebendysenterie der Reptilien. *Kleintierpraxis* **4**, 131–137.

Janakidevi, K. (1961a). A new species of *Chilomastix* Alexeieff 1912. (Protozoa. Retortomonadines Grassé 1952) from the Indian lizard. *Z. Parasitenk.* **20**, 563–567.

Janakidevi, K. (1961b). A new species of *Hexamastix* (Protozoa) parasitic in the spiny-tailed lizard *Uromastix hardwicki*. *Z. Parasitenk.* **21**, 151–154.

Janakidevi, K. (1961c). A new ciliate from the spiny-tailed lizard. *Z. Parasitenk.* **21**, 155–158.

Janakidevi, K. (1961d). A new species of *Proteromonas* from the spiny-tailed lizard. *Arch. Protistenk.* **105**, 450–454.

Janakidevi, K. (1961e). *Hexamastix dobelli* n. sp. a new Trichomonad, parasitic in the starred tortoise. *J. Protozool.* **8**, 294–296.

Janakidevi, K. (1961f). Description of a new protozoon, *Alexieffella cheloni* n. gen. n. sp. *Ann. Mag. Nat. Hist.* Ser. 13. **IV**, 192–202.

Janakidevi, K. (1961g). The morphology of *Monocercomonoides filamentum* n. sp., parasite of the Indian starred tortoise. *Arch. Protistenk.* **106**, 37–40.

Janakidevi, K. (1961h). *Tritrichomonas lissemyi* n. sp., a parasite protozoon from the turtle. *Ann. Mag. Nat. Hist.* Ser. 13. **IV**, 411–414.

Janakidevi, K. (1961i). On *Retortomonas cheloni* n. sp., a parasitic protozoon from the starred tortoise. *Parasitology* **52**, 165–168.

Johnston, T. H. (1932). The parasites of the "stumpy tail" lizard *Trachysaurus rugosus*. *Trans. Roy. Soc. Austr.* **56**, 62–70.

Knowles, R. G. and Gupta, B. M. D. (1930). On two intestinal protozoa of an Indian turtle. *Indian J. med. Res.* **18**, 97–104.

Kudo, R. (1919). "Studies on Myxosporidia." Illinois Biol. Monographs, Vol. 5, 3 and 4.

Laird, M. (1951). *Plasmodium lygosomae* n. sp., a parasite of a New Zealand skink, *Lygosoma moco* Gray. *J. Parasit.* **37**, 183–189.

Laird, M. (1960). Malayan Protozoa. 3. Saurian malaria parasites. *J. Protozool.* **7**, 245–250.

Lavier, G. (1927). *Protoopalina nyanza* n. sp., opaline parasite d'un reptile. *C.R. Soc. Biol., Paris* **97**, 1709–1710.

Lavier, G. (1938). Sur *Eimeria raillieti* Léger 1899, coccidie intestinale d'*Anguis fragilis. Ann. Parasit. hum. comp.* **16**, 215–219.

Lavier, G. (1942). Sur une localisation atypique du parasitisme dans le genre *Hexamita. C.R. Soc. Biol., Paris* **136**, 20–22.

Reichenow, E. (1953). "Lehrbuch der Protozoenkunde." (Doflein-Reichenow), 6th edn., Fischer, Jena.

Rodhain, J. and van Hoof, M. Th. (1935). Sur le rôle pathogène d'*Entamoeba invadens. C. R. Soc. Biol., Paris* **118**, 1646–1650.

Roudabush, R. L. (1937). Some Coccidia of reptiles found in N. America. *J. Parasit.* **23**, 345–359.

Saxe, L. H. and Schmidt, E. M. (1953). *Trimitus parvus* Grassé (protozoa, mastigophora) from a garter snake *Thamnophis radix. Proc. Iowa Acad. Sci.* **60**, 754–758.

Schöppler, H. (1917). Ueber eine pemphigusartige Erkrankung bei *Lacerta agilis*, durch Gregarinen hervorgerufen. *Zbl. Bakt.* I, **79**, 27–29.

Setna, S. B. and Bana, R. E. (1935). *Eimeria flaviviridis* n. sp. from the gallbladder of *Hemidactylus flaviviridis. J. roy. micr. Soc.* Ser. III, **55**, 256–260.

Shortt, H. E. and Swaminath, C. S. (1931). Life history and morphology of *Trypanosoma phlebotomi* (Mackie, 1914). *Indian J. med. Res.* **19**, 541–564.

Steck, F. (1962). Pathogenese und klinisches Bild der Amoebendysenterie der Reptilien. *Acta Trop.* **19**, 318–354.

Tiegs, O. W. (1931). Note on the occurrence of *Sarcocystis* in muscle of python. *Parasitology* **23**, 412–414.

Wood, W. F. (1953). Some observations on the intestinal protozoa of Californian lizards. *J. Parasit.* **21**, 165–174.

Yakimoff, W. L. and Gousseff, F. F. (1934). *Isospora phisalix* n. sp. eine neue Schlangencoccidie. *Arch. Protistenk.* **81**, 547–550.

Yakimoff, W. L. and Gousseff, F. F. (1935a). Une coccidie de serpent. *Ann. Parasit. hum. comp.* **13**, 28–31.

Yakimoff, W. L. and Gousseff, F. F. (1935b). On the coccidia of shrews, grass snakes and lizards. *J. Roy. micr. Soc.* Ser. III, **55**, 170–173.

C. TURBELLARIA

A few representatives of this group, the Temnocephala, may occasionally be found on turtles. The Sub-order varies from other turbellarians by the presence of peculiar tentacles and adhesive organs. They are harmless ectocommensals which feed on the remains of their host's diet. Some parasitic Temnocephala occur on crustaceans and snails in tropical climates. They were discovered in Chile in 1840 and were at first thought to be leeches (Hyman, 1951). Those which live on turtles pass their whole developmental cycle on the same host. A detailed account of these turbellarians was given by Baer (1931) and Bresslau and Reisinger (1926). Cordero (1946) described a most interesting case in which the Temnocephala were, in turn, parasitized by plerocercoids.

The particular species observed on turtles is *Temnocephalus brevicornis* Monticelli (Fig. 313. 3). It has been found in the arm-pit and on the tail of *Hydromedusa tectifera* Cope, *H. maximiliani* Mikan, *H. platanensis* Gray, *Platemys radiolata* Mikan and *Mesoclemmys gibba* Schweigg.

Merten (1922) suspected *Temnocephalus brasiliensis* to live on turtles. He described the morphology of this species and that of a variation, *Temnocephalus brevicornis* Monticelli which he calls *var. intermedia*. It seems possible that neither species is entirely specific with regard to their host. Boettger (1957) saw *T. brevicornis* not only on turtles but on freshwater crustaceans as well.

REFERENCES

Baer, J. G. (1931). Étude monographique du groupe des Temnocephales. *Bull. biol.* **65**, 1–57.
Boettger, C. R. (1957). Stammesgeschichte und Verbreitung der Turbellarien-gruppe *Temnocephalida. Abh. Braunschw. wiss. Ges.* **9**, 26–35.
Bresslau, E. and Reisinger, E. (1926). *Temnocephalida. In* "Handbuch der Zoologie" (Kükenthal, ed.), Vol. 2, 294–308.
Cordero, E. H. (1946). *Ophiotaenia cohospes* n. sp. de la tortuga fluvial *Hydromedusa tectifera* Cope, una larva plerocercoide en el parenquima de *Temnocephala brevicornis* Mont., y su probable metamorfosis. *Comm. zool. mus. hist. nat. Montevideo* **2**, Nr. 34, 1–12.
Hyman, L. H. (1951). "The Invertebrates", Vol. II. McGraw-Hill, New York.
Merten, H. (1922). Ergebnisse einer zoologischen Forschungsreise in Brasilien 1913–14 von E. Bresslau. Neue Beiträge zur Anatomie von Temnocephala. *Zool. Jahrb. Anat.* **43**, 539–556.

D. TREMATODA

Monogenea

The trematodes (flat-worms with suckers) are among the commonest of parasites. Many of them are found in reptilians, most of them belonging to the Class Digenea which need one or several intermediate hosts to complete their life cycle. A few, however, are found among the Monogenea which need no intermediate host and the Aspidobothria which have very large suckers, subdivided by septa. Other genera of Monogenea found in reptiles are those of *Polystoma* and *Polystomoidella*.

Rudolphi (1819) was the first to describe finding a monogenetic trematode in a reptile. He found the worm in the oral cavity of *Emys orbicularis* L. and called it *Polystoma ocellatum*. It is now known as *Polystomoides ocellatum* (Stunkard, 1924; Paul, 1938). The genus was established by Stunkard (1924). It represents only reptilian parasites, among them *Polystomoides multifalx* St. and *P. oris* Paul (1938) from

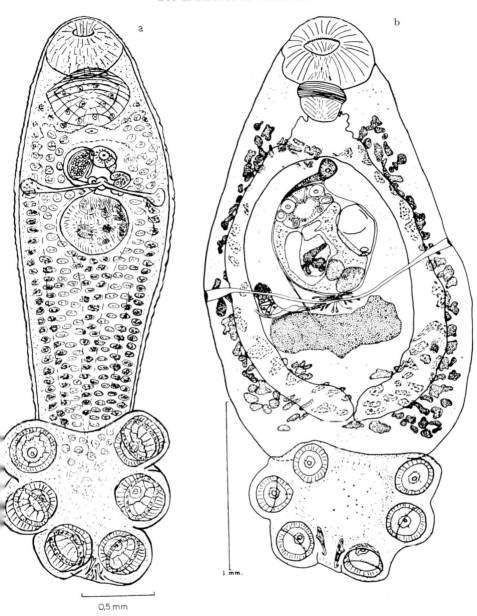

a

b

0,5 mm

1 mm.

FIG. 306. (a) *Polystomoides oris* Paul. (From Paul.); (b) *Polystomoidella oblonga* Wright. (From Oglesby.)

the mouth of *Chrysemys picta* Schn. (Fig. 306a). Paul recorded trematodes in eighteen out of fifty-seven turtles, some harbouring up to five worms. Oglesby (1961) published a detailed study on *Polystomoidella oblonga* Wright from the urinary bladder of *Sternotherus odoratus* Latreille (Fig. 306b).

The urinary bladder is the commonest habitat of monogenetic trematodes both in amphibians and reptiles. They are less frequently seen in the nasal or oral cavities, in the oesophagus or on the carapace. Only one species, *Neopolystoma orbiculare* has been found in the lungs.

Sproston (1949) gives the following key to the genus, limited to species found on reptiles:

(1) Adhesive organ without hooks   *Neopolystoma*
    Adhesive organ with one or two pairs of hooks   2
(2) One pair of hooks   *Polystomoidella*
    Two pairs of hooks   *Polystomoides*

The three genera differ from the main genus *Polystoma*, mainly found in amphibians, by a shorter uterus which contains only one egg and the presence of only one testis.

Sproston (1949) lists the following species as occurring on reptilians:

Neopolystoma domitilae Price in the urinary bladder of *Pseudemys ornata* Gray;

N. rugosum Price in the nostrils of *Trionyx ferox* Schn.;

N. orbiculare Price in the urinary bladder of *Pseudemys scripta elegans* Wied and related species like *Chrysemys picta* Schn., *C. picta marginata* Agassiz, *Chelodina longicollis* Shaw, *Malaclemmys centrata* Latr. and in the lungs and the gut of *Trionyx ferox*;

N. chelodinae Price in the urinary bladder of *Chelodina longicollis* Shaw;

N. exhamatum Price in the urinary bladder of *Clemmys japonica* Temm. and Schl.;

N. palpebrae Strelkow in *Trionyx sinensis* Wiegmann (Bychowsky, 1957);

N. terrapenis Price in the urinary bladder of *Terrapene carolina triunguis* Ag.;

Polystomoidella oblonga (Wright) Price in the urinary bladder and on the carapace of *Kinosternon scorpioides integrum* Le Conte, other species of *Kinosternon*, *Sternotherus carinatus* Gray, other species of *Sternotherus* and *Chelydra serpentina* L.;

P. hassalli Price (? = *oblonga*) in the urinary bladder of *Kinosternon* spp. and *Chelydra serpentina* L.;

P. whartoni Price in the urinary bladder of *Kinosternon* spp.;

Polystomoides ocellatus (Rud.) Ozaki, in the mouth, pharynx and nostrils of *Emys orbicularis* L., *Chelone mydas* L., and *Caretta caretta* L.;

P. coronatus Price in the mouth and the nostrils of various *Pseudemys*,
Chrysemys, *Graptemys*, *Malaclemmys* and *Trionyx* species as well as
in *Chelydra serpentina* L., and *Terrapene carolina triunguis* Agassiz.;

P. oris Paul in the mouth of *Chrysemys picta* Schn.;

P. japonicus Ozaki in the mouth and the pharynx of *Clemmys
japonica* Temm. and Schl.;

P. megaovum Ozaki in the urinary bladder of *Geoemyda spengleri*
Gmelin.;

P. kachugae Fukui and Ogata in the mouth of *Ocadia sinensis* Gray;

P. ocadiae Fukui and Ogata in the mouth of *Ocadia sinensis* Gray;

P. multifalx (Stunkard) Ozaki in the mouth and the pharynx of
Pseudemys scripta elegans Wied.;

P. digitatum MacCallum in *Trionyx s. spinifera* Le Sueur and *Trionyx
ferox* Schn. (perhaps synonymous with *P. coronatus*);

P. opacum Stunkard in *Trionyx ferox* Schn. and *Graptemys geographica* Le Sueur (probably synonymous with *P. coronatus*).

Aspidobothria

Family Aspidogastridae

Differing from all other trematodes the Aspidogastridae are equipped
with a very large ventral adhesive organ subdivided by septa into 27–
144 single suckers. The parasites penetrate deeply into the body of the
host. They have been seen in fish, molluscs, crustaceans and also in
chelonians. They have no typical metamorphosis and do not usually
change their host, but if their host is devoured by another animal they
may survive and appear in an accidental host.

Dollfus (1958) investigated the Aspidogastridae, supplying a key
and a morphological description of the family. Nothing is known so
far about a possible pathogenic effect of these worms on their hosts.
The author lists the following species as having been found in reptilians:

Lophotaspis interiora Ward and Hopkins in the gut of *Macrochelys
temmincki* Holbrook (= *Macroclemmys temmincki* Troost?);

L. orientalis Faust and Tang in stomach and gut of *Trionyx sinensis*
Wiegman, China;

L. vallei Stossich in the oesophagus and the stomach of *Caretta
caretta* L. Eastern mediterranean; east coast of tropical America;

Multicotyle purvisi Dawes from *Siebenrockiella crassicollis* Gray,
Malaya (adhesive organ with 144 suckers);

Lissemysia indica Simha in the gut of *Lissemys punctata* Gray, India;

Cotylaspis cokeri Barker and Pearsons in the gut of *Graptemys
pseudogeographica* Gray, N. America;

14*

C. lenoiri Poirier in the gut of *Cyclanorbis senegalenensis* Dum. and Bibr. Senegal, and *Trionyx triunguis* Forsk. Nile;

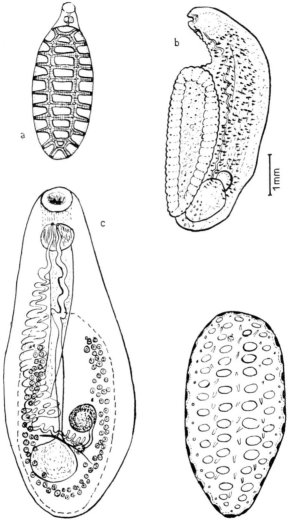

FIG. 307. a, *Cotylaspis cokeri* Barker and Pearsons; b, *Lophotaspis vallei* Stossich; c, *Lophotaspis orientalis* Faust and Tang. × 15. On the right an adhesive disk. (From Dollfus.)

C. sinensis Faust and Tang in the gut of *Trionyx sinensis* Wiegman, China;

C. stunkardi Rumbold in the gut of *Chelydra serpentina* L. N. America. Details of the parasites concerned are shown in the illustrations (Fig.

307). For the determination of species the original publication (Dollfus, 1958) should be consulted.

Digenetic Trematodes of the Intestinal Canal

About 200 different species of host-changing trematodes may be found, as mature worms in reptilians, mostly inhabiting the intestinal tract. The complete life cycle has only been worked out in a few species; the first intermediate host is, in most cases, a mollusc. The reptile usually becomes infected by feeding upon the second intermediate host. For the genus *Eustomos* mud snails (Lymnaeidae) serve as the first; dragonfly larvae as second intermediate hosts. In *Telorchis* the first host is again a snail of the genus *Physella*, while larval amphibians represent the second intermediate host.

Family Plagiorchidae

Many typical genera of this family, which makes up most of the digenetic trematodes occurring in reptilians, are found in this group:

Leptophallus. A genus particularly represented by L. *nigrovenosus* Bellingham frequently seen in the gut of snakes. First intermediate host lymnaeid snails, second host Amphibia (Fig. 308c);

Opisthioglyphe spp. parasitize snakes and chelonians. *O. ranae* Frölich (Fig. 309b) appears in snakes and amphibians. The snakes may become infected by feeding on the frogs;

Plagiorchis lives in chameleons, lizards and snakes. Example: *P. mentulatus* St. (Fig. 308a);

Astiotrema spp. which occur in snakes and chelonians, have been described by Mehra (1931b) (Fig. 308e);

Styphlodora. Dawes (1941b) found representatives of this genus in chelonians, snakes and varanids.

Rarer genera, occasionally seen in chelonians, are *Rhytidodes*; *Rhytodo-doides*; *Pachypsolus*; *Styphlotrema* and *Enodiotrema*. The original papers (Dawes, 1948; Yamaguti, 1958; Skrjabin, 1947) give details suitable for the determination of any of these species.

Renifer. Four species have been found in the gut of N. American snakes (Kagan, 1947). The Sub-family Reniferinae has been described by MacMullen and Talbot (1933);

Eustomos. *E. chelydrae* MacCallum (Fig. 310a) uses lymnaeid snails as first, dragonfly larvae as second intermediate host;

Zeugorchis spp. are frequently found in the stomach of snakes. Example: *Z. natricis* Holl and Allison (Fig. 310c);

Cercolecithos arrectus Molin parasitizes the gut of lizards;

Dasymetra spp., *Mediorina* spp. occur in snakes, *Tremiorchis* spp. in

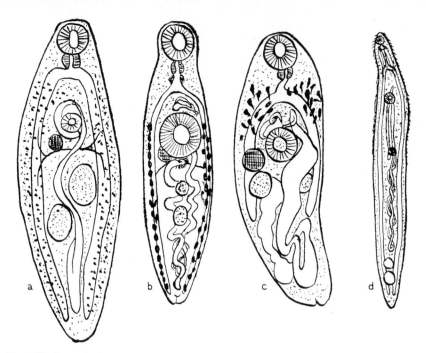

FIG. 308. Intestinal trematodes. I. a, *Plagiorchis mentulatus* Stossich; b, *Encyclometra caudata* Joyeux and Houdemer; c, *Leptophallus nigrovenosus* Bellingham; d, *Telorchis assula* Duj. (= *nematoides*) Mühling. (From Dawes.)

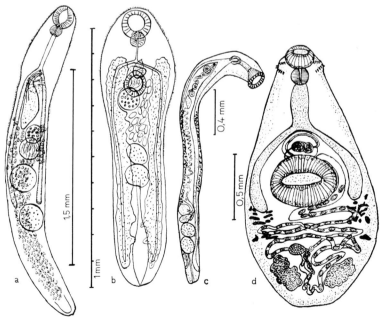

FIG. 309. Intestinal trematodes. II. a, *Astiotrema monticelli* Stossich. (After Dollfus.) b, *Opisthioglyphe ranae* Frölich (= *natricis* Dollfus); c, *Atrophocaecum indicum* Simha; d, *Singhiatrema singhia* Simha. (From Simha.)

Varanus; *Opisthogonimus interrogatus* Nicoll in snakes and *Micro-derma elinguis* Mehra in *Kachuga smithii* Gray.

Paralepoderma. The species *cloacicola* occurs in the common viper (*Vipera berus* L.). The first intermediate hosts are *Planorbis* snails. From them the parasite is transferred to frogs and toads but it can also accidentally appear in water beetles.

Spinometra. The genus was established by Mehra (1931a) for a parasite found on a turtle (*Spinometra kachugae* M.).

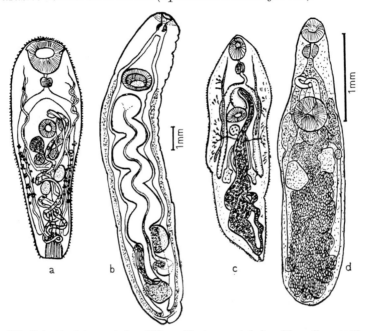

FIG. 310. Intestinal trematodes. III. a, *Eustomos chelydrae* Maccallum. × 32. (From Dawes.) b, *Odhneriotrema incommodum* Leidy. (From Dawes.) c, *Zeugorchis natricis* Holl and Allison. d, *Styphlodora compactum* Dawes. (From Dawes.)

Family Acanthostomatidae. Simha described *Atrophocaecum indicum* from Indian adders. Other Indian snakes were found infested by *Haplocaecum asymetricum* Simha (Fig. 309c). *Acanthostomum* occurs on crocodiles.

Family Allocreadidae. Only one species is known, *Crepidostomum cooperi* Hopkins from *Trionyx mutica* Webb.

Family Clinostomatidae. Several species of the genus *Odhneriotrema*; *O. microcephala* Travassos, and *O. incommodum* Leidy occur in crocodiles (Fig. 310b).

Family Cyathocotylidae. Simha describes *Gogata serpentum* v. *indicum* from the gut of several Indian snakes.

Family Dicrocoeliidae. *Brachycoelium salamandrae* Frölich, normally found in salamanders, occurs frequently in the slow-worm (*Anguis fragilis* L.). Simha described members of the genus *Paradistomoides* from lizards and chameleons.

Family Encyclometridae. *Encyclometra caudata* Joyeux and Baer, *E. natricis* Baylis and Cannon and *E. colubrimurorum* Rud. have been found in the gut of snakes, the latter species also in the oesophagus (Fig. 308b).

Family Echinostomidae. Species of *Singhiatrema* parasitize Indian snakes, *Paryphostomum* has been found in *Uromastix hardwicki* Gray.

Family Hemiuridae. Representatives of this family occur mainly in fish. The genera *Hemiurus* and *Lecithochirium* occur in chelonians, *Halipegus mehransis* Srivasta in the Indian snake *Ptyas mucosus* L.

Family Lecithodendriidae. Many species representing this family occur in lizards and chameleons, the latter may be parasitized by *Pleurogenoides gastroporus* Lühe and Travassos. Simha (1958) describes species of *Prosthodendrium* from Indian lizards as well as *Ganeo tigrinum* Mehra and Negi from Sinhalese chameleons. The genera *Orchidasma* and *Prosotocus* occur in lizards and chelonians; *Anchitrema sanguineum* Sansino and Looss also inhabits Sinhalese chameleons (Simha, 1958).

Family Microscaphidiidae. These are rarely seen parasites from marine turtles. Genera: *Polyangium, Octangium, Microscaphidium.*

Family Otobrephidae. These are parasites of Indian snakes.

Family Paramphistomidae. Chelonian parasites. Genera: *Parmaphistomum, Allostoma, Amphistoma, Stunkardia* (Bhalerao, 1931).

Family Pronocephalidae. Chelonian parasites. Genera: *Adenogaster, Pyelosomum, Diaschistorchis* (Rhode, 1962).

Family Proterodiplostomoidae. Simha (1958) found *Proalarioides tropidonotus* Vidyarthi in the gut of *Natrix piscator* Schn.

Family Telorchiidae. Odening (1960) reports *Telorchis assula* Duj. (= *T. ercolani* Mont.) as fairly common in *Natrix natrix* L. (Fig. 308d). Other representatives of this genus occur in snakes and chelonians. The life cycle of *Telorchis medius* Stunkard has been described. It begins with *Physella* snails. The infection is transmitted to a second host, an amphibian larva through which it reaches the final host, a snake or a turtle.

Digenetic Trematodes in the Gall Bladder, the Peritoneal Cavity, the Uterus and the Kidneys

Trematodes which have gained access to other organs of the host than the intestinal canal are a far greater menace to the health of the host than the former. Those found in the gall bladder are, in most cases, close relations of the intestinal species. Among the Plagiorchidae the genera *Allopharynx* and *Xenopharynx* are specialized in this direction (Simha, 1958) and inhabit the gall bladder of snakes. The same habitat is occupied by the Lecithodendriidae: *Mehraorchis chamaeleonis* Simha and *Paradistomum mutabile* Nicoll. In the gall bladder of lizards we find *Paradistomoides mutabile* Nicoll (Dicrocoeliidae).

The peritoneal cavity is not normally the seat of mature worms but is sometimes invaded by larval stages. The tortoise *Kachuga kachuga* Gray has been found peritoneally infected by *Isoparorchis hypselibagri* Billet (Family Sclerodistomatidae) (Simha, 1958).

Two plagiorchids, *Leptophyllum tamiamensis* McIntosh and *Zeugorchis aequatus* Stafford have been found in the uterus of snakes.

Even the kidney has, on occasion, been found invaded by mature worms. Snakes were found so infected by the plagiorchids *Paurophyllum simplexus* Byrd, Parker and Reiber and *P. megametricus* Byrd, Parker and Reiber (1940).

Digenetic Trematodes in the Lungs

The pulmonary parasites, very common in reptilians, deserve special attention. *Macrodera longicollis* Lühe, a common pulmonary parasite of snakes, may serve as an example (Fig. 311a). It is easily recognized by the club-shaped anterior end. In chelonians the commonest lung trematode is *Heronimus chelydrae* MacCallum, particularly found in *Chelydra serpentina* L. and *Chrysemys picta bellii* Gray (Fig. 311e). The first intermediate hosts are planorbid snails: *Gyraulus parvus* Say, physids (*Physa gyrini* Say), *Physa sayii* Tappan or *Valvata tricarinata* Say. Ulmer and Sommer (1957) succeeded in carrying out experimental infections. A sporocyst of this type of parasite is shown in Fig. 311f.

Several Plagiorchidae also occur in reptilian lungs. Apart from several species of *Styphlodora* we may find *Pneumatophilus variabilis* Leidy; *Caudorchis eurineus* Talbot as well as *Lechriorchis primus* Stafford; and *L. tygarti* Talbot. The latter four species live as mature worms in the lungs of several species of *Thamnophis* and *Natrix*. Talbot (1933) determined *Physella* as first, *Rana* tadpoles as second intermediate hosts.

Digenetic Trematodes of Liver and Circulatory System

Systematically there is close similarity between the hepatic and the circulatory trematodes. They are therefore treated together. The species coming under this heading all belong to the genus *Spirorchis*. Some types are highly specialized for a life in the circulatory system.

Simha (1958) found *Hepatohaematrema hepaticum* S. in the liver of *Kachuga kachuga* Gray. Martin and Bamberger (1952) gave a detailed description of trematodes found in reptilian blood vessels. They found *Haemoxenicon stunkardi* and *H. chelonenecon* in the veins of *Chelonia*

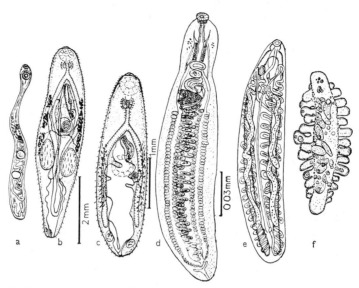

Fig. 311. Pulmonary and cardiac trematodes. a, *Macrodera longicollis* Lühe. (From Dawes.) b, *Lechriorchis primus* Stafford. (From Talbot.) c, *Caudorchis eurineus* Talbot. d, *Haemoxenicon chelonenecon* Martin and Bamberger. e, *Heronimus chelydrae* Mac-callum. × 4. (After Stunkard.) f, 24 days old sporocyst of the same species. (After Ulmer and Sommer.)

mydas L. and described the species in detail. The worms have a pre-dilection for the mesenteric veins which they sometimes block al-together. In the blood of marine turtles like *Chelone mydas* L. we may find *Learedius orientalis* Mehra, *L. learedi* Price and *L. similis* Price. *Amphiorchis amphiorchis* Price and *Monticellius indicus* Mehra also occur in marine turtles. Related species are: *Amphiorchis lateralis* Oguro from *Eretmochelys imbricata* L., the hawksbill turtle and *Carettacola bipora* Manter and Larson from *Caretta caretta* L., the loggerhead turtle. For a detailed description of these and the following trematodes the original papers must be consulted (see Yamaguti, 1958).

Both the circulatory and the cardiac trematodes have so far only been found in chelonians. Among them should be mentioned *Neospirorchis pricei* Manter and Larson from *Caretta caretta* L. and *Haplotrema synorchis* Luhmann as well as *H. constrictum* Leared from the same host.

Only one trematode, *Haplotrema polesianum* Ejsmont, has so far been found in the heart of the European turtle *Emys orbicularis* L.

Cercariae

Reptiles may occasionally carry encysted larval stages of digenetic trematodes, but they do not, in these cases, represent the natural second intermediate hosts; they only function as means of transport. Odening (1916) found large numbers of encapsulated cercariae of *Neodiplostomulum* sp. Nr. 2 Odening (? = *N. spathoides*) in the fatty tissue of a grass snake (*Natrix natrix* L.) and he compares these with similar types found in the Volga delta. The proper secondary intermediate hosts would in this case have been frogs, the final hosts birds of prey (Fig. 312).

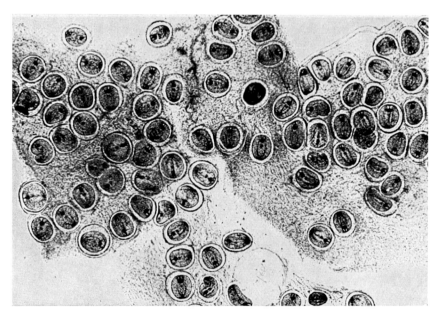

Fig. 312. *Neodiplostomulum* sp. No. 2 Odening (? = *spathioides* Dubois) from the fat body of a grass snake. Approx. × 25. (Photo.: Bockhardt. From Odening, 1961.)

The same author deals also with the appearance of the mesocercaria *Alaria alata* Göze in snakes. Here, too, the snakes serve only as secondary or transport intermediary hosts. The cercariae were found both in the grass snake (*Natrix natrix* L.) and the common viper (*Vipera berus* L.). The first intermediate hosts are, in this case, planorbid snails, the second ranid frogs and *Pelobates fuscus* Laur. The final host of *Alaria alata* is a carnivorous mammal. Small mammals may also on occasion function as secondary transport hosts for these cercariae.

REFERENCES

Bhalerao, G. D. (1931). Two new trematodes from reptiles: *Paryphostomum indicum* n. sp. and *Stunkardia dilymphosa* n. gen. n. sp. *Parasitology* **32**, 99–108.

Bychowsky, B. E. (1957). "Monogenetic Trematodes, their Systematics and Phylogeny." (W. J. Hargis, jr., ed.). Washington.

Byrd, E. E. (1936). A new trematode parasite from the mud turtle *Kinosternon subrubrum* Gray. *J. Parasit.* **22**, 413, 415.

Byrd, E. E., Parker, M. V. and Reiber, R. J. (1940). A new genus and two new species of digenetic trematodes with a discussion of the systematics of these and certain related forms. *J. Parasit.* **26**, 111–122.

Caballero, R. (1960). Estudio de trematodes digeneos de algunas tortugas comestibles de Mexico. Thesis Univ. Nac., Mexico.

Crandell, R. B. (1960). The life history and affinities of the turtle lung fluke *Heronimus chelydrae* MacCallum. *J. Parasit.* **46**, 289–307.

Dawes, B. (1941a). On *Multicotyle purvisi* n. g. n. sp., an Aspidogastrid trematode from the river turtle *Siebenrockiella crassicollis* in Malaya. *Parasitology* **33**, 300–305.

Dawes, B. (1941b). On *Styphlodora elegans* n. sp. and *Styphlodora compactum* n. sp. trematode parasites of *Python reticulatus* in Malaya, with a key to the species of the genus *Styphlodora* Looss 1889. *Parasitology* **33**, 445–458.

Dawes, B. (1956). "The Trematoda. With special reference to British and other European forms." Cambridge University Press.

Dollfus, R. P. (1958). Cours d'Helminthologie (1). I. Trematodes. Sousclasse *Aspidogastraea*. *Ann. Parasit. hum. comp.* **33**, 305–395.

Holl, F. J. and Allison, L. N. (1933). *Zeugorchis natricis* n. sp., a trematode from the water snake. *J. Parasit.* **21**, 274–276.

Kagan, F. G. (1947). A new species of *Renifer* (Trematoda) from the King Snake *Lampropeltis getulus*, with an emendation of the genus *Renifer* Pratt 1903. *J. Parasit.* **33**, 427–432.

Luhmann, M. (1933). Two new trematodes from the loggerhead turtle (*Caretta caretta*). *J. Parasit.* **21**, 274–276.

Martin, W. E. and Bamberger, J. W. (1952). New blood flukes (*Trematoda: Spirorchidae*) from the marine turtle *Chelonia mydas* L. *J. Parasit.* **38**, 105–110.

McIntosh, A. (1933). *Odhneriotrema incommodum* Leidy 1856, a trematode from the mouth of *Alligator mississippiensis* Daud. *J. Parasit.* **21**, 53–55.

McMullen, D. B. (1932). The life cycle of the turtle trematode *Cercorchis medius*. *J. Parasit.* **20**, 248–250.

McMullen, D. B. (1933). The life cycle and a discussion of the systematics of the turtle trematode, *Eustomos chelydrae*. *J. Parasit.* **21**, 52–53.

Mehra, H. R. (1931a). A new genus (*Spinometra*) of the Family Lepodermatidae Odhner (Trematoda) from a tortoise, with a systematic discussion and classification of the Family. *Parasitology* **23**, 157–178.

Mehra, H. R. (1938b). On two new species of the genus *Astiotrema* Loss belonging to the family Lepodermatidae Odhner. *Parasitology* **23**, 179–190.

Mehra, H. R. (1931c). On a new Trematode, *Microderma elinguis* n. g., n. sp. *Parasitology* **23**, 191–195.

Odening, K. (1960a). Zur Kenntnis einiger Trematoden aus Schlangen. *Zool. Anz.* **165**, 337–348.

Odening, K. (1960b). Studien an Trematoden aus Schlangen, Vögeln und Säugetieren. *Monat. dtsch. Akad. Wiss. Bln.* **2**, 438–445.

Odening, K. (1961a). Weitere Mittelungen über Trematodenlarven vom Typ *Neodiplostomulum* aus einheimischen *Natrix natrix* L. sowie über erste Versuche zur Erforschung der Biologie dieser Larven. *Ibid.* **3**, 59–69.

Odening, K. (1961b). Zur Parasitenfauna europäischer Schlangen, unter besonderer Berücksichtigung ihrer Rolle im Zyklus des Erregers der Alariose. *Biol. Beitr.* **1**, 172–136.

Oglesby, L. C. (1961). Ovoviviparity in the monogenetic Trematode *Polystomoidella oblonga*. *J. Parasit.* **47**, 237–243.

Paul, A. A. (1938). Life history studies of N. American freshwater Polystomes. *J. Parasit.* **24**, 469–510.

Rhode, K. (1962). A new Trematode, *Diaschistorchis multitesticularis* sp. n. from a Malayan tortoise, *Hieremys annandalei* Boulenger. *J. Parasit.* **48**, 296–297.

Rudolphi, C. A. (1819). "Entozoorum Synopsis." Berlin.

Schewtschenko, N. N. and Barabaschowa, V. N. (1958). Helminth fauna of *Lacerta agilis* and *Vipera berus* L. in the Charkow area. *Izd. Akad. Nauk. SSSR.*, Festschr. Skrjabin 389–394.

Siddiqui, W. A. (1958). On a new Trematode, *Astiotrema geomydia* (Fam. Plagiorchidae) from an Indian tortoise. *Z. Parasitenk.* **18**, 219–222.

Simha, S. S. (1958). Studies on the Trematode parasites of reptiles found in Hyderabad State, *Z. Parasitenk.* **18**, 161–218.

Simha, S. S. (1960). Observations on *Anchitrema sanguineum* Sansino 1894, Looss 1988. *J. biol. Sci.* **3**, 46–47.

Skrjabin, K. J. (1947). "Trematody shiwotnych i tscheloweka." Moscow.

Sproston, N. G. (1949). A synopsis of the Monogenetic Trematodes. *Trans. zool. Soc. Lond.* **25**, 185–600.

Stunkard, H. W. (1924). On some trematodes from Florida turtles. *Trans. Amer. micr. Soc.* **43**, 97–110.

Talbot, S. B. (1933). Life history studies on trematodes of the Sub-family Reniferinae. *Parasitology* **25**, 518–545.

Thapar, G. S. (1933). On a new Trematode of the genus *Astiotrema*, Looss 1900, from the intestine of a tortoise. *Chitra indica*. *J. Helminth.* **11**, 87–94.

Waitz, J. A. (1961). Parasites of Idaho reptiles. *J. Parasit.* **47**, 51.

Yamaguti, S. (1958). "Systema Helminthum", Vol. I. Interscience, London, New York.

E. TAPEWORMS (CESTOIDEA)

Sub-class Cestodes

Both the larvae and the mature stages of these worms may be encountered in reptilians, either in the intestine or in the peritoneal cavity. The reptiles become infected by feeding on other animals parasitized by larval cestodes. If the infestation is heavy, the reptiles may become weakened. Particularly large tapeworms may also be pathogenic simply because of their size.

The following cestodes have recently been described from reptiles from the Rhodesias (Mettrick, 1963):

Ophiotaenia ophiodes: From *Causus rhombeatus.*
Ophiotaenia punica: From *Causus rhombeatus.*
Ophiotaenia theileri: From *Causus rhombeatus.*
Ophiotaenia nigricollis sp. n.: From *Naja nigricollis crawshayi* Gthr.
Diphyllobothriidae:
Bothridium pithonis: From *Python sebae* var. *minus.*
Duthiersia fimbriata: From *Varanus niloticus.*
Anoplocephalidae:
Megacapsula leiperi: From *Pachydactylus bibroni.*
the latter is probably identical with *Oochoristica agamae* Baylis 1919.

Order Proteocephaloidea

Members of the genera *Acanthotaenia* and *Ophiotaenia* are commonly seen in the reptilian gut. The former genus is mostly found in lizards, the latter in snakes and chelonians.

Acanthotaenia, a genus with at least twelve species, is distinguished by the presence of fine spines on the scolex. These spines are missing in the allied genus *Ophiotaenia* (fifty species) (Figs. 313, 316a). Many of the species described are of uncertain validity and frequent synonymity cannot be excluded. Among the more commonly seen species are *Ophiotaenia perspicua* La Rue, *O. zschokkei* Rudin and *O. agkistrodontis* Harwood, Less frequently seen are *Crepidobothrium gerrardii* Baird which occurs in snakes and the doubtful species *Palaia varani* Shipley from *Varanus indicus* Daud.

The first intermediate host of all these Proteocephaloidea is a copepode which takes up cestode eggs with its food. The larva develops in the crustacean and changes into the procercoid. Although neither snakes nor lizards feed on copepodes the procercoid somehow gains access to these reptiles, perhaps by way of making use of other intermediate hosts like amphibian larvae or fish. *Ophiotaenia perspicua* La Rue is one of the few species where the life cycle has been experimentally determined.

Order Trypanorhyncha

Most of the members of this Order parasitize marine selachians (sharks and rays). It is therefore remarkable that they also occur in reptiles. The Trypanorhyncha are recognized by their long cephalic tentacles which are armed with hooks (Fig. 314).

Otobothrium cysticum Mayer has been found in the gut of the marine turtle *Chelonia mydas* L. The larva of the worm lives in marine fish which serve as food to the turtle which also serves as host to another cestode, *Tentacularia coryphaenae* Bosc. Larvae of this species have been discovered in fish of the genus *Coryphaena*.

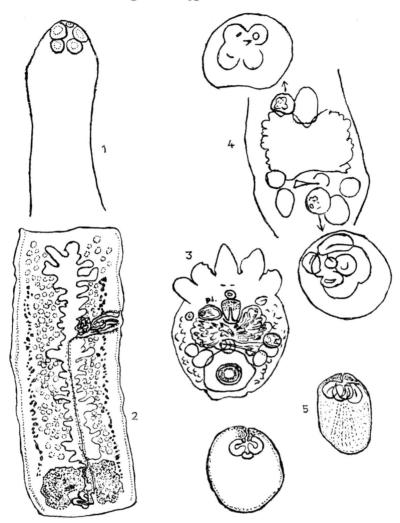

FIG. 313. 1 and 2. *Ophiotaenia cohospes* Cordero (1946). 3 and 4. *Temnocephala brevicornis* Monticelli. 5. Larval stages. (From Cordero, 1946.)

We may further note the appearance of Trypanorhyncha in marine snakes, even in crocodiles, and, in one case, in the peritoneal cavity of the horned viper *Aspis cerastes* L. whose habitat, the Sahara, is far distant from the sea (Dollfus, 1957) (Fig. 314).

Order Cyclophyllidea

Apart from the genus *Ophiotaenia*, reptilian cestodes are represented by another group, the *Oochoristica*. Wardle and McLeod (1952) dis-

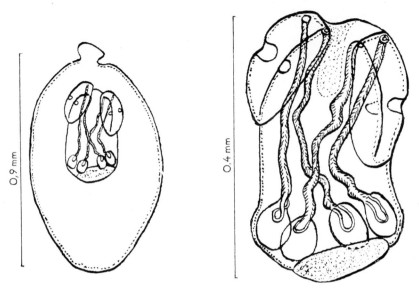

Fig. 314. Plerocercoid of *Otobothrium* (?). (After Dollfus.)

tinguish twenty-two species in lizards, snakes and chelonians. Commonly seen are, for instance, *Oochoristica bivitellolobata* Loewen (Fig. 316b), *O. parvovaria* Steelman (Fig. 316c), *O. americana* Harwood, *O. anniellae* Stunkard and Lynch and *O. whitentoni* Steelman (Fig. 316d). All these are worms of moderate length, their proglottids are longer than wide. Their life cycle is fairly well known. Ticks function as first intermediate hosts harbouring the tapeworm larva, the cysticercus.

The only species of the related genus *Nematotaenia*, so commonly seen in amphibians, which occurs in reptiles is *Nematotaenia tarentolae* Lopez-Neyra found in geckos (Fig. 315).

Ophiovalipora houdemeri Hsü occurs in *Elaphe carinata*. The intermediate host is thought to be an insect. The life cycle of *Pancerina varani* Stossich is as yet unknown.

Cestodes of the related genus *Joyeuxella* pass their larval stage in lizards. A coprophagous insect, probably a fly, serves as intermediate host. The final hosts are mammals which become infected by feeding on reptiles. *Joyeuxella pasqualii* Diamare is a tapeworm of dog, wolf or cat, *J. echinorhynchoides* Sonsino matures in the fox or the dog.

Order Pseudophyllida

Only a few members of this Order mature in reptiles, where their larvae are, however, frequently seen.

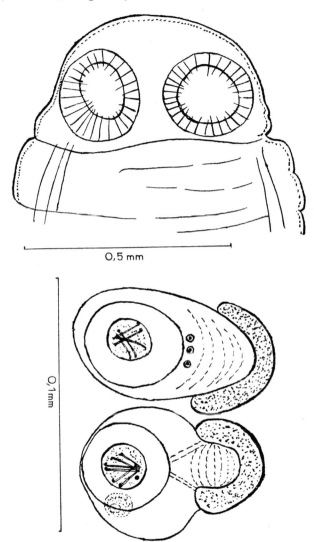

FIG. 315. Above: *Oochoristica rostellata* Zschokke var. *agamicola* Dollfus. Below: *Nematotaenia tarentolae* Lopez-Neyra. Two egg capsules with parauterine organs. (From Dollfus.)

The mature worm of *Spirometra serpentis* Yamaguti may be found in *Naja naja atra* Cantor. *Python molurus* L. may be infested by

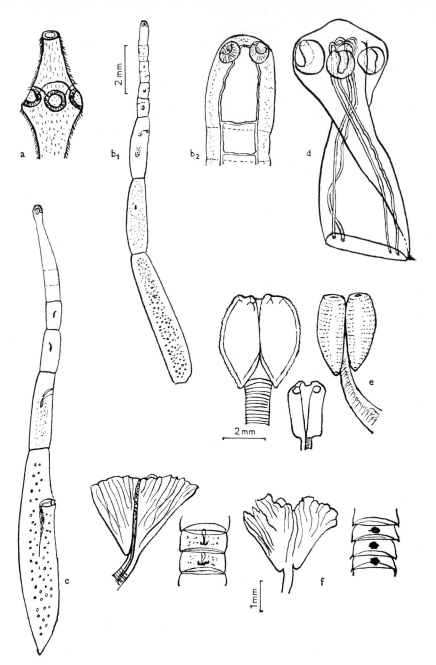

FIG. 316. Cestodes from reptiles. (From Wardle and MacLeod.) a, *Acanthotaenia shipleyi* Linstow. Scolex. (After Southwell.) b, *Oochoristica bivitellolobata* Loewen. c, *Oochoristica parvovaria* Steelman. d, *Oochoristica whitentoni* Steelman. e, *Bothridium pithonis* Blainville. (From Southwell and Joyeux, Du Noyer and Baer, 1931.) f, *Duthiersia expansa* Perrier. (From Woodland.)

Bothridium pithonis Blainville and *Varanus* species by *Duthiersia expansa* Perrier and *D. fimbriata* Diesing. A more rarely seen species is *Ancistrocephalus imbricatus* Diesing, a triaenophorid which occurs in the marine turtle *Thalassochelys caretta* L. These worms, too, are of medium size with oblong proglottids (*Spirometra*) or with a club-shaped (*Bothridium*) or lobed scolex (Fig. 316e, f). Small crustaceans like *Cyclops* are the first intermediate hosts. They pick up the cestode eggs from the bottom and then act as hosts to the larval procercoids. It is as yet not known whether direct transmission takes place from the copepode to the reptile or whether a second intermediate host is required.

Numerous Pseudophyllidea have been reported from reptiles. Larval stages of *Spirometra erinacei* Faust, Campbell and Kellogg have been seen in snakes and lizards. The first intermediate host is again a *Cyclops*, final hosts are E. Asian dogs and foxes. Other sparganids may occur in frogs and may be transferred to humans when these frogs are used to cure eye diseases, a method said to have been popular in E. Asia. Similar sparganids, whose final hosts are carnivorous cats, have been found in crocodiles. The larva of *Diphyllobothrium reptans* Diesing, which occurs in snakes, has been described as "*Spirometra reptans* Meggit". The final hosts are dogs. Schreitmüller and Lederer (1930) found in snakes another sparganid, *Plerocercoides panceri* Polonio (= *Ligula panceri* Polonio). The mature worm is again found in carnivorous cats. Differentiation between these species is difficult and the systematics of the group consequently as yet unsatisfactory.

REFERENCES

Beddard, P. E. (1913). On some species of *Ichthyotaenia* and *Ophiotaenia* from Ophidia. *Proc. zool. Soc. Lond.* **1913**, 153–168.

Cordero, E. H. (1946). *Ophiotaenia cohospes* n. sp. de la tortuga fluvial *Hydromedusa tectifera* Cope, una larva plerocercoide en el perenquina de *Temnocephala brevicornis* Mont., y su probable metamorfosis. *Comm. Zool. Mus. Hist. Nat. Montevideo* II, **34**, 1–12.

Dollfus, R. P. (1957). Présence accidentelle d'une larve de Cestode tetrarhynque chez un Ophidien terrestre d'Algérie. *Ann. Inst. Pasteur, Algérie* **35**, 70–72.

Harwood, P. D. (1933). The helminths parasitic in a water moccasin (snake) with a discussion of the character of the Proteocephalidae. *Parasitology* **25**, 130–142.

Hyman, L. H. (1951). "The Invertebrates", Vol. II. McGraw-Hill, New York.

Meggitt, F. J. (1933). On some tape worms from the bull snake (*Pituophis sayi*) with remarks on the species of the genus *Oochoristica* (*Cestoda*). *J. Parasit.* **20**, 181–189.

Mettrick, D. F. (1963). Some cestodes of reptiles and amphibians from the Rhodesias. *Proc. zool. Soc. Lond.* **141**, 239–250.

Mueller, J. P. (1951). Spargana from the Florida alligator. *J. Parasit.* **37**, 317–318.

Schreitmüller, W. and Lederer, G. (1930). "Krankheitserscheinungen an Fischen Reptilien und Lurchen." Wenzel, Berlin.

Southwell, T. (1928). Cestodes of the Order *Pseudophyllidea* recorded from India and Ceylon. *Amer. J. trop. Med.* **22**, 419–448.

Waitz, J. A. (1961). Parasites of Idaho reptiles. *J. Parasit.* **47**, 51.

Wardle, R. A. and McLeod, J. A. (1952). "The Zoology of Tape Worms." University of Minnesota Press, Minneapolis, U.S.A.

F. Acanthocephala

The Reptilia serve mainly as temporary or occasional hosts to these worms whose proboscis is armed with rows of barbed hooks. Of mature worms only one genus, *Neoechinorhynchus*, is sometimes seen in chelonians. Following upon the original description of one species of this genus (*N. emydis* Leidy) by Lincicome (1948), Cable and Hopp (1954) suggested that this description had probably been based on more than one species. The chelonian Acanthocephala are, in their view, very species-specific. They determined the further species *Neoechinorhynchus pseudemydis* and *N. chrysemydis*. There are further *N. emyditoides* Fisher and *N. stunkardi* Cable and Fisher (1961), the latter from *Graptemys pseudogeographica* Gray. Snails serve as primary intermediate hosts to all these species. The related species *N. rutili* Müller, a widely distributed parasite of fish, may occasionally be found in the stomach of turtles (Sprehn, 1959) (Fig. 317). The intermediate hosts are in this case *Sialis* larvae and Ostracodes (Finland).

Acanthocephalus anthuris Duj. (Fig. 318), commonly seen in amphibians, may also attack chelonians.

Acanthocephalus ranae Schrank, so commonly seen in frogs and toads, may be transferred to grass snakes (*Natrix natrix* L.) which infect themselves by feeding on the frogs. It is unlikely that they should feed on the intermediate hosts *Asellus aquaticus* L.

Snakes may serve as temporary hosts to species of the genera *Oligacanthorhynchus* and *Centrorhynchus*. The final hosts are in the main birds.

Frogs, lizards and adders function as intermediate hosts to *Centrorhynchus aluconis* Müller whose final hosts are ducks. *C. areolatus* Rud. and *C. lancea* Westrumb occur temporarily in *Coluber viridiaeneus;* the final hosts are birds of prey, intermediate hosts terrestrial insect larvae. Early stages of *C. lesiniformis* Molin and *C. leptorhynchus* Meyer have been found in *Natrix natrix* L. The first intermediate hosts of *C. cinctus* Rud. are terrestrial insects; further hosts amphibians and snakes, and final hosts birds of prey.

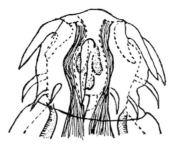

FIG. 317. *Neoechinorhynchus rutili* Müller. An occasional parasite in the stomach of *Emys orbicularis* L. Anterior extremity. (From Sprehn.)

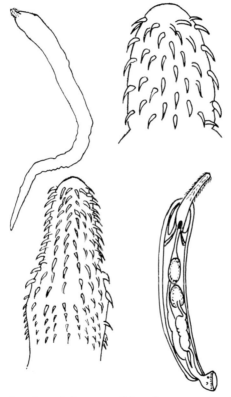

FIG. 318. Above: *Acanthocephalus ranae* Schrank, an occasional parasite of the grass snake. Left, the whole worm. ×4. Right, Anterior extremity. ×72. Below: *Acanthocephalus anthuris* Duj. ×72 and ×16. (From Lühe.)

The encysted juvenile forms of *C. buteonis* Schrank, a parasite of owls, have been found in lizards and snakes. These may also harbour *C. picae* Rud.

Rarer Acanthocephalus species, mentioned by Petrotschenko (1956/8) are: *Polyacanthorhynchus macrorhynchus* Baylis, a parasite of crocodiles, birds and fish and *Sphaerechinorhynchus rotundocapitatus* Johnston, which occurs in the Australian *Pseudechis porphyriacus* Shaw.

It seems, on the whole, as if reptilians infect themselves with Acanthocephala less through feeding on the first, but far more through ingesting second intermediary hosts, in particular Amphibia.

REFERENCES

Andruschko, A. M. and Markow, G. S. (1958). The helminth fauna of reptiles in the Kysil-Kum desert. *Isdt. Akad. Nauk. SSSR*. Festschr. Skrjabin, 32–37.

Cable, R. M. and Hopp, W. B. (1954). Acanthocephalan parasites of the genus *Neoechinorhynchus* in N. American turtles, with the description of two new species. *J. Parasit.* **40**, 674–680.

Cable, R. M. and Fisher, F. M. (1961). A fifth species of *Neoechinorhynchus* (Acanthocephala) in turtles. *J. Parasit.* **47**, 666–668.

Fisher, F. M. jr. (1960). On Acanthocephala of turtles, with the description of *Neoechinorhynchus emyditoides* n. sp. *J. Parasit.* **46**, 257–266.

Lincicome, D. R. (1948). Observations on *Neoechinorhynchus emydis* Leidy an acanthocephalan parasite of turtles. *J. Parasit.* **24**, 51–54.

Meyer, A. (1933). Acanthocephala. *In* Brohmer "Die Tierwelt Mitteleuropas" (Ehrmann and Ulmer, eds.). Quelle and Meyer, Leipzig.

Petrotschenko, V. J. (1956/8). "Akantocefaly domashnich i dikich shivotnych." (In Russian.) Moscow.

Sprehn, C. (1959). Acanthocephala. *In* "Die Tierwelt Mitteleuropas." (Supplement to Brohmer *et al.*). Quelle and Meyer, Leipzig.

G. NEMATODA

Nematodes are commonly seen in reptiles. They occur in the most varied organs, particularly in the intestine and the lungs. Their presence is the more serious to the host the more numerous the worms are, and this is particularly true in respect of the filaria inhabiting the bloodstream, where they can cause thrombosis and oedema. Single nematodes are rarely harmful, but may be dangerous to juvenile animals.

There is hardly a "pet" more widely distributed and more misunderstood than *Testudo graeca* L. the "European" or "Greek" tortoise which, in most cases, does not come from either Europe or Greece but from N. Africa. Those who keep these unfortunate reptiles in countries mostly much too cold for their comfort are sometimes alarmed to see that their pets are infested by intestinal worms. They may well be alarmed, for according to a recent investigation carried out by Shad (1963) Greek tortoises kept in his laboratory were found infected by eight different species of oxyurid worms. The account he gives of these worms is worth quoting. In ten female tortoises (weight and age are not given) he found the following species of *Tachygonetria:*

Species	No. of worms in 10 ♀ tortoises	Numbers of tortoises affected
1. *T. dentata*	7 138	10
2. *T. macrolaimus*	3 480	10
3. *T. conica*	1 942	10
4. *T. microstoma*	718	10
5. *T. robusta*	300	10
6. *T. stylosa*	723	7
7. *T. uncinata*	457	9
8. *T. numidica*	196	6

In other words, nearly half the tortoises were hosts to six different oxyurid species. They were all found in the colon from the ileo-colic juncture on down to the cloaca, but the distribution of the various species within the colon varied greatly. The author ascribes this "Niche diversification" to food or environmental preferences among the worms.

The following catalogue of nematodes parasitizing Reptilia is mainly based on the systematic papers of Yorke and Maplestone (1926), Chitwood and Chitwood (1950) and Skrjabin (1960).

Nematodes of the Intestinal Canal

Almost 500 different species of nematodes have been described from reptiles. Most of them inhabit the small intestine, some the colon and a few the stomach and the oesophagus.

(a) Ascaroidea

Ascarids are, as elsewhere, common intestinal parasites of reptiles, but we have no accounts so far of migrations within the host analogous to these occurring in mammals. Ash and Beaver (1962) investigated the occurrence of the ascarid *Ophidascaris labiatopapillosa* Walton and its life cycle. They discovered the larval stage of this parasite in the amphibium *Amphiuma tridactylum* Cuv. and in various frogs like *Rana pipiens* Gmel. and *Rana clamitans* Daud. The larvae were found either free or encysted in the liver or the mesenterium. The adult worm occurs in a variety of snakes of the genus *Natrix, Coluber, Lampropeltis* and *Heterodon.*

The following genera are more commonly encountered in reptiles:

Ascaris: One species only pathogenic for reptiles: *A. cephaloptera* Rud.

Hexametra: Ten intestinal parasites have been described from chameleons and from lizards (Fig. 319a).

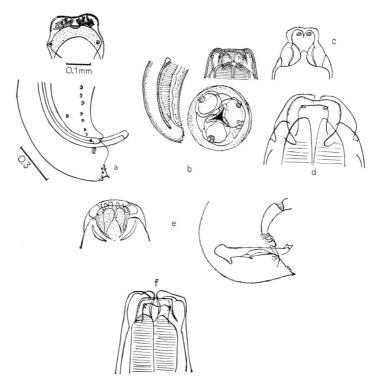

Fig. 319. Nematodes from the intestine of reptiles. *Ascaroidea, Anisakoidea.* a, *Hexametra sewelli* Baylis and Daubney. Anterior and posterior extremity. b, *Polydelphis dalmatina* Kreis. c, *Trispiculascaris trispiculascaris* Travassos, anterior extremity. (After Skrjabin from Yorke and Maplestone.) d, *Ophidascaris filaria* Baylis, anterior extremity. × 80. (From Yorke and Maplestone.) e, *Dujardinascaris helicina* Baylis. Anterior and posterior extremity. × 67. (After Baylis from Yorke and Maplestone.) f, *Angusticaecum holopterum* Baylis, anterior extremity. × 42. (From Yorke and Maplestone.)

Ophidascaris: More than twenty intestinal forms, mostly slender forms of medium size are known from snake and lizards. Genotype *O. filaria* Baylis (Fig. 319d).

The following species of *Ophidascaris* were listed by Baylis (1921):

Ophidascaris filaria Duj. 1845: From *Python molurus, Python reticulatus, Python sebae* and *Python spilotes*. It was also found in *Varanus* species in Zanzibar.

Ophidascaris radiosa Schneider 1866: From *Bitis gabonica*.

Ophidascaris obconica Baird 1860: From *Helicops angulatus* (Brazil).

Ophidascaris mombasica sp. nov.: From *Psammophis subtaeniatus* (Mombasa).

Ophidascaris gestri Parona 1890: From *Tropidonotus piscator* (*T. quincunciatus*).

Ophidascaris papillifera v. Linst: Undetermined snakes from the Bismarck archipelago.

Ophidascaris solitaria v. Linst.: From *Dipsadomorphus dendrophilus* (Siam).

Ophidascaris naiae Gedoelst 1916: From *Naja nigricollis* (Belgian Congo).

Ophidascaris intorta Gedoelst 1916: From *Bitis* spp. (Belgian Congo).

Polydelphis: Skrjabin described nine species, slender and of medium size, from snakes (Fig. 319b).

Baylis (loc. cit.) lists the following species of *Polydelphis*:

Polydelphis anoura Duj. 1845: From *Python molurus, Python sebae, Bitis arietans, Drymobius bifossatus* (= *Coluber lichtensteini*), *Coluber corais, Zamenis constrictor*.

Polydelphis attenuata Molin 1858: From *Python molurus, P. sebae, P. reticulatus, Bitis arietans*.

Polydelphis oculata v. Linst. 1899: From *Python reticulatus, P. sebae*.

Polydelphis quadricornis Wedl 1862: From *Naja haje, N. nigricollis, Bitis arietans, Pseudaspis cana, Crotalus* spp.

Polydelphis boddaerti Baird 1860: From *Drymobius boddaerti* (West Indies).

Polydelphis hexametra Gedoelst 1916: From *Chamaeleo dilepis* (Belgian Congo).

Polydelphis waterstoni sp. nov.: From *Zamenis gemonensis* var. *caspius* (Macedonia).

One of us (E. E.) recently found an undetermined species of *Polydelphis* in the sublingual pouch of a *Chamaeleo melleri* from Tanganyika.

Trispiculascaris: *Tr. trispiculascaris* Travassos inhabits the gut of crocodiles. It is the only species of the genus (Fig. 319c).

Other ascarid worms are listed by Baylis (loc. cit.) as occurring in crocodiles as follows:

Dujardinascaris helicina Baylis: From *Crocodilus niloticus* and other crocodile spp.

Typhlophorus lamellaris v. Linst.: From *Gavialis gangeticus*.

(b) Anisakoidea

The members of this family are intestinal parasites frequently transmitted by earthworms (*Porrocaecum*).

Dujardinascaris: At least eleven species from crocodiles (*D. helicina* Baylis, *D. longispicula* Baylis and others) (Fig. 319e).

Multicaecum: Five species from crocodiles.

Polycaecum: *P. gangeticum* Maplestone, a parasite of crocodiles.

Porrocaecum: One species, *P. sulcatum* Baylis in marine turtles.

Terranova crocodili Mosgowy: A parasite of crocodiles.

Angusticaecum: Parasites of crocodiles (*A. holopterum* Baylis) (Fig. 319f) has also been seen in various species of *Testudo* (Baylis, loc. cit.).

Metangusticaecum brasiliense Mosgowy: A parasite of crocodiles.

Amplicaecum: Six species at least have been described from snakes, chameleons, lizards. (*A. africanum* Taylor, *A. alatum* Baylis and others.)

Typhloporus lamellaris Linstow: A parasite of crocodiles.

(c) Trichostrongyloidea

These nematodes, usually large types occurring in mammals, can also infest reptiles. Their life cycles are as yet largely unknown but it can be assumed that, as a rule, the early development takes place in the soil and that the infective stage is that of the third larva.

Oswaldocruzia: Six species in lizards (*O. agamae* Sandground) and snakes (*O. denudata* Rud.)

Herpetostrongylus pythonis Baylis: An intestinal parasite of the python, *H. varani* Baylis.

(d) Trichocephaloidea

Some members of this Superfamily occur in reptiles. The exact mode of development is only known for *Theileriana variabilis* Chapin.

Sclerotrichum echinatum Rud.: A parasite of lizards.

Capillaria: A number of species living in lizards and snakes.

Eucoleus freitaslenti Skrjabin and Schichobalowa: From snakes.

Thominx serpentina Skrjabin and Schichobalowa: From *Chelydra serpentina*.

Theileriana variabilis Chapin: From *Testudo denticulata* L.

Sauricola: Two species in chelonians (Fig. 320).

(e) Oxyuroidea

This extremely numerous Superfamily provides about 150 reptilian parasites derived from various genera.

Oxyuris: None definitely described from reptiles. Forstner (1960), however, pictures *O. lata* as a chelonian parasite (Fig. 325, right).

Thelandros: After Skrjabin at least 12 reptilian species, small to medium in size, mostly slender (Fig. 323b).

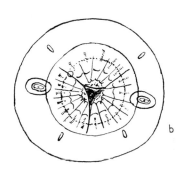

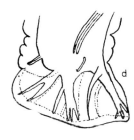

FIG. 320. Trichocephaloidea. *Sauricola sauricola* Chapin. a, anterior extremity. × 60; b, cross section through rostral region. × 240; c, ♀ posterior extremity. × 32; d, Bursa. × 60. (After Chapin from Yorke and Maplestone.)

Parapharyngodon: At least seventeen species living in the gut of lizards, snakes and chelonians (Fig. 321). As typical of the genus may be quoted *P. maplestoni* Chatterji from *Hemidactylus flaviviridis* Rüpp.

Thelastomoides: Three species from tortoises.

Ozolaimus: Two species from *Iguana tuberculata* Laur., *O. megatyphlon* Duj. (Fig. 322a), *O. cirratus* Linstow (Fig. 322b).

Macracis: Two species from lizards, *M. papillosa* Forstner from *Testudo graeca* L.

Travassozolaimus travassosi Vigueras: In chameleons.

Pharyngodon: Large genus. More than thirteen well-defined species occur in saurians. *P. spinicauda* in lizards. (Fig. 323a), *P. mammillatus* Linstow in *Eumeces* spp. (Fig. 321d).

15

Parathelandros: At least seven species from saurians, particularly geckos.

Spauligodon: At least ten species in saurians, particularly in geckos (Fig. 323c), distinguished by wing-like dilations of the posterior segments.

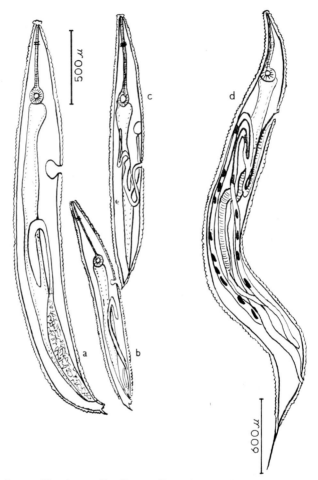

FIG. 321. Oxyuroidea in reptiles. I. a–c, *Parapharyngodon bulbosus* Freitas; a and b, ♂; c, ♀; d, *Pharyngodon mamillatus* Linstow ♀. (From Dollfus, after Skrjabin.)

Tachygonetria: At least twenty well-defined species from saurians and tortoises. *T. vivipara* Wedl (Fig. 323f), *T. dentata* Seurat (Fig. 325, middle), *T. longicollis* Seurat (Fig. 324 left), *T. robusta* Drasche (Fig. 325 left), *T. thapari* Dubiniana (Fig. 327). Most of

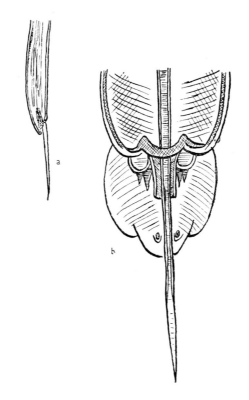

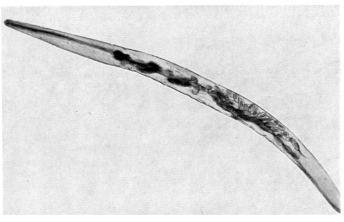

(c)

FIG. 322. Oxyuroidea in reptiles. II. a, *Ozolaimus megatyphlon* Rud.; b, *Ozolaimus cirratus* Linstow. (From Schneider and Linstow in Yorke and Maplestone.) c, *Macracis papillosa* Forstner ♀. × 15. (From Forstner.)

them slender, lancet-shaped medium-sized types without particular distinguishing marks.

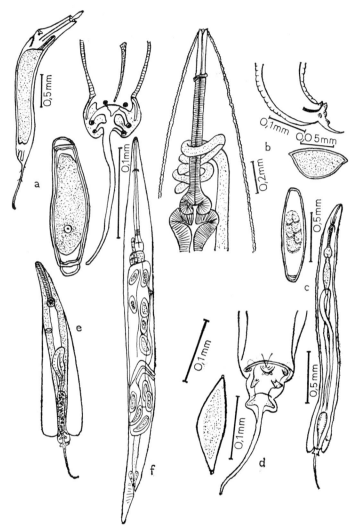

FIG. 323. Oxyuroidea in reptiles. III. a, *Pharyngodon spinicauda* Dies. ♀, egg and posterior extremity of ♂. (After Seurat.) b, *Thelandros hemidactylus* Pathwardhan, anterior extremity, ♂ posterior extremity and egg; c, *Parathelandros mabuyae* Sandground. Egg and ♂; d, *Spauligodon cubensis*. Read and Amrein. Egg and ♂ posterior extremity; e, *Spauligodon mearnsi* Edgerly ♂; f, *Tachygonetria* vivipa a Wedl. ♀. (After Seurat.)

Alaeuris: A few species from tortoises and iguanids (Fig. 326). The males are equipped with very long spiculae.

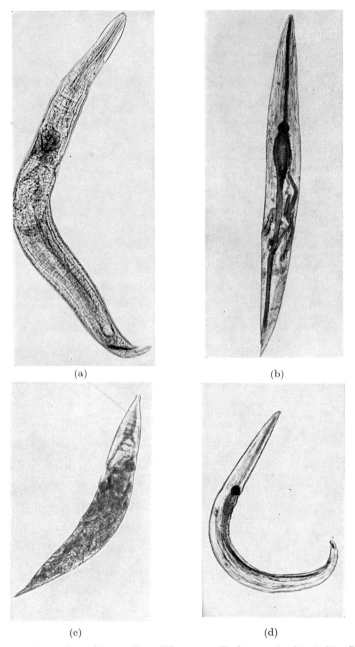

(a)

(b)

(c)

(d)

FIG. 324. Oxyuroidea in reptiles. IV. a, c, *Tachygonetria longicollis*. ♀ above, ♂ below. ×21. (After Forstner.) b, d, *Tachygonetria* sp. (= *testudinis* Forstner). ♀ above, ♂ below. (After Forstner.)

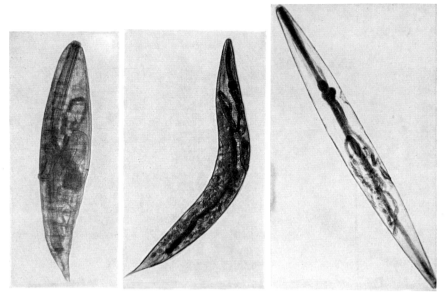

FIG. 325. Oxyuroidea in reptiles. V. Left, *Tachygonetria robusta* Drasche ♀.×21.
Middle, *Tachygonetria dentata* Seurat ♀.×21. (After Forstner.) Right, *Oxyuris* (?) *lata*
Forstner ♀.×15. (After Forstner.)

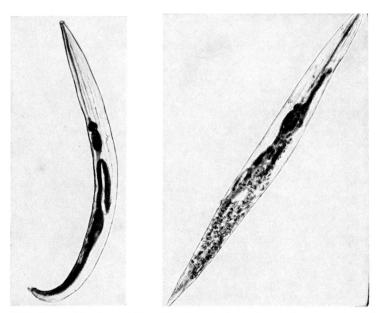

FIG. 326. Oxyuroidea in reptiles. VI. *Alaeuris forcipiformis* Forstner. Left, ♂.×21.
Right, ♀.×14. (From Forstner.)

Mehdiella: Parasites of tortoises (Fig. 328).

Paralaeuris dorochila Cuckler from the gut of *Conolophus subcristatus* Gray (Galapagos islands).

Pseudalaeuris: At least sixteen species from saurians and tortoises. *P. expansa* Walton from *Testudo horsfieldi* Gray. The males are recognized by the presence of numerous papilli at the anal extremity (Fig. 327).

Thaparia: A few species from tortoises.

Veversia: A few species from saurians.

Atractis: Parasites of tortoises (Fig. 329).

Labidurus: Parasites of tortoises (Fig. 330a).

Kathlania: Only one species, *K. leptura* Rud. from *Chelonia mydas* L.

Tonaudia: Only one species, *T. tonaudia* Lane, from *Chelonia mydas* L.

Spironoura: Several species from chelonians and snakes.

Zanclophorus: Parasites of chelonians (Fig. 330). *Z. ararath* Massimow.

Cissophyllus: Parasites of chelonians.

(f) Strongyloidea

As a rule parasites of the intestinal tract. Slender types of medium and large size, represented particularly by the Family Diaphanocephalidae genus *Kalicephalus*.

Strongyloides pererai Trav. in *Ophioides striatus* Wagler.

Diaphanocephalus: *D. galeatus* Railliet and Henry from *Tupinambis teguixin* L., *D. diesingi* Freitas and Lent from *Tupinambis nigropunctatus* sp.

Kalicephalus: Numerous genus with over fifty well-determined species from snakes. Typical is the broad shapeless cephalic extremity and the bursa (Fig. 331). Best known: *K. mucronatus* Molin, *K. boae*, Harwood, *K. minutus* Ortlepp, and *K. parvus* Ortlepp.

Occipitodontus: A few species from snakes.

Hexadontophorus: *H. ophisauri* Kreis, from *Ophisaurus* spp.

(g) Cosmocercoidea

Mainly parasites of fish and amphibians. Only a few species in reptilians.

Aplectana amhersti Azim in *Chrysolophus amhersti*.

Aplectana chamaeleonis Travassos in *Chamaeleo fischeri*.

Aplectana hylambatis Trav. in *Leptopelis aubryi* Dum.

Bellaplectana, *Neoxysomatium* and *Raillietnema* are occasionally found in amphibians and reptiles. *Raillietnema loveridgei* Trav. occurs in *Bdellophis vittatus* Boul., *Neopharyngodon gekko* Chakranarty and Bhaduri in *Gekko gekko* L.

(h) Heterakoidea

Meteterakis: A parasite of amphibians mainly. In reptilians we find:

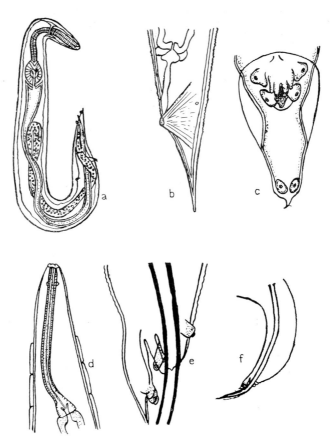

Fɪɢ. 327. Oxyuroidea in reptiles. VII. a–c, *Pseudalaeuris expansa* Rees. ♀ and ♂ posterior extremities. (From Rees.) d–f, *Alaeuris conspicua* Ortlepp. Anterior and posterior extremity of ♂ seen from above and sideways. (After Ortlepp.)

M. cophotis Freitas: In Agamids.

M. longispiculata Inglis (= *Spinicauda longicauda longispiculata* Baylis): In *Gekko gekko* L. (Fig. 332h-i).

M. louisi Inglis: In saurians.

M. mabuyae Inglis: In *Mabuya carinata* Schn.

M. varani Skrjabin, Schichobalowa and Lagodowskaja (= *Africana varani* Maplestone): In *Varanus bengalensis*.

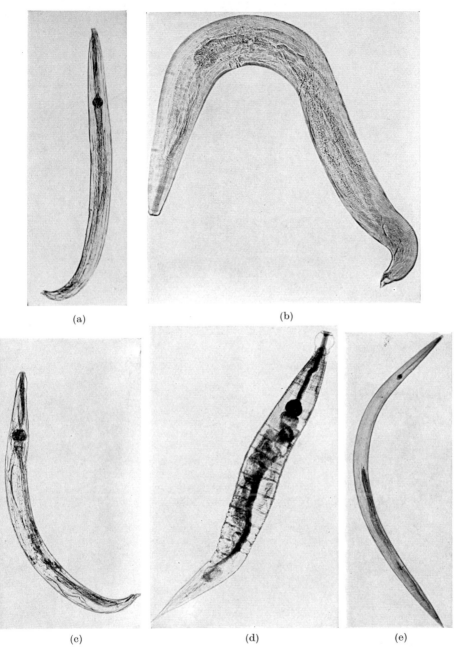

(a)   (b)

(c)   (d)   (e)

Fig. 328. Oxyuroidea in reptiles. VIII. a, *Mehdiella hamosa* Forstner ♂. × 30;
b, *Mehdiella cordata* Forstner ♂. × 72. (After Forstner.) c, *Mehdiella uncinata* Drasche
♂; d, *Mehdiella uncinata* ♀. Both × 25; e, *Mehdiella microstoma* Seurat ♂. × 15.
(After Forstner.)

15*

Spinicauda

At least seven species in saurians and chameleons. *Sp. spinicauda* Olfers occurs in *Podicnema teguexin* L. (Fig. 332a-d), *Sp. sonsinoi* Linstow in lizards and in *Chamaeleo vulgaris* L.

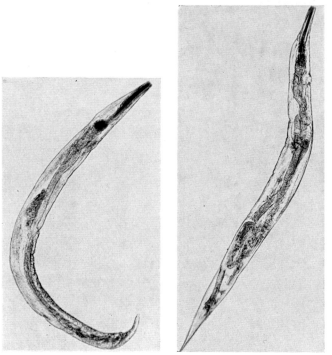

Fig. 329. Oxyuroidea in reptiles. IX. *Atractis dactylura* Duj. Left, ♂; right, ♀. × 30. (After Forstner.)

Africana

Three species in tortoises (*A. africana* Trav. Fig. 332k-l) and chameleons. (*A. acuticeps* Trav.)

Strongyluris

At least twenty-three species in saurians, chameleons and snakes.

St. brevicaudata Müller: Occurs in *Agama agama agama* L. and in *Chamaeleo dilepis* Leach (Fig. 332e-g).

St. chamaeleonis Baylis and Daubney: In *Chamaeleo vulgaris* L.

St. ornata Railliet and Henry: In *Stellio vulgaris* Latr.

Moaciria alvarengai Freitas: Occurs in *Lygosoma maculata* Blyth.

Ganguleterakis: According to Kreis (1940) some representatives of the genus parasitize reptilians.

(i) Camallanoidea

Parasites of stomach and intestine, mostly medium sized worms. *Camallanus*. Several species in chelonians.

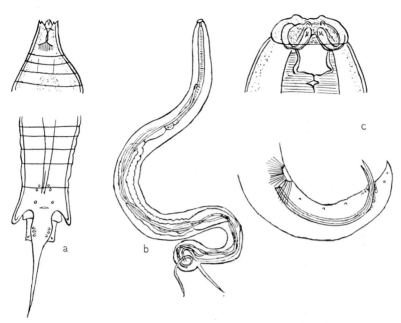

Fig. 330. Oxyuroidea in reptiles. X. a, *Labiduris gulosa* Rud. Anterior extremity. × 80. Posterior extremity of ♂. × 66. (After Schneider from Yorke and Maplestone.) b, *Tonaudia tonaudia* Lane ♂. × 10. (After Lane from Yorke and Maplestone.) c, *Zanclophorus annandalei* Baylis and Daubney. Anterior extremity above; ♂ posterior extremity below. × 18. (From Yorke and Maplestone.)

(j) Spiruroidea

A varied group of nematodes which change hosts during development. While fish, aquatic reptiles and amphibians ingest the larval stages of these worms when feeding on copepodes, terrestrial reptiles infect themselves through feeding on beetles and other insects. The reptiles function mainly as intermediate hosts, the final hosts being dogs.

Spiroxys: Several species in the stomach of chelonians.

Spirocerca: *S. lupi* Rud. The African lizard *Eremias arguta* ingests the larva by feeding on a beetle which serves as temporary transport host. The larva undergoes a resting period in the peritoneal cavity of the reptile. The final stage develops in a dog.

Physaloptera: Numerous species in the stomach and the gut of saurians, chameleons and snakes.

Abbreviata: Parasites of stomach and gut of saurians.

Skrjabinoptera: Particularly *S. colubri*, a common parasite of snakes. Other species in lizards.

Thubunaea: *T. pudica* Seurat, a parasite of chameleons (Fig. 333d-e).

Proleptus: A parasite of chelonians.

Gnathostoma: Parasites of crocodiles. First intermediate host: copepodes. Second: fish or amphibians, also reptiles.

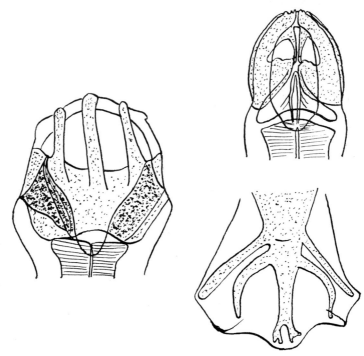

FIG. 331. Strongyloidea. *Kalicephalus minutus* Ortlepp. Left, Anterior extremity. × 240. Right above, Anterior extremity sideways. × 200. Below, Bursa. × 200. (After Baylis and Daubney from Yorke and Maplestone.)

Larval stages of *Gnathostoma* species are frequently seen in reptiles (Fig. 333f). For details see Daengsvang (1949) and Miyazaki and Ash (1959). Ash (1962) quotes the following reptiles as being natural second intermediate hosts of *Gnathostoma procyonis* Chandler: the snakes *Agkistrodon piscivorus* Lac., *Natrix r. rhombifera* Hallowell, *Natrix sipedon* L., *Lampropeltis getulus* L.; the chelonians *Kinosternon subrubrum hippocrepis* Gray, *Terrapene carolina major* Agassiz and *Alligator mississippiensis* Daud. The larvae, about 1 mm long, are found free in the tissue of the reptiles. The first intermediate hosts are

Cyclops species. The mature worms are found within small tumours of the gastric wall of herons.

Dermal oedema of the face and the limbs in Siam have been found to be caused by *Gnathostoma spinigerum* Owen (Daengsvang, 1949). Again *Cyclops* species function as first intermediate hosts. The second

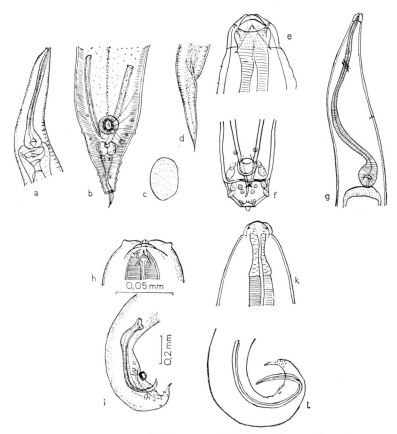

FIG. 332. Heterakoidea. a–d, *Spinicauda spinicauda* Olfers. a, Anterior extremity; b, ♂ posterior extremity; c, egg; d, ♀ posterior extremity. (After Travassos from Yorke and Maplestone.) e–g, *Strongyluris brevicaudata* Müller; e, anterior extremity. × 165; f, ♂ posterior extremity. × 45; g, anterior extremity. × 23. (From Yorke and Maplestone.) h–i, *Meteterakis longispiculata* Inglis; h, anterior extremity; i, ♂ posterior extremity; k–l, *Africana africana* Travassos; k, anterior extremity; l, ♂ posterior extremity. × 38. (From Yorke and Maplestone.)

hosts are fish and aquatic snakes of undetermined species, which carry the parasite in the muscular and intestinal tissues. People are warned therefore not to eat freshwater creatures raw or insufficiently cooked.

Tanqua: Parasites of varanids and snakes. Development as in the previous genus. *T. anomala* Linstow (Fig. 333b-c).

Hedruris: Gastric parasites of chelonians.

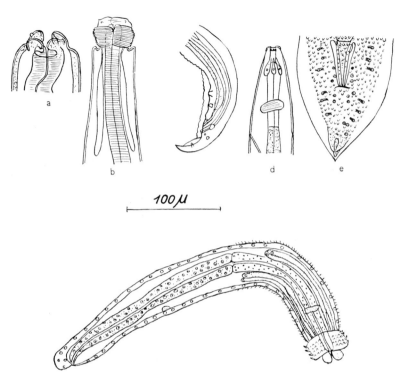

FIG. 333. Spiruroidea. a, *Spiroxys contorta*, anterior extremity. × 80. (After Baylis and Lane from Yorke and Maplestone.) b–c, *Tanqua anomala* Linstow, anterior extremity, ♂ posterior extremity. Both × 28. (After Yorke and Maplestone.) d–e, *Thubunaea pudica* Seurat, anterior extremity and ♂ posterior extremity. Both × 85. (After Seurat from Yorke and Maplestone.) f, Third larval stage of *Gnathostoma procyonis* Chandler from a Cyclops sp. (After Ash.)

Pulmonary Nematodes

Reptilian lungs may be infested by representatives of the Order Rhabdiasiodea or by *Pneumonema tiliquae* Johnston, a member of the Family Rictulariidae.

It is a peculiarity of the Rhabdiasioidea that they alternate between free-living and parasitic forms. The sexually mature free-living form produces filariform juveniles which search for the chance to penetrate the skin of a suitable host. Having gained access by this way or by becoming actually a part of the food on which the host feeds, the filariform worms find their way to the lungs. In the lungs the worms develop into hermaphrodites. Fertilized eggs are swallowed and hatch in the colon, producing rhabdiform larvae which are voided with the faeces and so deposited on the soil where they grow to sexual maturity.

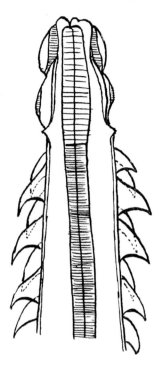

Fig. 334. *Pneumonia tiliquae* Johnston. Anterior extremity. × 215. (From Yorke and Maplestone.)

Rhabdiasioidea: Worms of the genus *Rhabdias* may be found in the lungs of chameleons, slow-worms and snakes. Sprehn (1961) mentions the species *Rhabdias dujardini* Maupas-Seurat and *Rh. entomelas* Duj. from *Anguis fragilis* L. and *Rh. fuscovenosa* Railliet from *Natrix natrix* L.

Pneumonema tiliquae Johnston (Fig. 334) is a pulmonary parasite of *Tiliqua scincoides* White.

Nematodes of the Circulatory and Lymphatic System

Nematodes parasitizing the circulatory and lymphatic systems of reptilians belong to the Superfamilies Dracunculoidea and Filarioidea. They affect particularly the subcutaneous connective tissue where they cause tumours, oedema and inflammation.

Dracunculoidea

Dracunculus: Five species, some of appreciable size. The juvenile
larvae live free at the bottom of ponds where they are taken up
by copepodes which are, in turn, eaten by the final host.

Dracunculus medinensis L.: The guinea worm, well-known in human
pathology, may occasionally also be found in the dermis of
reptilians. Desportes (1938) found the closely allied species *Filaria
oesophagea* Polonio (1895) in *Natrix natrix persa* Pallas. He found
in the mediastinum juvenile females of 27–85 mm length, adult
females of 28–44 mm length, males of 11–20 mm and embryos of

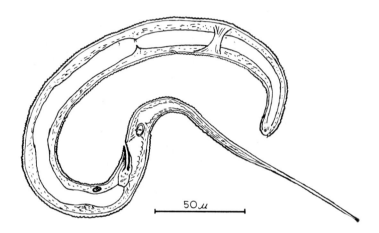

Fig. 335. Embryo of *Dracunculus oesophageus* Polonio. (After Desportes.)

just under 0·5 mm (Fig. 335). Experiments determined *Macro-
cyclops fuscus* Jur. as intermediate host. Desportes named the
species *Dracunculus oesophageus* Polonio.

D. globocephalus Mackie: Occurs in *Chelydra serpentina* L.

D. houdemeri Hsü: In *Natrix piscator* Schn.

D. dahomensis Neumann: In *Python* spp. *D. ophidensis* Brackett in
Thamnophis sirtalis L.

Even the expert may have difficulties in distinguishing between the
various *Dracunculus* species quoted. Mirza (1958) suggests assigning to
one and the same species all Dracunculids found in snakes.

Filarioidea

Short, slender worms transmitted by arthropods, mosquitoes and
mites. Reptilia may harbour sexually mature forms as well as juvenile

FIG. 336. *Python reticulatus* Schneider with dermal lesions caused by filarial infection. (Photo.: W. Frank.)

FIG. 337. Part of Fig. 336 at higher magnification, showing dermal destruction and loss of scales. (Photo.: W. Frank.)

FIG. 338. *Python reticulatus* Schneider. Early dermal destruction caused by filarial infection. On the right is an old wound. (Photo.: W. Frank.)

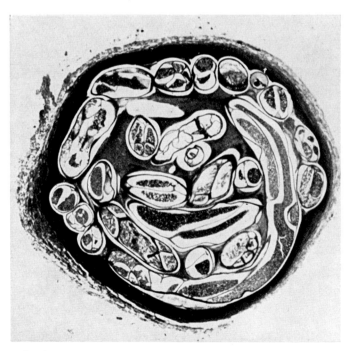

FIG. 339. Section through the mesenteric artery of *Python molurus bivittatus* Kühl filled with adult filarial worms of *Macdonaldius oschei* Chabaud and Frank. (Photo.: W. Frank)

larvae, microfilariae which, occurring in large numbers may block both circulatory and lymphatic vessels causing thrombosis and oedema.

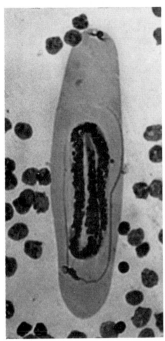

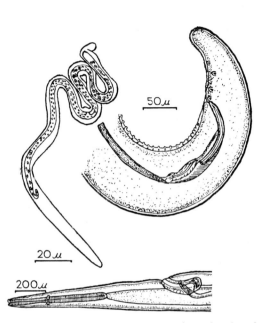

FIG. 340. *Macdonaldius oschei* Chabaud and Frank. Microfilaria in the vein of *Epicrates cenchris* L. Stained Giemsa. (Photo.: W. Frank.)

FIG. 341. *Macdonaldius andersoni* Chabaud and Frank. Above left, Microfilaria; right, posterior extremity. Below, anterior extremity. From Chabaud and Frank.

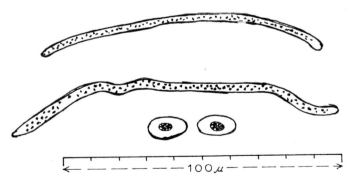

FIG. 342. Microfilariae of *Thamugadia physignathi* Cleland from the brain of *Physignathus lesueuri* Gray. Drawn by microprojection. (E. Elkan.)

Frank (1962) reports on the death of pythons in the Stuttgart Zoo. The animals died with large dermal lesions (Figs. 336–338) and the post-mortem examination revealed the presence of several hundreds of mature filaria in the mesenteric arteries as well as numerous "sheathed" stages of the microfilarial type *Macdonaldius oschei* Chabaud and Frank (Figs. 339–341). Altogether at least twelve genera are, with numerous species, represented in reptilians. Only in three of them has it been possible to determine the whole life cycle. The adult worms are mostly of medium length. In *Macdonaldius oschei* the females measure 62 mm; in *M. andersoni* 50 mm; the males 33 and 22 mm respectively. The caudal extremity of the males is armed with a number of spiculae and papillae. The diameter of the microfilaria in both species is 0·2 mm.

One of us (E. E.) had the opportunity of studying a case of extensive microfilarial infection in an Australian water dragon (*Physignathus lesueuri*) which died after 9 years of captivity in an English animal collection. The large, pale, friable and oedematous fat body contained numerous microfilaria (Fig. 342). These were, in fact, present in the blood vessels, particularly in the capillaries of every organ, and were particularly numerous in the brain, where some of them could be seen to lie outside the capillaries embedded in the brain substance itself. In spite of this massive infestation no organ showed any cellular reaction or signs of necrobiosis. The water dragon must have been infected before it reached England and must therefore have lived with the infection for at least 9 years, which makes it doubtful whether the filariae were the sole cause of death. They had, on the other hand, caused extensive degenerative changes in the kidneys (Fig. 343) where the parenchymatous epithelium had almost completely disappeared leaving only the meshwork of the interstitial reticulum behind. The number of worms in the renal capillaries, however, was rather smaller than that in the brain where no evidence of local damage could be demonstrated (Fig. 345). The parasite was determined as *Thamugadia physignathi* Cleland, described from the liver and the mesenteric vessels of *Physignathus lesueuri* Gray by Johnston (1912), Johnston and Cleland (1911) and by Johnston and Mawson (1953). The transmitting vector, probably a mosquito, is not known yet.

Hastospiculum: At least four species in the blood vessels of varanids and snakes.

Foleyella: Some species parasitize the blood of lizards. A well-known species is, for instance, *F. candazei* Fraipont from *Uromastix acanthinurus* Bell and *F. agamae* Rodhain from Agamids. W. Frank, in a personal communication to R.-Klinke (1962), reported

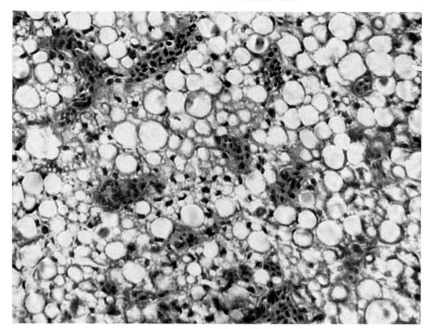

FIG. 343. Kidney of a specimen of *Physignathus lesueuri*, the water dragon, heavily infected with microfilaria of *Thamugadia physignathi*. Renal parenchyma almost completely destroyed.

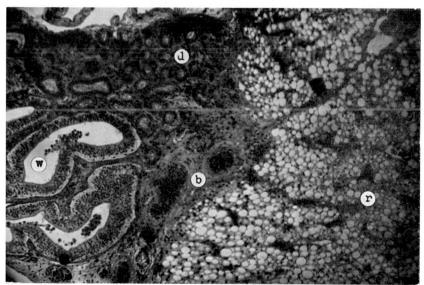

FIG. 344. As Fig. 343, showing the borderline between normal (left), and degenerate (right) tissue. *b*, Blood vessels; *d*, renal tubules; *r*, degenerate renal tissue; *w*, Wolffian duct. (Photo.: E. Elkan.)

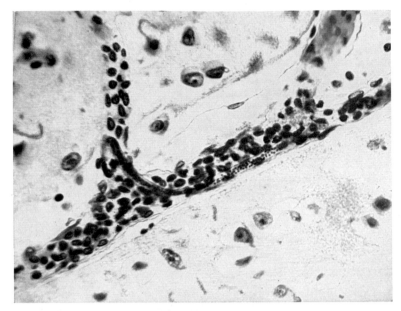

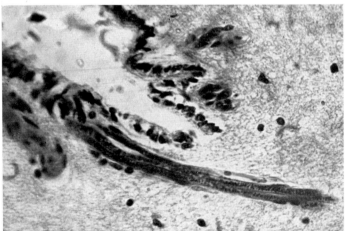

Fig. 345. Microfilaria of *Thamugadia physignathi* Cleland in the brain of *Physignathus lesueuri*. Intravascular worms (above), extravascular worms (below).

having again found *Foleyella furcata* Linstow 1899 in *Chamaeleo oustaleti* Mcqu.

Oswaldofilaria: Parasites of saurians and crocodiles. Mackerras (1953) determined the mosquitoes *Culex annulirostris* Skuse and *Culex fatigans* Wied as vectors of *Oswaldofilaria chlamydosauri* Breinl.

Macdonaldius: Five species in snakes, iguanids and *Heloderma*. Frank (1962) determined the mite *Ornithodoros talaje* Guérin and Méneville as vector of *Madonaldius oschei* Chabaud and Frank. For a detailed description see the original publication (Figs. 339–341).

Saurofilaria: Parasites of Mexican saurians.

Thamugadia: Parasites of saurians. cf. the earlier description of an infection of *Physignathus lesueuri* Gray.

Pseudothamugadia: Parasites of reptiles.

Saurositus: Haemoparasites of agamids (Macfie, 1924).

Conispiculum: Parasites of saurians. Pandit, Pandit and Iyer (1929) determined *Culex fatigans* as vector of *Conispiculum flavescens* P. P. and I.

Piratuba and *Cardianema*: Rarer haemoparasites of reptilians.

Micropleura: Haemofilaria of crocodiles. *M. vazi* Trav. in the peritoneal cavity of *Caiman sclerops* Gray.

The number of helminthic species found in reptiles closely approaches that of fish. The number of genera is slightly larger. Yamaguti (1961) lists:

28 Families of digenetic trematodes;

6 Families of cestodes;

31 Families of nematodes.

The nematodes embraced 105 genera with 583 species.

REFERENCES

Ash, L. R. and Beaver, P. C. (1962). A restudy of *Ophidascaris labiatopapillosa* occurring in the stomach of N. American snakes. *J. Parasit.* **48**, (Suppl.), 41.

Ash, L. R. (1962). Development of *Gnathostoma procyonis* Chandler 1942, in the first and second intermediate hosts. *J. Parasit.* **48**, 298–305.

Baylis, H. A. (1921). On the classification of the ascaridae. II. The *Polydelphis* group with some account of other ascarids parasitic in snakes. *Parasitology* **12**, 411–426.

Baylis, H. A. (1929). Some new parasitic nematodes and cestodes from Java. *Parasitology* **21**, 256–265.

Baylis, H. A. and Daubney, R. (1922). Reports on the parasitic nematodes in the collection of the Zoological Survey of India. *Mem. Ind. Mus.* **7**, 263–347.

Caballero, E. C. (1954). Nematodes de los Reptiles de Mexico. XI. Nuevo genero y nueva especie de Filaria de Iguanidos. *Rev. Parasit.* **15**, 305–313.

Chabaud, A. G. and Frank, W. (1961). Nouvelle filaire parasite des artères de pythons: *Macdonaldius oschei* n. sp. (Nematodes, Onchocercidae). *Z. Parasitenk.* **20**, 434–439.

Chabaud, A. G. and Frank, W. (1961). Nouvelle filaire, parasite des artères de l'*Heloderma suspectum* Cope: *Macdonaldius andersoni* n. sp. (Nematodes, Onchocercidae). *Ann. Parasit. hum. comp.* **36**, 127–136.

Chabaud, A. G. and Frank, W. (1961). Les filaires de l'Héloderme. Note additive. *Ann. Parasit. hum. comp.* **36**, 804–805.

Chitwood, B. G. and Chitwood, M. B. (1950). "An Introduction to Nematology." Washington.

Daengsvang, S. (1949). Human gnathostomiasis in Siam, with reference to the method of prevention. *J. Parasit.* **35**, 116–121.

Desportes, C. (1938). *Filaria oesophagea* Polonio 1895, parasite de la couleuvre d'Italie, est un Dracunculus très voisin de la filaire de medine. *Ann. Parasit. hum. comp.* **16**, 305–326.

Edgerley, R. H. (1952). Two new species of Nematoda, *Strongyluris riversidensis* and *Pharyngodon mearnsi* from Lizard *Streptosaurus mearnsi*. *Trans. Amer. micr. Soc.* **71**, 288–292.

Fitzsimmons, W. M. (1958). *Saurositus macfiei* sp. nov., a filarioid parasite of the lizard *Agama mossambica mossambica* Peters. *Ann. trop. Med. Par.* **52**, 257–260.

Forstner, M. J. (1960). Ein Beitrag zur Kenntnis parasitischer Nematoden aus griechischen Landschildkröten. *Z. Parasitenk.* **20**, 1–22.

Hsü, H. F. (1933). On *Dracunculus houdemeri* n. sp., *Dracunculus globocephalus* and *Dracunculus medinensis*. *Z. Parasitenk.* **6**, 101–118.

Inglis, W. G. (1958). A revision of the nematode genus *Meteterakis* Karve, 1930. *Parasitology* **48**, 9–31.

Johnston, T. H. and Cleland, B. (1911). The haematozoa of Australian reptilia. *Proc. Linn. Soc. N.S. Wales* **36**, 479–491.

Johnston, T. H. (1912). Notes on some Entozoa. *Proc. Roy. Soc. Queensland* **24**, 63–91.

Johnston, T. H. (1912). A census of Australian reptilian Entozoa. *Proc. Roy. Soc. Queensland* **24**, 233–249.

Johnston, T. H. and Mawson, P. M. (1943). Remarks on some nematodes from Australian reptiles. *Trans. Roy. Soc. S. Austr.* **67**, 183–186.

Kreis, H. A. (1940). Ein neuer parasitischer Nematode aus *Corucia zebrata* (Scincidae, Reptilia). *Ganguleterakis triaculeatus* n. sp. *Z. Parasitenk.* **6**, 332–338.

Kreis, H. A. (1940). Beiträge zur Kenntnis parasitischer Nematoden. IX. Parasitische Nematoden aus dem Naturhistorischen Museum Basel. *Zbl. Bakt.* Orig. **145**, 163–208.

Macfie, J. W. S. (1924). *Saurositus agamae* n. g., n. sp., a filarioid parasite of the lizard *Agama colonorum*. *Ann. trop. Med. Par.* **18**, 409–412.

Mackerras, M. F. (1953). Lizard Filaria: Transmission by mosquitoes of *Oswaldofilaria chlamydosauri* Breinl. (Nematoda, Filarioidea). *Parasitology* **43**, 1–3.

Mirza, M. B. (1958). On *Dracunculus* Reichard, 1759 and its species. *Z. Parasitenk.* **18**, 44–47.

Miyazaki, J. and Ash, L. R. (1959). On the gnathostome larvae found from snakes in New Orleans, U.S.A. (In Japanese.) *Jap. J. Parasit.* **8**, 351–352.

Ortlepp, R. J. (1933a). *Ozolaimus megatyphlon* Rud., a little known helminth from *Iguana tuberculata*. *Onderst. J. Vet. Sci. An. Ind.* **1**, 99–114.

Ortlepp, R. J. (1937b). On some South African reptilian oxyurids. *J. Vet. Sci. An. Ind.* **1**, 99–114.

Pandit, C. G., Pandit, S. R. and Iyer, P. V. S. (1929). The development of the filaria *Conispiculum guindiensis* (1929) in *Culex fatigans*, with a note on the transmission of the infection. *Ind. J. med. Res.* **17**, 421–429.

Patwardhan, S. S. (1935). Nematodes from the common wall lizard *Hemidactylus flaviviridis* Rüppel. *Proc. Ind. Acad. Sci.* **1**, (7) 376–380.

Read, C. P. and Amrein, Y. U. (1935). North American nematodes of the genus *Pharyngodon* Diesing. (Oxyuridae). *J. Parasit.* **39**, 365–370.

Rees, F. G. (1935). Two new species of *Tachygonetria* from the Indian tortoise *Testudo horsfieldi* Gray. *Proc. zool. Soc. Lond.* **3**, 599–603.

Sandground, J. H. (1936). Scientific results of an expedition to Rain Forest Regions in Eastern Africa. VI. Nematoda. *Bull. Mus. comp. Zool.* **79**, 341–366.

Seurat, L. G. (1912). Sur les Oxyures de *Uromastix acanthinurus* Bell. *C.R. Soc. Biol., Paris* **73**, 223–226.

Seurat, L. G. (1914). Sur un cas d'Endotokie Matricide chez un Oxyure. *C.R. Soc. Biol., Paris* **76**, 850–852.

Shad, A. G. (1963). Niche diversification in a parasitic species flock. *Nature, Lond.* **198**, 404–406.

Skrjabin, K. J. (1960). "Ossnowy Nematodologii." Moscow (in Russian).

Smith, A. J. (1910). A new filarial species (*F. mitchelli* n. sp.) found in *Heloderma suspectum*, and its larvae in a tick parasite upon the Gila Monster, with remarks upon ticks as possible intermediate hosts in filariasis. *Univ. Pennsylvan. Med. Bull.* **23**, 487–497.

Sonsino, P. (1889). Studi e notizie elminthologiche. *Atti Soc. tosc. sci. nat.* **6**, 224–237.

Waitz, J. A. (1961). Parasites of Idaho Reptiles. *J. Parasit.* **47**, 51.

Yamaguti, S. (1961). "Systema Helminthum", Vol. III. Interscience, London-New York.

Yorke, W. and Maplestone, P. A. (1926). "The Nematode Parasites of Vertebrates." Churchill, London.

H. Leeches

Leeches are mainly found on turtles and crocodiles. A review of the species likely to be encountered has been given by Autrum (1936). The genus *Haementeria* is particularly well represented with fifteen species from turtles and two from crocodiles. In Europe we find *Haementeria costata* Fr. Müller on *Emys orbicularis* L., in E. Asia and N. America *H. rugosa* Vervil. On crocodiles we find *H. fimbriata* Johansson (*Crocodilus niloticus* L.) and *H. maculata* Weber on Brazilian crocodiles. All these species seem to be exclusively adapted to life on one specific host; the finding of *Haementeria okadai* Oka, which ordinarily parasitizes frogs, in the mouth of a turtle, may have been a chance event. An interesting species is *Haementeria costata* Müller (= *Placobdella stepanowi* Blanchard) which transmits the blood parasite *Haemogregarina stepanowi* Danilewsky.

The species *Hemiclepsis marginata* O. F. Müller, on the other hand, which occurs from Europe to Japan, has a wide spectrum of hosts including besides fish and larval amphibians the turtle *Chinemys reevesii* Gray.

Actinobdella annectens Moore has been found on the common snapping turtle (*Chelydra serpentina* L.).

Members of the genus *Ozobranchus* not only suck blood like *Haementeria* but also transmit various diseases. *Ozobranchus shipleyi* Harding for instance has been found to transmit *Haemogregarina nicoriae* Castellani and Wiley in *Geoemyda trijuga* Schweigger. Other species of *Ozobranchus* are found on marine turtles and freshwater turtles as well as on crocodiles.

Nigrelli and Smith (1943) studied the histological evidence of the damage caused by attacks of leeches when they found *Ozobranchus* associated with fibroepitheliomata in the marine turtle *Chelonia mydas* L.

REFERENCES

Autrum, H. (1936). Hirudineen. Pt. I. *In* Bronn's "Klassen und Ordnungen des Tierreichs." Quelle and Meyer, Leipzig.
Nigrelli, R. F. and Smith, G. M. (1943). The occurrence of leeches, *Ozobranchus branchiatus*, on fibroepithelial tumours of marine turtles *Chelonia mydas*. *Zoologica* **28**, 107–108.

I. Mites (Acarina)

Mites are regarded with great apprehension by the herpetologist both as parasites and as transmitters of diseases. Unfortunately they occur in considerable numbers of reptiles. Some of them limit themselves to one or a few hosts, others show no sign of discrimination. One group, whose final hosts are mammals, pass their juvenile stages on reptilians. The mites fasten themselves in those areas of the skin most suitable for their requirements. Sometimes we may find them under scales, in the axilla, in the inguinal region around the root of the tail, sometimes around the eyes. Some species even penetrate the lungs of snakes. Epidemics of mite invasion occur particularly where many Reptilia are kept in close confinement. The situation can become very serious since the life of the host is threatened if the loss of blood caused by the mites is too severe (Fig. 346).

Approximately 250 different species of mites have so far been described, the commonest being *Ophionyssus natricis* Mégnin which attacks snakes.

In dealing with the individual species we follow the survey of Baker and Wharton (1952).

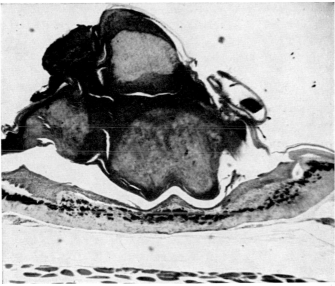

FIG. 346. A specimen of *Lacerta viridis* which was heavily infested with ticks. Above, Anterior part of the lizard showing dermal lesions. Below, Section through the skin showing excessive keratosis. (Photo.: E. Elkan.)

Mesostigmata

Heterozerconidae

Heterozercon oudemansi Finnegan (1931), found as an external parasite on a tropical snake.

Entonyssidae

Parasites of the trachea and the lungs of snakes. Fain (1961) gave a detailed description of these species and revised the family. He found 2% of all snakes investigated infested with these mites. According to

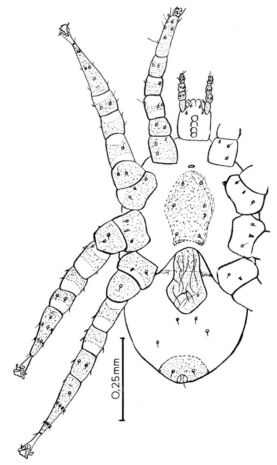

FIG. 347. *Entonyssus colubri* Hubbard. (After Fain, 1961.)

the state of development, larvae, protonymphs and deutonymphs are distinguished. The mode of transmission has not been determined but nymphs are more numerous in the trachea than in the lungs.

Entonyssus. Six species in Asia and N. America.

E. *halli* Ewing: From *Crotalus* spp. in Texas, particularly *Crotalus cinereus* Le Conte.

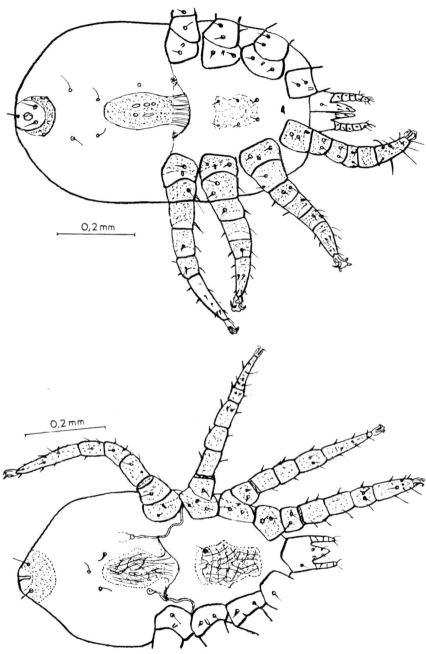

0,2 mm

0,2 mm

FIG. 348. Left, *Hamertonia radfordi* Fain. Right, *Entophiophaga natricoterei* Fain. (Both from Fain, 1961.)

E. rileyi Ewing: From a *Crotalus* sp. (*Crotalus cinereus* Le Conte) in Texas.

E. colubri Hubbard comb. Fain: From *Coluber flagellum flaviventris* Hallowell, *Coluber constrictor constrictor* L., *C. c. foxi* Baird and Girard (Fig. 347).

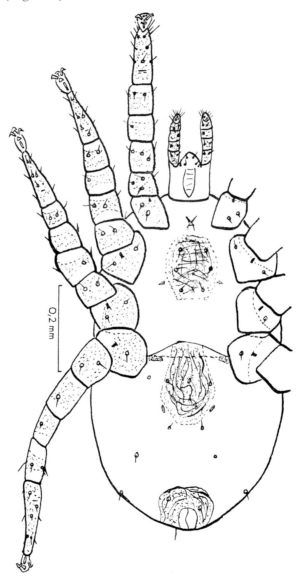

Fig. 349. *Entophionyssus glasmacheri* Vitzthum. (After Fain, 1961.)

E. asiaticus Fain: From *Natrix chrysarga* Schl., *N. subtruncata* Schl.

E. philippinensis Fain: From *Fordonia leucobalia* Schl. and *Natrix piscator* Schn.

E. javanicus Fain: From *Natrix vittata* L.

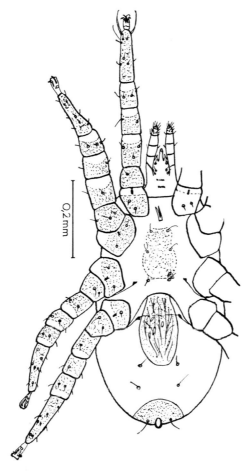

FIG. 350. *Viperacarus europaeus* Fain. (From Fain, 1961.)

Hamertonia bedfordi Radford: From *Dendroaspis angusticeps* Smith.

H. psammophis Till: From *Psammophis s. sibilans* L., *Rhamphiophis oxyrhynchus garambensis* Witte, *Meizodon coronatus* Schl. and *Dromophis lineatus* Dum. and Bibr.

H. radfordi Fain: From *Gastropyxis smaragdina* Schl. (Fig. 348, left).

Entophiophaga congolensis Fain: From *Dasypeltis scaber* L. and *Crotaphopeltis hotamboeia* Laur.

E. scaphiophis Fain: From *Scaphiophis a. albopunctata* Peters.

E. natriciterei Fain: From *Natriciteres o. olivacea* Peters (Fig. 348, right).

E. colubricola Fain: From *Coluber jugularis caspius* Gmelin.

Entophionyssus hamertoni Radford: From *Thamnophis sirtalis parietalis* Say and *T. s. sirtalis* L.

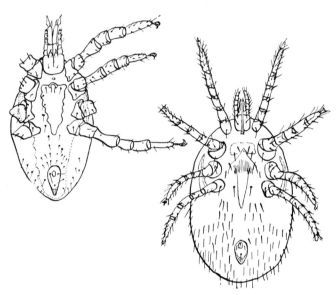

FIG. 351. *Ophionyssus natricis* Mégnin. Left, ♂. (After Radford.) Right, ♀. (After Hirst.)

E. glasmacheri Vitzthum comb. Fain: From *Elaphe quadrivittata* Holbrook, *E. guttata* L., *E. obsoleta* Say and *Pituophis sayi* Schl. (Fig. 349).

E. natricis Keegan comb. Fain: From *Natrix sipedon* L.

E. fragilis Keegan comb. Fain: From *Lampropeltis getulus* L.

E. heterodontos Keegan comb. Fain: From *Heterodon contortrix* L., *Heterodon platyrhinos* Cathesby and *Lampropeltis calligaster* Hln.

Viperacarus europaeus Fain: From *Vipera berus* L. (Fig. 350).

Cobranyssus schoutedeni Radford comb. Fain: From *Naja tripudians fasciatus* Gray.

Pneumophionyssus aristoterisi Fonseca: From *Erythrolamprus aesculapii* L.

Entophioptes liophis Fain: From *Liophis anomalus* Gthr.

Dermanyssidae

The Dermanyssidae are ectoparasites of saurians and snakes. Only *Mabuyonyssus* parasitizes the nostrils.

The commonest blood-sucking tick of snakes, usually found under the scales, is *Ophionyssus* (= *Serpenticola*) *natricis* Mégnin (Gervais) (= *serpentium* Hirst) (Fig. 351).

This tick, which feeds on the blood of snakes, is not only the nightmare of the herpetologist, on occasion it even infests humans. It has been reported (Privorn and Samsinak, 1958) that workers employed in a laboratory where many snakes were kept began to suffer from intense itching followed by the appearance of small boils. Schweizer (1952) tested various substances designed to kill the mites and to disinfect the cages. The most suitable of these proved to be paradichlorbenzol which is used in varying doses according to the species and the size of the snakes. Some snakes react by showing a transient form of paralysis while under treatment. A mixture of castor oil and 90% alcohol in equal parts has also been used successfully.

Ophionyssus variabilis Zemskaya: From *Echis carinata* Schn.

Neoliponyssus gordonensis Hirst: From *Mabuya quinquestriata* Lichtenst.

Neoliponyssus lacertinus Berlese: Occurs on lizards.

N. monodi Hirst: Occurs on *Acanthodactylus* spp.

N. saurarum Oudemans: Occurs on lizards.

Steatonyssus arabicus Hirst: Occurs on *Agama adramitana*.

Mabuyonyssus freedmanni Till was found on the head of *Mabuya quinquetaeniata margaritifer* Peters. Fain (1961) suggests that the usual seat of infection is the nostril.

Omentolaelaptidae

Omentolaelaps mehelyae Fain (Fig. 352) occurs under ventral and ventro-lateral scales of *Mehelya capensis savorgnani* Mocquard and *M. poensis* Smith in the Congo.

Laelaptidae

Ophidilaelaps imphalensis Radford (1947).

Haemolaelaps natricis Feider and Solomon: From *Natrix natrix* L.

Ixodorhynchus liponyssoides Ewing: From *colubrid* snakes.

I. johnstoni Fain: From *Heterodon p. platyrhinos* Latr.

I. leptodeirae Fain: From *Leptodeira maculata* Hallowell.

I. cubanensis Fain: From *Liophis andreae* Reinhardt.

Ixobioides butantanensis Fonseca: From colubrid snakes (Fig. 353).

I. fonsecae Fain: From *Xenodon guentheri* Boul.

16

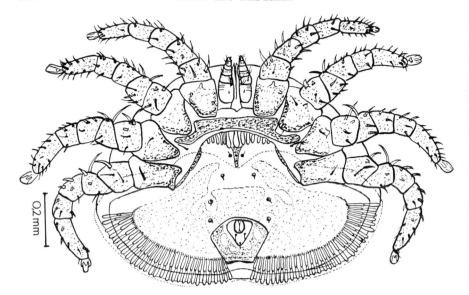

0.2 mm

Fig. 352. *Omentolaelaps mehelyae* Fain ♀. (From Fain, 1961.)

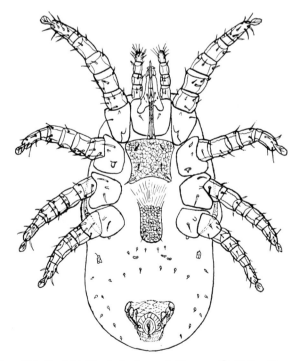

Fig. 353. *Ixodobioides butantanensis* Fonseca ♀. (After Fonseca.)

Hemilaelaps triangulus Ewing: From colubrid snakes, South U.S.A.

H. javanensis Fain: From *Lycodon subcinctus* Boie.

H. farrieri Tibbets: From colubrid snakes, Africa.

H. congolensis Fain: From *Causus rhombeatus* Licht.

H. causicola Fain: From *Causus rhombeatus* Lichtst.

H. dipsadoboae Fain: From *Dipsadoboa unicolor* Guenther.

H. radfordi Feider and Solomon: From *Natrix natrix* L.

H. feideri Fain: From *N. natrix helvetica* Lac.

H. caheni Fain: From *Bitis nasicornis* Shaw and *Naja melanoleuca* Hall.

H. piger Berlese: From *Coluber gemonensis* Laur., *Elaphe situla* L., *N. natrix* L.

H. imphalensis Radford: From *Coluber radiatus* Schlegel.

H. novae-guineae Fain: From *Dendrophis calligaster salmonis* Gthr.

H. ophidius Lavoipierre: From *Causus lichtensteini* Jan.

H. schoutedeni Fain: From *Boaedon fuliginosus* Boie.

H. upembae Fain: From *Boaedon fuliginosus* Boie.

Asiatolaelaps tanneri Tibbetts: From *Natrix tigrina lateralis* Berth.

A. evansi Fain: From *Elaphe flavolineata* Schl.

Strandtibbettsia gordoni Tibbetts: From *Natrix* spp.

S. brasiliensis Fain: From *Lycognathus cervinus* Laur.

Fig. 354. *Lacerta agilis*. Leg infested by ticks. (Photo.: Stemmler-Gyger.)

Paramegistidae

Ophiomegistus luzonensis Banks: From snakes of Pacific islands.
O. buloloensis Gthr.: From snakes of Pacific islands.
O. clelandi Womersley: From Australian snakes.

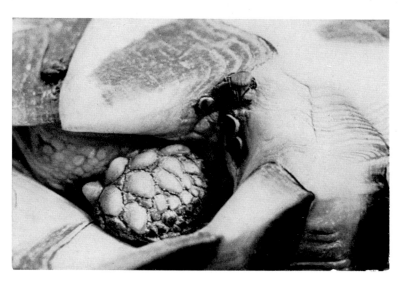

FIG. 355. *Testudo marginata*. Leg infested by ticks. (Photo.: Stemmler-Gyger.)

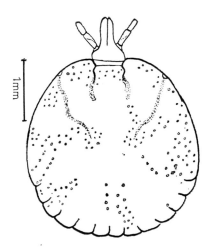

FIG. 356. *Amblyomma laticauda* Warburton (♂ of *Laticauda colubrina* Schneider).
(After Warburton.)

Ixodides

These ticks have commonly been found to parasitize reptiles, particularly tortoises (Figs. 355, 356), snakes and varanids. *Ixodes ricinus* L., which employs three hosts, may in the nymphal stage invade reptiles, the final host being a mammal (Jellison, 1933). The argasid *Ornithodorus talaje* Guérin-Ménéville must be regarded as particularly dangerous because it transmits diseases caused by spirochaetes like Q-fever and others and may also infest humans. *Haemofilaria* may equally be transmitted by this tick.

Argasidae

Ornithodoros talaje Guérin-Ménéville.

Ixodidae

Numerous species of the genera *Amblyomma* (Fig. 356), *Aponomma* (Fig. 357) and *Hyalomma* as well as *Ixodes ricinus* L. have been found

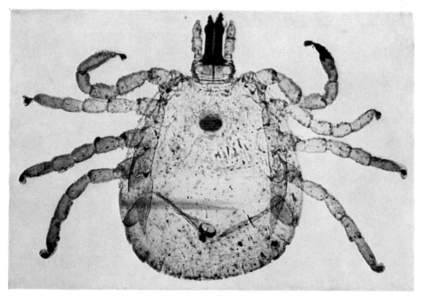

FIG. 357. *Aponomma latum* Koch. (Photo.: E. Elkan.)

on reptiles, particularly on tortoises, varanids and the larger snakes (Schulze, 1932, 1936; Dunn, 1918; Sambon, 1928; Krijgsman and Ponto, 1932; Warburton, 1932).

Trombidiformes

Pterygosomidae

We owe most of our knowledge on this family to R. F. Lawrence who reviewed it in 1935/36. He described mites infesting geckonids, agamids, gherrhosaurids and zonurids. On geckos he found:

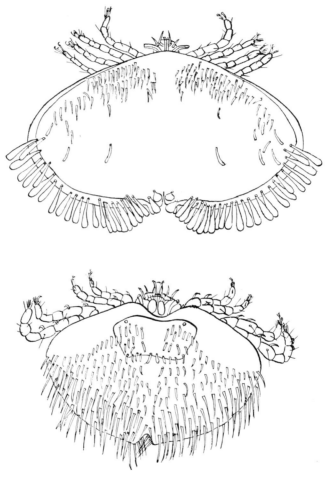

FIG. 358. Above: *Pterygosoma bedfordi* Lawr. Below: *Geckobia hemidactyli* Lawr.

Geckobia transvaalensis, G. ozambica, G. tasmani, G. oedurae, G. natalensis, G. hewitti, G. homopholus, G. namaquensis, G. rhoptropi, G. pachydactyli, G. hemidactyli (Fig. 358, below), *G. phyllodactyli,* and *G. karroica.*

The genus *Geckobia* was revised by Radford (1943). For further details see Hirst (1926) and Womersley (1941). They mention the following species:

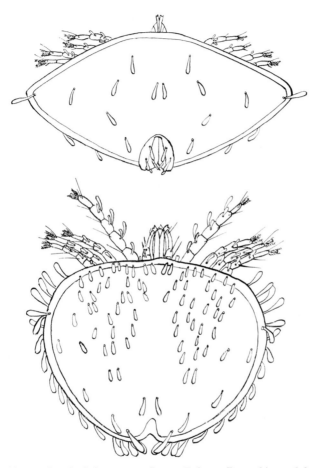

FIG. 359. Above: *Scaphothrix convexa* Lawr. Below: *Zonurobia cordylensis* Lawr.

Geckobia australis Hirst, *G. bataviensis* Vitzthum, *G. boulengeri* Hirst.
G. clelandi Hirst, *G. diversipilis* Hirst, *G. gehyrae* Hirst, *G. gleadoviana* Hirst.
G. gymnodactyli Womersley, *G. haplodactyli* Womersley, *G. hindustanica* Hirst.
G. indica Hirst, *G. latasti* Hirst, *G. loricata* Berlese, *G. papuana* Hirst.

G. malayana Hirst, *G. naultina* Womersley, *G. neumanni* Berlese, *G. similis* Tragardh.

G. socotrensis Hirst, *G. tarantulae* Tragardh.

G. turkestana Hirst.

FIG. 360. *Ixodiderma inverta* (legs not shown). Below: palps. (From Lawrence.)

Of the genus *Pterygosoma* they mention:

Pterygosoma inermis Tragardh, *P. neumanni* Berlese and *P. persicum* Hirst.

From S. African agamids Lawrence (1935/6) mentions:

Pterygosoma melanum Hirst.

P. agamae Peters and the new species *P. hirsti, P. armatum, P. bedfordi* (Fig. 358, above).

P. longipalpe, P. aculeatum, P. triangulare and *P. transvaalense.*

From Gherrosaurids he quotes:

Pterygosoma gherrosauri Lawr., *P. bicolor* Lawr. and *P. hystrix* Lawr. The genera of this family were found on zonurids, particularly *Zonurobia* species newly described as: *Zonurobia cordylensis* (Fig. 359, bottom), *Z. polyzonensis, Z. circularis, Z. semilunaris, Z. debilipes, Z. transvaalensis, Z. sanguinea, Z. subquadrata* and *Z. montana.*

To these should be added:

Scaphothriz convexa Lawr. (Fig. 359, top).

Ixodiderma inverta Lawr. (Fig. 360), *I. lacertae* Lawr., *I. pilosa* Lawr. Other authors described: *Pimeliaphilus insignis* Berlese, *P. tenuipes* Hirst, also occurring on geckonids.

Lane (1954), gave a detailed account of *Geckobiella texana* Banks found to infest *Sceloporus u. undulatus* Latr. (Fig. 361).

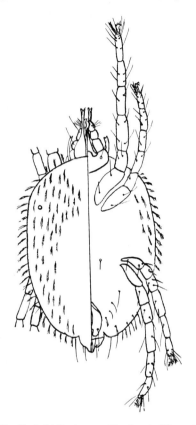

Fig. 361. *Geckobiella texana* Banks ♂. (From Lane.)

The following key for these species was given by Lawrence (1936):

1 With dorsal shield   2
  Without dorsal shield   3
2 Dorsal shield with a few, long hairs   *Pimeliaphilus*
  Dorsal shield with many but short hairs   *Geckobia*
3 Apex of hypostome broad, dorsal shield with few
   hairs   4

16*

Hypostome nearly parallel, dorsal shield with
    many hairs   5
4 Body longer than wide, large, skin leathery   *Ixodiderma*
  Body wider than long, small, skin not leathery   *Scaphothrix*
5 Back with a group of hairs on either side of mouth
    organs. Eyeless   *Pterygosoma*
  Back without group of hairs around mouth, eyes
    present   *Zonurobia*

Trombiculidae

Like so many other animals reptiles are frequently infested by
chigger mites. These mites infest mammals as well as cold-blooded
animals: they do not seem to be very particular about their hosts and
the list given below may be incomplete. It rests mainly on the reviews
by Audy (1961), Lawrence (1949) and Radford (1942a). All these
species are ectoparasitic. There have been recorded:

Trombicula agamae André: From saurians.

T. arenicola Loomis: From *Masticophis flagellum* Shaw and *Phyllo-rhynchus decurtatus* Cope.

T. hakei Radford: From *Coluber radiatus* Schlegel and *Naja tripudians fasciatus* Gray.

T. hasei Feider: From Rumanian lizards.

T. vanommereni Schierbeck : From humans and saurians (Radford).

T. (Eutrombicula) tropica Ewing: From *Anaidia bitaeniata* Blg.-Venezuela.

T. (Eu.) alfreddugesi Oudemanns: Infests chelonians, snakes, lizards and birds. In the U.S.A. it causes dermatitis in humans. In E. Asia it transmits the Tsutsugamushi disease (Ewing, 1944).

T. (Eu.) belkini Gould: From Californian lizards—*Phrynosoma coronatum* Gray and *Uta stansburiana* Baird and Girard.

T. (Eu.) gurneyi Ewing: From *Eumeces fasciatus* L.

T. (Eu.) insularis Ewing: From *Anolis cybotes* Cope.

T. (Eu.) ophidica Fonseca: From *Ophis merremi* Wagler.

T. (Eu.) tinami Oudemans: From *Crypturus noctivagus* Wied.

T. (Eutrombicula, Squamicola Lawrence) *draconis* Lawr.: From *Pseudocordylus s. subviridis.*

T. (Eu. Squ.) lawrenci Wharton and Fuller: From agamids.

T. (Eu. Squ.) montensis Lawr.: From *Pseudocordylus s. subviridis.*

Lawrence (1949) furthermore described the following species from
saurians:

T. (Eu. Squ.) gherrosauri, T. homopholis, T. pachydactyli, T. rhodes-iensis, T. rhoptropi.

T. (Fonseca) ewingi Fonseca: From *Ophis merremi*, Wagler.

T. (F.) travassosi Fonseca: From *Spilotes pullatus* L.

T. (Neotrombicula) tragardhiana Feider: From *Lacerta agilis* L.

Acomatacarus arizonensis Ewing: From *Phrynosoma coronatum blainvillei* Gray, *Sceloporus m. magister* Hallowell and other saurians.

Other species, found by Lawrence to infest saurians, are:

A. geckobius, A. lacertae, A. mabuyae, A. namaquensis.

Ascoschöngastia gherrosauri Lawr., *A. ophicola* Lawr., *A. tropidosauri* Lawr., *A. viperina* Lawr.

Euschöngastia lacertae Brennan: From *Sceloporus occidentalis* Baird and Girard, and *Gherronotus multicarinatus* Blainville.

Eu. longitarsala Powder and Loomis: From *Uta stansburiana* Baird and Girard, *Phrynosoma coronatum* Gray, *Phrynosoma platyrhinos* and other Californian lizards.

Neoschöngastia scelopori Ewing: From *Sceloporus spinosus* Wiegm.

Odontacarus australis Ewing: From *Tropidurus peruvianus* Lesson.

O. shawi Brennan: From *Gecko coleonyx variegatus* Baird, *Masticophis flagellum* Shaw and other Californian lizards and snakes.

Sauracarella africana Lawr., *S. montana* Lawr., *S. whartoni* Lawr.

Sauriscus ewingi Lawr.

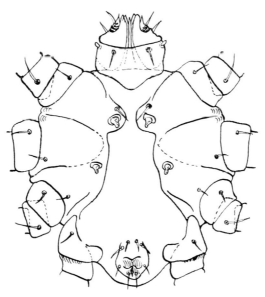

FIG. 362. *Ophioptes tropicalis* Ewing. (From Ewing.)

Schöngastia mabuyana Lawr., *Sch. platysauri* Lawr., *Sch. pseudo-
   cordyli* Lawr.
Sch. scincicola Lawr.
For details the original papers should be consulted.

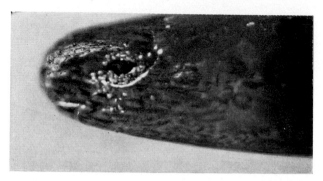

Fig. 363. *Anguis fragilis* ♀. Eye region infested with the hypopus stage of the tick
Caloglyphus. (Photo.: E. Elkan.)

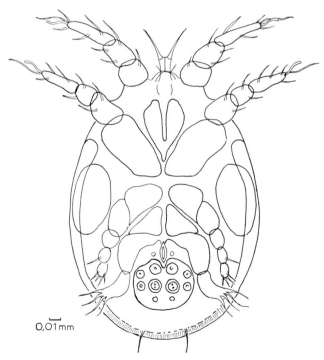

0,01mm

Fig. 364. Hypopus stage of the tick *Caloglyphus*. Drawn by microprojection. (E.
Elkan.)

Myobiidae

This is a small group of mites which live on the scales of S. American snakes. *Ophioptes parkeri* Sambon, *O. tropicalis* Ewing (Fig. 362), *O. oudemansi* Sambon.

Erythraeidae

Species of the genus *Leptus*, occurring on lizards inhabiting Pacific islands were described by Baker and Wharton (1952).

Sarcoptiformes

One of us (E. Elkan) had occasion to observe the infestation of a slow-worm (*Anguis fragilis* L.) with numerous specimens of the hypopus stage of a *Caloglyphus* species. Since, at the hypopus stage, these juvenile mites have no functional mouth organs, they were apparently using the slow-worm as an intermediate transport host and the case cannot be regarded as one of true parasitism (Figs. 363, 364).

REFERENCES

André, M. (1929). Nouvelle forme larvaire de *Thrombicula*, parasite sur un saurien de Palestine. *Bull. Mus. Nat. Hist. Nat.* 401–405.
Audy, J. R. (1961). African *Trombiculidae* (*Acarina*). 2. The genera *Eutrombicula* Ew. and *Sauriscus* Lawr. with description of a new subgenus, *Squamicola*. *Ann. Natal. Mus.* **15**, 135–140.
Baker, E. W. and Wharton, G. W. (1925). "An Introduction to Acarology." New York.
Camin, J. H. (1948). Mite transmission of a haemorrhagic septicaemia in snakes. *J. Parasit.* **34**, 545–554.
Camin, J. H. (1953). Observations on the life history and sensory behaviour of the snake mite. (*Ophionyssus natricis* Gervais) (Acarina, Macronyssidae). *Chicago Acad. Sci. Publ.* 10.
Dunn, L. H. (1918). Studies on the Iguana tick *Amblyomma dissimilis* in Panama. *J. Parasit.* **5**, 1–10.
Ewing, H. E. (1934). A new pit-producing mite from the scales of a S. American snake. *Parasitology* **20**, 53–56.
Ewing, H. E. (1944). The trombiculid mites (Chigger mites) and their relation to disease. *J. Parasit.* **30**, 339–365.
Fain, A. (1961). Les Acariens parasites endopulmonaires des serpents (*Entonyssidae Mesostigmata*). *Bull. Inst. Roy. Soc. Nat. Belg.* **37**, 1–135.
Fain, A. (1961b). Espèces et genres nouveaux dans la famille *Ixodorhynchidae* Ewing 1922 (*Acarina: Mesostigmata*). *Rev. Zool. Bot. Afr.* **64**, 175–182.
Fain, A. (1961c). Une nouvelle famille d'Acariens, parasite de serpents du genre *Mehelya* au Congo: *Omentolaelaptidae* fam. nov. (Mesostigmata). *Rev. Zool. Bot. Afr.* **64**, 283–296.
Fain, A. (1962). Les Acariens mesostigmatiques ectoparasites des Serpents. *Bull. Inst. R. Sci. Nat. Belg.* **38**, 18, 1–149.
Feider, Z. (1958). Sur une larve du genre *Trombicula* (*Acari*) parasite sur les lézards de la Roumanie. *Z. Parasitenk.* **18**, 441–456.

Finnegan, S. (1931). On a new species of mite of the family Heterozerconidae, parasitic on a snake. *Proc. zool. Soc. Lond.*, 1349–1357.

Fonseca, F. da, (1934). Der Schlangenparasit *Ixobioides butantanensis* novi generis n. sp. (*Acarina, Ixodorhynchidae*, nov. fam.). *Z. Pa asitenk.* **6**, 508–527.

Fonseca, F. da (1948). A monograph of the genera and species of *Macronyssidae* Oudemans 1936, (syn. *Liponyssidae* Vitzthum 1931 Acari). *Proc. zool. Soc. Lond.* **118**, 249–334.

Hirst, S. (1915). On a blood-sucking gamasid mite (*Ichoronyssus serpentinus* sp. n?) parasitic on Couper's snake. *Proc. zool. Soc. Lond.*, 383–386.

Hirst, S. (1926). On the parasitic mites of the suborder *Prostigmata* (*Trombidioidea*) found on lizards. *J. Linn. Soc. Zool.* **36**, 173–200.

Jellison, W. L. (1933). The parasitism of Lizards by *Ixodes ricinus californicus*. *J. Parasit.* **20**, 243–244.

Johnston, D. (1962). Ixodorhynchine mites ectoparasites of snakes. 1. Descriptions of a new genus and three new species from the nearctic region. (Acarina Mesostigmata). *Bull. Ann. Soc. R. Ent. Belg.* **98**, Nr. 11.

Krijgsman, B. J. and Ponto, S. A. S. (1932). Die Verbreitung der Zecken in Niederländisch-Ostindien. *Z. Parasitenk.* **4**, 140–146.

Lane, J. E. (1954). A redescription of the American lizard mite *Geckobiella texana* Banks 1904 with notes on the systematics of the species. (*Acarina: Pterygosomidae*). *J. Parasit.* **40**, 93–99.

Lawrence, R. F. (1935). Prostigmatic mites of S. African lizards. *Parasitology* **27**, 1–45.

Lawrence, R. F. (1936). The prostigmatic mites of S. African lizards. *Parasitology* **28**, 1–39.

Lawrence, R. F. (1949). The larval trombiculid mites of S. African vertebrates. *Ann. Natal. Mus.* **11**, 405–486.

Powder, W. A. and Loomis, R. B. (1962). A new species and new records of Chiggers (*Acarina: Trombiculidae*) from reptiles of S. California. *J. Parasit.* **48**, 204–208.

Privora, M. and Samsinak, K. (1958). Milben als Menschenplage. *Z. Parasitenk.* **18**, 257–269.

Radford, C. D. (1942a). The larval Trombiculinae (Acarina: Trombidiinae) with descriptions of twelve new species. *Parasitology* **34**, 55–81.

Radford, C. D. (1942b). New parasitic mites (*Acarina*). *Parasitology* **34**, 295–307.

Radford, C. D. (1943). Genera and species of parasitic mites (*Acarina*). *Parasitology* **35**, 58–81.

Sambon, L. W. (1928). The parasitic acarians of animals and the part they play in the causation of the eruptive fevers and other diseases of man. *Ann. trop. Med. Parasit.* **22**, 67–132.

Schmidt, F. L. (1928). *Entonyssus vitzthumi* (Acarina), a new ophidian lung mite. *J. Parasit.* **26**, 309–313.

Schroeder, C. R. (1934). Snake mite (*Ophionyssus serpentinum*). *J. Econ. Ent.* **27**, 1004–1014.

Schulze, P. (1932). Neue und wenig bekannte Arten der Zeckengattungen *Amblyomma* und *Aponomma*. *Z. Parasitenk.* **4**, 459–476.

Schulze, P. (1936). Neue und wenig bekannte Amblyommen und Aponommen aus Afrika, Südamerika, Indien, Borneo und Australien. (*Ixodidae*). *Z. Parasitenk.* **8**, 419–637.

Schweizer, H. (1952). Die Blutmilbe (*Ophionyssus natricis* Gerv./Mégn.) der "Stallfeind" des Schlangenpflegers und ihre Vernichtung. *Aqu. Terr. Z.* **5**, 103–105.

Strandtmann, R. W. and Wharton, G. W. (1958). "A Manual of Mesostigmatic Mites Parasitic on Vertebrates." Maryland.

Till, W. M. (1957). Mesostigmatic mites, living as parasites of reptiles in the Ethiopian region (*Acarina: Laelaptidae*). *J. Ent. Soc. S. Afr.* **20** (1) 120–143.

Warburton, C. (1932). On five new species of ticks (*Arachnida: Ixodidae*). *Parasitology* **24**, 558–568.

Womersley, H. (1941). New species of *Geckobia* (*Acarina: Pterygosomidae*) from Australia and New Zealand. *Trans. Roy. Soc. S. Austr.* **65**, 323–328.

J. Tongue Worms (Linguatulida)

These parasites, which are not worms but related to the Arachnida, may be found infesting tropical snakes and saurians. Fain (1961) found 11% of fifty-two examined specimens of *Naja* in the National Parks of Albert and Gramba (Belgian Congo) infected with *Cubirea pomeroyi* Woodl. Sixteen specimen of the genus *Mehelya* from the same area were parasitized by *Porocephalus subulifer* Leuckart. An infection with two different species of tongue worms was found in two cases only. In general the infections seem to exclude each other.

Most linguatulids are entoparasites and live, in reptiles, in the bronchi, the lungs, rarely in the heart or in the head. Only in a few cases has it been possible to determine their life cycle. Most of them seem to require two hosts. Reptiles become infected by feeding on primary hosts containing juvenile stages. These may be fish, amphibians, reptiles and mammals, rarely birds. Some species seem to complete their whole development without change of host. In such a case larvae and adults are found side by side. This, as Fain (1961) points out, is however no final proof, since the larvae need not have developed in the same host but may have been taken up with infected food. The presence of very young stages between the embryo and the third larva might be more suggestive (Fig. 372). Fain and Mortelmans (1960) found, in the trachea of a Komodo dragon, a female with mature eggs as well as encysted second and later larvae of *Sambonia lohrmanni* Noc and Giglioni, and considered this as sufficient proof for continuous development in one and the same host. But it may happen that linguatulid larvae re-encyst on entry into a new host before attaining sexual maturity. Fain (1961), whose original papers should be consulted for the determination of species, distinguished fifty different types of Linguatulida, as follows:

Order Cephalobaenida

Cephalobaenidae

Pulmonary parasites.

Cephalobaena tetrapoda Heymons: In S. American snakes of the genera *Bothrops, Lachesis, Leptophis* (Fig. 365a).

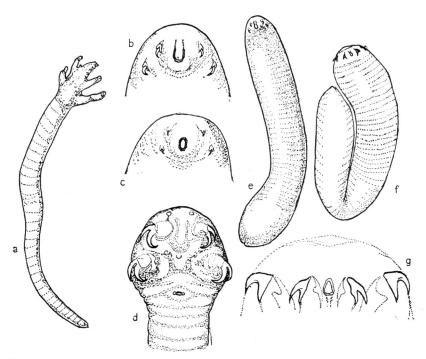

FIG. 365. a, *Cephalobaena tetrapoda* Heymons ♀. (After Heymons.) b, and e, *Alofia platycephala* Giglioli ♀. (After Heymons.) c, *Sebekia oxycephala* Sambon ♀. (After Heymons.) d, *Leiperia gracilis* Heymons and Vitzthum. Head of immature worm. (From Heymons.) f, *Elenia lialisi* Heymons second larval stage. (After Heymons.) g, Head of *Elenia lialisi* Heymons.

Raillietiella geckonis Sambon: Adult in geckonids and agamids.

R. affinis Bovien: In *Gecko verticillatus* Laur.

R. mabuiae Heymons: In *Mabuya sulcata* Peters (Fig. 366, left).

R. gehyrae Bovien: In *Gehyra multilata* Wiegm.

R. hemidactyli Hett.: In S.E. Asian geckonids.

R. kochi Heymons: In varanids.

R. shipleyi Heymons: In varanids.

R. orientalis Sambon: Adult in Eurasian snakes, larval in a species of *Naja* from the Congo.

R. boulengeri Sambon (Fig. 366, middle and right): larval and adult in African snakes.

R. agcoi Tubangui and Masilungan: In Philippine cobras.

R. mediterranea Sambon: Larval in toads, adult in *Coluber* spp.

R. furcocerca Sambon: In S. American snakes.

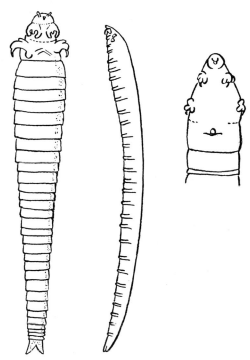

Fig. 366. Left, *Raillietiella mabuiae* Heymons. Middle and right, *Raillietiella boulengeri* Vaney and Sambon. (From Kükenthal, 1926.)

R. bicaudata Heymons and Vitzthum: In N. American snakes.

R. giglioli Hett: In *Amphisbaena alba* L.

R. chamaeleonis Gretillat and Brygoo: In Chamaeleonids.

R. schoutedeni Fain: In *Monopellis schoutedeni* Witte (Fig. 367).

Megadrepanoides solomonensis Self and Kunz: In the lungs of *Varanus indicus* Daud.

M. varani Self and Kunz: In the lungs of *Varanus indicus* Daudin.

Order Porocephalida

Sebekidae

Sebekia oxycephala Sambon: in the lungs of American crocodiles (adult). Larval in American fish and snakes (Fig. 365c).

S. wedli Gigliolo: Adult in African crocodiles.

S. acuminata Travassos: In Brazilian crocodiles.

S. divesta Giglioli: In American crocodiles.

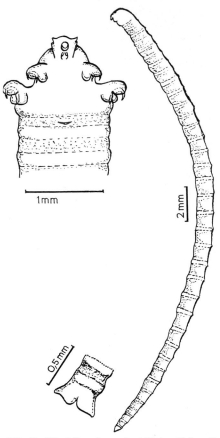

FIG. 367. *Raillietiella schoutedeni* Fain. (After Fain.)

S. samboni Travassos: In Brazilian crocodiles.

S. cesarisi Giglioli: In African crocodiles.

S. jubini Sambon: In the nasal pit of *Crocodilus siamensis* Sch.

Diesingia megastoma Diesing: In *Hydraspis geoffroyana* Wagler.

Alofia platycephala Giglioli: In S. American crocodiles (Fig. 365b, e).

A. indica Hett: In crocodiles from the Ganges.

Leiperia gracilis Heymans and Vitzthum: Adult in S. American crocodiles, larval in fish, turtles and snakes (= *Pentastomum gracile*
Diesing) (Fig. 365d).

L. cincinnalis Sambon: Adult in lungs, heart and aorta of *Crocodilus niloticus* Laur. Larval in several spp. of fish (= *Porocephalus nematoides* de Beauchamp) (Fig. 372b).

Subtriquetridae

Adult in the oral cavity and the pharynx of crocodiles, larval in the intestine and swim-bladder of fish.

Subtriquetra subtriquetra Sambon: In S. American crocodiles.

S. shipleyi Hett: In the pharynx of Indian crocodiles.

S. megacephala Sambon: In the cephalic tissues of *Crocodilus palustris* L.

Sambonidae

Sambonia lohrmanni Noc and Giglioli: Larval and adult in the lungs of African varanids (Fig. 368).

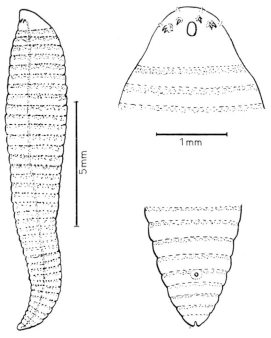

FIG. 368. *Sambonia lohrmanni* Noc and Giglioli. (After Fain and Mortelmans.)

Elenia australis Heymons: In Australian varanids.

E. lialisi Heymons: Larval in *Lialis jicari* Blgr. (Fig. 365f.).

Waddycephalus teretiusculus Sambon: Larval and adult in Australian snakes (Fig. 369a).

Porocephalidae

Larval in mammals, adult in the lungs of snakes.

Porocephalus crotali Humboldt: Larval in mammals (mice), snakes and amphibians. Adult in crotalid snakes.

P. clavatus Sambon: Larvae encysted in mammals; adult in boid and viperid snakes.

P. stilesi Sambon: In S. American snakes.

P. subulifer Sambon: Larval in snakes and mammals, adult in African snakes (Fig. 370, right).

P. benoiti Fain: In African snakes.

P. pomeroyi Woodland: In African snakes.

Kiricephalus coarctatus Sambon: In American snakes, larval encysted in snakes and mammals (Fig. 369b).

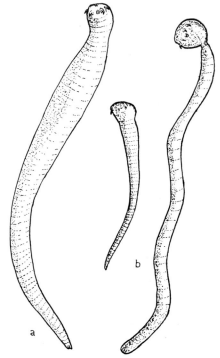

Fig. 369. a, *Waddycephalus teretiusculus* Sambon ♀; b, *Kiricephalus coarctatus* Sambon: left, ♂; right, ♀. (After Heymons.)

K. pattoni Sambon: Larval in snakes and amphibians, adult in Indian, Madagascar and Australian snakes.

K. tortus Sambon: In *Dipsadomorphus irregularis* Merrem.

Armilliferidae

Nymphs mostly in mammals, rarely in birds, adult in the lungs of snakes.

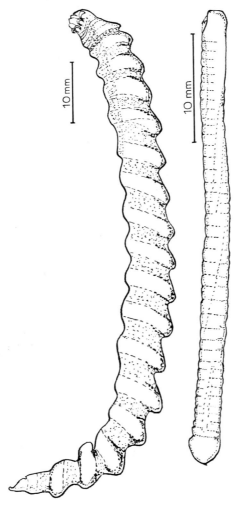

FIG. 370. Left, *Armillifer armillatus* Wyman; right, *Porocephalus subulifer* Leuckart. (After Fain.)

Armillifer armillatus Sambon (Figs. 370, left; 371, right). In boid, viperid and colubrid snakes, larval in mammals including humans, rarely in birds.

A. grandis Sambon: Larval in birds. Adult in African viperid snakes.

A. moniliformis Sambon: Larval in monkeys, tarsians and carnivores.
Adult in Asian pythons.

Cubirea annulata Kishida: In African snakes.

C. pomeroyi Kishida: In *Naja* spp.

Gigliolella brumpti Chabaud and Choquet: In snakes from Madagascar.

Ligamifer mazzai Heymons: In Asian and Australian snakes. Perhaps
transmitted by marsupials.

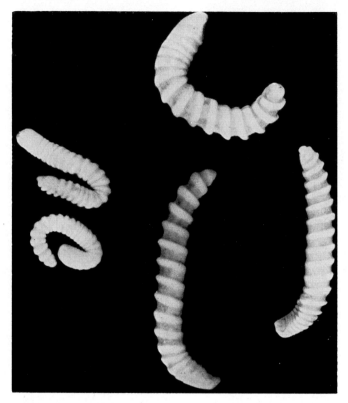

FIG. 371. Left, Two larvae of *Armillifer grandis* Hett; right, three larvae of *Armillifer armillatus* Wyman. (After Fain.)

REFERENCES

Fain, A. (1961). Les Pentastomides de l'Afrique Centrale. *Ann. Koninkl. Mus. Tervuren* **92**, 1–115.

Fain, A. and Mortelmans, J. (1960). Observations sur le cycle évolutif de *Sambonia lohrmanni* chez le Varan. Preuve d'un dévelopement direct chez les Pentastomida. *Bull. Acad. Roy. Belg.* 5. ser. **46**, 518–531.

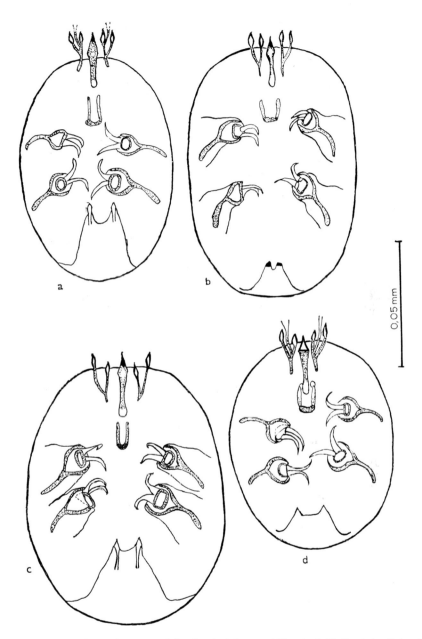

FIG. 372. a, Embryonic stage of *Sambonia lohrmanni* Noc and Giglioni; b, *Leiperia cincinnalis* Sambon; c, *Armillifer armillatus* Wyman; d, *Porocephalus subulifer* Leuckart. (After Fain.)

Gretillat, S. and Brygoo (1959). *Raillietiella chamaeleonis* n. sp. première espèce de *Cephalobaenidae* (*Pentastomida*) signalée à Madagascar. *Ann. Parasit.* **34**, 112–120.

Hett, M. L. (1924). On the family *Linguatulidae. Proc. zool. Soc. Lond.* 107–160.

Heymons, R. (1932). Ein Beitrag zur Kenntnis der Pentastomiden Australiens und benachbarter Gebiete. *Z. Parasitenk.* **4**, 409–430.

Heymons, R. (1935). Beiträge zur Systematik der Pentastomiden. II. Einige bemerkenswerte Pentastomiden aus Lacertiliern. *Z. Parasitenk.* **10**, 676–690.

Heymons, R. and Graf Vitzthum, H. (1935). Beiträge zur Systematik der Pentastomiden. *Z. Parasitenk.* **8**, 1–103.

Self, J. P. and Murry, F. S. (1948). *Porocephalus crotali* Humboldt (Pentastomida) in Oklahoma. *J. Parasit.* **34**, 21–23.

Woodland, W. N. F. (1920). On a remarkable new species of *Porocephalus* (*P. pomeroyi* sp. n.) from the foregut of a Nigerian cobra. *Parasitology* **12**, 337–340.

K. Insects

Insects may damage Reptilia directly and indirectly; directly through stinging and blood-sucking and through the proteolytic action of fly larvae. Peters (1948) and Rainey (1953) reported on cases of this kind in chelonians. Equally Graham-Jones (1961) mentions that flies frequently deposit their eggs in the cloacal and tail region of chelonians. The larvae, when hatched, penetrate the host tissue and may cause deep wounds extending under the carapace. Any visible larvae should be removed. The tortoises should be bathed twice daily and treated with antiseptic powder. If not too heavily damaged the animals may be saved.

Indirect insect damage to reptiles may be caused by mosquitoes and flies which transmit blood parasites. The following might be mentioned:

Culex fatigans Wied	⎫
C. annulirostis Skuse	⎬ transmit filariae.
Culex tarsalis L.	transmits viruses.
Phlebotomus spp.	transmit *Bartonella* spp., *Leishmania* spp. and trypanosomes.
Glossina palpalis Rob. and Desv.	⎫
G. tachinoides Westwood	⎬ transmit trypanosomes.

In a few cases even fleas have been found on reptiles. Jäth (1952) encountered these insects on *Lacerta vivipara* Jacquin and on *Natrix natrix* L. Fleas have also been found on the green lizard *Lacerta v. viridis* Laur. which had hatched from the faeces of dogs and were determined as *Ctenocephalus canis* L. (T. Schellkopf in Jäth, 1952).

We may finally mention *Triatoma rubrovaria* Pinto, a bug which has been found to carry spores of the protozoon *Hepatozoon triatomae*

Osimani which is a parasite of lizards. The bugs, most probably, transmit the infection.

REFERENCES

Graham-Jones, O. (1961). Notes on the common tortoise. *Vet. Rec.* **73**, 313–321.
Jäth, H. (1952). Flöhe als Irrgäste auf Reptilien. *Aqu. Terr. Z.* **5**, 276.
Peters, J. A. (1948). The box turtle as a host for dipterous parasites. *Amer. Midl. Nat.* **40**, 472–474.
Rainey, D. G. (1953). Death of an ornate box turtle parasitized by dipterous larvae. *Herpetologica* **9**, 109–110.

L. DISEASES CAUSED BY FUNGI

Contrary to our findings in fish and amphibians mycotic diseases in reptiles are rare. We quote the few accounts of such infections which have been published.

Meyn (1942) described the appearance of *Actinomyces bovis* Harz em. Boström in a captive snake. Equally Rodhain and Mattlet (1950) found fungal threads in a tracheal tumour of a snake. From these a *Cephalosporium* type fungus could be grown in culture.

Blanchard (1890) found various stages of a hypomycetous fungus in tumours of a green lizard (*Lacerta viridis* L.). Both the surface layers and the deeper parts of the tumours contained whitish conidia, divided into chambers and having a length of up to 15 μ. The deeper layers showed a dense network of chambered, laterally compressed threads resembling *Fusarium* or *Selenosporium*. Species of the former genus may be found on animal corpses. The fungus also had great similarity to *Selenosporium urticum*, a species which grows on decaying plants, and the author suggests that it may have been identical with the latter species.

One of us (E. E.) saw a mycotic infection in a specimen of *Coronella austriaca* kept in company with a specimen of *Natrix sipedon*. The latter died first, showing no other sign of illness than a small swelling under one scale. A month after this the smooth snake showed signs of disease. The nostrils were blocked, the oral mucosa swollen, one eye more prominent than the other and the whole gular region oedematous. The oedema disappeared after the snake had been killed. Post-mortem examination revealed numerous white spots on the liver (Fig. 373). These contained no acid-fast bacilli but many hyphenous fungal threads. Attempts to grow bacteria from any part of the snake failed. The fungal threads were Gram-positive and stained well by the periodic acid–Schiff technique. The peripheral part of the foci and the surrounding tissue contained large numbers of eosinophil granulocytes.

Fungal mycelia were also found (E. E.) on the peritoneal surface of abdominal organs in a specimen of *Chinemys reevesii* Gray which had suffered from an extensive disease of the Harderian gland (Fig. 374). It was not possible to determine the exact nature of these fungi.

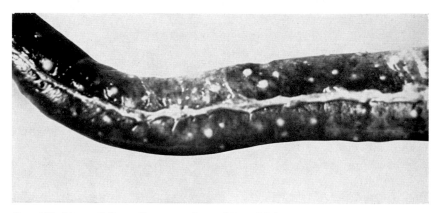

FIG. 373. Liver of *Coronella a. austriaca* with multiple fungal abscesses. × 4. (Photo.: E. Elkan.)

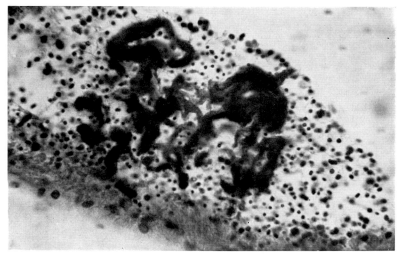

FIG. 374. Fungal mycelium in the peritoneal cavity of *Chinemys reevesii* Gray in a specimen also suffering from a diseased Harderian gland. × 250. (Photo.: E. Elkan.)

Some authors consider that fungi may be responsible for an oral disease of tortoises, sometimes described as mouth cancer (Graham-Jones, 1961).

Interesting observations on zoophagous fungi were published by Hunt (1957). He found that the lungs of tortoises were frequently the seat of fungi of an *Aspergillus* type. In severe cases such an infection may entirely destroy and obliterate parts of the organ. Confinement of several animals in close quarters increases the danger of transmission. The author concluded that about 3% of all deaths in captive tortoises were caused by pulmonary mycosis.

Fungal infection may even extend to the carapace of tortoises. Infection by *Mucor* species has been observed in such cases but the exact pathogens have not been determined. The ventral shield is more frequently affected than the dorsal carapace. All types of chelonians may be so affected with the exception of marine species, where the disease is much rarer. A species very commonly affected is *Sternotherus carinatus* Gray.

Four specimens of giant tortoises (*Testudo elephantopus, T. gigantea elephantina*) died in the Chicago Zoological Park (Georg *et al.*, 1962). The first showed a lung infection with *Aspergillus amstelodami* and *Geotrichum candidum*. The second, also a Galapagos tortoise, was infected with *Beauveria bassiana*, the third, an aldabra tortoise, with *Paecilomyces fumoso-roseus*, in the fourth no certain cause of death was ascertained. The two Galapagos tortoises had been in captivity for 30 years. The authors stress the difficulty in imitating the exact environmental conditions to which these giant tortoises are geared. Their particular temperature requirements cannot always be maintained and they may become victims of bacterial and fungal infections against which they have no natural immunity.

Among the reptiles most difficult to keep in captivity are the chameleons. In spite of all our efforts most of them die within a year and the exact cause of death usually remains unexplained. We were therefore particularly interested in the case of a two-banded chameleon (*Chamaeleo bitaeniatus* Fischer 1884) which, as related by its owner, had developed a "paraplegia" and had to be killed because it could no longer maintain its hold on branches and fell to the ground unless helped. The dissection of *Chamaeleo bitaeniatus* is difficult because the entire peritoneum is intensely black through the presence of innumerable melanophores. The fact that this chameleon died from an extensive disease of the liver was therefore only discovered when sections of this organ were examined (Fig. 375a). These showed the liver permeated by foci of necrotic material surrounded first by a shell of granulation tissue and then by a second shell of fibrous tissue. Application of the periodic acid–Schiff technique showed the granulation zone to be heavily permeated by a yeast-like fungus, the individual cells measuring between $2.5 \times 3 \, \mu$ to $7 \times 8 \, \mu$. They showed no sign of capsule formation but some filamentation with branching and septation, the hyphae being between 1.5 and $2.0 \, \mu$ thick. Dr. J. G. Murray of the Mycological

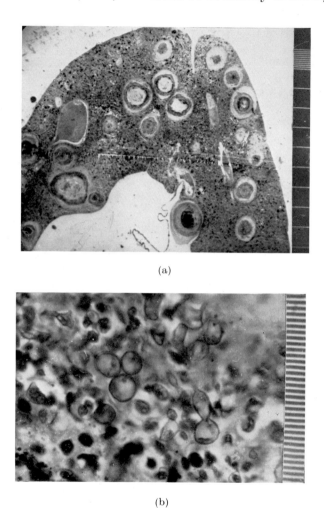

(a)

(b)

Fig. 375. *Chamaeleo bitaeniatus* Fischer. Adult female. Infection of liver with *Candida albicans*. (a) H. and E. Low power. Scale: 0.1 and 0.01. (b) PAS-haematoxylin-tetrazin. Scale $1.67 \, \mu$. (Photo.: E. Elkan.)

Reference Laboratory of the London School of Hygiene who examined the material considered the offending organism to be most likely *Candida albicans*. Considering how extensively the liver of this reptile was affected its death is perhaps not surprising. What seems more extraordinary is the fact that nothing abnormal and in particular no fungus could be found in any of the other viscera although a thorough search was made in microscopic sections. Further material of this kind would be of great interest particularly since we should like to know whether chameleons frequently die of fungal infections or whether this was an unusual and isolated case (Fig. 375b).

REFERENCES

Blanchard, R. (1890). Sur une remarquable dermatose causée chez le lézard vert par un champion du genre *Selenosporium*. *Mem. Soc. Zool. Fr.* **3**, 241–255.

Georg, L. K., Williamson, W. M., Tilden, E. B. and Getty, R. E. (1962). Mycotic pulmonary disease of captive giant tortoises due to *Beauveria bassiana* and *Poecilomyces fumoso-roseus*. *Sabouraudia* **2**, 80–86.

Graham-Jones, O. (1961). Notes on the Common Tortoise. *Vet. Rec.* **73**, 313–321.

Hunt, T. J. (1957). Notes on diseases and mortality in testudines. *Herpetologica* **13**, 19–23.

Meyn, A. (1942). Actinomyces Infektion bei einer Schlange. *Zool. Garten* N.F. **14**, 251.

Rodhain J. and Mattlet, G. (1950). Une tumeur mycosique chez la couleuvre vipérine *Tropidonotus natrix*. *Ann. Parasit.* **25**, 77–79

CHAPTER 21

Non-Parasitic and Environmental Diseases

A. TUMOURS

Like the fish and the Amphibia, reptiles may be afflicted by a variety of tumours which may be genuine or of the pseudotumour variety. The genuine tumours may be benign, causing displacement of neighbouring

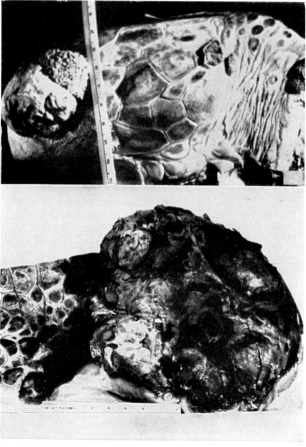

FIG. 376. Dermal papillomata in *Chelonia mydas* L. Above, tumour above the eye; below, tumour on the tail. (From Lucké and Schlumberger.)

organs only, or malign, infiltrating the neighbourhood and metastasizing. Lucké and Schlumberger (1949) reviewed the material available.

Dermal tumours (epitheliomata and papillomata) were described by Schwarz (1923) on *Tupinambis teguixin*; by Lucké and Schlumberger (1948) on *Pelusios odoratus* Latr.; and by Lucké, Smith and Coates (1938) on *Chelonia mydas* (Fig. 376). Smith and Coates suggest that the dermal fibroepitheliomata seen on the skin of marine turtles may have been caused by a virus because similar eruptions were seen on the skin of the indigenous human population. They also report the occasional presence of trematode eggs in these tumours.

Papillomata are commonly seen in the skin of lizards particularly in *Lacerta agilis* L. In its harmless form the disease is often referred to as "pox". Stolk and Plehn (1911) reported on such tumours in lizards which, in more extended form, may lead to the development of "tree bark tumours"; the histology of these was investigated by Klein (1952). The tumours may assume very bizarre shapes (Fig. 378) due to the development of a mixed fibroepithelial papilloma involving the epidermis and the corium. The cause of this disease, which has also been seen in freshly caught animals, is not known. Blanchard (1890) assigned responsibility to fungi of the *Selenosporium* type. Later authors could not confirm these findings. Papillary dermal carcinomata were seen by Bergmann (1941) in *Homalopsis buccata* L. and by Koch (1904) in *Lacerta agilis*. Similar observations were made by Pick and Poll (1903) and Plimmer (1912). Schlumberger (1958) published the figure of an epithelioma on the foot of *Heloderma*, the gila monster. In this case squamous epithelium had invaded the adjacent fibromuscular tissue (Fig. 377) and even the underlying bone was affected.

One of us (E.E.) recently saw a very young chameleon (*Ch. bitaeniatus*) of 5 cm length whose mother had died of a liver infection by the fungus *Candida albicans*. Exactly the same fungus was seen growing in small patches on the skin of the youngster where it caused appreciable thickening of the stratum corneum and a thinning out of the layer of dermal melanophores. This picture seems to represent the typical reptilian reaction to any agent which chronically irritates the skin. Both fungi and viruses seem to be able occasionally to breach the epidermal defences in which case the disease progresses towards papillomatosis or even ulceration.

The oral tissue of reptiles is frequently affected by tumours. These were reviewed by Schlumberger (1953). At that time twenty cases had been reported from chelonians, crocodiles, lizards and snakes, not always arising from the same cause. Some of the tumours were multiple chondromata arising from cartilage, as for instance a tumour seen in a

monitor lizard by Bland-Sutton (1885). The picture was also shown of
a spongy carcinoma of the parotid in the Teju, *Tupinambis nigropunctatus* (Fig. 380).

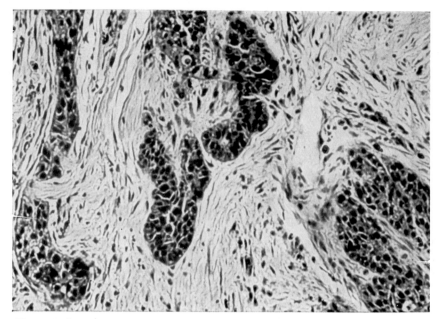

FIG. 377. Strands of a malign epithelioma invading the leg of a gila monster (*Heloderma suspectum*). × 220. (After Schlumberger in Cohrs, Jaffé and Meesen.)

Schlumberger mentions a pelvic tumour in a specimen of *Python
reticulatus* from the Zoological Gardens of Philadelphia, accompanied
by two melanomas elsewhere. We shall also have to report on a case
of a melanosarcoma affecting the lip of a snake. Another oral tumour
of a specimen of *Python sebae* Gm. was mentioned by Vaillant and
Pettit (1902).

An ocular tumour in the turtle *Chelonia mydas* L. was seen by Lucké
(1938).

We have already mentioned the occurrence of chondromata and
osteomata in reptiles. Stolk (1958) for instance saw numerous small
tumours in the tail of a *Lacerta viridis* L. and he could show that the
tumour originated in the vertebral column. They contained osteoblasts,
fibroblasts, bundles of collagen fibres and small fragments of bone. It
was thought unlikely that the condition should have been the result of
an injury. We may here also mention a case of bony tumours and malformation seen in a specimen of *Crocodilus porosus* Schneider by Kälin

(1937). Both exostoses and bony tumours were found in the same animal.

Tumours of internal organs have been found in the lungs (Bland-Sutton, 1885), the kidneys and the pancreas. A papillary adenocarcin-

Fig. 378. *Lacerta ocellata* with tree bark tumours of the skin. (Photo.: Foersch.)

Fig. 379. Maxillary osteoma in *Lacerta viridis*. (Photo.: E. Elkan.)

oma of the kidney was seen by Patay (1933) in a specimen of *Natrix natrix* L. Ratcliffe (1935, 1943) described adenocarcinomata and other neoplasms of the pancreas.

Neural tumours are rare in reptiles. However, Scott and Beattie (1927) found a tumour of the cerebellum in *Crocodilus porosus* Schn.

Coloured tumours, particularly melanomata which occur in reptiles are rightly regarded with much apprehension. Ball (1946) reported on a remarkable case of melanoma in a specimen of *Pituophis melanoleucus*

17

Daudin. A melanoma appeared on the body of a female and on the lip of the male. The latter grew very rapidly to a size of $4 \times 2 \cdot 5$ cm.

Pseudotumours, i.e. tumours due to parasitic infection, are frequently seen. To this group belong the gular tumours which were found to

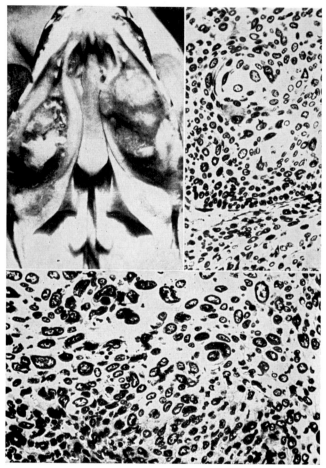

Fig. 380. Oral cancer in *Tupinambis nigropunctatus* Spix. Above left, ventral view of maxillary region; above right and below, sections through the tumour. $\times 211$. (From Lucké and Schlumberger.)

contain bacteria of the species "*Bacterium*" *sauromali* Conti and Crawley (1939). Another tumour (Rodhain and Mettlet, 1950) contained fungal threads. It should also be mentioned that tumours may be caused through filariosis and through trematodes which encyst in reptiles. A papilloma of the gall bladder associated with a trematode infection was described by Smith and Nigrelli (1941). The same authors (1943) reported on a chelonian fibroepithelioma connected with leeches of the genus *Ozobranchus*. Smith and Coates (1938) finally found trematode eggs in the fibroepithelioma of a marine turtle.

REFERENCES

Ball, H. A. (1946). Melanosarcoma and rhabdomyoma in two pine snakes *Pituophis melanoleucus*. *Cancer Res.* **6**, 134–138.

Bergmann, R. A. M. (1941). Tumoren bij Slangen. *Geneesk. Tijdschr. Ned. Ind.* **81**, 547–577.

Blanchard, R. (1890). Sur une remarquable dermatose causée chez le lézard vert par un champignon du genre *Selenosporium*. *Mém. Soc. Zool., Fr.* **3**, 241–255.

Bland-Sutton, J. (1885). Tumours in animals. *J. Anat. Phys.* **19**, 415–475.

Conti, F. and Crawley, J. H. (1939). A new bacterial species isolated from the Chuckawalla (*Sauromalus varius*). *J. Bact.* **37**, 647–653.

Kälin, J. A. (1937). Über Skeletanomalien bei Crocodiliden. *Z. Morph. Ökol. Tiere* **32**, 327–437.

Klein, B. M. (1952). Die Borkengeschwulst der Eidechsen. *Mikrokosmos* **42**, 49–52.

Koch, M. (1904). Demonstration einiger Geschwülste bei Tieren. *Verh. dtsch. Path. Ges.* **7**, 136–147.

Lucké, B. (1938). Studies on tumours in cold-blooded vertebrates. *Ann. Rep. Tortugas Lab. Carneg. Inst. Wash.* 1937/38. 92–94.

Lucké, B. and Schlumberger, M. G. (1949). Neoplasia in cold-blooded vertebrates. *Phys. Rev.* **29**, 91–216.

Nigrelli, R. F. and Smith, G. M. (1943). The occurrence of leeches, *Ozobranchus branchiatus*, in fibroepithelial tumours of marine turtles *Chelonia mydas*. *Zoologica* **2**, 107–108.

Patay, R. (1933). Sur un cas d'épithélioma du rein chez *Tropidonotus natrix* (Ophidien colubridé). *C. R. Soc. Biol., Paris* **114**, 65–67.

Pick, L. and Poll, M. (1903). Über einige bemerkenswerte Tumorbildungen aus der Thierpathologie, insbesondere über gutartige und krebsige Neubildungen bei Kaltblütern. *Berl. klin. Wschr.* **40**, 510–572.

Plehn, M. (1911). Über Geschwülste bei niederen Wirbeltieren. 2. *Conf. int. Étude Cancer*, 221–242.

Plimmer, M. G. (1912). Report on the deaths which occurred in the Zoological Gardens during 1911. *Proc. zool. Soc. Lond.*, 235–240.

Plimmer, M. G. (1913). Report on the deaths which occurred in the Zoological Gardens during 1912. *Proc. zool. Soc. Lond.*, 141–149.

Ratcliffe, H. L. (1935). Carcinoma of the pancreas in Say's pine snake (*Pituophis sayi*). *Amer. J. Cancer* **24**, 78–79.

Ratcliffe, H. L. (1943). Neoplastic disease of the pancreas of snakes (Serpentes). *Amer. J. Path.* **19**, 359–366.

Rodhain, J. and Mettlet, G. (1950). Une tumeur mycosique chez la couleuvre viperine *Tropidonotus natrix*. *Ann. Parasit.* **25**, 77–79.

Schlumberger, H. G. (1953). Comparative pathology of oral neoplasms. *Oral. Surg.* **6**, 1078–1094.

Schlumberger, H. G. and Lucké, B. (1948). Tumours of fishes, amphibians and reptiles. *Cancer Res.* **8**, 657–754.

Schlumberger, H. G. (1958). Krankheiten der Fische, Amphibien und Reptilien. *In* "Pathologie der Laboratoriumstiere" (Cohrs, Jaffé and Meesen, eds.). Springer, Berlin, Göttingen, Heidelberg.

Schnabel, R. (1954). Papillome an einer Smaragdeidechse (*Lacerta viridis*). *Zool. Garten* **2**, 270–278.

Schwarz, F. (1923). Über zwei Geschwülste bei Kaltblütern. *Z. Krebsforsch.* **20**, 353–357.

Scott, H. H. and Beattie, J. (1927). Neoplasm in a porose crocodile. *J. Path. Bact.* **30**, 41–66.

Smith, G. M. A. and Coates, C. (1938). Fibro-epithelial growths of the skin in large marine turtles, *Chelonia mydas*. *Zoologica* **23**, 93–98.

Smith, G. M. A. (1939). The occurrence of trematode ova, *Haplotrema constrictum*, on fibroepithelial tumours of the marine turtle *Chelonia mydas*. *Zoologica* **24**, 379–389.

Smith, G. M. A. and Nigrelli, R. F. (1941). A papillomatous tumour of the gall bladder associated with infection by flukes, occurring in the marine turtle *Chelonia mydas*. *Zoologica* **26**, 13–16.

Stolk, R. (1953). Hyperkeratosis and carcinoma planocellulare in the lizard, *Lacerta agilis*. *Koninkl. Ned. Akad. Wetensch.* Ser. C. **56**, 157–163.

Stolk, R. (1958). Tumours of reptiles. Multiple osteomas in the lizard *Lacerta viridis*. *Beaufortia* **7**, 1–9.

Vaillant, B. and Pettit, A. (1902). Lesions stomacales observés chez un Python de Seba. *Bull. Mus. Hist. Nat., Paris* **8**, 593–595.

B. Diseases due to Faulty Environment

Unsuitable nutrition and unsuitable environment may both cause diseases in reptiles. Animals may fall ill because they have not enough or not the right food; they may suffer from lack of sunshine, particularly from lack of u.v. radiation; or from the lack of space, and enforced immobility. Into the same group belong the harmful effects of excessive air, and soil humidity factors which frequently interfere with the health of captive reptiles.

Among the alimentary disturbances vitamin deficiencies are common but not always easily recognized. They may manifest themselves as inflammation of areas of skin or of the eyes, as oedema, difficulties in skin shedding, refusal to feed at all, oral oedema and inflammation, listlessness, fading of coloration, and an inclination to hide in the most inaccessible corner of the cage. In short, they may cause the greatest variety of symptoms and give, at first sight, no hint towards a correct diagnosis. Since small doses of vitamins are harmless and since it may take some time before the root of the trouble is discovered, it may be advisable to feed with a few drops of a multivitamin mixture wherever reptiles fail to thrive for obvious reasons. Lack of vitamin A may damage the eyes (Fig. 381), persistent softness of the carapace of tortoises is often regarded as a form of rickets due to lack of vitamin D and it must not be forgotten that, apart from the vitamin, tortoises also appreciate the addition of crushed bones to their diet. Rickets is by no means

FIG. 381. *Lacerta t. taurica* Pallas imported from Greece. Oedema of eyes due to avitaminosis. Young specimen. (Photo.: Stemmler-Gyger.)

FIG. 382. Ornamental turtles affected by rickets showing distorted carapace. (Photo.: Stemmler-Morath.)

uncommon in captive animals. Hamerton and Scott, in their reports on the death of animals in a zoological garden, make repeated mention of such cases (1933 also 1926–28). Equally Kälin (1937) saw skeletal

damage due to rickets in crocodiles (Fig. 382) and damage of this kind
is particularly common at the end of a hibernation period when the
feeding of egg-shells or crushed bone is of particular importance.
Kästle (personal communication) reports that he succeeded in curing
tail deformities by giving calcium and a multivitamin preparation.

Vitamin deficiency probably causes many other, not easily recognizable symptoms. Inflammatory processes of the intestinal tract
(mouth and gut), so frequently seen in captive animals are, if not due to
parasites, often caused by a vitamin B deficiency, and can be cured by
adding this vitamin to the food.

The thyroid gland often gives cause to irregularities either in the form
of hyper- or hypo-thyroidism. Hypo-thyroidism produces goitre in
reptiles as well as in fish and amphibians, where, however, the condition
is much more common than in reptiles. Schlumberger (1955) reported
on three cases of goitre, two in tortoises and one in a lizard, all of
which had been inmates of zoological gardens for several years. He
suggests that the condition was caused by lack of iodine.

Since the production of vitamin D is linked up with the action of
u.v. rays, environmental and metabolic factors are closely linked and
interdependent. Mistakes may be aggravated by faulty or oscillating
temperature or humidity.

It remains of course frequently impossible to determine the adverse
environmental factors harmful to reptiles, particularly if these are
found diseased in their natural environment. Fig. 383, for instance,
shows an Aesculapian snake (*Elaphe l. longissima* Laur.), caught in
the Tessin, with a patchy disease of the skin. No parasites were found
and it was thought that the skin degeneration was caused by other
noxious factors in the snake's habitat. It has to be considered, however, that the spectrum of possible parasites is a wide one and that
these may not always be visible even if a hand lens is used. Animals
weakened by malnutrition and/or internal parasites may eventually
be killed by bacterial infection. The possible variations in the pathology
of lower vertebrates are so great that we must not be surprised at the
number deaths which remain undiagnosed to the last.

Into this group belong at the moment the disturbances of the equili–
brium so often seen in captive *Xenopus* and the distressing *disease of
the eyelids* which affects so many of the terrapins and ornamental
turtles imported from overseas.

This disease was well-known to Klingelhöffer, a German ophthalmo-
logist, who mentions, in his textbook on herpetology, that unfortunately
the hard heads of terrapins were too difficult to section. And so this
eye specialist who would have been so well-qualified to find the cause

of this mysterious disease had to leave the work to posterity. Meanwhile he suggested that the disease was due to avitaminosis.

FIG. 383. *Elaphe l. longissima* from the Tessin with dermal disease, photographed soon after capture. (Photo.: Stemmler-Gyger.)

A host of different causes has, in the meantime, been blamed for this disease: faulty temperature, faulty diet, too little or too much lime in the water, bacterial infection, etc. All we know is that, while most animals die from it, some survive the disease and even regain their eyesight.

The affected specimens always belong to the genera *Clemmys*, *Emys*, *Chinemys*, *Pseudemys*, *Chrysemys* or *Pseudomedusa* and it may occur in young, freshly imported turtles or in old stock. The nictitating membrane becomes inflamed, thickened, and too easily visible with the naked eye. It closes too slowly and does not cover the eyeball quite. Its capillaries are engorged. Within a day or two first the upper, then the lower eyelid become swollen. Soon they fuse so firmly that they cannot even be separated with a blunt instrument (Fig. 384a and b). The turtle, totally blinded, mostly refuses to feed and eventually dies from inanition. But not always. Some observers have seen a hard mass eventually detaching itself from the eye, revealing a perfectly intact

eyeball underneath. The disease is usually bilateral, but unilateral
cases have also been seen. These animals are more likely to survive
because they continue to feed.

(a)

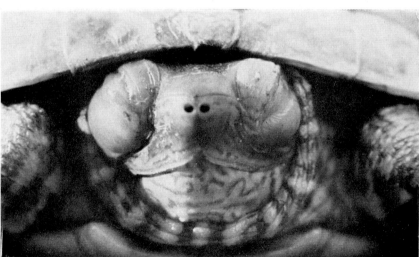

(b)

FIG. 384. *Clemmys caspica leprosa* Loveridge and Williams. Disease of the Harderian gland. (a) First week. (Photo.: E. Elkan.) (b) Anterior view.

Modern histological methods make the sectioning of turtle-heads
quite feasible and the inspection of material from these cases produces

a surprising result (Fig. 385). The seat of the disease is not the eyelid proper but the Harderian gland, a structure closely joined to it. The eyeball is not affected at all.

The Harderian gland, named after the Swiss anatomist Harder who discovered it in 1694 in deer, lies in the orbital cavity opposite the lachrymal gland and is present in most animals from the amphibians upwards. In man the gland is only represented by a rudimentary body, the caruncula lacrimalis. In crocodiles, snakes and the tuatara (*Sphenodon*) the lachrymal gland is missing and only the Harderian gland is developed. It has been taken for granted that it is the function of these glands to moisten and to lubricate the very vulnerable corneal surface of the eyeball. But it remained difficult to see why these glands were equally well, if not better, developed in aquatic species, whose eyes, permanently bathed in water, would not seem to need either cleaning or lubrication. The investigations of Schmidt-Nielsen and Fange (1958) have solved this enigma. These authors showed that the ophthalmic glands secrete, apart from serous fluid and a little mucus, large quantities of salt (NaCl). "Salty tears" are known well enough, but we have now learnt that, while the human kidney is quite able to excrete surplus salt without aid from any other excretory organ, the kidney of the lower vertebrate is apparently not so efficient, and we can now understand the astonishingly large size of the Harderian gland in marine animals which cannot well avoid swallowing a good deal of salt with their food.

The normal lachrymal and Harderian glands, though not identical, are of very similar structure. They are tubular-acinous glands similar to the salivary glands. Statements to the effect that these glands might be sebaceous are incorrect. They are largely serous; only the excretory ducts are partly lined with goblet cells capable of producing a small amount of mucus.

Sections through the orbit of a diseased animal show the normal glandular structure completely lost. The epithelium has changed from the glandular to the squamous type; the acini are grossly dilated and distended by masses of keratinic debris which cannot be expelled (Figs. 385, 386). In short, the gland has undergone complete metaplasia, the centre being usually marked by a large accumulation of eosinophile granulocytes forming a kind of abscess. Eosinophilia is marked throughout, particularly in the liver, where capillaries and biliary ducts are surrounded by agglomerations of acidophile granulocytes. The centre of the keratinic masses in the glandular acini is usually marked by one or several degenerate nuclei, probably the remains of the original glandular epithelium.

17*

It would be easier to explain this extraordinary histological picture if occlusion of the excretory duct of the Harderian gland could be demonstrated. Such an occlusion might occur in consequence of bacterial

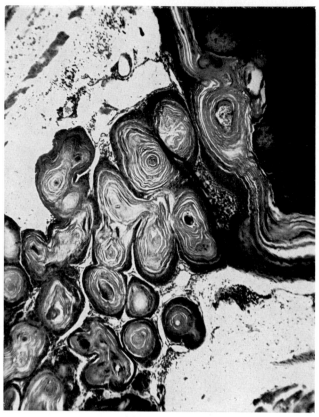

FIG. 385. *Chinemys reevesii* Gray. Section through the orbital region showing extensive metaplasia of the Harderian gland with accumulation of keratinic masses in the acini. Stain, Mallory. × 50. (Photo.: E. Elkan.)

infection. So far only some acid-fast mycobacteria were encountered and these are too common and too ubiquitous to be regarded as significant. No trace of the duct could be found in the grossly pathologic glands and further lengthy and time-consuming research will be needed to clarify the many problems that remain.

A signpost may be seen in the following observation. When heads of just-hatched Malayan turtles (*Dermochelys coriacea* L.) were sectioned the upper region of the nasal cavity was filled with numerous, so far unidentified, nematodes. The structure of the mucous membrane was intensely damaged by the worms. Parasites are only too often the cause of morbidity in lower vertebrates and it is by no means impossible that nematodes might obstruct the excretory ducts of the ophthalmic

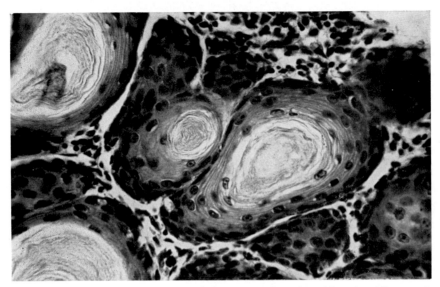

FIG. 386. As Fig. 385, × 300, showing inflammatory invasion with eosinophile granulo-cytes and extensive metaplasia of the Harderian gland. (Photo.: E. Elkan.)

glands. In that case the central nuclei in the keratinic masses might represent the remains of such worms. At the time of writing we can only offer this partial solution of the problem. The rest must be handed on to yet further generations of herpetologists.

Ornamental terrapins which are widely distributed as pets and rarely kept in suitable conditions often show a patchy white discoloration of the carapace accompanied by listlessness and refusal to feed. Successes obtained in treating the condition with multiple vitamin preparations make it appear very likely that the disease is caused by a form of avit-aminosis. Heat, light and a variety of—preferable live—food is of the greatest importance for these small terrapins which, although sold by the thousand, are not really suitable "pets" at all.

Mertens (1927) reported on a disease of the ear and the labyrinth in a lizard (*Anolis porcatus* Gray). He noticed semispherical tumours on both sides of the head which, when opened, discharged a white chalky mass. The condition was caused by excessive chalk deposit in the saccus endolymphaticus. This sac always and quite normally con-tains chalk deposits in reptiles and in amphibians. The reason for the excessive deposits and the consequent distension of the sacs is not known. Krefft (1926) reported on similar "chalk tumours" and one of us (R.-K.) saw the same condition in a specimen of *Phelsuma d. dubia* Boettger (Fig. 387). Incision of the swellings again produced a thick mass which solidified on discharge.

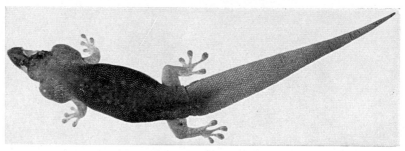

FIG. 387. *Phelsuma d. dubia* Boettger with abnormally distended chalk sacs. Eyes removed by dissection. (Orig.)

REFERENCES

Ashley, L. M. (1955). "Laboratory Anatomy of the Turtle." Wm. C. Brown publ. Dubuque. Iowa, U.S.A.

Bojanus, L. H. (1819/21). "Anatomia Testudinis Europaeae." Vilna, p. 135. Glandula lacrymalis externa. III; Illustration reprinted in Owen, R. "Anatomy of Vertebrates" (1866), Vol. I, p. 340.

Boycott, B. B. and Robins, M. W. (1961). The care of young red-eared terrapins (*Pseudemys scripta elegans*) in the laboratory. *Brit. J. Herpet.* **2**, 206–210.

Franz, V. (1924). Mikroskopische Anatomie der Hilfsteile des Sehorgans der Wirbeltiere. *Erg. Anat. Entwges.* **25**, 241–390.

Gegenbaur, C. (1898). "Vergleichende Anatomie der Wirbeltiere", Vol. I, Leipzig.

Graham-Jones, O. (1961). Some clinical conditions affecting the N. African tortoise ("Greek tortoise") *Testudo graeca*. *Vet. Rec.* **73**, 371–421.

Griffiths, I. and Carter, E. (1958). Sectioning refractory animal tissue. *Stain Technology* **33**, 209–214.

Hamerton, A. E. (1933). Report on deaths occurring in the Society's gardens during the year 1932. *Proc. zool. Soc. Lond.*, pp. 451–462.

Harder, J. J. (1693/4). Glandula nova lachrymalis una cum ductu secretorio in Ericiis et in Damis ab Hardere descripta. "Acta Eruditorum." publ. Lipsiae.

Harris, V. A. (1963). "The Anatomy of the Rainbow Lizard (*Agama agama* L.)." Hutchinson Trop. Monographs. London.

Hunt, T. J. (1956). Deaths of *Testudo elegans* from intestinal obstruction. *Brit. J. Herpet.* **2**, 35.

Hunt, T. J. (1957). Note on diseases and mortality in testudines. *Herpetologica* **13**, 19–23.

Kälin, J. A. (1937). Uber Skeletanomalieen bei Crocodiliden. *Z. Morph. Ökol. Tiere* **32**, 327–347.

Kaplan, H. M. (1957). The care and diseases of laboratory turtles. *Proc. Anim. Care Panel* **7**, 259–272.

Klingelhöffer, W. (1955). "Terrarienkunde", 2nd edn. Kernen, Stuttgart.

Krefft, P. (1926). "Das Terrarium", 3rd edn. Berlin.

Lever, F. V. (1954). "Histopathology of the Skin." Lippincott, Philadelphia.

Loveridge, A. (1947). Bone making material for turtles. *Copeia* 1947, p. 136.

Mertens, R. (1927). Über eine merkwürdige Erkrankung des Gehörorgans bei *Anolis* und anderen Eidechsen. *Bl. Aqu. Terrk.* **38**, 13–14.

Noble, K. (1931). "The Biology of the Amphibia." McGraw-Hill, New York.

Paule, W. J. (1953). Some comparative observations on orbital glands, with special references to the turtle. *Anat. Rec.* **115**, 408. Abstr. No. 282.

Peters, A. (1890). Beitrag zur Kenntnis der Harderschen Drüse. *Arch. mikr. Anat.* **36**.

Piersol, G. A. (1887). Beiträge zur Histologie der Harderschen Drüsen der Amphibien. *Arch. mikr. Anat.* **29**.

Pillet, A. and Bignon, F. (1885). La glande lachrymale d'une tortue géante (*Chelone viridis*). *Bull. Soc. Zool. Fr.* **10**, 60–66.

Plimmer, K. G. (1915). Reports on deaths which occurred in the Zoological Gardens during 1914 together with a list of the blood parasites found during the year. *Proc. zool. Soc. Lond.* 1915, 123–130.

Pope, C. H. (1956). "The Reptile World." Routledge and Kegan Paul, London.

Sardemann, E. (1888). Beiträge zur Anatomie der Tränendrüse. *Ber. Naturf. Ges. Freiburg* **3**, 95–128.

Schlumberger, H. G. (1955). Spontaneous goiter and cancer of the thyroid in animals. *Ohio J. Sci.* **55**, 23–43.

Schmidt-Nielsen, K. and Fange, R. (1958). Salt glands in marine reptiles. *Nature, Lond.* **182**, 781–785.

Scott, H. (1926–28). Report on the deaths occurring in the Society's gardens during the year 1925, 1926, 1927. *Proc. zool. Soc. Lond.* 1926, 231–244; 1927, 73–198; 1928, 81–119.

Schreitmüller, W. and Lederer, G. (1930). "Krankheitserscheinungen bei Fischen Reptilien und Lurchen." Berlin.

Wallis, G. L. (1942). "The Vertebrate Eye." Cranbrook Inst. of Science, Bloomfield Hills, Michigan, U.S.A.

Weber, M. (1887). Über die Nebenorgane des Auges der Reptilien. *Arch. Nat. gesch.* **43**, 261–342.

Weichert, C. K. (1958). "The Anatomy of the Chordates." McGraw-Hill, New York.

C. Injuries through Physical Factors

Animals may suffer from excessive insolation as well as through lack of sunshine. Mosauer and Lazier (1933), examining deserticolous reptiles, found that snakes may be killed during excessively long periods of heat. Three experimental snakes were exposed to an air temperature of 35·5°C in the Coachella valley of California.

The first specimen died after 6 min with a rectal temperature of 47°C; the second after 10·5 min with a rectal temperature of 46·6°C; the third after 9 min, rectal temperature 47°C. Temperatures over 46°C were obviously fatal for these snakes. Mosauer (1936) found, furthermore, that the species *Uma notata* Baird, *Dipsosaurus dorsalis* Baird and

Girard and *Crotalus cerastes* Hallowell die once their body temperature exceeds 44·2–53°C. In the Californian deserts soil temperatures up to 62°C were observed in the morning between 9 and 15.30 h. Experimental data indicate optimal temperatures for deserticolous saurians to lie between 35 and 40°C, a rise above 45–50°C being invariably fatal. Blum and Spealman (1933) published similar findings. They found that rattlesnakes are not damaged by increased insolation as long as the temperature does not exceed the supportable limit. The snakes died as soon as the temperature of the surrounding air reached 49°C.

The reaction of reptiles to cold is similar to that of amphibians. Excessively low temperatures are particularly dangerous for aquatic specimens like turtles. Some species tolerate excessive changes badly. *Sphenodon punctatus* Gray has, according to Dawbin (1962), in its natural habitat a remarkable tolerance to varying temperatures. It still feeds at 7°C and tolerates up to 40°C in the open air.

A case of incredible tolerance to cold in terrapins has been reported by Cable (1933). He found on January 30th two specimens of *Terrapene c. carolina* L. with their heads frozen into the ice. When thawed out they seemed to be entirely undamaged. Other specimens taken from the water which had a temperature of 10°C had a body temperature as low as 9·5°C.

Reptilian species adjusted to dry and warm air do not tolerate humidity. They may also be damaged by a draughty cage or by cages the walls of which are made of particularly rough material. Cement in particular should be given a carefully smoothed surface.

REFERENCES

Blum, H. F. and Spealman, C. R. (1933). Note on the killing of rattlesnakes by "sunlight". *Copeia* **3**, 150–151.
Cable, A. R. (1933). Hibernation of the box turtle. *Copeia* **3**, 13–14.
Dawbin, W. H. (1962). The tuatara in its natural habitat. *Endeavour* **21**, Nr. 81, 16–24.
Mosauer, W. (1936). The toleration of solar heat in desert reptiles. *Ecology* **17**, 56–66.
Mosauer, W. and Lazier, E. L. (1933). Death from insolation in desert snakes. *Copeia* **3**, 149.

D. POISONING

Reptiles may be poisoned either by their keepers if chemicals are used to free cages from mites, ants or other insects, or if, in the wild, they unsuccessfully attack insects which retaliate with poisonous stings.

The modern insecticides, so popular with gardeners, are particularly harmful to small reptiles. Manufacturers (Geigy and Co. Pest Control Dept.) have issued a warning against the use of these substances for the disinfection of cages of small animals. Both snakes and lizards have proved extraordinarily sensitive to the smallest doses of DDT and many other modern insecticides under whatever alluring name they may appear. The animals die within a few hours after the slightest contact with any of these substances. The effect shows itself in loss of equilibrium, irregular muscular contractions, cramp and breathing difficulties. Very slightly poisoned specimens may recover in a water bath of several days' duration at 25–30°C, the cage temperature being raised to 30°C at the same time.

Schweizer (1952) gives exact dosage figures for insecticides where these are considered necessary to combat mites in reptile cages.

Some frogs and toads have a very effective armour in the form of poisonous skin glands. They should not be used as food for reptiles. Schreitmüller and Lederer (1930) mention fatalities caused by feeding with common toads (*B. bufo* L.).

Even where the animals have been removed from a cage and this has been cleaned and disinfected, every trace of the chemicals used should be carefully washed off before the reptiles are readmitted to their quarters. They may be sensitive to the slightest smell or a small degree of pollution of their water.

REFERENCES

Geigy and Co. Ltd. Pest Control Dept. (1947). DDT Insektizide, Reptilien und Amphibien. *Aqu. Z. Jg.* 1947, 150.
Schreitmüller, W. and Lederer, G. (1930). "Krankheitserscheinungen bei Fischen, Reptilien und Lurchen." Wenzel, Berlin.
Schweizer, H. (1952). Die Blutmilbe (*Ophionyssus natricis* Gerv. Mégn.) der "Stallfeind" des Schlangenpflegers und ihre Vernichtung. *Aqu. Terr. Z.* **5**, 103–105.

Chapter 22

Wound Healing and Regeneration

In the matter of wound healing and regeneration the reptiles stand somewhere midway between the Amphibia and the mammals. The topic has been dealt with by Barber (1944), Fujinami (1901) and Wallis (1927, 1938). There are also a number of accounts of fractures and their mode of healing in reptiles (Wallis, 1928; Korschelt and Stock, 1928; Korschelt, 1932; Lehmensick, 1934; Pritchard and Ruzicka, 1950).

Authors have always been interested in the regeneration of lost limbs. It was extensively discussed by Fraisse as early as 1885. The organ showing the best regenerative ability in reptiles is the tail (Korschelt, 1927/31; Slotopolsky, 1921/22). Occasionally, as shown by Werber (1905), parts of the dentigerous cranial parts may regenerate. Legs regenerate very incompletely, rarely producing more than tail-like stumps. Guyénot and Matthey (1928), Marcucci (1930) and Hell-mich (1951) published a number of observations on the regeneration of the extremities in lizards. Marcucci (1930) in particular collected a great deal of material. He found that amputated toes rarely produced more than tail-like, sometimes forked stumps, sometimes no more than a short truncated appendix. Different species showed slight variations in their ability to regenerate. Regeneration in *Lacerta muralis* Laur. was found to be more complete than that in *Lacerta ocellata* Daud. Complete regeneration of a limb has never been observed in any species, nor is the regenerated part ever able to assume the function of the lost limb.

Slotopolsky (1922) studied the processes connected with the autotomy and regeneration of the lacertid tail. He showed that the vertebrae in the predestined breaking spot have a small gap which, however, does not extend to the whole cross section of the vertebra. This crack can usually be found in the sixth caudal vertebra but it may already be found in the fifth. Regeneration is subject to individual variation. The last six vertebrae are not replaced. Partial rupture and lateral incisions produce multiple regenerated buds. Dawbin (1962) pictures a forked tail in *Sphenodon punctata*.

Fractures of bones have always aroused much interest and have particularly been studied in lizards. Wallis (1927/28) maintained that the conditions of healing in reptiles varied basically from those in mammals. He worked on *Lacerta sicula* Raf. and divided the recovery period into four phases: during the first phase fibrous callus is laid down while the periosteum produces only very little of it. Hyaline

(a)

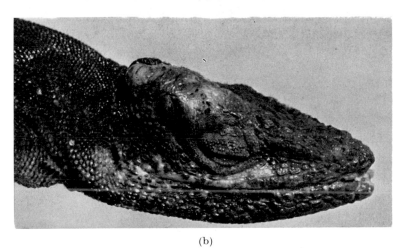

(b)

Fig. 388. *Anolis carolinensis* with a healing wound caused through biting.
(Photo.: Kästle.)

cartilaginous callus appears next, enveloping the fractured ends of the bone. The two surfaces unite by fibrous tissue. The cartilaginous callus eventually calcifies and envelops the fracture area (Fig. 388). Enchondral ossification is very slow in appearing. It goes parallel with the general calcification of the cartilaginous callus, the periostal bony callus gradually enveloping the cartilaginous parts. Fibrous callus eventually transforms itself into cartilage. Once the two fractured surfaces are united the intervening cartilage is absorbed and the cavity restored. The healing process is completely suspended if the period of hibernation intervenes and is only resumed in the following spring.

Compared with events in a rat, fractures heal more slowly in the lizard. Cold-blooded animals produce predominantly cartilaginous callus, while bony callus is at an early stage produced in mammals.

Pritchard and Ruzicka (1950) confirmed these observations and found, further, that similar conditions prevail in the frog.

REFERENCES

Barber, L. W. (1944). Correlation between wound healing and regeneration in forelimbs and tail of lizards. *Anat. Rec.* **89**, 441–451.

Dawbin, W. H. (1962). The tuatara in its natural habitat. *Endeavour* **21**, Nr. 81, 16–24.

Fraisse, B. (1885). "Die Regeneration von Geweben und Organen bei Wirbeltieren, besonders bei Amphibien und Reptilien." Kassel and Berlin.

Fujinami, A. (1901). Gewebsveränderungen bei der Heilung von Knochen-frakturen (Reptilien). *Beitr. path. Anat.* **29**, 432–485.

Guyénot, E. and Matthey, R. (1928). Les processus regénératifs dans la patte posterieure du lézard. *Roux' Arch.* **113**, 520–529.

Hellmich, G. (1951). A case of limb regeneration in the Chilean iguanid *Liolaemus*. *Copeia* 1951, 241–242.

Korschelt, E. (1927/31). "Regeneration und Transplantation." Berlin.

Korschelt, E. (1932). Über Frakturen und Skeletanomalieen der Wirbeltiere. II. Vögel, Reptilien, Amphibien und Fische. *Beitr. path. Anat.* **89**, 668–717.

Korschelt, E. and Stock, H. (1928). "Geheilte Knochenbrüche bei wildlebenden und in Gefangenschaft gehaltenen Tieren." Berlin.

Lehmensick, R. (1934). Über Panzerverletzungen bei Schildkröten. *Zool. Anz.* **105**, 325–331.

Marcucci, E. (1930). Il potere rigenerativo degli arti nei rettili. *Arch. zool. Ital.* **14**, 227–252.

Pritchard, J. J. and Ruzicka, A. J. (1950). Comparison of fracture repair in the frog, lizard and rat. *J. Anat.* **84**, 236–261.

Slotopolsky, B. (1921/22). Beiträge zur Kenntnis der Verstümmelungs- und Regenerationsvorgänge am Lacertilierschwanz. *Zool. Jahrb. Anat.* **43**, 219–322.

Wallis, K. (1927). Zur Knochenhistologie und Kallusbildung beim Reptil (*Clemmys leprosa*). *Z. Zellforsch.* **6**, 1–26.

Wallis, K. (1928). Über den Knochenkallus beim Kaltblüter (Eidechse). *Z. Zellforsch.* **7**, 257–289.

Werber, J. (1905). Regeneration der Kiefer bei der Eidechse *Lacerta agilis*. *Roux' Arch.* **19**, 248–258.

CHAPTER 23

Developmental Abnormalities

Under this heading we shall have to consider the appearances of double and multiple monsters as well as abnormal development of single organs, albinism and melanism.

FIG. 389. Siamese twins in *Anguis fragilis* L. Head and body joined down to the last third of the body. (Photo.: Stemmler-Gyger.)

FIG. 390. Anomaly in the development of the carapace of a Greek tortoise *Testudo h. hermanni* Gmelin with unpaired supracaudal scale (typical of *T. graeca* L.) and incised edge of carapace (typical of *T. marginata* Schoepff). (From Wermuth.)

Double monsters have frequently been seen in chelonians. Hildebrand (1930, 1938) described cases with double heads, double tails as

well as complete or incomplete "Siamese twins". Into the former
category belonged a pair of *Pseudemys floridana* Le Conte, the twins
being united by the posterior part of the ventral shield only. Another
pair, in this case of *"Chrysemys scaber"*, were joined laterally.

Fig. 389 shows the remarkable case of a slow-worm (*Anguis fragilis*
L.) brought to our notice by the kindness of O. Stemmler of Basle. Here
we have two complete animals endowed with only one head. The
opposite malformation, where one body carries two heads, seems to
be more common in snakes. Willis (1932) reported on a double embryo
in a lizard.

Fig. 391. *Python molurus* from India. Albinotic specimen with black-blue eyes.
Specimen in the collection of the Mus. Nat. Hist. Bern. (Photo.: Stemmler-Gyger.)

Fig. 392. *Vipera aspis aspis* L. caught at Innertkirchen Switzerland. Melanotic
female. (Photo.: Stemmler-Gyger.)

Among other deformations may be seen truncation of the head, malformation of the mouth and deficiencies in the dentigerous bones. Kälin (1937) saw such cases in crocodiles, all caused by skeletal anomalies. Wermuth (1961) described an anomaly in a specimen of *Testudo h. hermanni* Gmelin, the Greek tortoise. The animal had a single supracaudal scale which is typical for *T. graeca* L. and a serrated edge of the carapace which is typical for *T. marginata* Schoepff (Fig. 390). Anomalies of the carapace are fairly common in chelonians (Mertens, 1936). They may be combined with other abnormal developments.

Albinotic animals are most striking among colour deviations in reptiles (Fig. 391). Melanism, the opposite, also occurs frequently (Fig. 392). Schetty (1950) reported on a melanotic lizard (*Lacerta viridis viridis* Laur.).

Fig. 393. One-year-old specimen of *Vipera aspis aspis* L. with two separate dorsal rows of patches. (Photo.: Bertolf.)

It seems doubtful whether the appearance of accessory parietal organs described for instance by Haffner (1955) for *Lacerta vivipara* Jaquin should be included among the anomalies since they are extraordinarily common in reptiles, particularly so in lizards. Haffner himself found such rudimentary eyes in one-sixth of his material. Attempts at lens and retina formation can clearly be seen in these organs which, in some cases, are paired and often connected with the mesencephalon by a thin strand of optic nerve. There is always a gap in the bony skull

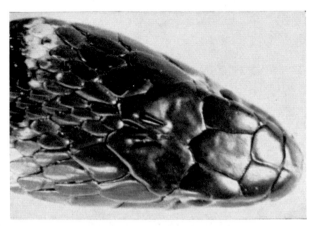

FIG. 394. Dorsal view of the head of a *Natrix natrix* L. with one central and two lateral parietal fossae. (Photo.: E. Elkan.)

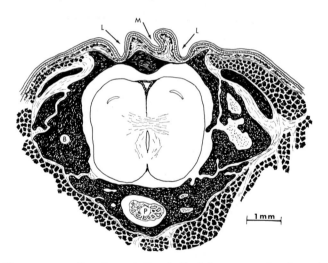

FIG. 395. Transverse section through the skull of the grass snake shown in Fig. 394. Note the extreme attenuation of the bony brain capsule opposite the two lateral grooves (*L*). There is no corresponding attenuation opposite the median groove (*M*). *B*, brain capsule; *P*, pituitary gland. Drawn by microprojection. (E. Elkan.)

dorsal to the parietal eye, matched in some cases by a pitted scale or a pair of pitted scales on the surface. As shown in Fig. 394 these gaps can appear in a variety of patterns. The grass snake in question—probably a great rarity—had two parietal and one median groove.

When, during a period of hibernation, the snake died, sections were made through the head. These showed extreme attenuation of the bone opposite the trough of the lateral dermal grooves. At the level of the median groove the bone was unaffected. No abnormality of the brain could be seen and we are left to speculate on the phylogenetic significance of this syndrome (Fig. 395).

Hermaphroditic sexual organs are of more obvious teratological interest. Risley (1941) reported on a specimen of *Chrysemys picta marginata* Agassiz which proved to be a complete hermaphrodite equipped with two testicles, a well-developed left oviduct and nine oocytes in the right and thirty-two in the left testis. Another turtle (*Malaclemys terrapin centrata* Latreille) showed some degree of female pseudohermaphroditism. The juvenile animal was equipped with ovaries and an ovarian medullary tumour composed of testicular tissue.

We owe further observations on chelonian hermaphrodites to Fantham (1905) and Matthey (1927). Fantham reported on a Greek tortoise (*T. graeca* L.) which developed a complete male genital system and mature oocytes. Matthey's specimen (*Emys orbicularis* L.) had hermaphroditic gonads, an oviduct and parts of the male copulatory organ.

Lantz (1923) saw a hermaphroditic specimen of *Lacerta saxicola defilippi* Cam. Judging by the number of cases reported, hermaphroditism is rarer in reptiles than in amphibians and fish.

Forbes (1941) tried to influence the sex of reptiles artificially. He inserted peritoneal implants of cristalline testosterone or oestroform into specimens of *Sceloporus spinosus floridanus* Stejn. After $6\frac{1}{2}$ weeks the animals showed testicular atrophy, hyperplasia of the Müllerian ducts and hypertrophy of the epididymis and the vasa deferentia. Oestroform implantation produced testicular atrophy with loss of spermatogenesis, atrophy of spermatic ducts and the epididymis and hyperplasia of the Müllerian ducts.

REFERENCES

Clay, W. M. (1935). The occurrence of albinos in a brood of the common water snake *Natrix sipedon*. *Copeia* 1935, 115.
Cunningham, B. (1937). "Axial Bifurcation in Serpents." Durham.
Dawbin, W. H. (1962). The tuatara in its natural habitat. *Endeavour* **21**, No. 81, 16–24.
Fantham, H. B. (1905). On hermaphroditism and vestigial structures in the reproductive organs of *Testudo graeca*. *Amer. Mag. Nat. Hist.* 7 ser. **16**, 120–125.
Forbes, T. R. (1941). Observations on the urogenital anatomy of the adult male lizard *Sceloporus* and on the action of implanted pellets of testosterone and of oestrone. *J. Morph.* **68**, 71–69.

Glaesner, L. (1924). Über drei Doppelbildungen von *Chelonia mydas*. *Zool. Anz.* **60**, 185–194.

Haffner, K. v. (1955). Über accescorische Parietalorgane und Nebenparietalaugen als degenerative Bildungen am Parietalauge. *Mitt. Hamb. Zool. Mus. Inst.* **53**, 25–32.

Hildebrandt, S. F. (1930). Duplicity and other abnormalities in diamond-back terrapins. *J. Elisha Mitchell Sci. Soc.* **46**, 41–53.

Kälin, J. A. (1937). Über Skeletanomalien bei Crocodiliden. *Z. Morph. Ökol. Tiere* **32**, 327–347.

Lantz, L. A. (1923). Hermaphroditisme partiel chez *Lacerta saxicola*. *Bull. Soc. Zool. Fr.* **48**, 289–290.

Matthey, R. (1927). Intersexualité chez une tortue (*Emys europea*). *C.R. Soc. Biol.*, *Paris* **97**, 369–371.

Mertens, R. (1936). Eine bemerkenswerte Variation des Schildkrötenpanzers. "*Isis*" *Mitt. München Jg.* 1934/36, 15–19.

Meisenheimer, J. (1930). "Geschlecht und Geschlechter im Tierreich". Vol. II, Fischer, Jena.

Müller, L. (1927). Neigung zum Melanismus bei Reptilien von der Insel Milos. *Bl. Aqu. Terrk.* **38**, 217–273.

Procter, J. B. (1926). A note on an albino Grass-snake. *Proc. zool. Soc. Lond.*, 1095–1096.

Risley, P. L. (1950). Some observations on hermaphroditism in turtles. *J. Morph.* **68**, 101–119.

Schetty, P. (1950). Eine melanotische Smaragdeidechse *Lacerta v. viridis* Laur. *Wschr. Aqu. Terrk.* **44**, 278–280.

Schweizer, H. (1951). Über eine der *Vipera aspis hugyi* Schinz sehr nahestehende südalpine Population von *Vipera aspis aspis* L. *Aqu. Terr. Z.* **4**, 78–81.

Wermuth H. (1961). Anomalien bei einer griechischen Landschildkröte (*Testudo hermanni hermanni* Gmelin). *S.B. Ges. naturf. Fr. Berl.* N.F. **1**, 139–142.

Willis, R. A. (1932). A monstrous twin embryo in a lizard, *Tiliqua scincoides*. *J. Anat.* **66**, 189–201.

CHAPTER 24

The Organic Systems of Reptiles and their Importance in Reptilian Pathology

This chapter makes an attempt to classify the diseases of reptiles according to the organs in which they occur, particularly with a view to the fact that disease of one organ can have the most varied effects on others and on the animal as a whole.

We are helped in this task by the reports issued by those in charge of large animal collections like the London Zoo, which issues annual reports on the deaths of the animals in the Gardens and their causes.

Since our table can hardly hope to be complete even at the time of writing and since the science of animal pathology is undergoing a period of rapid growth, the reader who is interested in detail will want to refer to the wealth of original papers published in the journals of pathology and zoology of all countries.

The surface may be affected by injuries, swelling, tumours, inflammations, infestation by worms and mites or by avitaminosis. Discoloration may be congenital or, particularly in the case of inflammation, a sign of serious illness.

The intestinal canal is, of all the organic systems, the one most exposed to disease. Hunt (1957), investigating the cause of death in chelonians, found diseases of the gut to be responsible in 40% of his cases. Of these again most concerned the stomach and the intestine which were frequently infected by amoebae, sometimes by faulty feeding, occasionally by avitaminosis. Faulty nourishment combined with lack of exercise tends to produce constipation in captive animals. Hunt mentions (1956) the case of a *Pseudemys scripta elegans* Wied. which died from intestinal obstruction after having eaten the seed of *Curica papaya* L. The large intestine was stretched to capacity and on the point of rupturing.

The respiratory organs are almost equally exposed to disease. In Hunt's (1957) statistic they supplied 35% of all deaths in chelonians, including inflammation, abscesses and gangrene. Pulmonary atelectasis, a state in which the lungs are collapsed and contain no air, was described by Schreitmüller and Lederer (1930). Just as in amphibians, mycoses, aspergilloses and infection with acid-fast cold-water bacilli play their part and are very likely to gain entry through the bronchi or the lungs.

The blood, if diseased, will probably be found to be invaded by Protozoa, filaria, trematodes or other parasites.

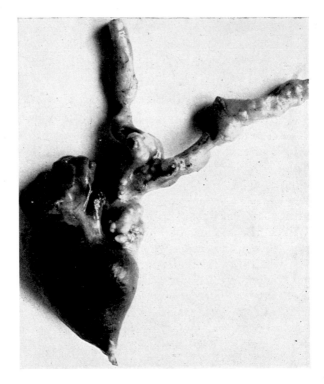

Fig. 396. *Iguana iguana* L. Heart and main blood vessels with extensive deposits of cholesterol. (Photo.: W. Frank.)

The skeletal system is much exposed to disease and deformation.

Osteomalacia and osteoporosis may appear in consequence of lack of vitamin D and of enteritis (Wallis, 1927). Osteogenetic tumours have also been described.

The urogenital system, though not as exposed as the other organs, may be the seat of disease. Hunt (1927) mentions cases of fatal nephritis in turtles. Nephrolithiasis is more commonly seen in tortoises. In very dry surroundings these sometimes fail to void their urine, a condition which may lead to autointoxication. Cases of excessive deposition of urates resembling gout have been seen by Appleby and Giller (1960). They reported on nine cases of urate deposits in joints, the liver and the heart (cf. Zwart, 1963, and Fig. 397). We owe to the kindness of Dr. W. Frank, Stuttgart, the picture (Fig. 396) of a large lizard (*Iguana iguana*) with excessive deposits of cholesterol in the walls of the large blood vessels. The same author provided the picture of the heart of a gavial which suffered from severe gout. This animal died when the heart was entirely encrusted with deposits of uric acid (Fig. 397).

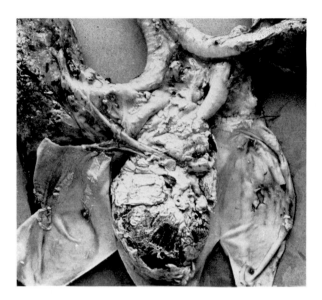

FIG. 397. Malay gavial (*Tomistoma schlegali*) suffering from severe gout. Heart and main blood vessels encrusted with uric acid deposits. (Photo.: W. Frank.)

Diseases of the sexual system concern particularly the eggs (Hunt's (1957) egg-necrosis) or the ovary. Klingelhöffer (1955) mentions the dangerous situation which arises when the process of oviposition is disturbed. This condition affects many captive reptilians, particularly tortoises and chameleons, and is probably due to a combination of causes. At the time of writing any attempt at treatment seems to be as dangerous as the condition itself.

Of the sensory organs the eye disease of terrapins is by far the most commonly seen. Since there have been no reports on this disease in wild animals it must be due to factors connected with captivity. Infection of the excretory ducts of the Harderian gland is the most likely cause, but it remains difficult to explain why in one and the same cage some of the specimens should contract the disease and others not.

REFERENCES

Appleby, E. C. and Giller, W. G. (1960). Some cases of gout in reptiles. *J. Path. Bact.* **30**, 427–430.

Hamerton, A. E. (1935). Report on deaths occurring in the Society's gardens during the year 1932. *Proc. zool. Soc. Lond.* 1935, 451–482.

Hunt, T. J. (1956). Deaths of *Testudo elegans* from intestinal obstruction. *Brit. J. Herpet.* **2**, 35.

Hunt, T. J. (1957). Notes on diseases and mortality in testudines. *Herpetologica* **13**, 19–23.

Klingelhöffer, W. (1959). "Terrarienkunde." 2nd edn. Kernen, Stuttgart.

Schreitmueller, W. and Lederer, G. (1930). "Krankheitserscheinungen bei Fischen, Reptilien und Lurchen." Wenzel, Berlin.

Scott, H. (1926–28). Report on the deaths occurring in the Society's gardens during the years 1925, 1926, 1927. *Proc. zool. Soc. Lond.* 1926, 231–244; 1927, 173–198; 1928, 81–119.

Wallis, K. (1927). Zur Knochenhistologie und Kallusbildung beim Reptil (*Clemys leprosa* Schweigg.). *Z. Zellforsch.* **6**, 1–16.

Zwart, P. (1963). Studies on Renal Pathology in Reptiles. Diss. Utrecht.

Chapter 25

Table of Localization, Symptoms and Possible Causes of Diseases in Reptiles

Localization	Symptoms	Possible causes
Skin and carapace	Small tumours	Cold-water tuberculosis, fungi
	Abscesses	Filariae; dracunculids
	Larger tumours	Filariae; malignancy
	Hyperkeratosis	Mites; fungi
	Oedema; ulceration	Mites; blood filariae
	Softening of carapace	Avitaminosis; faulty feeding
Eye	Blindness	Disease of the Harderian gland; infection
Mouth	Mouth permanently open	Inflammation of mucous membrane; blockage of nasal passage; nematodes; lack of vitamins
	Mouth containing cheesy masses	Intestinal disease
Intestines	Inflammation	Flagellates; sporozoa; ciliates; entamoeba; helminths; avitaminosis; faulty nutrition
	Prolapse	Constipation
Extremities	Solid tumours; difficulties in movements	Gout
Liver and gall bladder	White foci	Sporozoa; tuberculosis; malignancy; fungus infection
Peritoneal cavity	Ascites, clear or sanguinous	Any severe systemic disease and infection; congestion of liver; ovarian necrosis; helminthiasis
Skeleton	Softening or brittleness of bones; malformation; bony tumours	Faulty feeding; avitaminosis D; Malignant disease
Lungs; trachea; bronchi	Inflammation; obstruction; atelectasis	Bacterial infection; parasitic worms

Localization	Symptoms	Possible causes
Circulatory system and heart	Circulating blood parasites	Filaria;dracunculids;trematodes
	Obstruction of blood vessels	Trypanosoma
	Intracellular parasites	Haemosporidia; Adeleidea; Piroplasma
Muscles and nerves	Tumours	Parasitic protozoa
Sexual organs	Degeneration; atrophy	Sporozoa; obstructed oviposition
Kidney	Degeneration; urate deposits	Faulty metabolism; parasitic fungi and Protozoa
Urinary bladder	Inflammation	Trematodes
General symptoms	Listlessness; apathy	Metabolic disturbances; parasites; faulty temperature or humidity; lack of sunshine; unsuitable cage
	Growth disturbances	Irregularities of the endocrine system

CHAPTER 26

Treatment

A. DRUGS*

Drug	Application	Diagnosis
Alcohol, diluted	External, with brush	White spots in turtles
Antibiotics	Mixed with food	Infections
Borax solution	External as drops	Eye infections
Chinosol	Solution, as bath	Inflammation of mouth
Chloramphenicol	Oral or added to the water	*Aeromonas hydrophila*
Chlorcamphor sol.	External	Mites
Cuprex	Solution	Disinfection of cages
Enterovioform	Mixed with food	Amoebiasis
Formalin	5–10% solution	Disinfection of cages; preservation of dead specimens
Gammexan	External, with brush	Mites
Helminal	Mixed with food	Helminths
Iodine	External, with brush	Skin injuries
Cod liver oil, also as ointment	External Internal	Parasites Rickets
Lugol's solution	External, with brush	Skin defects and inflammation
Nematolyt-Vet.	With food	Helminthiasis
Paraffin liqu.	1 ml per anum	Constipation
Protargol	5% sol. as eye drops or bath	Ophthalmic inflammations
Castor oil	1 : 1 with absol. alcohol, external, with brush	Mites
Salt (NaCl)	Mild solutions as bath	White spots in turtles
Santonin	Very small doses with food every 6–7 days	Helminthiasis
Socatyl (Ciba)	Solution in water	Diarrhoea
Sulphanilamide	Solution: externally	Inflammation of the eyes Inflammation of the mouth
Proflavin emulsion	Externally	Skin defects and inflammation
Vitamin drugs f.i. Vigartol	Mix with food	Avitaminosis

* The table can only give some preliminary hints at the use of drugs. Treatment by physical means is discussed under section B.

B. Biological and Physical Methods of Treatment

Wherever possible these methods should be preferred to treatment with drugs or chemicals. They include strict imitation of natural surroundings including soil, opportunities for climbing and hiding, provision of clean water of suitable temperature, control of general air temperature and humidity, air currents and nutrition. It can be seen from this list that the task of producing ideal conditions for captive reptiles is by no means an easy one. Where it is fulfilled however the keeper may well claim that the animals in his care are better provided for than they ever would be in their natural surroundings which may well be lacking in one or several of the conditions mentioned. It is also obvious that, just as we cannot keep tropical and arctic plants in the same hothouse, reptiles from different habitats cannot be accommodated in one and the same cage. Nor should it be taken for granted that several members of the same species will live in eternal peace with each other. They may do so for a while and deceive the keeper until he is one morning faced with the results of a great fight, the reasons for which he will never learn.

There is an extensive literature on the choice and preparation of suitable foods for captive reptiles. Some species will adapt themselves to substitutes where the natural food cannot be supplied. Others are entirely unadaptable and no attempt should be made to keep them in cages where they will only succumb to a lingering death from starvation. It is perhaps not surprising to notice that the larger a reptile at the time of its capture the more depressing is the effect of captivity on its appetite. Snakes so afflicted may starve for months and may then suddenly, and for no obvious reasons, break their fast and develop a perfectly normal appetite. The fact that they can usually be seen lying coiled up under or over the source of heat shows the importance of such installations, nor should the provision of water baths be neglected in purely terrestrial animals. An occasional water spray, depositing dew drops on plants, is a useful adjunct. Like the Amphibia the reptiles have an enormous tenacity of life and there must be many specimens in collections which have outlived generations of their keepers.

CHAPTER 27

Reptilia and Human Hygiene

In a few cases it is just possible that reptiles may transmit diseases to man. This applies particularly to *Salmonella* infections, where it is however rarely possible to assert with certainty in which direction the infection was transmitted, since both humans and reptiles may carry the infection without showing signs of disease. Children playing with captive pets are of course most likely to infect themselves in this way, and there have been several reports of outbreaks of salmonellosis in homes with freshly imported turtles or tortoises.

Bartonella bacilliformis Strong, which causes Oroya fever in S. America, is suspected of being carried by reptiles, from whom it is transferred to humans by *Phlebotomus* flies.

Ticks, particularly the genera *Amblyomma* and *Ornithodoros*, undoubtedly play a part in transmitting diseases in the countries where they occur. *O. talaje* Guérin-Menéville, for instance, transmits the American relapsing fever, *Amblyomma* species *Rickettsiae*. The Tsut-sugamushi disease and the scrub typhus are equally transmitted by mites, particularly a *Trombicula* species, which sucks blood from lizards and humans.

The question of the transmissibility of virus diseases by reptiles has lately been studied in America. Thomas and Ecklund (1962) succeeded in transmitting the WEE (Western Equine Encephalomyelitis) virus to snakes with the aid of the mosquito *Culex tarsalis*. The virus remained viable in the snakes (*Thamnophis ordinoides* Baird and Girard) for some time. The importance of this procedure lies in the fact that the disease does not only affect horses but may be transferred to humans.

The trypanosomes and malarial parasites infesting reptiles are species specific and, vice versa, reptiles do not admit human blood parasites.

Of helminths (nematodes) only *Gnathostoma* species might be transmitted from reptiles to humans. *Gnathostoma spinigerum* Owen, which occurs in S.E. Asia, produces oedema of the skin, particularly in the face and the hands. The first intermediate hosts are *Cyclops* spp., the second fish, frogs and aquatic snakes of undetermined species. The remaining reptilian helminths do not seem transmissible to man.

18

The rightly feared common blood mite of snakes (*Ophionyssus natricis*) may occasionally be transferred to humans. Cases have been reported of workers dealing with infested snakes suffering from itching skin lesions. The common tick of sheep may infest other mammals and man and has also been found on some of the larger tropical species of snakes.

The tick *Hyalomma* (now *Hyalommasta*) *aegyptium* L. 1758 is not indigenous to northern countries but is frequently imported attached to tortoises which are unfortunately still regularly imported as pets in great numbers. The tick, according to Arthur (1963), has not so far established itself in England but biologists have been suspicious of its supposed ability to migrate to mammals like hedgehogs, donkeys, hamsters and dogs. It has also been suspected of transmitting bovine piroplasmosis and other diseases but further verification of these observations is required. So far as the buyers of tortoises are concerned they are well advised to inspect new purchases thoroughly for the presence of ticks. They can easily be dealt with by a little D.D.T. powder or a drop of methylated spirit. It is not advisable to try to remove the live tick from the tortoise; once killed it will shrivel up and fall off spontaneously.

REFERENCES

Arthur, D. R. (1963). "British Ticks." Butterworths, London.
Thomas, L. A. and Eklund, C. M. (1962). Overwintering of Western Equine Encephalomyelitis virus in Garter snakes experimentally infected by *Culex tarsalis*. *Proc. Soc. exp. Biol.*, *N.Y.* **109**, 421–424.

Zoological Names, Trivial Names and Main Habitat of Species Mentioned in the Text

Most names in the glossary are taken from the " List of the Vertebrated Animals ",
Vol. III, published by the Zoological Society of London in 1929.

Zoological names	Trivial names	Main habitat
Acanthodactylus erythrurus (= *A. vulgaris*)	Spanish fringe-fingered lizard	Southwest Europe, North Africa
Abramis brama	Bream	Fresh waters of North and Central Europe
Acerina cernua	Ruffe or Pope	Fresh waters of Europe
Acipenser sturio	Sturgeon	European seas. Atlantic coast of N. America
Agama adramitana		North Africa
Agama stellio	Hardoun. Starred lizard	Middle East, Asia Minor, Egypt
Agkistrodon piscivorus	Cotton-mouth moccassin Water moccassin	West Virginia, Florida, Gulf States, Southern N. America
Alburnus alburnus	Bleak	Fresh waters of North and Central Europe
Alytes obstetricans	Midwife toad	Southern Europe. Spain
Ambystoma tigrinum	Tiger salamander Larval form: Axolotl	Southern U.S.A., Mexico
Ameiurus nebulosus	Dwarf catfish	Fresh waters of North America
Ameiva ameiva	Surinam lizard	South and Central America
Amia calva	Bowfin	Lakes and swamps of North America
Amphisbaena alba	White burrowing lizard Red worm lizard	Brazil
Amphiuma	Blind eel (amphibian)	Southern States of the U.S.A.
Amyda (= *Trionyx*) *ferox*	Fierce soft-shelled turtle	S.E. U.S.A., S. Carolina to Florida and Louisiana
Amyda (= *Trionyx*) *spinifera*	Spiny soft-shelled turtle	Southern States of North America
Anabantidae	Labyrinth fishes	Fresh waters of Southern Asia and Africa
Anarrhichas lupus	Sea wolf	Seas of Northern Europe and America
Anguilla anguilla	Eel	Rivers of Europe. Atlantic ocean
Anguis fragilis	Slow-worm	Europe, Western Asia, North-West Africa, Eastern Siberia
Anolis equestris	Greater Cuban anolis lizard	West Indies, Cuba

Zoological names	Trivial names	Main habitat
Anolis porcatus	A lizard	South-Eastern States of U.S.A., Cuba
Anoptichthys jordani	Blind characid fish	Mexican caves
Aphanius	Top minnow	Spain, Italy, Near East
Aplodinotus grunniens	American freshwater drum	Guatemala to Canada
Argulus foliaceus	Fish louse	Parasitic on fish
Asellus aquaticus	Water louse. Sow bug	Fresh waters, Europe
Aspis cerastes	Horned viper	North Africa
Barbus barbus	Barbel	Fresh waters, Europe
Basiliscus vittatus	Banded basilisk (Lizard)	Central America
Betta splendens	Regan's Siamese fighting fish	Fresh waters of Siam and the Malay States
Bitis arietans (= *Bitis lachesis*)	Puff adder	Africa, from Morocco to Cape of Good Hope
Bitis nasicornis	Nose-horned viper	West Africa, Liberia, Gabon, Congo
Blicca björkna	White bream	Fresh waters, Temperate zone
Boaedon f. fuliginosus	Sooty snake	Africa
Boaedon lineatus	African lined snake	Africa
Bombina	Fire-bellied toad	Europe
Bothrops jararaca (= *Bothrops atrox*)	Fer-de-lance (snake)	Central and South America, Trinidad, Martinique, St. Lucia, Tobago
Bufo americanus	Northern toad	Eastern North America
Bufo bufo (= *B. vulgaris*)	Common toad	Europe, Temperate Asia
Bufo boreas	Mountain toad. Californian toad	Western North America
Bufo calamita	Natterjack	Europe
Bufo lentiginosus (= *B. americanus*)	American toad	Eastern North America
Bufo marinus	Giant toad. Marine toad	Tropical America
Bufo melanostictus	Indian toad, Common Asiatic toad	India, Tropical Asia, Malay States
Bufo regularis	Common African toad	Africa
Bufo valliceps	Helmet-headed toad	Southern part of U.S.A., Mexico
Bufo viridis	Green toad	Europe, North Africa, Western Asia
Bulimus	A water snail	Europe
Callorhynchus	Plow-nosed or Elephant-chimaera	Southern oceans, New Zealand, Tasmania
Carassius carassius	Goldfish. Crucian carp	Fresh waters of Europe and N.E. Asia
Cardium edule	Common cockle	European marine waters
Caretta caretta	Loggerhead turtle	Tropical and subtropical seas
Carnegiella strigata	Hatchet belly	South America, Panama to La Plata
Causus lichtensteini	West African viper	West Africa

Zoological names	Trivial names	Main habitat
Causus rhombeatus	Night adder. Cape viper	Tropical and South Africa
Centrarchidae	Sunfishes	Eastern North America
Ceramodactylus doriae	A lizard	Persia, Arabia
Chalcides ocellatus	Eyed skink	Morocco, Egypt, S.W. Asia, S. Europe
Chelodina longicollis	Long-necked terrapin Snake tortoise	South and S.E. Australia
Chelonia mydas (= Ch. viridis)	Green turtle	Tropical and subtropical seas, Ascension island
Chelydra serpentina	Snapping turtle, Alligator terrapin	Eastern North America
Chimaera monstrosa	Rabbit fish	Temperate zone of Atlantic ocean
Chinemys reevesii	Chinese turtle	China, Japan. Fresh waters and swamps
Chitra indica	Long-headed soft-shelled turtle	Northern India, Burma, Siam, Malay peninsula
Chrysemys picta	Painted terrapin	Eastern North America
Chrysolophus amhersti	Lady Amherst's pheasant	Szechuan, West China, East Tibet
Clarias	Amphibious catfish	Fresh and brackish waters of S.E. Asia
Clemmys caspica leprosa	Caspian terrapin	Western Asia, S.E. Europe, Persia, Mesopotamia, Cyprus, Crete
Clemmys guttata	Speckled terrapin	Eastern North America
Clemmys japonica	Japanese terrapin, Ishi-game	Japan
Clemmys leprosa	Spanish terrapin	Iberian peninsula, N.W. Africa, Senegambia
Clupea harengus	Herring	North Atlantic and North Pacific Ocean, Channel, Baltic sea
Cnemidophorus lemniscatus	Strand race runner	Tropical America
Colisa lalia	Dwarf gourami (a fish)	Fresh waters of Northern India
Coluber constrictor	Racer. American black snake	North America
Coluber flagellum	Coach whip snake	North America
Coluber gemonensis (= Coluber jugularis)	European whip snake	Southern Europe, S.W. Asia, Western Persia
Coluber radiatus (= Elaphe radiata)	Rayed snake	India, S.W. Asia, Southern China, Malay States
Conger conger	Conger eel	Marine, world-wide
Conolophus subcristatus	Galapagos land iguana	Galapagos and Seymour Islands
Constrictor constrictor	Boa constrictor	South America, Brazil, Venezuela, N.E. Peru, Guianas
Cordylus (= Zonurus) giganteus	Girdled lizard	South Africa

Zoological names	Trivial names	Main habitat
Coregonus vandesius	Whitefish	Great lakes of North America
Corydoras paleatus	Coat-of-mail catfish	Fresh waters, Eastern South America
Crenicichla	Pike cichlids	Fresh waters, Eastern South America
Crocodilus niloticus	Nile crocodile	North-East Africa, Madagascar
Crocodilus palustris	Marsh crocodile	India, Burma, Baluchistan
Crocodilus porosus	Estuarine crocodile	East India, Ceylon, South China, N. Australia, Solomon and Fiji islands
Crotalus cerastes	Horned rattlesnake, Sidewinder	Western North America, California, Arizona
Crotaphopeltis (= *Leptodeira*) *hotamboiea*	Rufescent snake	Southern and tropical Africa
Crypturus noctivagus	Banded Tinamon Bird	Eastern Brazil
Ctenosaurus acanthura	Spring-tailed iguana	Southern States of N. America, Mexico
Cyclanorbis senegalensis	Senegal soft-shelled turtle	Tropical Africa
Cynops pyrrhogaster	Japanese newt	Japan
Cyprinus carpio	Carp	Fresh waters, Europe, Temperate Asia
Cystobranchus mammillatus	Burbot leech	Fresh waters, Temperate zones
Cystobranchus respirans	Barbel leech	Fresh waters, Temperate zones
Dasypeltis scaber	Egg eating snake, Rough-keeled snake	Africa. Cape province to Egypt and Abyssinia
Dendraspis angusticeps	Green mamba	South and tropical Africa, Kenya, Angola
Dendrophis calligaster solomonensis	A snake	Solomon islands
Dermochelys coriacea	Giant leatherback turtle	Tropical seas, Malaya
Desmognathus fuscus	Northern dusky salamander	North America
Diemyctilus viridescens	Red-spotted newt	North America
Diploglossus	Galliwasp lizard	Central America
Dipsadoboa unicolor	Gunther's green snake	West Africa, Sierra Leone, Congo
Dipsadomorphus irregularis	A snake	Celebes, Moluccas, Papuasia, Solomon Islands
Dipsosaurus dorsalis	Desert pygmi iguana	California
Discoglossus pictus	Painted frog	South Europe, Spain, N.W. Africa
Draco volans	Flying lizard	Indo-China, Burma, Malay States, Philippines
Dromophis lineatus	A snake	Tropical Africa
Drymarchon corais	Gopher or Corais snake	Southern U.S.A., Brazil, Bolivia

Zoological names	Trivial names	Main habitat
Echis carinata	Carpet viper	N. Africa, S.W. Asia, India, Ceylon, Egypt
Elaphe flavolineata	Common Malayan racer	Malay States
Elaphe guttata	Corn snake	North America
Elaphe longissima	Aesculapian snake	Europe, W. Asia, Italy, S. Russia
Elaphe obsoleta	Pilot black snake	North America, Gulf States
Elaphe quadrivittata	Chicken snake	North America
Elaphe quatuorlineata	Aldrovandi's snake	S.E. Europe, W. Asia, S. Russia, Persia
Elaphe radiata (= *Coluber radiatus*)	Rayed snake	S.W. Asia, India, South-West China, Malay States
Elaphe situla	Leopard snake	Southern Europe, West Asia
Elaps (= *Micrurus*)	Coral snakes	Central and South America
Emys orbicularis	Pond tortoise	Europe, W. Asia, North-West Africa
Eretmochelys imbricata	Hawk-billed turtle	Tropical and subtropical seas
Erythrolamprus aesculapii	Red and black coral snake	Tropical America, Brazil, Peru, Guianas
Esox lucius	Pike	Fresh waters, Europe, N. Asia, North America
Eumeces fasciatus	American five-lined skink	Arizona, Canada
	American blue-tailed skink	New England to Florida, Mississippi
Fordonia leucobalia	Fordonia water snake	South Asia, Australasia, Indo-China, Malay States
Fundulus	Tooth carp	Fresh waters, Eastern N. America, West Africa
Gadus aeglefinus	Haddock	Atlantic ocean, North Sea
Gadus morrhua (= *Gadus callarias*)	Atlantic cod	Atlantic ocean
Gasterosteus aculeatus	Three-spined stickleback	Fresh waters, Northern Europe
Gastropyxis smaragdina	Emerald tree snake	Tropical Africa
Gavialis gangeticus	Gharial, Ganges crocodile	Ganges river, India
Gecko gecko (= *Gecko verticillatus*)	Great house gecko	S.E. Asia, N.E. India, Burma, Siam, Malay States
Gehyra multilata (= *Peropus mutilatus*)	Peron's house gecko	Islands of Indian and Pacific ocean, Indo-China, Hawaii, Mexico
Geoemyda trijuga	Ceylon terrapin	South Asia, India, Ceylon, Burma
Gherronotus multicarinatus	Alligator lizard	California
Gherrosaurus	African lizards	Tropical, Southern and South Africa
Glossina palpalis	Tsetse fly	Tropical Africa
Gobio gobio	Gudgeon	Fresh waters, Europe

Zoological names	Trivial names	Main habitat
Goniocephalus	Angle-headed agama	S.E. Asia, East India
Gordius aquaticus	Hair worm, "Water calf"	Fresh waters, temperate zones
Graptemys geographica	Erie map terrapin	North America
Graptemys pseudo-geographica	Small-headed map terrapin	North America
Heloderma suspectum	Gila monster Arizona poisonous lizard	Arizona, Utah, Nevada
Hemichromis bimaculatus	Jewel fish, Red cichlid	River Nile, Sahara rivers, Congo
Hemidactylus frenatus	Bridled house gecko	India, Indo-China, Australia, Malaya, South Africa, Mexico
Heterodon contortrix	Hog-nosed snake, Puffing adder	North America
Heterodon platyrhinos (= *H. contortrix*)	Hog-nosed snake Puffing adder	Southern States of N. America
Hieremys annandalei	Siam turtle	Siam, Cambodia, Malaysia
Hippocampus	Sea horse	Southern European seas
Hippoglossus vulgaris	Halibut	Temperate seas
Homalopsis buccata	Puff-faced water snake	S.E. Asia, Burma to Java, East India
Hydraspis geoffroyana	Geoffroy's terrapin	Southern Brazil
Hydromedusa maximiliani	Maximilian's terrapin	South America, Brazil
Hydromedusa tectifera	Cope's terrapin	Southern Brazil
Hyla arborea	European tree frog	Europe, Temperate Asia, N. Africa
Hyphessobrycon flammeus	Flame or Neon fish	Fresh waters, Brazil
Idus idus (= *Leuciscus idus*)	Ide or Orfe	Fresh waters of Central and N. Europe
Kachuga	Indian terrapin	Northern India, Burma
Katsuwonus pelamis	Skipjack, Bonito	Tropical seas
Kinosternon scorpiodes	Scorpion mud terrapin	South America, Brazil, Guianas
Kinosternon subrubrum	Pennsylvania mud terrapin or Mud turtle	Southern States of North America
Lacerta agilis	Sand lizard	Europe, Asia, Russia
Lacerta muralis	Wall lizard	Europe, S. Russia, Persia, Greece
Lacerta ocellata (= *L. lepida*)	Eyed lizard	Southwestern Europe Northwest Africa
Lacerta viridis	Green lizard	Europe, Asia, Southern Russia, Persia
Lacerta vivipara	Viviparous lizard	Europe, Asia
Lampetra planeri	Brook lamprey	Streams of Europe, Siberia Japan

Zoological names	Trivial names	Main habitat
Lampropeltis calligaster	Red-bellied king snake	North America
Lampropeltis getulus	King snake	North America, Mexico
Latastia longicauda revoili	A lizard	Somaliland
Leiolepisma (= *Lygosoma*)	Slender skink	New Zealand
Lepomis megalotis	Long-eared sunfish	Fresh waters of Eastern N. America
Leptodeira maculata (= *Crotaphopeltis m.*)	Cat's eye snake	South America
Leptopelis aubryi	A tree frog	Cameroon, West Africa
Leuciscus idus (*Idus idus*)	Ide or Orfe	Fresh waters of Central and N. Europe
Leuciscus leuciscus	Dace	Rivers of Central and N. Europe
Leuciscus rutilus (= *Rutilus rutilus*)	Roach	Rivers of North and Central Europe
Lialis jicarii	Jicari's flap-footed lizard	New Guinea
Liolaemus nigromaculatus	Black-spotted lizard	Chile
Liophis andreae	Andrea's Cuban snake	West Indies, Cuba
Liophis anomala	Parana beauty snake	South America, Brazil, Argentine
Liparidae	Snailfishes	Atlantic and Pacific oceans
Liparis vulgaris (= *Liparis liparis*)	Striped sea snailfish	North Atlantic
Lissemys indica	Indian flap-shelled turtle	India, Ceylon, Burma
Lissemys punctata	Asiatic soft-shelled turtle	Pakistan, Indo-China
Lophius piscatorius	Angler fish	European and African marine waters
Loricaria	A catfish	Fresh waters, South America
Lota lota	Burbot	Fresh waters of Europe
Lucioperca lucioperca	Giant pike-perch	Fresh waters of Eastern Europe
Lycodon	Oriental wolf snakes	South Asia, India, Ceylon, Cochin-China, Philippines, Malay States
Lycodon subcinctus	Banded wolf snake	S.E. China, Malay States
Lycognathus cervinus	A snake	Brazil, Bolivia, Guianas, Trinidad
Lygosoma	Slender skink	New Zealand
Lygosoma moco	Moco skink	New Zealand
Lymnaea	Pond snails	Fresh water, Temperate regions
Mabuya agilis	Raddi's skink	Tropical America, Ecuador, Brazil
Mabuya quinquetaeniata	African blue-tailed or five-lined skink	Egypt to Angola, East Africa, Senegambia
Mabuya raddoni	Raddon's skink	West Africa, Sierra Leone, Gabon, Congo
Mabuya striata	Grant's skink or long-toed skink	South and East Africa

18*

Zoological names	Trivial names	Main habitat
Macroclemys temmincki	Alligator snapping turtle	E.North America, Texas, Georgia, Florida, North Missouri
Malaclemys centrata (= *Malacoclemys terrapin*)	Carolina diamond-backed terrapin. Salt-water terrapin	Carolina, Florida
Malapterus electricus	Electric catfish	Tropical Africa
Mastacembelidae	Spiny eels	Fresh waters of India and Africa
Megalobatrachus japonicus (= *M. maximus*)	Giant salamander	Japan
Mehelya capensis	Cape file snake	East Africa, South Africa
Meizodon (= *Natrix*) *longicauda* (= *Natrix fuliginoides*)	Smoky snake	West Africa
Merluccius merluccius	Marine pike, European hake	Atlantic ocean, Mediterranean
Mesoclemmys (= *Hydraspis*) *gibba*	Gordon's terrapin	Brazil, Trinidad, Guianas
Monopeltis	Burrowing lizards	Central Africa
Mugil cephalus	Grey mullet	European, Asiatic and American seas
Mytilus edulis	Common mussel	Lakes and rivers, temperate zone
Naja melanoleuca	Black and white cobra	Tropical Africa
Naja naja	Indian cobra	Southern Asia, India, China, Malaysia
Naja tripudians fasciata	Cobra	India, China
Naja nigricollis	Black-necked cobra	Africa, Egypt, Angola, Transvaal, Natal
Natrix ferox (= *Tropidonotus ferox*)	Fierce snake	West Africa, Sierra Leone, Calabar
Natrix (= *Tropidonotus*) *natrix*	Grass snake	Europe, Central Asia, North East Africa
Natrix olivacea	Black-backed grass snake	Tropical Africa
Natrix piscator	Indian river snake	India, Indo-China, Malay States
Natrix rhombifera	Hallowell's rhomb snake	North America, Mexico
Natrix tigrina	Chinese tiger snake	N.E. Asia, Japan, Korea, China
Natrix vittata	Long-lined snake	Malay States, Java, Celebes
Necturus maculosus	Mudpuppy. Water dog	Southern North America
Nemacheilus barbatula	Stone loach	Fresh waters of Europe
Nematoda	Round worms	Parasitic
Nematomorpha	Gordian worms	Fresh waters, Temperate zones
Notophthalmus meridionalis	Texas newt	Southern States of N. America, Texas
Notopterus	Featherback fish, Razor-finned fish	Fresh waters of India

Zoological names	Trivial names	Main habitat
Ocadia sinensis	Bennet's terrapin	East Asia, China, Formosa
Ophicephalus	Spotted snake-headed fish	Fresh waters of Southern Asia
Ophis merremi	Merrem's Boipeva snake	South America, Brazil
Ophisaurus	Glass snake	Southeastern Europe, S.W. Asia
Osmerus eperlanus	Smelt, Soarling	Coasts of N. and Central Europe
Pelobates fuscus	European spadefoot	Southern Europe, Spain
Pelusios	Box turtles	Africa, N. America
Pelusios (= *Sternothaerus*) *odoratus*	Stinkpot, Musk turtle	New England, S. Ontario, S. Florida, Wisconsin, Texas
Pelusios sinuatus	Natal terrapin	S.E. Africa, Natal, Somaliland, Seychelle islands
Pelusios subniger	Black terrapin	West Africa, Liberia, Congo
Perca fluviatilis	Perch	Fresh waters of Europe
Petromyzon marinus	Sea lamprey	Coasts and rivers of Europe and North America
Phelsuma madagascariensis	Green gecko	Seychelles, Madagascar, East coast of Africa
Phoxinus phoxinus	Minnow	Fresh waters of Europe
Phrynosoma coronatum (= *Ph. blainvillii*)	Blainville's horned lizard	California
Phrynosoma solare	Regal horned lizard	Southern Arizona, N. California, Mexico
Phyllorhynchus	Leafnosed snakes	Southwestern U.S.A.
Physignathus lesueuri	Water dragon	Australia
Pituophis melanoleucus	Northern Pine snake	Southern New Jersey to S. Carolina
Pituophis melanoleucus sayi	Bull snake	U.S.A. Texas to Minnesota
Planorbis	Flat coiled snail	Fresh water of temperate zones
Platemys (= *Hydraspis*) *radiolata*	Milkan's terrapin	Brazil
Platydactylus (= *Tarentola*) *mauretanica*	Moorish gecko	Mediterranean coast, Spain to Egypt, Dalmatia, Ionian Islands
Pleurodeles waltli	Pleurodele or Spanish newt	Spain, North Africa
Pleuronectes flesus (= *Platichthys fl.*)	Flounder	European seas and estuaries
Polypterus senegalus	Sail-finned fish	Rivers of tropical West Africa
Proteus anguineus	Olm	Adelsberg cave, Yugoslavia, Carinthia, Dalmatia
Psammodromus algirus	Algerian sand lizard	S.W. Europe, Northwestern Africa
Psammodromus hispanicus	Spanish sand lizard	Iberian peninsula
Psammophis sibilans	Sand snake African beauty snake	Egypt, Senegambia, Angola, Nyasaland

Zoological names	Trivial names	Main habitat
Pseudechis porphyriacus	Purplish death adder	Australia
Pseudemys elegans	Elegant terrapin	North America
Pseudemys floridana	Florida Cooter or Terrapin	Eastern N. America, S. Georgia, Florida
Pseudemys (= *Terrapene*) *ornata*	Ornate box turtle or terrapin	Central America, Mexico
Pseudemys scripta elegans	Red-eared turtle	U.S.A. Georgia to North Carolina
Pseudocordylus	Small-scaled girdled lizard "Dasadder"	South Africa, Cape province
Pterophyllum scalare	Angel fish	Fresh waters of Brazil
Ptyas mucosa	Greater Indian Rat snake	Asia, India, Indo-China, Ceylon, Malay States
Putorius putorius (= *Mustelus putorius*)	Polecat	Europe
Pygosteus pungitius (= *Gasterosteus p.*)	Ten-spined stickleback	Fresh waters of N. Europe, Baltic sea
Python molurus	Indian python	East India, Ceylon
Python reticulatus	Reticulate python	East India, Burma, Indo-China, Malay States
Python spilotes	Diamond or Carpet python	Australia, New Guinea
Raia erinacea	Little or hedgehog skate	Marine waters, Temperate zones
Rana arvalis (= *R. terrestris*)	Field frog	Eastern Europe, Western Asia
Rana boyli	Yellow-legged frog	California
Rana catesbeiana	American bull frog	North America
Rana clamitans	Spring frog	North America
Rana dalmatina	Agile frog	Southern Europe
Rana esculenta	Edible frog	Southern Europe
Rana pipiens	Leopard frog	North America
Rana ridibunda	Marsh frog	Eastern Europe, Kent marshes
Rana rugosa	Japanese wart frog	Japan
Rana sylvatica	Eastern wood frog	Canada, U.S.A.
Rana temporaria	Grass frog	Europe, Northern Asia
Rasbora heteromorpha	Harlequin fish Asiatic minnow	Malay peninsula, Sumatra
Rhamphiophis oxyrhynchus	African sharp-snouted snake	Tropical Africa
Rhodeus amarus	Bitterling	Fresh waters of Central Europe
Rutilus rutilus	Roach	Rivers of North and Central Europe
Salamandra atra	Black salamander	Alpine region
Salamandra salamandra (= *S. maculosa*)	Spotted salamander	Europe
Salmo gairdneri	Rainbow trout	Rivers of North and Western America

Zoological names	Trivial names	Main habitat
Salmo salar	Salmon	Atlantic and rivers of W. Europe and North America
Salmo trutta fario	Common trout, Brown trout	Coast, rivers and streams of Europe and Eastern Asia
Salvelinus fontinalis	Brook trout, Common American char	Rivers and lakes of North America
Sauromalus ater	Chuckawalla lizard	Lower California
Sauromalus varius	Chuckawalla lizard	California
Scaphiophis albopunctata	Beaked snake	East Africa
Scardinius erythrophthalmus	Rudd	Fresh waters of Europe and Asia Minor
Scincus officinalis (= *Scincus scincus*)	Skink	N. Africa, Algeria to Egypt
Sceloporus graciosus	Mountain swift, Graceful fence lizard	Western and Northern U.S.A., California
Sceloporus magister	Desert spiny lizard	Southern States of U.S.A.
Sceloporus spinosus	Spiny fence lizard	Southern States of U.S.A. Mexico
Sceloporus undulatus	Fence lizard	Eastern U.S.A., New Jersey to Florida
Scomber scombrus	Mackerel	Atlantic ocean
Sialis lutaria	Alder fly	Europe
Siebenrockiella crassicollis	Black thick-necked tortoise	Malay peninsula
Silurus glanis	Wels. European catfish	Fresh waters, Central and Eastern Europe
Siredon mexicanum	Axolotl	Mexico
Siren lacertina	Mud eel	Fresh waters of Southern U.S.A.
Sphenodon punctatus	Tuatara lizard	Little islands near New Zealand
Spilotes pullatus	Cainana rat snake	South America
Squalius cephalus (= *Leuciscus cephalus*)	Chub	Rivers of Europe and Asia Minor
Sternotherus carinatus	Keeled-back musk turtle	Southeastern U.S.A.
Sternotherus odoratus	Stink pot, Mud terrapin	Southern States of N. America
Storeria dekayi	De Kay's snake	Northeastern U.S.A., Mexico
Sus scrofa	Wild pig	Europe
Tarentola mauretanica	Moorish gecko	Mediterranean coast, Spain to Egypt, Dalmatia, Ionian islands
Taricha granulosa	Rough-skinned newt	Southeast U.S.A.
Terrapene carolina	Eastern or Carolina box turtle	Eastern States of U.S.A. Maine to Illinois, Tenessee, Georgia
Terrapene major	Gulf coast box turtle Greater American box turtle	Southern States of U.S.A.
Terrapene trinunguis	Three-toes box turtle	Southern States of U.S.A.

Zoological names	Trivial names	Main habitat
Testudo denticulata	Brazilian tortoise Hercules tortoise	Tropical America, Guianas, Brazil, N.E. Peru, Venezuela, Colombia, Panama
Testudo elegans	Starred tortoise	India, Ceylon
Testudo elephantina (= *T. gigantea*)	Giant tortoise	Indian ocean islands, Aldabra islands
Testudo elephantopus (= *T. nigrita*)	Porter's blackish tortoise	Galapagos islands, Indefatigable islands
Testudo gigantea (= *T. elephantina*)	Giant tortoise	Indian ocean islands, Aldabra islands
Testudo graeca	Greek tortoise	Southern Europe, North Africa, Western Asia, Near East
Testudo hermanni	Spur-tailed Mediterranean tortoise	Southern Europe, Greece, Albania, Sardinia, Sicily
Testudo marginata	Tafrail tortoise	Southeast Europe, Greece
Thalassochelys caretta (= *Caretta caretta*)	Loggerhead turtle	Tropical and subtropical seas
Thamnophis ordinoides	Elegant garter snake	N.W. America, California
Thamnophis parietalis	Red-sided garter snake	Western North America
Thamnophis radix	Eastern plains garter snake	Eastern North America
Thamnophis sirtalis	Garter snake	North America, Southern Canada, British Columbia
Thymallus thymallus (= *Thymallus vulgaris*)	Grayling	Fresh waters, N. and Central Europe
Tilapia galilea	Galilee cichlid	Northern Israel
Tiliqua scincoides	Northern blue-tongued skink	Australia, Tasmania
Tinca tinca (= *Tinca vulgaris*)	Tench	Fresh waters of Europe, Asia minor and West Siberia
Trachysaurus rugosus	Stump-tailed skink	Australia
Trichogaster leeri	Pearl gourami	Siam, Malaga, Sumatra, Fresh waters
Trichogaster trichopterus	Three-spot gourami	Fresh waters of India, Malaya, Indo-China
Trigla gurnardus	Gurnard	European seas
Trionyx gangeticus	Ganges soft-shelled turtle	India, Ganges water system
Trionyx mutica	Pointed nose soft-shelled turtle	N. America, Mississippi, St. Lawrence
Trionyx sinensis	Chinese soft-shelled turtle	E. Asia, China, Hainan, Formosa, Japan
Trionyx spinifera	Spiny soft-shelled turtle	Mississippi and St. Lawrence basins
Trionyx triunguis	Nile soft-shelled turtle	Tropical Africa
Triturus alpestris	Alpine newt	Central Europe
Triturus cristatus	Crested newt	Europe
Triturus helveticus (= *Tr. palmatus*)	Palmate newt	Europe
Triton taeniatus (= *Triturus vulgaris*)	Common newt	Europe

Zoological names	Trivial names	Main habitat
Triturus vulgaris	Common newt	Europe
Tropidonotus (= *Natrix*) *ferox*	Fierce snake	West Africa
Tropidonotus (= *Natrix*) *natrix*	Grass snake	Palaeoarctic regions, Europe, West and Central Asia, Tunisia, Algeria
Tropidurus peruvianus	Lesson's Peruvian lizard	Peru, Chile
Tropidurus torquatus	Wied's ring-necked lizard	Brazil, Guianas
Tupinambis nigropunctatus	Black-pointed Tegu	Guianas, Brazil, Eastern Peru
Tupinambis teguixin	Great Tegu, Teguexin	Uruguay, Brazil, Guianas
Uma notata	Fringe-toed iguana	Southwestern U.S.A.
Unio	Freshwater mussel	Temperate zones, Northern hemisphere
Uromastix acanthinurus	Bell's dabb lizard	Morocco, Algeria
Uromastix hardwicki	General Hardwicke's lizard	Northwest India, Baluchistan
Uta stansburiana	Side-blotched lizard	California
Valvata	Valve snails	Fresh waters, Temperate zones
Vipera aspis	Asp viper	S. Europe, Italy, Balkan States
Vipera aspis hugyi	Asp viper	South Italy, Sicily
Vipera berus	Northern viper or Adder	Europe, Northern Asia
Xantusia henshawi	Henshaw's lizard	Southern California
Xenodon güntheri (= *Ophis g.*)	Günther's snake	South America, Tropical regions
Xenopus laevis	Claw-footed toad. "Platanna"	Cape province
Xiphophorus helleri	Swordtail	Fresh waters, S. Mexico, Guatemala
Zonurus giganteus (= *Cordylus g.*)	Girdled lizard	South Africa

Trivial name	Zoological name
Agama, angle-headed	*Goniocephalus*
Alder fly	*Sialis lutaria*
Axolotl	Larval form of *Ambystoma mexicanum* (= *A. tigrinum*), *Siredon mexicanum*
Cockle, common	*Cardium edule*
Crocodile, estuarine	*Crocodilus porosus*
Crocodile, Ganges	*Gavialis gangeticus*
Crocodile, marsh	*Crocodilus palustris*
Crocodile, Nile	*Crocodilus niloticus*
Eel, blind	*Amphiuma*
Fishes	
Angel fish	*Pterophyllum scalare*
Angler	*Lophius piscatorius*
Barbel	*Barbus barbus*
Bitterling	*Rhodeus amarus*
Bleak	*Alburnus alburnus*
Bonito	*Katsuwonus pelamis*
Bowfin	*Amia calva*
Bream	*Abramis brama*
Bream, white	*Blicca björkna*
Burbot	*Lota lota*
Carp	*Cyprinus carpio*
Carp, crucian	*Carassius carassius*
Catfish, European	*Silurus glanis*
Catfish, amphibian	*Clarias*
Catfish, coat of mail	*Corydoras palaeatus*
Catfish, dwarf	*Ameiurus nebulosus*
Catfish, electric	*Malapterurus electricus*
Chimaera, plow-nosed or Elephant	*Callorhynchus*
Chub	*Squalius cephalus*
Cichlid, Galilee	*Tilapia galilea*
Cod, Atlantic	*Gadus morrhua* (= *G. callarius*)
Conger eel	*Conger conger*
Dace	*Leuciscus leuciscus*
Drum, fresh water, American	*Aplodinotus grunniens*
Eel	*Anguilla anguilla*
Eel, spiny	Mastacembelidae
Featherback	*Notopterus*
Fighting fish, Regan's or Siamese	*Betta splendens*
Flame	*Hyphessobrycon flammeus*
Flounder	*Pleuronectes* (= *Platichthys*) *flesus*
Goldfish	*Carassius carassius*

Trivial name	Zoological name
Fishes—(contd.)	
Gourami, dwarf	*Colisa* (= *Trichogaster*) *lalia*
Gourami, pearl	*Trichogaster leeri*
Gourami, three-spot	*Trichogaster* (= *Osphromenus*) *trichopterus*
Grayling	*Thymallus*
Gudgeon	*Gobio gobio*
Gurnard	*Trigla gurnardus*
Haddock	*Gadus aeglefinus*
Hake, European	*Merluccius merluccius*
Halibut	*Hippoglossus vulgaris*
Harlequin	*Rasbora heteromorpha*
Hatchet belly	*Carnegiella strigata*
Herring	*Clupea harengus*
Ide	*Idus* (= *Leuciscus*) *idus*
Jewel fish	*Hemichromis bimaculatus*
Labyrinth fishes	Anabantidae
Lamprey, brook	*Lampetra planeri*
Lamprey, sea	*Petromyzon marinus*
Mackerel	*Scomber scombrus*
Minnow	*Phoxinus phoxinus*
Minnow, Asiatic	*Rasbora heteromorpha*
Mullet, grey	*Mugil cephalus*
Neon fish	*Hyphessobrycon flammeus*
Orfe	*Idus* (= *Leuciscus*) *idus*
Perch	*Perca fluviatilis*
Pike	*Esox lucius*
Pike, cichlid	*Crenichla*
Pike, marine	*Merluccius merluccius*
Pike, perch, giant	*Lucioperca lucioperca*
Pope	*Acerina cernua*
Rabbit fish	*Chimaera monstrosa*
Red cichlid	*Hemichromis bimaculatus*
Roach	*Rutilus rutilus* (= *Leuciscus rutilus*)
Rudd	*Scardinius erythrophthalmus*
Ruffe	*Acerina cernua*
Sail-finned fish	*Polypterus senegalensis*
Salmon	*Salmo salar*
Sea horse	*Hippocampus*
Sea snail, striped	*Liparis vulgaris* (= *Liparis liparis*)
Sea wolf	*Anarrhichas lupus*
Skate, little or hedgehog	*Raia erinacea*
Skipjack	*Katsuwonus pelamis*
Smelt or Sparling	*Osmerus eperlanus*
Snail fishes	Liparidae
Spotted, snake-headed fish	*Ophicephalus*
Stickleback, 3-spined	*Gasterosteus aculeatus*
Stickleback, 10-spined	*Pygosteus* (= *Pungitius*) *pungitius*
Stone loach	*Nemacheilus barbatula*
Sturgeon	*Acipenser sturio*
Sunfishes	Centrarchidae
Sunfish, long-eared	*Lepomis megalotis*

Trivial name	Zoological name

Fishes—(*contd.*)
  Swordtail   *Xiphophorus helleri*
  Tench   *Tinca tinca* (= *Tinca vulgaris*)

Trivial name	Zoological name
Fishes—(*contd.*)	
Swordtail	*Xiphophorus helleri*
Tench	*Tinca tinca* (= *Tinca vulgaris*)
Tooth carps	*Cyprinodontidae*
Top minnow	*Aphanius*
Trout, brook	*Salvelinus fontinalis*
Trout, common	*Salmo trutto fario*
Trout, rainbow	*Salmo gairdneri*
Wels	*Silurus glanis*
Whitefish	*Coregonus vandesius*
Fish louse	*Argulus*
Flatworms	Cestoda (segmented)
Fluke	Trematoda (unsegmented)
Frogs	
Agile	*Rana dalmatica*
Bull, American	*Rana catesbeiana*
Edible	*Rana esculenta*
Field	*Rana arvalis*
Grass	*Rana temporaria*
Leopard	*Rana pipiens*
Marsh	*Rana ridibunda*
Painted	*Discoglossus pictus*
Spadefoot, European	*Pelobates fuscus*
Spring	*Rana clamitans*
Tree, European	*Hyla arborea*
Wart, Japanese	*Rana rugosa*
Wood, Eastern	*Rana sylvatica*
Yellow-legged	*Rana boyli*
Geckos	
Bridled house gecko	*Hemidactylus frenatus*
Great house gecko	*Gecko gecko*
Green gecko	*Phelsuma madagascariensis*
Moorish gecko	*Tarentola mauretanica*
Peron's house gecko	*Gehyra* (= *Peropus*) *mutilatus*
Gharial	*Gavialis gangeticus*
Gila monster	*Heloderma suspectum*
Gordian worms	Nematomorpha
Hair worm	*Gordius aquaticus*
Hardoun	*Agama stellio*
Iguana, desert pygmi	*Dipsosaurus dorsalis*
Iguana, land, Galapagos	*Conolophus subristatus*
Iguana, spiny tailed	*Ctenosaurus acanthura*
Iguanid, fringe-toed	*Uma notata*
Leech, barbel	*Cystobranchus respirans*
Leech, burbot	*Cystobranchus mammillatus*

Trivial name	Zoological name

Lizards
  Alligator — *Gherronotus multicarinatus*
  Anolis, greater Cuban — *Anolis equestris*
  Basilisk, banded — *Basiliscus vittatus*
  Black-spotted — *Liolaemus nigromaculatus*
  Blainville's horned — *Phrynosoma coronatum*
  Burrowing — *Monopeltis*
  Chuckawalla — *Sauromalus ater* or *S. varius*
  Crag — *Pseudocordylus*
  Dabb, Bell's — *Uromastix acanthinurus*
  Dasadder — *Pseudocordylus*
  Eyed — *Lacerta ocellata* (= *L. lepida*)
  Fence — *Sceloporus undulatus*
  Flying — *Draco volans*
  Galliwasp — *Diploglossus*
  General Hardwicke's — *Uromastix hardwicki*
  Girdled — *Cordylus* (= *Zonurus*) *giganteus*
  Green — *Lacerta viridis*
  Henshaw's — *Xanthusia henshawi*
  Jicari's flap-footed — *Lialis jicarii*
  Lesson's Peruvian — *Tropidurus*
  Mountain swift — *Sceloporus graciosus*
  Red worm — *Amphisbaena*
  Regal, horned — *Phrynosoma solare*
  Ring-necked, Wied's — *Tropidurus torquatus*
  Sand — *Lacerta agilis*
  Sand, Algerian — *Psammodromus algirus*
  Sand, Spanish — *Psammodromus hispanicus*
  Side-blotched — *Uta stansburiana*
  Small-scaled, girdled — *Pseudocordylus*
  Spiny, desert — *Sceloporus magister*
  Spiny, fence — *Sceloporus spinosus*
  Starred — *Agama stellio*
  Strand race-runner — *Cnemidophorus lemniscatus*
  Surinam — *Ameiva ameiva*
  Tuatara — *Sphenodon punctatus*
  Viviparous — *Lacerta vivipara*
  Wall — *Lacerta muralis*
  White, burrowing — *Amphisbaena alba*

Mud eel — *Siren lacertina*
Mudpuppy — *Necturus maculosus*
Mussel, common — *Mytilus edulis*
Mussel, freshwater — *Unio*

Newts
  Alpine — *Triturus alpestris*
  Common — *Triturus vulgaris* (= *Tr. taeniatus*)
  Crested — *Triturus cristatus*
  Japanese — *Cynops pyrrhogaster*
  Palmate — *Triturus helveticus* (= *Tr. palmatus*)

Trivial name	Zoological name
Newts—*(contd.)*	
Pleurodele, Spanish	*Pleurodeles waltli*
Red-spotted	*Diemyctilus viridescens*
Rough-skinned	*Taricha granulosa*
Texas	*Notophthalmus meridionalis*
Olm	*Proteus anguineus*
Pheasant, Lady Amherst's	*Chrysolophus amhersti*
Polecat	*Putorius putorius* (= *Mustelus putorius*)
Pig, wild	*Sus scrofa*
Pond snail	*Lymnaea palustris*
Round worms	Nematoda
Salamander	
Black	*Salamandra atra*
Giant	*Megalobatrachus japonicus*
Northern dusky	*Desmognathus fuscus*
Spotted	*Salamandra salamandra* (= *S. maculosa*)
Tiger	*Ambystoma tigrinum*
Skink	
Blue-tailed or five-lined African	*Mabuya quinquetaeniata*
Blue-tailed, American	*Eumeces fasciatus*
Blue-tongued, Northern	*Tiliqua scincoides*
Common	*Scincus officinalis* (= *Sc. scincus*)
Eyed	*Chalcides ocellatus*
Five-lined, American	*Eumeces fasciatus*
Grant's	*Mabuya striata*
Moco	*Lygosoma moco*
Raddi's	*Mabuya agilis*
Raddon's	*Mabuya raddoni*
Slender	*Leiolepisma* (= *Lygosoma*)
Stump-tailed	*Trachysaurus rugosus*
Snail, flat-coiled	*Planorbis*
Snail, valve	*Valvata*
Slow-worm	*Anguis fragilis*
Sow bug	*Asellus aquaticus*
Snakes	
Aesculapian	*Elaphe longissima*
Aldrovandi's	*Elaphe quatuorlineata*
Andrea's Cuban	*Liophis andreae*
Beaked	*Scaphiophis albopunctata*
Beauty, African	*Psammophis sibilans*
Beauty, Parana	*Liophis anomala*
Black, American	*Coluber constrictor*
Black-backed grass	*Natrix olivacea*
Boa constrictor	*Constrictor constrictor*
Bull	*Pituophis melanoleucus*
Chicken	*Elaphe quadrivittata*
Coach, whip	*Coluber flagellum*

Trivial name	Zoological name
Snakes—(*contd.*)	
Cobra, black and white	*Naja melanoleuca*
Cobra, black-necked	*Naja nigricollis*
Black, Indian	*Naja naja* or *Naja tripudians fasciatus*
Corais	*Drymarchon corais*
Coral	*Elaps* (= *Micrurus*)
Coral, red and black	*Erythrolamprus aesculapii*
Corn	*Elaphe guttata*
Cotton-mouthed moccasin	*Agkistrodon piscivorus*
Death adder, purplish	*Pseudechis porphyricus*
de Kaye's	*Storeria dekayi*
Egg-eating	*Dasypeltis scaber*
Emerald tree	*Gastropyxis smaragdina*
Fer-de-lance	*Bothrops atrox* (= *B. jararaca*)
Fierce	*Natric ferox* (= *Tropidonotus ferox*)
File, Cape	*Mehelya capensis*
Fordonia water	*Fordonia leucobalia*
Garter	*Thamnophis sirtalis*
Garter, Eastern plains	*Thamnophis radix*
Garter, elegant	*Thamnophis ordinoides*
Garter, red-sided	*Thamnophis parietalis*
Glass	*Ophisaurus*
Gopher	*Drymarchon corais*
Grass	*Natrix* (= *Tropidurus*) *natrix*
Green mamba	*Dendraspis angusticeps*
Green, Günther's	*Dipsadoboa unicolor*
Günther's	*Xenodon güntheri*
Hallowell's rhomb	*Natrix rhombifera*
Hog-nosed	*Heterodon contortrix* (= *H. platyrhinus*)
King	*Lampropeltis getulus*
King, red-bellied	*Lampropeltis calligaster*
Leaf-nosed	*Phyllorhynchus*
Leopard	*Elaphe situla*
Lined, African	*Boaedon lineatus*
Long-lined	*Natrix vittata*
Mamba, green	*Dendraspis angusticeps*
Merrem's Boipeva	*Ophis merremi*
Northern pine	*Pituophis melanoleucus*
Pilot-black	*Elaphe obsolita*
Puff adder	*Bitis arietans* (= *Bitis lachesis*)
Puff-faced water	*Homalopsis buccata*
Puffing adder	*Heterodon contortrix* or *H. platyrhinus*
Python, diamond or carpet	*Python spilotes*
Python, Indian	*Python molurus*
Python, reticulate	*Python reticulatus*
Racer	*Coluber constrictor*
Racer, common Malayan	*Elaphe flavolineata*
Rat, Cainana	*Spilotes pullatus*
Rat, greater Indian	*Ptyas mucosus*
Rough-keeled	*Dasypeltis scaber*
Rattlesnake, horned	*Crotalus cerastes*
Rayed	*Coluber radiatus* (= *Elaphe radiata*)

Trivial name	Zoological name

Snakes—(*contd.*)
  River, Indian — *Natrix piscator*
  Rufescent — *Crotaphopeltis* (= *Leptodeira*) *hotamboeia*
  Sand — *Psammophis sibilans*
  Sharp-snouted, African — *Rhamphiophis oxyrrhynchus*
  Sidewinder — *Crotalus cerastes*
  Sooty — *Boaedon fuliginosus fuliginosus*
  Tiger, Chinese — *Natrix tigrina*
  Water moccasin — *Agkistrodon piscivorus*
  Whip — *Coluber gemonensis*
  Wolf, banded — *Lycodon subcinctus*
  Wolf, oriental — *Lycodon* sp.

Tegu
  Tegu, black-pointed — *Tupinambis nigropunctatus*
  Tegu, great or Teguexin — *Tupinambis teguixin*

Terrapin
  Alligator — *Chelydra serpentina*
  Bennett's — *Ocadia sinensis*
  Black — *Pelusios subniger*
  Caspian — *Clemmys caspica leprosa*
  Ceylon — *Geoemyda trijuga*
  Cope's — *Hydromedusa tectifera*
  Diamond-back, Carolina — *Malaclemys* (= *Malacoclemmys*) *terrapin*
  Elegant — *Pseudemys elegans*
  Erie, map — *Graptemys geographica*
  Florida cooter or terrapin — *Pseudemys floridana*
  Geoffroy's — *Hydraspis geoffroyana*
  Gordon's — *Mesoclemys* (= *Hydraspis*) *gibba*
  Indian — *Kachuga* sp.
  Japanese — *Clemmys japonica*
  Long-necked — *Chelodina longicollis*
  Maximilian's — *Hydromedusa maximiliani*
  Mikan's — *Platemys radiolata*
  Mud, Pennsylvanian — *Kinosternon subrubrum*
  Natal — *Pelusios sinuatus*
  Painted — *Chrysemys picta*
  Scorpion, mud — *Kinosternon scorpioides*
  Small-headed map — *Graptemys pseudogeographica*
  Spanish — *Clemmys leprosa*
  Speckled — *Clemmys guttata*
  Stinkpot, mud — *Sternotherus odoratus*
  Tinamon, banded — *Crypturus noctivagus*

Toad
  American — *Bufo americanus* (= *B. lentiginosus*)
  Claw-footed, S. African — *Xenopus laevis*
  Common African — *Bufo regularis*
  Common, European — *Bufo bufo*
  Fire-belly — *Bombina bombina*

Trivial name	Zoological name
Toads—(*contd.*)	
Giant marine	*Bufo marinus*
Green	*Bufo viridis*
Helmet-headed	*Bufo valliceps*
Indian or common Asiatic	*Bufo melanostictus*
Midwife	*Alytes obstetricans*
Mountain	*Bufo boreas*
Natterjack	*Bufo calamita*
Northern	*Bufo americanus* (= *B. lentiginosus*)
Tortoises	
Black, thick-necked	*Siebenrockiella crassicollis*
Brazilian	*Testudo denticulata*
Giant	*Testudo elephantina* (= *T. gigantea*)
Greek	*Testudo graeca*
Hercules	*Testudo denticulata*
Pond, European	*Emys orbicularis*
Porter's blackish	*Testudo elephantopus* (= *T. nigrita*)
Snake	*Chelodina longicollis*
Spur-tailed mediterranean	*Testudo hermanni*
Starred	*Testudo elegans*
Tafrail	*Testudo marginata*
Tsetse fly	*Glossina palpalis*
Tuatara	*Sphenodon punctatus*
Turtles	
Alligator, snapping	*Macroclemys temmincki*
Box	*Pelusios* sp.
Box, Carolina	*Terrapene carolina*
Box, Eastern	*Terrapene carolina*
Box, Gulf coast	*Terrapene major*
Box, ornate	*Pseudemys ornata*
Chinese	*Chinemys reevesii*
Flap-shelled, Indian	*Lissemys indica*
Green	*Chelonia mydas* (= *Ch. viridis*)
Hawk-billed	*Eretmochelys imbricata*
Keel-back musk	*Sternotherus carinatus*
Leatherback	*Dermochelys coriacea*
Loggerhead	*Caretta caretta* (= *Thalassochelys caretta*)
Mud, Pennsylvanian	*Kinosternon subrubrum*
Musk	*Pelusios odoratus*
Red-eared	*Pseudemys scripta elegans*
Siam	*Hieremys annandalei*
Snapping	*Chelydra serpentina*
Soft-shelled, Asiatic	*Lissemys punctata*
Soft-shelled, Chinese	*Trionyx sinensis*
Soft-shelled, fierce	*Trionyx* (= *Amyda*) *ferox*
Soft-shelled, Ganges	*Trionyx gangeticus*
Soft-shelled, long-headed	*Chitra indica*

Trivial name	Zoological name
Soft-shelled, Nile	*Trionyx triunguis*
Soft-shelled, pointed-nose	*Trionyx mutica*
Soft-shelled, Senegal	*Cyclanorbis senegalensis*
Soft-shelled, spiny	*Trionyx (= Amyda) spinifera*
Stink pot	*Pelusios odoratus*
Three-toed	*Terrapene triunguis*
Vipers	
Asp	*Vipera aspis*
Cape	*Causus rhombeatus*
Carpet	*Echis carinata*
Horned	*Aspis cerastes*
Night (or Night-adder)	*Causus rhombeatus*
Northern (or Adder)	*Vipera berus*
Nose-horned	*Bitis nasicornis*
West African	*Causus lichtensteini*
Water louse	*Asellus aquaticus*
Water calf	*Gordius aquaticus*
Water dog	*Necturus maculatus*
Water dragon	*Physignathus lesueuri*

SUBJECT INDEX